W9-ABC-482

A TREASURY OF GREAT MYSTERIES

VOLUME 2

edited by HOWARD HAYCRAFT

and JOHN BEECROFT

SIMON AND SCHUSTER, NEW YORK

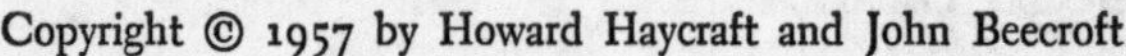

Library of Congress Catalog Card Number 57-6099

Printed in the United States of America

THE BIG SLEEP

by Raymond Chandler

CHAPTER ONE

IT WAS ABOUT eleven o'clock in the morning, mid October, with the sun not shining and a look of hard wet rain in the clearness of the foothills. I was wearing my powder-blue suit, with dark blue shirt, tie and display handkerchief, black brogues, black wool socks with dark blue clocks on them. I was neat, clean, shaved and sober, and I didn't care who knew it. I was everything the well-dressed private detective ought to be. I was calling on four million dollars.

The main hallway of the Sternwood place was two stories high. Over the entrance doors, which would have let in a troop of Indian elephants, there was a broad stained-glass panel showing a knight in dark armor rescuing a lady who was tied to a tree and didn't have any clothes on but some very long and convenient hair. The knight had pushed the vizor of his helmet back to be sociable, and he was fiddling with the knots on the ropes that tied the lady to the tree and not getting anywhere. I stood there and thought that if I lived in the house, I would sooner or later have to climb up there and help him. He didn't seem to be really trying.

There were French doors at the back of the hall, beyond them a wide sweep of emerald grass to a white garage, in front of which a slim dark young chauffeur in shiny black leggings was dusting a maroon Packard convertible. Beyond the garage were some decorative trees trimmed as carefully as poodle dogs. Beyond them a large greenhouse with a domed roof. Then more trees and beyond everything the solid, uneven, comfortable line of the foothills.

On the east side of the hall a free staircase, tile-paved, rose to a gallery with a wrought-iron railing and another piece of stained-glass romance. Large hard chairs with rounded red plush seats were backed into the vacant spaces of the wall round about. They didn't look as if anybody had ever sat in them. In the middle of the west wall there was a big empty fireplace with a brass screen in four hinged panels, and over the fireplace a marble mantel with cupids at the corners. Above the mantel there was a large oil portrait, and above the portrait two bullet-torn or moth-eaten cavalry pennants crossed in a glass frame. The portrait was a stiffly posed job of an officer in full regimentals of about the time of the Mexican war. The officer had a neat black imperial, black mustachios, hot hard coal-black eyes, and the general look of a man it would pay to get along with. I thought this might be General Sternwood's grandfather. It could hardly be the General himself, even though I had heard he was pretty far gone in years to have a couple of daughters still in the dangerous twenties.

I was still staring at the hot black eyes when a door opened far back under the stairs. It wasn't the butler coming back. It was a girl.

She was twenty or so, small and delicately put together, but she looked durable. She wore pale blue slacks and they looked well on her. She walked as if she were floating. Her hair was a fine tawny wave cut much shorter than the current fashion of pageboy tresses curled in at the bottom. Her eyes were slate-gray, and had almost no expression when they looked at me. She came over near me and smiled with her mouth and she had little sharp predatory teeth, as white as fresh orange pith and as shiny as porcelain. They glistened between her thin too taut lips. Her face lacked color and didn't look too healthy.

"Tall, aren't you?" she said.

"I didn't mean to be."

Her eyes rounded. She was puzzled. She was thinking. I could see, even on that short acquaintance, that thinking was always going to be a bother to her.

"Handsome too," she said. "And I bet you know it."

I grunted.

"What's your name?"

"Reilly," I said. "Doghouse Reilly."

"That's a funny name." She bit her lip and turned her head a little and looked at me along her eyes. Then she lowered her lashes until they almost cuddled her cheeks and slowly raised them again, like a theater curtain. I was to get to know that trick. That was supposed to make me roll over on my back with all four paws in the air.

"Are you a prizefighter?" she asked, when I didn't.

"Not exactly. I'm a sleuth."

"A–a–" She tossed her head angrily, and the rich color of it glistened in the rather dim light of the big hall. "You're making fun of me."

"Uh-uh."

"What?"

"Get on with you," I said. "You heard me."

"You didn't say anything. You're just a big tease." She put a thumb up and bit it. It was a curiously shaped thumb, thin and narrow like an extra finger, with no curve in the first joint. She bit it and sucked it slowly, turning it around in her mouth like a baby with a comforter.

"You're awfully tall," she said. Then she giggled with secret merriment. Then she turned her body slowly and lithely, without lifting her feet. Her hands dropped limp at her sides. She tilted herself towards me on her toes. She fell straight back into my arms. I had to catch her or let her crack her head on the tessellated floor. I caught her under her arms and she went rubber-legged on me instantly. I had to hold her close to hold her up. When her head was against my chest she screwed it around and giggled at me.

"You're cute," she giggled. "I'm cute too."

I didn't say anything. So the butler chose that convenient moment to come back through the French doors and see me holding her.

It didn't seem to bother him. He was a tall, thin, silver man, sixty or close to it or a little past it. He had blue eyes as remote as eyes could be. His skin was smooth and bright and he moved like a man with very sound muscles. He walked slowly across the floor towards us and the girl jerked away from me. She flashed across the room to the foot of the stairs and went up them like a deer. She was gone before I could draw a long breath and let it out.

The butler said tonelessly: "The General will see you now, Mr. Marlowe."

I pushed my lower jaw up off my chest and nodded at him. "Who was that?"

"Miss Carmen Sternwood, sir."

"You ought to wean her. She looks old enough."

He looked at me with grave politeness and repeated what he had said.

CHAPTER TWO

WE WENT OUT at the French doors and along a smooth red-flagged path that skirted the far side of the lawn from the garage. The boyish-looking chauffeur had a big black and chromium sedan out now and was dusting that. The path took us along to the side of the greenhouse and the butler opened a door for me and stood aside. It opened into a sort of vestibule that was about as warm as a slow oven. He came in after me, shut the outer door, opened an inner door and we went through that. Then it was really hot. The air was thick, wet, steamy and larded with the cloying smell of tropical orchids in bloom. The glass walls and roof were heavily misted and big drops of moisture splashed down on the plants. The light had an unreal greenish color, like light filtered through an aquarium tank. The plants filled the place, a forest of them, with nasty meaty leaves and stalks like the newly washed fingers of dead men. They smelled as overpowering as boiling alcohol under a blanket.

The butler did his best to get me through without being smacked in the face by the sodden leaves, and after a while we came to a clearing in the middle of the jungle, under the domed roof. Here, in a space of hexagonal flags, an old red Turkish rug was laid down and on the rug was a wheel chair, and in the wheel chair an old and obviously dying man watched us come with black eyes from which all fire had died long ago, but which still had the coal-black directness of the eyes in the portrait that hung above the mantel in the hall. The rest of his face was a leaden mask, with the bloodless lips and the sharp nose and the sunken temples and the outward-turning earlobes of approaching dissolution. His long narrow body was wrapped—in that heat—in a traveling rug and a faded red bathrobe. His thin clawlike hands were folded loosely on the rug, purple-nailed. A few locks of dry white hair clung to his scalp, like wild flowers fighting for life on a bare rock.

The butler stood in front of him and said: "This is Mr. Marlowe, General."

The old man didn't move or speak, or even nod. He just looked at me lifelessly. The butler pushed a damp wicker chair against the backs of my legs and I sat down. He took my hat with a deft scoop.

Then the old man dragged his voice up from the bottom of a well and said: "Brandy, Norris. How do you like your brandy, sir?"

"Any way at all," I said.

The butler went away among the abominable plants. The General spoke again, slowly, using his strength as carefully as an out-of-work showgirl uses her last good pair of stockings.

"I used to like mine with champagne. The champagne as cold as Valley Forge and about a third of a glass of brandy beneath it. You may take your coat off, sir. It's too hot in here for a man with blood in his veins."

I stood up and peeled off my coat and got a handkerchief out and mopped my face and neck and the backs of my wrists. St. Louis in August had nothing on that place. I sat down again and felt automatically for a cigarette and then stopped. The old man caught the gesture and smiled faintly.

"You may smoke, sir. I like the smell of tobacco."

I lit the cigarette and blew a lungful at him and he sniffed at it like a terrier at a rathole. The faint smile pulled at the shadowed corners of his mouth.

"A nice state of affairs when a man has to indulge his vices by proxy," he said dryly. "You are looking at a very dull survival of a rather gaudy life, a cripple paralyzed in both legs and with only half of his lower belly. There's very little that I can eat and my sleep is so close to waking that it is hardly worth the name. I seem to exist largely on heat, like a newborn spider, and the orchids are an excuse for the heat. Do you like orchids?"

"Not particularly," I said.

The General half-closed his eyes. "They are nasty things. Their flesh is too much like the flesh of men. And their perfume has the rotten sweetness of a prostitute."

I stared at him with my mouth open. The soft wet heat was like a pall around us. The old man nodded, as if his neck was afraid of the weight of his head. Then the butler came pushing back through the jungle with a teawagon, mixed me a brandy and soda, swathed the copper ice bucket with a damp napkin, and went away softly among the orchids. A door opened and shut behind the jungle.

I sipped the drink. The old man licked his lips watching me, over and over again, drawing one lip slowly across the other with a funereal absorption, like an undertaker dry-washing his hands.

"Tell me about yourself, Mr. Marlowe. I suppose I have a right to ask?"

"Sure, but there's very little to tell. I'm thirty-three years old, went to college once and can still speak English if there's any demand for it. There isn't much in my trade. I worked for Mr. Wilde, the District Attorney, as an investigator once. His chief investigator, a man named Bernie Ohls, called me and told me you wanted to see me. I'm unmarried because I don't like policemen's wives."

"And a little bit of a cynic," the old man smiled. "You didn't like working for Wilde?"

"I was fired. For insubordination. I test very high on insubordination, General."

"I always did myself, sir. I'm glad to hear it. What do you know about my family?"

"I'm told you are a widower and have two young daughters, both pretty and both wild. One of them has been married three times, the last time to an ex-bootlegger who went in the trade by the name of Rusty Regan. That's all I heard, General."

"Did any of it strike you as peculiar?"

"The Rusty Regan part, maybe. But I always got along with bootleggers myself."

He smiled his faint economical smile. "It seems I do too. I'm very fond of Rusty. A big curly-headed Irishman from Clonmel, with sad eyes and a smile as wide as Wilshire Boulevard. The first time I saw him I thought he might be what you are probably thinking he was, an adventurer who happened to get himself wrapped up in some velvet."

"You must have liked him," I said. "You learned to talk the language."

He put his thin bloodless hands under the edge of the rug. I put my cigarette stub out and finished my drink.

"He was the breath of life to me—while he lasted. He spent hours with me, sweating like a pig, drinking brandy by the quart and telling me stories of the Irish revolution. He had been an officer in the I.R.A. He wasn't even legally in the United States. It was a ridiculous marriage of course, and it probably didn't last a month, as a marriage. I'm telling you the family secrets, Mr. Marlowe."

"They're still secrets," I said. "What happened to him?"

The old man looked at me woodenly. "He went away, a month ago. Abruptly, without a word to anyone. Without saying good-by to me. That hurt a little, but he had been raised in a rough school. I'll hear from him one of these days. Meantime I am being blackmailed again."

I said: "Again?"

He brought his hands from under the rug with a brown envelope in them. "I should have been very sorry for anybody who tried to blackmail me while Rusty was around. A few months before he came—that is to say about nine or ten months ago—I paid a man named Joe Brody five thousand dollars to let my younger daughter Carmen alone."

"Ah," I said.

He moved his thin white eyebrows. "That means what?"

"Nothing," I said.

He went on staring at me, half frowning. Then he said: "Take this envelope and examine it. And help yourself to the brandy."

I took the envelope off his knees and sat down with it again. I wiped off the palms of my hands and turned it around. It was addressed to General Guy Sternwood, 3765 Alta Brea Crescent, West Hollywood, California. The address was in ink, in the slanted printing engineers use. The envelope was slit. I opened it up and took out a brown card and three slips of stiff paper. The card was of thin brown linen, printed in gold: "Mr. Arthur Gwynn Geiger." No address. Very small in the lower left-hand corner: "Rare Books and De Luxe Editions." I turned the card over. More of the slanted printing on the back. "Dear Sir: In spite of the legal uncollectibility of the enclosed, which frankly represent gambling debts, I assume you might wish them honored. Respectfully, A. G. Geiger."

I looked at the slips of stiffish white paper. They were promissory notes filled out in ink, dated on several dates early in the month before, September. "On Demand I promise to pay to Arthur Gwynn Geiger or Order the sum of One Thousand Dollars ($1000.00) without interest. Value Received. Carmen Sternwood."

The written part was in a sprawling moronic handwriting with a lot of fat curlicues and circles for dots. I mixed myself another drink and sipped it and put the exhibit aside.

"Your conclusions?" the General asked.

"I haven't any yet. Who is this Arthur Gwynn Geiger?"

"I haven't the faintest idea."

"What does Carmen say?"

"I haven't asked her. I don't intend to. If I did, she would suck her thumb and look coy."

I said: "I met her in the hall. She did that to me. Then she tried to sit in my lap."

Nothing changed in his expression. His clasped hands rested peacefully on the edge of the rug, and the heat, which made me feel like a New England boiled dinner, didn't seem to make him even warm.

"Do I have to be polite?" I asked. "Or can I just be natural?"

"I haven't noticed that you suffer from many inhibitions, Mr. Marlowe."

"Do the two girls run around together?"

"I think not. I think they go their separate and slightly divergent roads to perdition. Vivian is spoiled, exacting, smart and quite ruthless. Carmen is a child who likes to pull wings off flies. Neither of them has any more moral sense than a cat. Neither have I. No Sternwood ever had. Proceed."

"They're well educated, I suppose. They know what they're doing."

"Vivian went to good schools of the snob type and to college. Carmen went to half a dozen schools of greater and greater liberality, and ended up where she started. I presume they both had, and still have, all the usual vices. If I sound a little sinister as a parent, Mr. Marlowe, it is because my hold on life is too slight to include any Victorian hypocrisy." He leaned his head back and closed his eyes, then opened them again suddenly. "I need not add that a man who indulges in parenthood for the first time at the age of fifty-four deserves all he gets."

I sipped my drink and nodded. The pulse in his lean gray throat throbbed visibly and yet so slowly that it was hardly a pulse at all. An old man two thirds dead and still determined to believe he could take it.

"Your conclusions?" he snapped suddenly.

"I'd pay him."

"Why?"

"It's a question of a little money against a lot of annoyance. There has to be something behind it. But nobody's going to break your heart, if it hasn't been done already. And it would take an awful lot of chiselers an awful lot of time to rob you of enough so that you'd even notice it."

"I have pride, sir," he said coldly.

"Somebody's counting on that. It's the easiest way to fool them. That or the police. Geiger can collect on these notes, unless you can show fraud. Instead of that he makes you a present of them and admits they are gambling debts, which gives you a defense, even if he had kept the notes. If he's a crook, he knows his onions, and if he's an honest man doing a little loan business on the side, he ought to have his money. Who was this Joe Brody you paid the five thousand dollars to?"

"Some kind of gambler. I hardly recall. Norris would know. My butler."

"Your daughters have money in their own right, General?"

"Vivian has, but not a great deal. Carmen is still a minor under her mother's will. I give them both generous allowances."

I said: "I can take this Geiger off your back, General, if that's what you want. Whoever he is and whatever he has. It may cost you a little money, besides what you pay me. And of course it won't get you anything. Sugaring them never does. You're already listed on their book of nice names."

"I see." He shrugged his wide sharp shoulders in the faded red bathrobe. "A moment ago you said pay him. Now you say it won't get me anything."

"I mean it might be cheaper and easier to stand for a certain amount of squeeze. That's all."

"I'm afraid I'm rather an impatient man, Mr. Marlowe. What are your charges?"

"I get twenty-five a day and expenses—when I'm lucky."

"I see. It seems reasonable enough for removing morbid growths from people's backs. Quite a delicate operation. You realize that, I hope. You'll make your operation as little of a shock to the patient as possible? There might be several of them, Mr. Marlowe."

I finished my second drink and wiped my lips and my face. The heat didn't get any less hot with the brandy in me. The General blinked at me and plucked at the edge of his rug.

"Can I make a deal with this guy, if I think he's within hooting distance of being on the level?"

"Yes. The matter is now in your hands. I never do things by halves."

"I'll take him out," I said. "He'll think a bridge fell on him."

"I'm sure you will. And now I must excuse myself. I am tired." He reached out and touched the bell on the arm of his chair. The cord was plugged into a black cable that wound along the side of the deep dark green boxes in which the orchids grew and festered. He closed his eyes, opened them again in a brief bright stare, and settled back among his cushions. The lids dropped again and he didn't pay any more attention to me.

I stood up and lifted my coat off the back of the damp wicker chair and went off with it among the orchids, opened the two doors and stood outside in the brisk October air getting myself some oxygen. The chauffeur over by the garage had gone away. The butler came along the red path with smooth light steps and his back as straight as an ironing board. I shrugged into my coat and watched him come.

He stopped about two feet from me and said gravely: "Mrs. Regan would like to see you before you leave, sir. And in the matter of money the General has instructed me to give you a check for whatever seems desirable."

"Instructed you how?"

He looked puzzled, then he smiled. "Ah, I see, sir. You are, of course, a detective. By the way he rang his bell."

"You write his checks?"

"I have that privilege."

"That ought to save you from a pauper's grave. No money now, thanks. What does Mrs. Regan want to see me about?"

His blue eyes gave me a smooth level look. "She has a misconception of the purpose of your visit, sir."

"Who told her anything about my visit?"

"Her windows command the greenhouse. She saw us go in. I was obliged to tell her who you were."

"I don't like that," I said.

His blue eyes frosted. "Are you attempting to tell me my duties, sir?"

"No. But I'm having a lot of fun trying to guess what they are."

We stared at each other for a moment. He gave me a blue glare and turned away.

CHAPTER THREE

THIS ROOM WAS too big, the ceiling was too high, the doors were too tall, and the white carpet that went from wall to wall looked like a fresh fall of snow at Lake Arrowhead. There were full-length mirrors and crystal doodads all over the place. The ivory furniture had chromium on it, and the enormous ivory drapes lay tumbled on the white carpet a yard from the windows. The white made the ivory look dirty and the ivory made the white look bled out. The windows stared towards the darkening foothills. It was going to rain soon. There was pressure in the air already.

I sat down on the edge of a deep soft chair and looked at Mrs. Regan. She was worth a stare. She was trouble. She was stretched out on a modernistic chaise-longue with her slippers off, so I stared at her legs in the sheerest silk stockings. They seemed to be arranged to stare at. They were visible to the knee and one of them well beyond. The knees were dimpled, not bony and sharp. The calves were beautiful, the ankles long and slim and with enough melodic line for a tone poem. She was tall and rangy and strong-looking. Her head was against an ivory satin cushion. Her hair was black and wiry and parted in the middle and she had the hot black eyes of the portrait in the hall. She had a good mouth and a good chin. There was a sulky droop to her lips and the lower lip was full.

She had a drink. She took a swallow from it and gave me a cool level stare over the rim of the glass.

"So you're a private detective," she said. "I didn't know they really existed, except in books. Or else they were greasy little men snooping around hotels."

There was nothing in that for me, so I let it drift with the current. She put her glass down on the flat arm of the chaise-longue and flashed an emerald and touched her hair. She said slowly: "How did you like Dad?"

"I liked him," I said.

"He liked Rusty. I suppose you know who Rusty is?"

"Uh-huh."

"Rusty was earthy and vulgar at times, but he was very real. And he was a lot of fun for Dad. Rusty shouldn't have gone off like that. Dad feels very badly about it, although he won't say so. Or did he?"

"He said something about it."

"You're not much of a gusher, are you, Mr. Marlowe? But he wants to find him, doesn't he?"

I stared at her politely through a pause. "Yes and no," I said.

"That's hardly an answer. Do you think you can find him?"

"I didn't say I was going to try. Why not try the Missing Persons Bureau? They have the organization. It's not a one-man job."

"Oh, Dad wouldn't hear of the police being brought into it." She looked at me smoothly across her glass again, emptied it, and rang a bell. A maid came into the room by a side door. She was a middle-aged woman with a long yellow gentle face, a long nose, no chin, large wet eyes. She looked like a nice old horse that had been turned out to pasture after long service. Mrs. Regan waved the empty glass at her and she mixed another drink and handed it to her and left the room, without a word, without a glance in my direction.

When the door shut Mrs. Regan said: "Well, how will you go about it then?"

"How and when did he skip out?"

"Didn't Dad tell you?"

I grinned at her with my head on one side. She flushed. Her hot black eyes looked mad. "I don't see what there is to be cagey about," she snapped. "And I don't like your manners."

"I'm not crazy about yours," I said. "I didn't ask to see you. You sent for me. I don't mind your ritzing me or drinking your lunch out of a Scotch bottle. I don't mind your showing me your legs. They're very swell legs and it's a pleasure to make their acquaintance. I don't mind if you don't like my manners. They're pretty bad. I grieve over them during the long winter evenings. But don't waste your time trying to cross-examine me."

She slammed her glass down so hard that it slopped over on an ivory cushion. She swung her legs to the floor and stood up with her eyes sparking fire and her nostrils wide. Her mouth was open and her bright teeth glared at me. Her knuckles were white.

"People don't talk like that to me," she said thickly.

I sat there and grinned at her. Very slowly she closed her mouth and looked down at the spilled liquor. She sat down on the edge of the chaise-longue and cupped her chin in one hand.

"My God, you big dark handsome brute! I ought to throw a Buick at you."

I snicked a match on my thumbnail and for once it lit. I puffed smoke into the air and waited.

"I loathe masterful men," she said. "I simply loathe them."

"Just what is it you're afraid of, Mrs. Regan?"

Her eyes whitened. Then they darkened until they seemed to be all pupil. Her nostrils looked pinched.

"That wasn't what he wanted with you at all," she said in a strained voice that still had shreds of anger clinging to it. "About Rusty. Was it?"

"Better ask him."

She flared up again. "Get out! Damn you, get out!"

I stood up. "Sit down!" she snapped. I sat down. I flicked a finger at my palm and waited.

"Please," she said. "Please. You could find Rusty—if Dad wanted you to."

That didn't work either. I nodded and asked: "When did he go?"

"One afternoon a month back. He just drove away in his car without saying a word. They found the car in a private garage somewhere."

"They?"

She got cunning. Her whole body seemed to go lax. Then she smiled at me winningly. "He didn't tell you then." Her voice was almost gleeful, as if she had outsmarted me. Maybe she had.

"He told me about Mr. Regan, yes. That's not what he wanted to see me about. Is that what you've been trying to get me to say?"

"I'm sure I don't care what you say."

I stood up again. "Then I'll be running along." She didn't speak. I went over to the tall white door I had come in at. When I looked back she had her lip between her teeth and was worrying it like a puppy at the fringe of a rug.

I went out, down the tile staircase to the hall, and the butler drifted out of somewhere with my hat in his hand. I put it on while he opened the door for me.

"You made a mistake," I said. "Mrs. Regan didn't want to see me."

He inclined his silver head and said politely: "I'm sorry, sir. I make many mistakes." He closed the door against my back.

I stood on the step breathing my cigarette smoke and looking down a succession of terraces with flowerbeds and trimmed trees to the high iron fence with gilt spears that hemmed in the estate. A winding driveway dropped down between retaining walls to the open iron gates. Beyond the fence the hill sloped for several miles. On this lower level faint and far off I could just barely see some of the old wooden derricks of the oilfield from which the Sternwoods had made their money. Most of the field was public park now, cleaned up and donated to the city by General Sternwood. But a little of it was still producing in groups of wells pumping five or six barrels a day. The Sternwoods, having moved up the hill, could no longer smell the stale sump water or the oil, but they could still look out of their front windows and see what had made them rich. If they wanted to. I didn't suppose they would want to.

I walked down a brick path from terrace to terrace, followed along inside the fence and so out of the gates to where I had left my car under a pepper tree on the street. Thunder was crackling in the foothills now and the sky above them was purple-black. It was going to rain hard. The air had the damp foretaste of rain. I put the top up on my convertible before I started downtown.

She had lovely legs. I would say that for her. They were a couple of pretty smooth citizens, she and her father. He was probably just trying me out; the job he had given me was a lawyer's job. Even if Mr. Arthur Gwynn Geiger, *Rare Books and De Luxe Editions*, turned out to be a blackmailer, it was still a lawyer's job. Unless there was a lot more to it than met the eye. At a casual glance I thought I might have a lot of fun finding out.

I drove down to the Hollywood public library and did a little superficial research in a stuffy volume called Famous First Editions. Half an hour of it made me need my lunch.

CHAPTER FOUR

A. G. GEIGER'S PLACE was a store frontage on the north side of the boulevard near Las Palmas. The entrance door was set far back in the middle and there was a copper trim on the windows, which were backed with Chinese screens, so I couldn't see into the store. There was a lot of oriental junk in the windows. I didn't know whether it was any good, not being a collector of antiques, except unpaid bills. The entrance door was plate glass, but I couldn't see much through that either, because the store was very dim. A building entrance adjoined it on one side and on the other was a glittering credit jewelry establishment. The jeweler stood in his entrance, teetering on his heels and looking bored, a tall handsome white-haired Jew in lean dark clothes, with about nine carats of diamond on his right hand. A faint knowing smile curved his lips when I turned into Geiger's store. I let the door close softly behind me and walked on a thick blue rug that paved the floor from wall to wall. There were blue leather easy chairs with smoke stands beside them. A few sets of tooled leather bindings were set out on narrow polished tables, between book ends. There were more tooled bindings in glass cases on the walls. Nice-looking merchandise, the kind a rich promoter would buy by the yard and have somebody paste his bookplate in. At the back there was a grained wood partition with a door in the middle of it, shut. In the corner made by the partition and one wall, a woman sat behind a small desk with a carved wooden lantern on it.

She got up slowly and swayed towards me in a tight black dress that didn't reflect any light. She had long thighs and she walked with a certain something I hadn't often seen in bookstores. She was an ash blonde with greenish eyes, beaded lashes, hair waved smoothly back from ears in which large jet buttons glittered. Her fingernails were silvered. In spite of her get-up she looked as if she would have a hall bedroom accent.

She approached me with enough sex appeal to stampede a business men's lunch and tilted her head to finger a stray, but not very stray, tendril of softly glowing hair. Her smile was tentative, but could be persuaded to be nice.

"Was it something?" she enquired.

I had my horn-rimmed sunglasses on. I put my voice high and let a bird twitter in it. "Would you happen to have a Ben Hur 1860?"

She didn't say: "Huh?" but she wanted to. She smiled bleakly. "A first edition?"

"Third," I said. "The one with the erratum on page 116."

"I'm afraid not—at the moment."

"How about a Chevalier Audubon 1840—the full set, of course?"

"Er—not at the moment," she purred harshly. Her smile was now hanging by its teeth and eyebrows and wondering what it would hit when it dropped.

"You *do* sell books?" I said in my polite falsetto.

She looked me over. No smile now. Eyes medium to hard. Pose very straight and stiff. She waved silver fingernails at the glassed-in shelves. "What do they look like—grapefruit?" she enquired tartly.

"Oh, that sort of thing hardly interests me, you know. Probably has duplicate sets of steel engravings, tuppence colored and a penny plain. The usual vulgarity. No. I'm sorry. No."

"I see." She tried to jack the smile back up on her face. She was as sore as an alderman with the mumps. "Perhaps Mr. Geiger—but he's not in at the moment." Her eyes studied me carefully. She knew as much about rare books as I knew about handling a flea circus.

"He might be in later?"

"I'm afraid not until late."

"Too bad," I said. "Ah, too bad. I'll sit down and smoke a cigarette in one of these charming chairs. I have rather a blank afternoon. Nothing to think about but my trigonometry lesson."

"Yes," she said. "Ye-es, of course."

I stretched out in one and lit a cigarette with the round nickel lighter on the smoking stand. She still stood, holding her lower lip with her teeth, her eyes vaguely troubled. She nodded at last, turned slowly and walked back to her little desk in the corner. From behind the lamp she stared at me. I crossed my ankles and yawned. Her silver nails went out to the cradle phone on the desk, didn't touch it, dropped and began to tap on the desk.

Silence for about five minutes. The door opened and a tall hungry-looking bird with a cane and a big nose came in neatly, shut the door behind him against the pressure of the door closer, marched over to the corner and placed a wrapped parcel on the desk. He took a pinseal wallet with gold corners from his pocket and showed the blonde something. She pressed a button on the desk. The tall bird went to the door in the paneled partition and opened it barely enough to slip through.

I finished my cigarette and lit another. The minutes dragged by. Horns tooted and grunted on the boulevard. A big red interurban car grumbled past. A traffic light gonged. The blonde leaned on her elbow and cupped a hand over her eyes and stared at me behind it. The partition door opened and the tall bird with the cane slid out. He had another wrapped parcel, the shape of a large book. He went over to the desk and paid money. He left as he had come, walking on the balls of his feet, breathing with his mouth open, giving me a sharp side glance as he passed.

I got to my feet, tipped my hat to the blonde and went out after him. He walked west, swinging his cane in a small tight arc just above his right shoe. He was easy to follow. His coat was cut from a rather loud piece of horse robe with shoulders so wide that his neck stuck up out of it like a celery stalk and his head wobbled on it as he walked. We went a block and a half. At the Highland Avenue traffic signal I pulled up beside him and let him see me. He gave me a casual, then a suddenly sharpened side glance, and quickly turned away. We crossed Highland with the green light and made another block. He stretched his long legs and had twenty yards on me at the corner. He turned right. A hundred feet up the hill he stopped and hooked his cane over his arm and fumbled a leather cigarette case out of an inner pocket. He put a cigarette in his mouth, dropped his match, looked back when he picked it up, saw me watching him from the corner, and straightened up as if somebody had booted him from behind. He almost raised dust going up the block, walking with long gawky strides and jabbing his cane into the sidewalk. He turned left again. He had at least half a block on me when I reached the place where he had turned. He had me wheezing. This was a narrow tree-lined street with a retaining wall on one side and three bungalow courts on the other.

He was gone. I loafed along the block peering this way and that. At the second bungalow court I saw something. It was called "The La Baba," a quiet dim place with a double row of tree-shaded bungalows. The central walk was lined with Italian cypresses trimmed short and chunky, something the shape of the oil jars in Ali Baba and the Forty Thieves. Behind the third jar a loud-patterned sleeve edge moved.

I leaned against a pepper tree in the parkway and waited. The thunder in the foothills was rumbling again. The glare of lightning was reflected on piled-up black clouds off to the south. A few tentative raindrops splashed down on the sidewalk and made spots as large as nickels. The air was as still as the air in General Sternwood's orchid house.

The sleeve behind the tree showed again, then a big nose and one eye and some sandy hair without a hat on it. The eye stared at me. It disappeared. Its mate reappeared like a woodpecker on the other side of the tree. Five minutes went by. It got him. His type are half nerves. I heard a match strike and then whistling started. Then a dim shadow slipped along the grass to the next tree. Then he was out on the walk coming straight towards me, swinging the cane and whistling. A sour whistle with jitters in it. I stared vaguely up at the dark sky. He passed within ten feet of me and didn't give me a glance. He was safe now. He had ditched it.

I watched him out of sight and went up the central walk of the La Baba and parted the branches of the third cypress. I drew out a wrapped book and put it under my arm and went away from there. Nobody yelled at me.

CHAPTER FIVE

BACK ON THE BOULEVARD I went into a drugstore phone booth and looked up Mr. Arthur Gwynn Geiger's residence. He lived on Laverne Terrace, a hillside street off Laurel Canyon Boulevard. I dropped my nickel and dialed his number just for fun. Nobody answered. I turned to the classified section and noted a couple of bookstores within blocks of where I was.

The first I came to was on the north side, a large lower floor devoted to stationery and office supplies, a mass of books on the mezzanine. It didn't look the right place. I crossed the street and walked two blocks east to the other one. This was more like it, a narrowed cluttered little shop stacked with books from floor to ceiling and four or five browsers taking their time putting thumb marks on the new jackets. Nobody paid any attention to them. I shoved on back into the store, passed through a partition and found a small dark woman reading a law book at a desk.

I flipped my wallet open on her desk and let her look at the buzzer pinned to the flap. She looked at it, took her glasses off and leaned back in her chair. I put the wallet away. She had the fine-drawn face of an intelligent Jewess. She stared at me and said nothing.

I said: "Would you do me a favor, a very small favor?"

"I don't know. What is it?" She had a smoothly husky voice.

"You know Geiger's store across the street, two blocks west?"

"I think I may have passed it."

"It's a bookstore," I said. "Not your kind of bookstore. You know darn well."

She curled her lip slightly and said nothing. "You know Geiger by sight?" I asked.

"I'm sorry. I don't know Mr. Geiger."

"Then you couldn't tell me what he looks like?"

Her lip curled some more. "Why should I?"

"No reason at all. If you don't want to, I can't make you."

She looked out through the partition door and leaned back again. "That was a sheriff's star, wasn't it?"

"Honorary deputy. Doesn't mean a thing. It's worth a dime cigar."

"I see." She reached for a pack of cigarettes and shook one loose and reached for it with her lips. I held a match for her. She thanked me, leaned back again and regarded me through smoke. She said carefully:

"You wish to know what he looks like and you don't want to interview him?"

"He's not there," I said.

"I presume he will be. After all, it's his store."

"I don't want to interview him just yet," I said.

She looked out through the open doorway again. I said: "Know anything about rare books?"

"You could try me."

"Would you have a Ben Hur, 1860, Third Edition, the one with the duplicated line on page 116?"

She pushed her yellow law book to one side and reached a fat volume up on the desk, leafed it through, found her page, and studied it. "Nobody would," she said without looking up. "There isn't one."

"Right."

"What in the world are you driving at?"

"The girl in Geiger's store didn't know that."

She looked up. "I see. You interest me. Rather vaguely."

"I'm a private dick on a case. Perhaps I ask too much. It didn't seem much to me somehow."

She blew a soft gray smoke ring and poked her finger through. It came to pieces in frail wisps. She spoke smoothly, indifferently. "In his early forties, I should judge. Medium height, fattish. Would weigh about a hundred and sixty pounds. Fat face, Charlie Chan moustache, thick soft neck. Soft all over. Well dressed, goes without a hat, affects a knowledge of antiques and hasn't any. Oh yes. His left eye is glass."

"You'd make a good cop," I said.

She put the reference book back on an open shelf at the end of her desk, and opened the law book in front of her again. "I hope not," she said. She put her glasses on.

I thanked her and left. The rain had started. I ran for it, with the wrapped book under my arm. My car was on a side street pointing at the boulevard almost opposite Geiger's store. I was well sprinkled before I got there. I tumbled into the car and ran both windows up and wiped my parcel off with my handkerchief. Then I opened it up.

I knew about what it would be, of course. A heavy book, well bound, handsomely printed in handset type on fine paper. Larded with full-page arty photographs. Photos and letterpress were alike of an indescribable filth. The book was not new. Dates were stamped on the front endpaper, in and out dates. A rent book. A lending library of elaborate smut.

I rewrapped the book and locked it up behind the seat. A racket like that, out in the open on the boulevard, seemed to mean plenty of protection. I sat there and poisoned myself with cigarette smoke and listened to the rain and thought about it.

CHAPTER SIX

RAIN FILLED the gutters and splashed knee-high off the sidewalk. Big cops in slickers that shone like gun barrels had a lot of fun carrying giggling girls across the bad places. The rain drummed hard on the roof of the car and the burbank top began to leak. A pool of water formed on the floorboards for me to keep my feet in. It was too early in the fall for that kind of rain. I struggled into a trench coat and made a dash for the nearest drugstore and bought myself a pint of whiskey. Back in the car I used enough of it to keep warm and interested. I was long overparked, but the cops were too busy carrying girls and blowing whistles to bother about that.

In spite of the rain, or perhaps even because of it, there was business done at Geiger's. Very nice cars stopped in front and very nice-looking people went in and out with wrapped parcels. They were not all men.

He showed about four o'clock. A cream-colored coupe stopped in front of the store and I caught a glimpse of the fat face and the Charlie Chan moustache as he dodged out of it and into the store. He was hatless and wore a belted green leather raincoat. I couldn't see his glass eye at that distance. A tall and very good-looking kid in a jerkin came out of the store and rode the coupe off around the corner and came back walking, his glistening black hair plastered with rain.

Another hour went by. It got dark and the rain-clouded lights of the stores were soaked up by the black street. Street-car bells jangled crossly. At around five-fifteen the tall boy in the jerkin came out of Geiger's with an umbrella and went after the cream-colored coupe. When he had it in front Geiger came out and the tall boy held the umbrella over Geiger's bare head. He folded it, shook it off and handed it into the car. He dashed back into the store. I started my motor.

The coupe went west on the boulevard, which forced me to make a left turn and a lot of enemies, including a motorman who stuck his head out into the rain to bawl me out. I was two blocks behind the coupe before I got in the groove. I hoped Geiger was on his way home. I caught sight of him two or three times and then made him turning north into Laurel Canyon Drive. Halfway up the grade he turned left and took a curving ribbon of wet concrete which was called Laverne Terrace. It was a narrow street with a high bank on one side and a scattering of cabin-like houses built down the slope on the other side, so that their roofs were not very much above road level. Their front windows were masked by hedges and shrubs. Sodden trees dripped all over the landscape.

Geiger had his lights on and I hadn't. I speeded up and passed him on a curve, picked a number off a house as I went by and turned at the end of the block. He had already stopped. His car lights were tilted in at the garage of a small house with a square box hedge so arranged that it masked the front door completely. I watched him come out of the garage with his umbrella up and go in through the hedge. He didn't act as if he expected anybody to be tailing him. Light went on in the house. I drifted down to the next house above it, which seemed empty but had no signs out. I parked, aired out the convertible, had a drink from my bottle, and sat. I didn't know what I was waiting for, but something told me to wait. Another army of sluggish minutes dragged by.

Two cars came up the hill and went over the crest. It seemed to be a very quiet street. At a little after six more bright lights bobbed through the driving rain. It was pitch black by then. A car dragged to a stop in front of Geiger's house. The filaments of its lights glowed dimly and died. The door opened and a woman got out. A small slim woman in a vagabond hat and a transparent raincoat. She went in through the box maze. A bell rang faintly, light through the rain, a closing door, silence.

I reached a flash out of my car pocket and went downgrade and looked at the car. It was a Packard convertible, maroon or dark brown. The left window was down. I felt for the license holder and poked light at it. The registration read: Carmen Sternwood, 3765 Alta Brea Crescent, West Hollywood. I went back to my car again and sat and sat. The top dripped on my knees and my stomach burned from the whiskey. No more cars came up the hill. No lights went on in the house before which I was parked. It seemed like a nice neighborhood to have bad habits in.

At seven-twenty a single flash of hard white light shot out of Geiger's house like a wave of summer lightning. As the darkness folded back on it and ate it up a thin tinkling scream echoed out and lost itself among the rain-drenched trees. I was out of the car and on my way before the echoes died.

There was no fear in the scream. It had a sound of half-pleasurable shock, an accent of drunkenness, an overtone of pure idiocy. It was a nasty sound. It made me think of men in white and barred windows and hard narrow cots with leather wrist and ankle straps fastened to them. The Geiger hideaway was perfectly silent again when I hit the gap in the hedge and dodged around the angle that masked the front door. There was an iron ring in a lion's mouth for a knocker. I reached for it, I had hold of it. At that exact instant, as if somebody had been waiting for a cue, three shots boomed in the house. There was a sound that might have been a long harsh sigh. Then a soft messy thump. And then rapid footsteps in the house—going away.

The door fronted on a narrow run, like a footbridge over a gully, that filled the gap between the house wall and the edge of the bank. There was no porch, no solid ground, no way to get around to the back. The back entrance was at the top of a flight of wooden steps that rose from the alley-like street below. I knew this because I heard a clatter of feet on the steps, going down.

Then I heard the sudden roar of a starting car. It faded swiftly into the distance. I thought the sound was echoed by another car, but I wasn't sure. The house in front of me was as silent as a vault. There wasn't any hurry. What was in there was in there.

I straddled the fence at the side of the runway and leaned far out to the draped but unscreened French window and tried to look in at the crack where the drapes came together. I saw lamplight on a wall and one end of a bookcase. I got back on the runway and took all of it and some of the hedge and gave the front door the heavy shoulder. This was foolish. About the only part of a California house you can't put your foot through is the front door. All it did was hurt my shoulder and make me mad. I climbed over the railing again and kicked the French window in, used my hat for a glove and pulled out most of the lower small pane of glass. I could now reach in and draw a bolt that fastened the window to the sill. The rest was easy. There was no top bolt. The catch gave. I climbed in and pulled the drapes off my face.

Neither of the two people in the room paid any attention to the way I came in, although only one of them was dead.

CHAPTER SEVEN

IT WAS A WIDE ROOM, the whole width of the house. It had a low beamed ceiling and brown plaster walls decked out with strips of Chinese embroidery and Chinese and Japanese prints in grained wood frames. There were low bookshelves, there was a thick pinkish Chinese rug in which a gopher could have spent a week without showing his nose above the nap. There were floor cushions, bits of odd silk tossed around, as if whoever lived there had to have a piece he could reach out and thumb. There was a broad low divan of old rose tapestry. It had a wad of clothes on it, including lilac-colored silk underwear. There was a big carved lamp on a pedestal, two other standing lamps with jade-green shades and long tassels. There was a black desk with carved gargoyles at the corners and behind it a yellow satin cushion on a polished black chair with carved arms and back. The room contained an odd assortment of odors, of which the most emphatic at the moment seemed to be the pungent aftermath of cordite and the sickish aroma of ether.

On a sort of low dais at one end of the room there was a high-backed teakwood chair in which Miss Carmen Sternwood was sitting on a fringed orange shawl. She was sitting very straight, with her hands on the arms of the chair, her knees close together, her body stiffly erect in the pose of an Egyptian goddess, her chin level, her small bright teeth shining between her parted lips. Her eyes were wide open. The dark slate color of the iris had devoured the pupil. They were mad eyes. She seemed to be unconscious, but she didn't have the pose of unconsciousness. She looked as if, in her mind, she was doing something very important and making a fine job of it. Out of her mouth came a tinny chuckling noise which didn't change her expression or even move her lips.

She was wearing a pair of long jade earrings. They were nice earrings and had probably cost a couple of hundred dollars. She wasn't wearing anything else.

She had a beautiful body, small, lithe, compact, firm, rounded. Her skin in the lamplight had the shimmering luster of a pearl. Her legs didn't quite have the raffish grace of Mrs. Regan's legs, but they were very nice. I looked her over without either embarrassment or ruttishness. As a naked girl she was not there in that room at all. She was just a dope. To me she was always just a dope.

I stopped looking at her and looked at Geiger. He was on his back on the floor, beyond the fringe of the Chinese rug, in front of a thing that looked like a totem pole. It had a profile like an eagle and its wide round eye was a camera lens. The lens was aimed at the naked girl in the chair. There was a blackened flash bulb clipped to the side of the totem pole. Geiger was wearing Chinese slippers with thick felt soles, and his legs were in black satin pajamas and the upper part of him wore a Chinese embroidered coat, the front of which was mostly blood. His glass eye shone brightly up at me and was by far the most lifelike thing about him. At a glance none of the three shots I heard had missed. He was very dead.

The flash bulb was the sheet lightning I had seen. The crazy scream was the doped and naked girl's reaction to it. The three shots had been somebody else's idea of how the proceedings might be given a new twist. The idea of the lad who had gone down the back steps and slammed into a car and raced away. I could see merit in his point of view.

A couple of fragile gold-veined glasses rested on a red lacquer tray on the end of the black desk, beside a potbellied flagon of brown liquid. I took the stopper out and sniffed at it. It smelled of ether and something else, possibly laudanum. I had never tried the mixture but it seemed to go pretty well with the Geiger menage.

I listened to the rain hitting the roof and the north windows. Beyond was no other sound, no cars, no siren, just the rain beating. I went over to the divan and peeled off my trench coat and pawed through the girl's clothes. There was a pale green rough wool dress of the pull-on type, with half sleeves. I thought I might be able to handle it. I decided to pass up her underclothes, not from feelings of delicacy, but because I couldn't see myself putting her pants on and snapping her brassiere. I took the dress over to the teak chair on the dais. Miss Sternwood smelled of ether also, at a distance of several feet. The tinny chuckling noise was still coming from her and a little froth oozed down her chin. I slapped her face. She blinked and stopped chuckling. I slapped her again.

"Come on," I said brightly. "Let's be nice. Let's get dressed."

She peered at me, her slaty eyes as empty as holes in a mask. "Gugugoterell," she said.

I slapped her around a little more. She didn't mind the slaps. They didn't bring her out of it. I set to work with the dress. She didn't mind that either. She let me hold her arms up and she spread her fingers out wide, as if that was cute. I got her hands through the sleeves, pulled the dress down over her back, and stood her up. She fell into my arms giggling. I set her back in the chair and got her stockings and shoes on her.

"Let's take a little walk," I said. "Let's take a nice little walk."

We took a little walk. Part of the time her earrings banged against my chest and part of the time we did the splits in unison, like adagio dancers. We walked over to Geiger's body and back. I had her look at him. She thought he was cute. She giggled and tried to tell me so, but she just bubbled. I walked her over to the divan and spread her out on it. She hiccuped twice, giggled a little and went to sleep. I stuffed her belongings into my pockets and went over behind the totem pole thing. The camera was there all right, set inside it, but there was no plateholder in the camera. I looked around on the floor, thinking he might have got it out before he was shot. No plateholder. I took hold of his limp chilling hand and rolled him a little. No plateholder. I didn't like this development.

I went into a hall at the back of the room and investigated the house. There was a bathroom on the right and a locked door, a kitchen at the back. The kitchen window had been jimmied. The screen was gone and the place where the hook had pulled out showed on the sill. The back door was unlocked. I left it unlocked and looked into a bedroom on the left side of the hall. It was neat, fussy, womanish. The bed had a flounced cover. There was perfume on the triple-mirrored dressing table, beside a handkerchief, some loose money, a man's brushes, a keyholder. A man's clothes were in the closet and a man's slippers under the flounced edge of the bed cover. Mr. Geiger's room. I took the keyholder back to the living room and went through the desk. There was a locked steel box in the deep drawer. I used one of the keys on it. There was nothing in it but a blue leather book with an index and a lot of writing in code, in the same slanting printing that had written to General Sternwood. I put the notebook in my pocket, wiped the steel box where I had touched it, locked the desk up, pocketed the keys, turned the gas logs off in the fireplace, wrapped myself in my coat and tried to rouse Miss Sternwood. It couldn't be done. I crammed her vagabond hat on her head and swathed her in her coat and carried her out to her car. I went back and put all the lights out and shut the front door, dug her keys out of her bag and started the Packard. We went off down the hill without lights. It was less than ten minutes' drive to Alta Brea Crescent. Carmen spent them snoring and breathing ether in my face. I couldn't keep her head off my shoulder. It was all I could do to keep it out of my lap.

CHAPTER EIGHT

THERE WAS dim light behind narrow leaded panes in the side door of the Sternwood mansion. I stopped the Packard under the porte-cochere and emptied my pockets out on the seat. The girl snored in the corner, her hat tilted rakishly over her nose, her hands hanging limp in the folds of the raincoat. I got out and rang the bell. Steps came slowly, as if from a long dreary distance. The door opened and the straight, silvery butler looked out at me. The light from the hall made a halo of his hair.

He said: "Good evening, sir," politely and looked past me at the Packard. His eyes came back to look at my eyes.

"Is Mrs. Regan in?"

"No, sir."

"The General is asleep, I hope?"

"Yes. The evening is his best time for sleeping."

"How about Mrs. Regan's maid?"

"Mathilda? She's here, sir."

"Better get her down here. The job needs the woman's touch. Take a look in the car and you'll see why."

He took a look in the car. He came back. "I see," he said. "I'll get Mathilda."

"Mathilda will do right by her," I said.

"We all try to do right by her," he said.

"I guess you have had practice," I said.

He let that one go. "Well, good-night," I said. "I'm leaving it in your hands."

"Very good, sir. May I call you a cab?"

"Positively," I said, "not. As a matter of fact I'm not here. You're just seeing things."

He smiled then. He gave me a duck of his head and I turned and walked down the driveway and out of the gates.

Ten blocks of that, winding down curved rain-swept streets, under the steady drip of trees, past lighted windows in big houses in ghostly enormous grounds, vague clusters of eaves and gables and lighted windows high on the hillside, remote and inaccessible, like witch houses in a forest. I came out at a service station glaring with wasted light, where a bored attendant in a white cap and a dark blue windbreaker sat hunched on a stool, inside the steamed glass, reading a paper. I started in, then kept going. I was as wet as I could get already. And on a night like that you can grow a beard waiting for a taxi. And taxi drivers remember.

I made it back to Geiger's house in something over half an hour of nimble walking. There was nobody there, no car on the street except my own car in front of the next house. It looked as dismal as a lost dog. I dug my bottle of rye out of it and poured half of what was left down my throat and got inside to light a cigarette. I smoked half of it, threw it away, got out again and went down to Geiger's. I unlocked the door and stepped into the still warm darkness and stood there, dripping quietly on the floor and listening to the rain. I groped to a lamp and lit it.

The first thing I noticed was that a couple of strips of embroidered silk were gone from the wall. I hadn't counted them, but the spaces of brown plaster stood out naked and obvious. I went a little farther and put another lamp on. I looked at the totem pole. At its foot, beyond the margin of the Chinese rug, on the bare floor another rug had been spread. It hadn't been there before. Geiger's body had. Geiger's body was gone.

That froze me. I pulled my lips back against my teeth and leered at the glass eye in the totem pole. I went through the house again. Everything was exactly as it had been. Geiger wasn't in his flounced bed or under it or in his closet. He wasn't in the kitchen or the bathroom. That left the locked door on the right of the hall. One of Geiger's keys fitted the lock. The room inside was interesting, but Geiger wasn't in it. It was interesting because it was so different from Geiger's room. It was a hard bare masculine bedroom with a polished wood floor, a couple of small throw rugs in an Indian design, two straight chairs, a bureau in dark grained wood with a man's toilet set and two black candles in foot-high brass candlesticks. The bed was narrow and looked hard and had a maroon batik cover. The room felt cold. I locked it up again, wiped the knob off with my handkerchief, and went back to the totem pole. I knelt down and squinted along the nap of the rug to the front door. I thought I could see two parallel grooves pointing that way, as though heels had dragged. Whoever had done it had meant business. Dead men are heavier than broken hearts.

It wasn't the law. They would have been there still, just about getting warmed up with their pieces of string and chalk and their cameras and dusting powders and their nickel cigars. They would have been very much there. It wasn't the killer. He had left too fast. He must have seen the girl. He couldn't be sure she was too batty to see him. He would be on his way to distant places. I couldn't guess the answer, but it was all right with me if somebody wanted Geiger missing instead of just murdered. It gave me a chance to find out if I could tell it leaving Carmen Sternwood out. I locked up again, choked my car to life and rode off home to a shower, dry clothes and a late dinner. After that I sat around in the apartment and drank too much hot toddy trying to crack the code in Geiger's blue indexed notebook. All I could be sure of was that it was a list of names and addresses, probably of the customers. There were over four hundred of them. That made it a nice racket, not to mention any blackmail angles, and there were probably plenty of those. Any name on the list might be a prospect as the killer. I didn't envy the police their job when it was handed to them.

I went to bed full of whiskey and frustration and dreamed about a man in a bloody Chinese coat who chased a naked girl with long jade earrings while I ran after them and tried to take a photograph with an empty camera.

CHAPTER NINE

THE NEXT MORNING was bright, clear and sunny. I woke up with a motorman's glove in my mouth, drank two cups of coffee and went through the morning papers. I didn't find any reference to Mr. Arthur Gwynn Geiger in either of them. I was shaking the wrinkles out of my damp suit when the phone rang. It was Bernie Ohls, the D.A.'s chief investigator, who had given me the lead to General Sternwood.

"Well, how's the boy?" he began. He sounded like a man who had slept well and didn't owe too much money.

"I've got a hangover," I said.

"Tsk, tsk." He laughed absently and then his voice became a shade too casual, a cagey cop voice. "Seen General Sternwood yet?"

"Uh-huh."

"Done anything for him?"

"Too much rain," I answered, if that was an answer.

"They seem to be a family things happen to. A big Buick belonging to one of them is washing about in the surf off Lido fish pier."

I held the telephone tight enough to crack it. I also held my breath.

"Yeah," Ohls said cheerfully. "A nice new Buick sedan all messed up with sand and sea water. . . . Oh, I almost forgot. There's a guy inside it."

I let my breath out so slowly that it hung on my lip. "Regan?" I asked.

"Huh? Who? Oh, you mean the ex-legger the eldest girl picked up and went and married. I never saw him. What would he be doing down there?"

"Quit stalling. What would anybody be doing down there?"

"I don't know, pal. I'm dropping down to look see. Want to go along?"

"Yes."

"Snap it up," he said. "I'll be in my hutch."

Shaved, dressed and lightly breakfasted I was at the Hall of Justice in less than an hour. I rode up to the seventh floor and went along to the group of small offices used by the D.A.'s men. Ohls' was no larger than the others, but he had it to himself. There was nothing on his desk but a blotter, a cheap pen set, his hat and one of his feet. He was a medium-sized blondish man with stiff white eyebrows, calm eyes and well-kept teeth. He looked like anybody you would pass on the street. I happened to know he had killed nine men—three of them when he was covered, or somebody thought he was.

He stood up and pocketed a flat tin of toy cigars called Entractes, jiggled the one in his mouth up and down and looked at me carefully along his nose, with his head thrown back.

"It's not Regan," he said. "I checked. Regan's a big guy, as tall as you and a shade heavier. This is a young kid."

I didn't say anything.

"What made Regan skip out?" Ohls asked. "You interested in that?"

"I don't think so," I said.

"When a guy out of the liquor traffic marries into a rich family and then waves good-by to a pretty dame and a couple million legitimate bucks—that's enough to make even me think. I guess you thought that was a secret."

"Uh-huh."

"Okey, keep buttoned, kid. No hard feelings." He came around the desk tapping his pockets and reaching for his hat.

"I'm not looking for Regan," I said.

He fixed the lock on his door and we went down to the official parking lot and got into a small blue sedan. We drove out Sunset, using the siren once in a while to beat a signal. It was a crisp morning, with just enough snap in the air to make life seem simple and sweet, if you didn't have too much on your mind. I had.

It was thirty miles to Lido on the coast highway, the first ten of them through traffic. Ohls made the run in three quarters of an hour. At the end of that time we skidded to a stop in front of a faded stucco arch and I took my feet out of the floorboards and we got out. A long pier railed with white two-by-fours stretched seaward from the arch. A knot of people leaned out at the far end and a motorcycle officer stood under the arch keeping another group of people from going out on the pier. Cars were parked on both sides of the highway, the usual ghouls, of both sexes. Ohls showed the motorcycle officer his badge and we went out on the pier, into a loud fish smell which one night's hard rain hadn't even dented.

"There she is—on the power barge," Ohls said, pointing with one of his toy cigars.

A low black barge with a wheelhouse like a tug's was crouched against the pilings at the end of the pier. Something that glistened in the morning sunlight was on its deck, with hoist chains still around it, a large black and chromium car. The arm of the hoist had been swung back into position and lowered to deck level. Men stood around the car. We went down slippery steps to the deck.

Ohls said hello to a deputy in green khaki and a man in plain clothes. The barge crew of three men leaned against the front of the wheelhouse and chewed tobacco. One of them was rubbing at his wet hair with a dirty bath-towel. That would be the man who had gone down into the water to put the chains on.

We looked the car over. The front bumper was bent, one headlight smashed, the other bent up but the glass still unbroken. The radiator shell had a big dent in it, and the paint and nickel were scratched up all over the car. The upholstery was sodden and black. None of the tires seemed to be damaged.

The driver was still draped around the steering post with his head at an unnatural angle to his shoulders. He was a slim dark-haired kid who had been good-looking not so long ago. Now his face was bluish white and his eyes were a faint dull gleam under the lowered lids and his open mouth had sand in it. On the left side of his forehead there was a dull bruise that stood out against the whiteness of the skin.

Ohls backed away, made a noise in his throat and put a match to his little cigar. "What's the story?"

The uniformed man pointed up at the rubbernecks on the end of the pier. One of them was fingering a place where the white two-by-fours had been broken through in a wide space. The splintered wood showed yellow and clean, like fresh-cut pine.

"Went through there. Must have hit pretty hard. The rain stopped early down here, around nine p.m. The broken wood's dry inside. That puts it after the rain stopped. She fell in plenty of water not to be banged up worse, not more than half tide or she'd have drifted farther, and not more than half tide going out or she'd have crowded the piles. That makes it around ten last night. Maybe nine-thirty, not earlier. She shows under the water when the boys come down to fish this morning, so we get the barge to hoist her out and we find the dead guy."

The plainclothesman scuffed at the deck with the toe of his shoe. Ohls looked sideways along his eyes at me, and twitched his little cigar like a cigarette.

"Drunk?" he asked, of nobody in particular.

The man who had been toweling his head went over to the rail and cleared his throat in a loud hawk that made everybody look at him. "Got some sand," he said, and spat. "Not as much as the boy friend got—but some."

The uniformed man said: "Could have been drunk. Showing off all alone in the rain. Drunks will do anything."

"Drunk, hell," the plainclothesman said. "The hand throttle's set halfway down and the guy's been sapped on the side of the head. Ask me and I'll call it murder."

Ohls looked at the man with the towel. "What do you think, buddy?"

The man with the towel looked flattered. He grinned. "I say suicide, Mac. None of my business, but you ask me, I say suicide. First off the guy plowed an awful straight furrow down that pier. You can read his tread marks all the way nearly. That puts it after the rain like the Sheriff said. Then he hit the pier hard and clean or he don't go through and land right side up. More likely turned over a couple of times. So he had plenty of speed and hit the rail square. That's more than half-throttle. He could have done that with his hand falling and he could have hurt his head falling too."

Ohls said: "You got eyes, buddy. Frisked him?" he asked the deputy. The deputy looked at me, then at the crew against the wheelhouse. "Okey, save that," Ohls said.

A small man with glasses and a tired face and a black bag came down the steps from the pier. He picked out a fairly clean spot on the deck and put the bag down. Then he took his hat off and rubbed the back of his neck and stared out to sea, as if he didn't know where he was or what he had come for.

Ohls said: "There's your customer, Doc. Dove off the pier last night. Around nine to ten. That's all we know."

The small man looked in at the dead man morosely. He fingered the head, peered at the bruise on the temple, moved the head around with both hands, felt the man's ribs. He lifted a lax dead hand and stared at the fingernails. He let it fall and watched it fall. He stepped back and opened his bag and took out a printed pad of D.O.A. forms and began to write over a carbon.

"Broken neck's the apparent cause of death," he said, writing. "Which means there won't be much water in him. Which means he's due to start getting stiff pretty quick now he's out in the air. Better get him out of the car before he does. You won't like doing it after."

Ohls nodded. "How long dead, Doc?"

"I wouldn't know."

Ohls looked at him sharply and took the little cigar out of his mouth and looked at that sharply. "Pleased to know you, Doc. A coroner's man that can't guess within five minutes has me beat."

The little man grinned sourly and put his pad in his bag and clipped his pencil back on his vest. "If he ate dinner last night, I'll tell you—if I know what time he ate it. But not within five minutes."

"How would he get that bruise—falling?"

The little man looked at the bruise again. "I don't think so. That blow came from something covered. And it had already bled subcutaneously while he was alive."

"Blackjack, huh?"

"Very likely."

The little M.E.'s man nodded, picked his bag off the deck and went back up the steps to the pier. An ambulance was backing into position outside the stucco arch. Ohls looked at me and said: "Let's go. Hardly worth the ride, was it?"

We went back along the pier and got into Ohls' sedan again. He wrestled it around on the highway and drove back towards town along a three-lane highway washed clean by the rain, past low rolling hills of yellow-white sand terraced with pink moss. Seaward a few gulls wheeled and swooped over something in the surf and far out a white yacht looked as if it was hanging in the sky.

Ohls cocked his chin at me and said: "Know him?"

"Sure. The Sternwood chauffeur. I saw him dusting that very car out there yesterday."

"I don't want to crowd you, Marlowe. Just tell me, did the job have anything to do with him?"

"No. I don't even know his name."

"Owen Taylor. How do I know? Funny about that. About a year or so back we had him in the cooler on a Mann Act rap. It seems he run Sternwood's hotcha daughter, the young one, off to Yuma. The sister ran after them and brought them back and had Owen heaved into the icebox. Then next day she comes down to the D.A. and gets him to beg the kid off with the U. S. 'cutor. She says the kid meant to marry her sister and wanted to, only the sister can't see it. All *she* wanted was to kick a few high ones off the bar and have herself a party. So we let the kid go and then darned if they don't have him come back to work. And a little later we get the routine report on his prints from Washington, and he's got a prior back in Indiana, attempted hold-up six years ago. He got off with a six months in the county jail, the very one Dillinger bust out of. We hand that to the Sternwoods and they keep him on just the same. What do you think of that?"

"They seem to be a screwy family," I said. "Do they know about last night?"

"No. I gotta go up against them now."

"Leave the old man out of it, if you can."

"Why?"

"He has enough troubles and he's sick."

"You mean Regan?"

I scowled. "I don't know anything about Regan, I told you. I'm not looking for Regan. Regan hasn't bothered anybody that I know of."

Ohls said: "Oh," and stared thoughtfully out to sea and the sedan nearly went off the road. For the rest of the drive back to town he hardly spoke. He dropped me off in Hollywood near the Chinese Theater and turned back west to Alta Brea Crescent. I ate lunch at a counter and looked at an afternoon paper and couldn't find anything about Geiger in it.

After lunch I walked east on the boulevard to have another look at Geiger's store.

CHAPTER TEN

THE LEAN BLACK-EYED credit jeweler was standing in his entrance in the same position as the afternoon before. He gave me the same knowing look as I turned in. The store looked just the same. The same lamp glowed on the small desk in the corner and the same ash blonde in the same black suede-like dress got up from behind it and came towards me with the same tentative smile on her face.

"Was it–?" she said and stopped. Her silver nails twitched at her side. There was an overtone of strain in her smile. It wasn't a smile at all. It was a grimace. She just thought it was a smile.

"Back again," I chirped airily, and waved a cigarette. "Mr. Geiger in today?"

"I'm–I'm afraid not. No–I'm afraid not. Let me see–you wanted . . . ?"

I took my dark glasses off and tapped them delicately on the inside of my left wrist. If you can weigh a hundred and ninety pounds and look like a fairy, I was doing my best.

"That was just a stall about those first editions," I whispered. "I have to be careful. I've got something he'll want. Something he's wanted for a long time."

The silver fingernails touched the blonde hair over one small jet-buttoned ear. "Oh, a salesman," she said. "Well–you might come in tomorrow. I think he'll be here tomorrow."

"Drop the veil," I said. "I'm in the business too."

Her eyes narrowed until they were a faint greenish glitter, like a forest pool far back in the shadow of trees. Her fingers clawed at her palm. She stared at me and chopped off a breath.

"Is he sick? I could go up to the house," I said impatiently. "I haven't got forever."

"You–a–you–a–" her throat jammed. I thought she was going to fall on her nose. Her whole body shivered and her face fell apart like a bride's pie crust. She put it together again slowly, as if lifting a great weight, by sheer will power. The smile came back, with a couple of corners badly bent.

"No," she breathed. "No. He's out of town. That–wouldn't be any use. Can't you–come in–tomorrow?"

I had my mouth open to say something when the partition door opened a foot. The tall dark handsome boy in the jerkin looked out, pale-faced and tight-lipped, saw me, shut the door quickly again, but not before I had seen on the floor behind him a lot of wooden boxes lined with newspapers and packed loosely with books. A man in very new overalls was fussing with them. Some of Geiger's stock was being moved out.

When the door shut I put my dark glasses on again and touched my hat. "Tomorrow, then. I'd like to give you a card, but you know how it is."

"Ye-es. I know how it is." She shivered a little more and made a faint sucking noise between her bright lips. I went out of the store and west on the boulevard to the corner and north on the street to the alley which ran behind the stores. A small black truck with wire sides and no lettering on it was backed up to Geiger's place. The man in the very new overalls was just heaving a box up on the tailboard. I went back to the boulevard and along the block next to Geiger's and found a taxi standing at a fireplug. A fresh-faced kid was reading a horror magazine behind the wheel. I leaned in and showed him a dollar: "Tail job?"

He looked me over. "Cop?"

"Private."

He grinned. "My meat, Jack." He tucked the magazine over his rear view mirror and I got into the cab. We went around the block and pulled up across from Geiger's alley, beside another fireplug.

There were about a dozen boxes on the truck when the man in overalls closed the screened doors and hooked the tailboard up and got in behind the wheel.

"Take him," I told my driver.

The man in overalls gunned his motor, shot a glance up and down the alley and ran away fast in the other direction. He turned left out of the alley. We did the same. I caught a glimpse of the truck turning east on Franklin and told my driver to close in a little. He didn't or couldn't do it. I saw the truck two blocks away when we got to Franklin. We had it in sight to Vine and across Vine and all the way to Western. We saw it twice after Western. There was a lot of traffic and the fresh-faced kid tailed from too far back. I was telling him about that without mincing words when the truck, now far ahead, turned north again. The street at which it turned was called Brittany Place. When we got to Brittany Place the truck had vanished.

The fresh-faced kid made comforting sounds at me through the panel and we went up the hill at four miles an hour looking for the truck behind bushes. Two blocks up, Brittany Place swung to the east and met Randall Place in a tongue of land on which there was a white apartment house with its front on Randall Place and its basement garage opening on Brittany. We were going past that and the fresh-faced kid was telling me the truck couldn't be far away when I looked through the arched entrance of the garage and saw it back in the dimness with its rear doors open again.

We went around to the front of the apartment house and I got out. There was nobody in the lobby, no switchboard. A wooden desk was pushed back against the wall beside a panel of gilt mailboxes. I looked the names over. A man named Joseph Brody had Apartment 405. A man named Joe Brody had received five thousand dollars from General Sternwood to stop playing with Carmen and find some other little girl to play with. It could be the same Joe Brody. I felt like giving odds on it.

I went around an elbow of wall to the foot of tiled stairs and the shaft of the automatic elevator. The top of the elevator was level with the floor. There was a door beside the shaft lettered "Garage." I opened it and went down narrow steps to the basement. The automatic elevator was propped open and the man in new overalls was grunting hard as he stacked heavy boxes in it. I stood beside him and lit a cigarette and watched him. He didn't like my watching him.

After a while I said: "Watch the weight, bud. She's only tested for half a ton. Where's the stuff going?"

"Brody, four-o-five," he grunted. "Manager?"

"Yeah. Looks like a nice lot of loot."

He glared at me with pale white rimmed eyes. "Books," he snarled. "A hundred pounds a box, easy, and me with a seventy-five pound back."

"Well, watch the weight," I said.

He got into the elevator with six boxes and shut the doors. I went back up the steps to the lobby and out to the street and the cab took me downtown again to my office building. I gave the fresh-faced kid too much money and he gave me a dog-eared business card which for once I didn't drop into the majolica jar of sand beside the elevator bank.

I had a room and a half on the seventh floor at the back. The half-room was an office split in two to make reception rooms. Mine had my name on it and nothing else, and that only on the reception room. I always left this unlocked, in case I had a client, and the client cared to sit down and wait.

I had a client.

CHAPTER ELEVEN

SHE WORE brownish speckled tweeds, a mannish shirt and tie, hand-carved walking shoes. Her stockings were just as sheer as the day before, but she wasn't showing as much of her legs. Her black hair was glossy under a brown Robin Hood hat that might have cost fifty dollars and looked as if you could have made it with one hand out of a desk blotter.

"Well, you *do* get up," she said, wrinkling her nose at the faded red settee, the two odd semi-easy chairs, the net curtains that needed laundering and the boy's size library table with the venerable magazines on it to give the place a professional touch. "I was beginning to think perhaps you worked in bed, like Marcel Proust."

"Who's he?" I put a cigarette in my mouth and stared at her. She looked a little pale and strained, but she looked like a girl who could function under a strain.

"A French writer, a connoisseur in degenerates. You wouldn't know him."

"Tut, tut," I said. "Come into my boudoir."

She stood up and said: "We didn't get along very well yesterday. Perhaps I was rude."

"We were both rude," I said. I unlocked the communicating door and held it for her. We went into the rest of my suite, which contained a rust-red carpet, not very young, five green filing cases, three of them full of California climate, an advertising calendar showing the Quints rolling around on a sky-blue floor, in pink dresses, with seal-brown hair and sharp black eyes as large as mammoth prunes. There were three near-walnut chairs, the usual desk with the usual blotter, pen set, ashtray and telephone, and the usual squeaky swivel chair behind it.

"You don't put on much of a front," she said, sitting down at the customer's side of the desk.

I went over to the mail slot and picked up six envelopes, two letters and four pieces of advertising matter. I hung my hat on the telephone and sat down.

"Neither do the Pinkertons," I said. "You can't make much money at this trade, if you're honest. If you have a front, you're making money—or expect to."

"Oh—are you honest?" she asked and opened her bag. She picked a cigarette out of a French enamel case, lit it with a pocket lighter, dropped case and lighter back into the bag and left the bag open.

"Painfully."

"How did you get into this slimy kind of business then?"

"How did you come to marry a bootlegger?"

"My God, let's not start quarreling again. I've been trying to get you on the phone all morning. Here and at your apartment."

"About Owen?"

Her face tightened sharply. Her voice was soft. "Poor Owen," she said. "So you know about that."

"A D.A.'s man took me down to Lido. He thought I might know something about it. But he knew much more than I did. He knew Owen wanted to marry your sister—once."

She puffed silently at her cigarette and considered me with steady black eyes. "Perhaps it wouldn't have been a bad idea," she said quietly. "He was in love with her. We don't find much of that in our circle."

"He had a police record."

She shrugged. She said negligently: "He didn't know the right people. That's all a police record means in this rotten crime-ridden country."

"I wouldn't go that far."

She peeled her right glove off and bit her index finger at the first joint, looking at me with steady eyes. "I didn't come to see you about Owen. Do you feel yet that you can tell me what my father wanted to see you about?"

"Not without his permission."

"Was it about Carmen?"

"I can't even say that." I finished filling a pipe and put a match to it. She watched the smoke for a moment. Then her hand went into her open bag and came out with a thick white envelope. She tossed it across the desk.

"You'd better look at it anyway," she said.

I picked it up. The address was typewritten to Mrs. Vivian Regan, 3765 Alta Brea Crescent, West Hollywood. Delivery had been by messenger service and the office stamp showed 8.35 a.m. as the time out. I opened the envelope and drew out the shiny 4¼ by 3¼ photo that was all there was inside.

It was Carmen sitting in Geiger's high-backed teakwood chair on the dais, in her earrings and her birthday suit. Her eyes looked even a little crazier than as I remembered them. The back of the photo was blank. I put it back in the envelope.

"How much do they want?" I asked.

"Five thousand—for the negative and the rest of the prints. The deal has to be closed tonight, or they give the stuff to some scandal sheet."

"The demand came how?"

"A woman telephoned me, about half an hour after this thing was delivered."

"There's nothing in the scandal sheet angle. Juries convict without leaving the box on that stuff nowadays. What else is there?"

"Does there have to be something else?"

"Yes."

She stared at me, a little puzzled. "There is. The woman said there was a police jam connected with it and I'd better lay it on the line fast, or I'd be talking to my little sister through a wire screen."

"Better," I said. "What kind of jam?"

"I don't know."

"Where is Carmen now?"

"She's at home. She was sick last night. She's still in bed, I think."

"Did she go out last night?"

"No. I was out, but the servants say she wasn't. I was down at Las Olindas, playing roulette at Eddie Mars' Cypress Club. I lost my shirt."

"So you like roulette. You would."

She crossed her legs and lit another cigarette. "Yes. I like roulette. All the Sternwoods like losing games, like roulette and marrying men that walk out on them and riding steeplechases at fifty-eight years old and being rolled on by a jumper and crippled for life. The Sternwoods have money. All it has bought them is a rain check."

"What was Owen doing last night with your car?"

"Nobody knows. He took it without permission. We always let him take a car on his night off, but last night wasn't his night off." She made a wry mouth. "Do you think–?"

"He knew about this nude photo? How would I be able to say? I don't rule him out. Can you get five thousand in cash right away?"

"Not unless I tell Dad–or borrow it. I could probably borrow it from Eddie Mars. He ought to be generous with me, heaven knows."

"Better try that. You may need it in a hurry."

She leaned back and hung an arm over the back of the chair. "How about telling the police?"

"It's a good idea. But you won't do it."

"Won't I?"

"No. You have to protect your father and your sister. You don't know what the police might turn up. It might be something they couldn't sit on. Though they usually try in blackmail cases."

"Can you do anything?"

"I think I can. But I can't tell you why or how."

"I like you," she said suddenly. "You believe in miracles. Would you have a drink in the office?"

I unlocked my deep drawer and got out my office bottle and two pony glasses. I filled them and we drank. She snapped her bag shut and pushed her chair back.

"I'll get the five grand," she said. "I've been a good customer of Eddie Mars. There's another reason why he should be nice to me, which you may not know." She gave me one of those smiles the lips have forgotten before they reach the eyes. "Eddie's blonde wife is the lady Rusty ran away with."

I didn't say anything. She stared tightly at me and added: "That doesn't interest you?"

"It ought to make it easier to find him–if I was looking for him. You don't think he's in this mess, do you?"

She pushed her empty glass at me. "Give me another drink. You're the hardest guy to get anything out of. You don't even move your ears."

I filled the little glass. "You've got all you wanted out of me–a pretty good idea I'm not looking for your husband."

She put the drink down very quickly. It made her gasp—or gave her an opportunity to gasp. She let a breath out slowly.

"Rusty was no crook. If he had been, it wouldn't have been for nickels. He carried fifteen thousand dollars, in bills. He called it his mad money. He had it when I married him and he had it when he left me. No—Rusty's not in on any cheap blackmail racket."

She reached for the envelope and stood up. "I'll keep in touch with you," I said. "If you went to leave me a message, the phone girl at my apartment house will take care of it."

We walked over to the door. Tapping the white envelope against her knuckles, she said: "You still feel you can't tell me what Dad—"

"I'd have to see him first."

She took the photo out and stood looking at it, just inside the door. "She has a beautiful little body, hasn't she?"

"Uh-huh."

She leaned a little towards me. "You ought to see mine," she said gravely.

"Can it be arranged?"

She laughed suddenly and sharply and went halfway through the door, then turned her head to say coolly: "You're as cold-blooded a beast as I ever met, Marlowe. Or can I call you Phil?"

"Sure."

"You can call me Vivian."

"Thanks, Mrs. Regan."

"Oh, go to hell, Marlowe." She went on out and didn't look back.

I let the door shut and stood with my hand on it, staring at the hand. My face felt a little hot. I went back to the desk and put the whiskey away and rinsed out the two pony glasses and put them away.

I took my hat off the phone and called the D.A.'s office and asked for Bernie Ohls.

He was back in his cubbyhole. "Well, I let the old man alone," he said. "The butler said he or one of the girls would tell him. This Owen Taylor lived over the garage and I went through his stuff. Parents at Dubuque, Iowa. I wired the Chief of Police there to find out what they want done. The Sternwood family will pay for it."

"Suicide?" I asked.

"No can tell. He didn't leave any notes. He had no leave to take the car. Everybody was home last night but Mrs. Regan. She was down at Las Olindas with a playboy named Larry Cobb. I checked on that. I know a lad on one of the tables."

"You ought to stop some of that flash gambling," I said.

With the syndicate we got in this county? Be your age, Marlowe. That sap mark on the boy's head bothers me. Sure you can't help me on this?"

I liked his putting it that way. It let me say no without actually lying. We said good-by and I left the office, bought all three afternoon papers and rode a taxi down to the Hall of Justice to get my car out of the lot. There was nothing in any of the papers about Geiger. I took another look at his blue notebook, but the code was just as stubborn as it had been the night before.

CHAPTER TWELVE

THE TREES on the upper side of Laverne Terrace had fresh green leaves after the rain. In the cool afternoon sunlight I could see the steep drop of the hill and the flight of steps down which the killer had run after his three shots in the darkness. Two small houses fronted on the street below. They might or might not have heard the shots.

There was no activity in front of Geiger's house or anywhere along the block. The box hedge looked green and peaceful and the shingles on the roof were still damp. I drove past slowly, gnawing at an idea. I hadn't looked in the garage the night before. Once Geiger's body slipped away I hadn't really wanted to find it. It would force my hand. But dragging him to the garage, to his own car and driving that off into one of the hundred odd lonely canyons around Los Angeles would be a good way to dispose of him for days or even for weeks. That supposed two things: a key to his car and two in the party. It would narrow the sector of search quite a lot, especially as I had had his personal keys in my pocket when it happened.

I didn't get a chance to look at the garage. The doors were shut and padlocked and something moved behind the hedge as I drew level. A woman in a green and white check coat and a small button of a hat on soft blonde hair stepped out of the maze and stood looking wild-eyed at my car, as if she hadn't heard it come up the hill. Then she turned swiftly and dodged back out of sight. It was Carmen Sternwood, of course.

I went on up the street and parked and walked back. In the daylight it seemed an exposed and dangerous thing to do. I went in through the hedge. She stood there straight and silent against the locked front door. One hand went slowly up to her teeth and her teeth bit at her funny thumb. There were purple smears under her eyes and her face was gnawed white by nerves.

She half smiled at me. She said: "Hello," in a thin, brittle voice. "Wha–what–?" That tailed off and she went back to the thumb.

"Remember me?" I said. "Doghouse Reilly, the man that grew too tall. Remember?"

She nodded and a quick jerky smile played across her face.

"Let's go in," I said. "I've got a key. Swell, huh?"

"Wha–wha–?"

I pushed her to one side and put the key in the door and opened it and pushed her in through it. I shut the door again and stood there sniffing. The place was horrible by daylight. The Chinese junk on the walls, the rug, the fussy lamps, the teakwood stuff, the sticky riot of colors, the totem pole, the flagon of ether and laudanum–all this in the daytime had a stealthy nastiness, like a fag party.

The girl and I stood looking at each other. She tried to keep a cute little smile on her face but her face was too tired to be bothered. It kept going blank on her. The smile would wash off like water off sand and her pale skin had a harsh granular texture under the stunned and stupid blankness of her eyes. A whitish tongue licked at the corners of her mouth. A pretty, spoiled and not very bright little girl who had gone very, very wrong, and nobody was doing anything about it. To hell with the rich. They made me sick. I rolled a cigarette in my fingers and pushed some books out of the way and sat on the end of the black desk. I lit my cigarette, puffed a plume of smoke and watched the thumb and tooth act for a while in silence. Carmen stood in front of me, like a bad girl in the principal's office.

"What are you doing here?" I asked her finally.

She picked at the cloth of her coat and didn't answer.

"How much do you remember of last night?"

She answered that—with a foxy glitter rising at the back of her eyes. "Remember what? I was sick last night. I was home." Her voice was a cautious throaty sound that just reached my ears.

"Like hell you were."

Her eyes flicked up and down very swiftly.

"Before you went home," I said. "Before I took you home. Here. In that chair—" I pointed to it—"on that orange shawl. You remember all right."

A slow flush crept up her throat. That was something. She could blush. A glint of white showed under the clogged gray irises. She chewed hard on her thumb.

"You—were the one?" she breathed.

"Me. How much of it stays with you?"

She said vaguely: "Are you the police?"

"No. I'm a friend of your father's."

"You're not the police?"

"No."

She let out a thin sigh. "Wha—what do you want?"

"Who killed him?"

Her shoulders jerked, but nothing more moved in her face. "Who else—knows?"

"About Geiger? I don't know. Not the police, or they'd be camping here. Maybe Joe Brody."

It was a stab in the dark but it got a yelp out of her. "Joe Brody! Him!"

Then we were both silent. I dragged at my cigarette and she ate her thumb.

"Don't get clever, for God's sake," I urged her. "This is a spot for a little old-fashioned simplicity. Did Brody kill him?"

"Kill who?"

"Oh, Christ," I said.

She looked hurt. Her chin came down an inch. "Yes," she said solemnly. "Joe did it."

"Why?"

"I don't know." She shook her head, persuading herself that she didn't know.

"Seen much of him lately?"

Her hands went down and made small white knots. "Just once or twice. I hate him."

"Then you know where he lives."

"Yes."

"And you don't like him any more?"

"I hate him!"

"Then you'd like him for the spot."

A little blank again. I was going too fast for her. It was hard not to. "Are you willing to tell the police it was Joe Brody?" I probed.

Sudden panic flamed all over her face. "If I can kill the nude photo angle, of course," I added soothingly.

She giggled. That gave me a nasty feeling. If she had screeched or wept or even nosedived to the floor in a dead faint, that would have been all right. She just giggled. It was suddenly a lot of fun. She had had her photo taken as Isis and somebody had swiped it and somebody had bumped Geiger off in front of her and she was drunker than a Legion convention, and it was suddenly a lot of nice clean fun. So she giggled. Very cute. The giggles got louder and ran around the corners of the room like rats behind the wainscoting. She started to go hysterical. I slid off the desk and stepped up close to her and gave her a smack on the side of the face.

"Just like last night," I said. "We're a scream together. Reilly and Sternwood, two stooges in search of a comedian."

The giggles stopped dead, but she didn't mind the slap any more than last night. Probably all her boy friends got around to slapping her sooner or later. I could understand how they might. I sat down on the end of the black desk again.

"Your name isn't Reilly," she said seriously. "It's Philip Marlowe. You're a private detective. Viv told me. She showed me your card." She smoothed the cheek I had slapped. She smiled at me, as if I was nice to be with.

"Well, you do remember," I said. "And you came back to look for that photo and you couldn't get into the house. Didn't you?"

Her chin ducked down and up. She worked the smile. I was having the eye put on me. I was being brought into camp. I was going to yell "Yippee!" in a minute and ask her to go to Yuma.

"The photo's gone," I said. "I looked last night, before I took you home. Probably Brody took it with him. You're not kidding me about Brody?"

She shook her head earnestly.

"It's a pushover," I said. "You don't have to give it another thought. Don't tell a soul you were here, last night or today. Not even Vivian. Just forget you were here. Leave it to Reilly."

"Your name isn't—" she began, and then stopped and shook her head vigorously in agreement with what I had said or with what she had just thought of. Her eyes became narrow and almost black and as shallow as enamel on a cafeteria tray. She had had an idea. "I have to go home now," she said, as if we had been having a cup of tea.

"Sure."

I didn't move. She gave me another cute glance and went on towards the front door. She had her hand on the knob when we both heard a car coming. She looked at me with questions in her eyes. I shrugged. The car stopped, right in front of the house. Terror twisted her face. There were steps and the bell rang. Carmen stared back at me over her shoulder, her hand clutching the door knob, almost drolling with fear. The bell kept on ringing. Then the ringing stopped. A key tickled at the door and Carmen jumped away from it and stood frozen. The door swung open. A man stepped through it briskly and stopped dead, staring at us quietly, with complete composure.

CHAPTER THIRTEEN

HE WAS a gray man, all gray, except for his polished black shoes and two scarlet diamonds in his gray satin tie that looked like the diamonds on roulette layouts. His shirt was gray and his double-breasted suit of soft, beautifully cut flannel. Seeing Carmen he took a gray hat off and his hair underneath it was gray and as fine as if it had been sifted through gauze. His thick gray eyebrows had that indefinably sporty look. He had a long chin, a nose with a hook to it, thoughtful gray eyes that had a slanted look because the fold of skin over his upper lid came down over the corner of the lid itself.

He stood there politely, one hand touching the door at his back, the other holding the gray hat and flapping it gently against his thigh. He looked hard, not the hardness of the tough guy. More like the hardness of a well-weathered horseman. But he was no horseman. He was Eddie Mars.

He pushed the door shut behind him and put that hand in the lap-seamed pocket of his coat and left the thumb outside to glisten in the rather dim light of the room. He smiled at Carmen. He had a nice easy smile. She licked her lips and stared at him. The fear went out of her face. She smiled back.

"Excuse the casual entrance," he said. "The bell didn't seem to rouse anybody. Is Mr. Geiger around?"

I said: "No. We don't know just where he is. We found the door a little open. We stepped inside."

He nodded and touched his long chin with the brim of his hat. "You're friends of his, of course?"

"Just business acquaintances. We dropped by for a book."

"A book, eh?" He said that quickly and brightly and, I thought, a little slyly, as if he knew all about Geiger's books. Then he looked at Carmen again and shrugged.

I moved towards the door. "We'll trot along now," I said. I took hold of her arm. She was staring at Eddie Mars. She liked him.

"Any message—if Geiger comes back?" Eddie Mars asked gently.

"We won't bother you."

"That's too bad," he said, with too much meaning. His gray eyes twinkled and then hardened as I went past him to open the door. He added in a casual tone: "The girl can dust. I'd like to talk to you a little, soldier."

I let go of her arm. I gave him a blank stare. "Kidder, eh?" he said nicely. "Don't waste it. I've got two boys outside in a car that always do just what I want them to."

Carmen made a sound at my side and bolted through the door. Her steps faded rapidly downhill. I hadn't seen her car, so she must have left it down below. I started to say: "What the hell—!"

"Oh, skip it," Eddie Mars sighed. "There's something wrong around here. I'm going to find out what it is. If you want to pick lead out of your belly, get in my way."

"Well, well," I said, "a tough guy."

"Only when necessary, soldier." He wasn't looking at me any more. He was walking around the room, frowning, not paying any attention to me. I looked out above the broken pane of the front window. The top of a car showed over the hedge. Its motor idled.

Eddie Mars found the purple flagon and the two gold-veined glasses on the desk. He sniffed at one of the glasses, then at the flagon. A disgusted smile wrinkled his lips. "The lousy pimp," he said tonelessly.

He looked at a couple of books, grunted, went on around the desk and stood in front of the little totem pole with the camera eye. He studied it, dropped his glance to the floor in front of it. He moved the small rug with his foot, then bent swiftly, his body tense. He went down on the floor with one gray knee. The desk hid him from me partly. There was a sharp exclamation and he came up again. His arm flashed under his coat and a black Luger appeared in his hand. He held it in long brown fingers, not pointing it at me, not pointing it at anything.

"Blood," he said. "Blood on the floor there, under the rug. Quite a lot of blood."

"Is that so?" I said, looking interested.

He slid into the chair behind the desk and hooked the mulberry-colored phone towards him and shifted the Luger to his left hand. He frowned sharply at the telephone, bringing his thick gray eyebrows close together and making a hard crease in the weathered skin at the top of his hooked nose. "I think we'll have some law," he said.

I went over and kicked at the rug that lay where Geiger had lain. "It's old blood," I said. "Dried blood."

"Just the same we'll have some law."

"Why not?" I said.

His eyes went narrow. The veneer had flaked off him, leaving a well-dressed hard boy with a Luger. He didn't like my agreeing with him.

"Just who the hell are you, soldier?"

"Marlowe is the name. I'm a sleuth."

"Never heard of you. Who's the girl?"

"Client. Geiger was trying to throw a loop on her with some blackmail. We came to talk it over. He wasn't here. The door being open we walked in to wait. Or did I tell you that?"

"Convenient," he said. "The door being open. When you didn't have a key."

"Yes. How come *you* had a key?"

"Is that any of your business, soldier?"

"I could make it my business."

He smiled tightly and pushed his hat back on his gray hair. "And I could make your business my business."

"You wouldn't like it. The pay's too small."

"All right, bright eyes. I own this house. Geiger is my tenant. Now what do you think of that?"

"You know such lovely people."

"I take them as they come. They come all kinds." He glanced down at the Luger, shrugged and tucked it back under his arm. "Got any good ideas, soldier?"

"Lots of them. Somebody gunned Geiger. Somebody got gunned by Geiger, who ran away. Or it was two other fellows. Or Geiger was running a cult and made blood sacrifices in front of that totem pole. Or he had chicken for dinner and liked to kill his chickens in the front parlor."

The gray man scowled at me.

"I give up," I said. "Better call your friends downtown."

"I don't get it," he snapped. "I don't get your game here."

"Go ahead, call the buttons. You'll get a big reaction from it."

He thought that over without moving. His lips went back against his teeth. "I don't get that, either," he said tightly.

"Maybe it just isn't your day. I know you, Mr. Mars. The Cypress Club at Las Olindas. Flash gambling for flash people. The local law in your pocket and a well-greased line into L.A. In other words, protection. Geiger was in a racket that needed that too. Perhaps you spared him a little now and then, seeing he's your tenant."

His mouth became a hard white grimace. "Geiger was in what racket?"

"The smut book racket."

He stared at me for a long level minute. "Somebody got to him," he said softly. "You know something about it. He didn't show at the store today. They don't know where he is. He didn't answer the phone here. I came up to see about it. I find blood on the floor, under a rug. And you and a girl here."

"A little weak," I said. "But maybe you can sell the story to a willing buyer. You missed a little something, though. Somebody moved his books out of the store today—the nice books he rented out."

He snapped his fingers sharply and said: "I should have thought of that, soldier. You seem to get around. How do you figure it?"

"I think Geiger was rubbed. I think that is his blood. And the books being moved out gives a motive for hiding the body for a while. Somebody is taking over the racket and wants a little time to organize."

"They can't get away with it," Eddie Mars said grimly.

"Who says so? You and a couple of gunmen in your car outside? This is a big town now, Eddie. Some very tough people have checked in here lately. The penalty of growth."

"You talk too damned much," Eddie Mars said. He bared his teeth and whistled twice, sharply. A car door slammed outside and running steps came through the hedge. Mars flicked the Luger out again and pointed it at my chest. "Open the door."

The knob rattled and a voice called out. I didn't move. The muzzle of the Luger looked like the mouth of the Second Street tunnel, but I didn't move. Not being bullet proof is an idea I had had to get used to.

"Open it yourself, Eddie. Who the hell are you to give me orders? Be nice and I might help you out."

He came to his feet rigidly and moved around the end of the desk and over to the door. He opened it without taking his eyes off me. Two men tumbled into the room, reaching busily under their arms. One was an obvious pug, a good-looking pale-faced boy with a bad nose and one ear like a club steak. The other man was slim, blond, deadpan, with close-set eyes and no color in them.

Eddie Mars said: "See if this bird is wearing any iron."

The blond flicked a short-barreled gun out and stood pointing it at me. The pug sidled over flatfooted and felt my pockets with care. I turned around for him like a bored beauty modeling an evening gown.

"No gun," he said in a burry voice.

"Find out who he is."

The pug slipped a hand into my breast pocket and drew out my wallet. He flipped it open and studied the contents. "Name's Philip Marlowe, Eddie. Lives at the Hobart Arms on Franklin. Private license, deputy's badge and all. A shamus." He slipped the wallet back in my pocket, slapped my face lightly and turned away.

"Beat it," Eddie Mars said.

The two gunmen went out again and closed the door. There was the sound of them getting back into the car. They started its motor and kept it idling once more.

"All right. Talk," Eddie Mars snapped. The peaks of his eyebrows made sharp angles against his forehead.

"I'm not ready to give out. Killing Geiger to grab his racket would be a dumb trick and I'm not sure it happened that way, assuming he has been killed. But I'm sure that whoever got the books knows what's what, and I'm sure that the blonde lady down at his store is scared batty about something or other. And I have a guess who got the books."

"Who?"

"That's the part I'm not ready to give out. I've got a client, you know."

He wrinkled his nose. "That—" he chopped it off quickly.

"I expected you would know the girl," I said.

"Who got the books, soldier?"

"Not ready to talk, Eddie. Why should I?"

He put the Luger down on the desk and slapped it with his open palm. "This," he said. "And I might make it worth your while."

"That's the spirit. Leave the gun out of it. I can always hear the sound of money. How much are you clinking at me?"

"For doing what?"

"What did you want done?"

He slammed the desk hard. "Listen, soldier. I ask you a question and you ask me another. We're not getting anywhere. I want to know where Geiger is, for my own personal reasons. I didn't like his racket and I didn't protect him. I happen to own this house. I'm not so crazy about that right now. I can believe that whatever you know about all this is under glass, or there would be a flock of johns squeaking sole leather around this dump. You haven't got anything to sell. My guess is you need a little protection yourself. So cough up."

It was a good guess, but I wasn't going to let him know it. I lit a cigarette and blew the match out and flicked it at the glass eye of the totem pole. "You're right," I said. "If anything has happened to Geiger, I'll have to give what I have to the law. Which puts it in the public domain and doesn't leave me anything to sell. So with your permission I'll just drift."

His face whitened under the tan. He looked mean, fast and tough for a moment. He made a movement to lift the gun. I added casually: "By the way, how is Mrs. Mars these days?"

I thought for a moment I had kidded him a little too far. His hand jerked at the gun, shaking. His face was stretched out by hard muscles. "Beat it," he said quite softly. "I don't give a damn where you go or what you do when you get there. Only take a word of advice, soldier. Leave me out of your plans or you'll wish your name was Murphy and you lived in Limerick."

"Well, that's not so far from Clonmel," I said. "I hear you had a pal came from there."

He leaned down on the desk, frozen-eyed, unmoving. I went over to the door and opened it and looked back at him. His eyes had followed me, but his lean gray body had not moved. There was hate in his eyes. I went out and through the hedge and up the hill to my car and got into it. I turned it around and drove up over the crest. Nobody shot at me. After a few blocks I turned off, cut the motor and sat for a few moments. Nobody followed me either. I drove back into Hollywood.

CHAPTER FOURTEEN

IT WAS ten minutes to five when I parked near the lobby entrance of the apartment house on Randall Place. A few windows were lit and radios were bleating at the dusk. I rode the automatic elevator up to the fourth floor and went along a wide hall carpeted in green and paneled in ivory. A cool breeze blew down the hall from the open screened door to the fire escape.

There was a small ivory pushbutton beside the door marked "405." I pushed it and waited what seemed a long time. Then the door opened noiselessly about a foot. There was a steady, furtive air in the way it opened. The man was long-legged, long-waisted, high-shouldered and he had dark brown eyes in a brown expressionless face that had learned to control its expressions long ago. Hair like steel wool grew far back on his head and gave him a great deal of domed brown forehead that might at a careless glance have seemed a dwelling place for brains. His somber eyes probed at me impersonally. His long thin brown fingers held the edge of the door. He said nothing.

I said: "Geiger?"

Nothing in the man's face changed that I could see. He brought a cigarette from behind the door and tucked it between his lips and drew a little smoke from it. The smoke came towards me in a lazy, contemptuous puff and behind it words in a cool, unhurried voice that had no more inflection than the voice of a faro dealer.

"You said what?"

"Geiger. Arthur Gwynn Geiger. The guy that has the books."

The man considered that without any haste. He glanced down at the tip of his cigarette. His other hand, the one that had been holding the door, dropped out of sight. His shoulder had a look as though his hidden hand might be making motions.

"Don't know anybody by that name," he said. "Does he live around here?"

I smiled. He didn't like the smile. His eyes got nasty. I said: "You're Joe Brody?"

The brown face hardened. "So what? Got a grift, brother—or just amusing yourself?"

"So you're Joe Brody," I said. "And you don't know anybody named Geiger. That's very funny."

"Yeah? You got a funny sense of humor maybe. Take it away and play on it somewhere else."

I leaned against the door and gave him a dreamy smile. "You got the books, Joe. I got the sucker list. We ought to talk things over."

He didn't shift his eyes from my face. There was a faint sound in the room behind him, as though a metal curtain ring clicked lightly on a metal rod. He glanced sideways into the room. He opened the door wider.

"Why not—if you think you've got something?" he said coolly. He stood aside from the door. I went past him into the room.

It was a cheerful room with good furniture and not too much of it. French windows in the end wall opened on a stone porch and looked across the dusk at the foothills. Near the windows a closed door in the west wall and near the entrance door another door in the same wall. This last had a plush curtain drawn across it on a thin brass rod below the lintel.

That left the east wall, in which there were no doors. There was a davenport backed against the middle of it, so I sat down on the davenport. Brody shut the door and walked crab-fashion to a tall oak desk studded with square nails. A cedarwood box with gilt hinges lay on the lowered leaf of the desk. He carried the box to an easy chair midway between the other two doors and sat down. I dropped my hat on the davenport and waited.

"Well, I'm listening," Brody said. He opened the cigar box and dropped his cigarette stub into a dish at his side. He put a long thin cigar in his mouth. "Cigar?" He tossed one at me through the air.

I reached for it. Brody took a gun out of the cigar box and pointed it at my nose. I looked at the gun. It was a black Police .38. I had no argument against it at the moment.

"Neat, huh?" Brody said. "Just kind of stand up a minute. Come forward just about two yards. You might grab a little air while you're doing that." His voice was the elaborately casual voice of the tough guy in pictures. Pictures have made them all like that.

"Tsk, tsk," I said, not moving at all. "Such a lot of guns around town and so few brains. You're the second guy I've met within hours who seems to think a gat in the hand means a world by the tail. Put it down and don't be silly, Joe."

His eyebrows came together and he pushed his chin at me. His eyes were mean.

"The other guy's name is Eddie Mars," I said. "Ever hear of him?"

"No." Brody kept the gun pointed at me.

"If he ever gets wise to where you were last night in the rain, he'll wipe you off the way a check raiser wipes a check."

"What would I be to Eddie Mars?" Brody asked coldly. But he lowered the gun to his knee.

"Not even a memory," I said.

We stared at each other. I didn't look at the pointed black slipper that showed under the plush curtain on the doorway to my left.

Brody said quietly: "Don't get me wrong. I'm not a tough guy—just careful. I don't know hell's first whisper about you. You might be a lifetaker for all I know."

"You're not careful enough," I said. "That play with Geiger's books was terrible."

He drew a long slow breath and let it out silently. Then he leaned back and crossed his long legs and held the Colt on his knee.

"Don't kid yourself I won't use this heat, if I have to," he said. "What's your story?"

"Have your friend with the pointed slippers come on in. She gets tired holding her breath."

Brody called out without moving his eyes off my stomach. "Come on in, Agnes."

The curtain swung aside and the green-eyed, thigh-swinging ash blonde from Geiger's store joined us in the room. She looked at me with a kind of mangled hatred. Her nostrils were pinched and her eyes had darkened a couple of shades. She looked very unhappy.

"I knew damn well you were trouble," she snapped at me. "I told Joe to watch his step."

"It's not his step, it's the back of his lap he ought to watch," I said.

"I suppose that's funny," the blonde squealed.

"It has been," I said. "But it probably isn't any more."

"Save the gags," Brody advised me. "Joe's watchin' his step plenty. Put some light on so I can see to pop this guy, if it works out that way."

The blonde snicked on a light in a big square standing lamp. She sank down into a chair beside the lamp and sat stiffly, as if her girdle was too tight. I put my cigar in my mouth and bit the end off. Brody's Colt took a close interest in me while I got matches out and lit the cigar. I tasted the smoke and said:

"The sucker list I spoke of is in code. I haven't cracked it yet, but there are about five hundred names. You got twelve boxes of books that I know of. You should have at least five hundred books. There'll be a bunch more out on loan, but say five hundred is the full crop, just to be cautious. If it's a good active list and you could run it even fifty per cent down the line, that would be one hundred and twenty-five thousand rentals. Your girl friend knows all about that. I'm only guessing. Put the average rental as low as you like, but it won't be less than a dollar. That merchandise costs money. At a dollar a rental you take one hundred and twenty-five grand and you still have your capital. I mean, you still have Geiger's capital. That's enough to spot a guy for."

The blonde yelped: "You're crazy, you goddam egg-headed—!"

Brody put his teeth sideways at her and snarled: "Pipe down, for Chrissake. Pipe down!"

She subsided into an outraged mixture of slow anguish and bottled fury. Her silvery nails scraped on her knees.

"It's no racket for bums," I told Brody almost affectionately. "It takes a smooth worker like you, Joe. You've got to get confidence and keep it. People who spend their money for second-hand sex jags are as nervous as dowagers who can't find the rest room. Personally I think the blackmail angles are a big mistake. I'm for shedding all that and sticking to legitimate sales and rentals."

Brody's dark brown stare moved up and down my face. His Colt went on hungering for my vital organs. "You're a funny guy," he said tonelessly. "Who has this lovely racket?"

"*You* have," I said. "Almost."

The blonde choked and clawed her ear. Brody didn't say anything. He just looked at me.

"What?" the blonde yelped. "You sit there and try to tell us Mr. Geiger ran that kind of business right down on the main drag? You're nuts!"

I leered at her politely. "Sure I do. Everybody knows the racket exists. Hollywood's made to order for it. If a thing like that has to exist, then right out on the street is where all practical coppers want it to exist. For the same reason they favor red light districts. They know where to flush the game when they want to."

"My God," the blonde wailed. "You let this cheesehead sit there and insult me, Joe? You with a gun in your hand and him holding nothing but a cigar and his thumb?"

"I like it," Brody said. "The guy's got good ideas. Shut your trap and keep it shut, or I'll slap it shut for you with this." He flicked the gun around in an increasingly negligent manner.

The blonde gasped and turned her face to the wall. Brody looked at me and said cunningly: "*How* have I got that lovely racket?"

"You shot Geiger to get it. Last night in the rain. It was dandy shooting weather. The trouble is he wasn't alone when you whiffed him. Either you didn't notice that, which seems unlikely, or you got the wind up and lammed. But you had nerve enough to take the plate out of his camera and you had nerve enough to come back later on and hide his corpse, so you could tidy up on the books before the law knew it had a murder to investigate."

"Yah," Brody said contemptuously. The Colt wobbled on his knee. His brown face was as hard as a piece of carved wood. "You take chances, mister. It's kind of goddamned lucky for you I *didn't* bop Geiger."

"You can step off for it just the same," I told him cheerfully. "You're made to order for the rap."

Brody's voice rustled. "Think you got me framed for it?"

"Positive."

"How come?"

"There's somebody who'll tell it that way. I told you there was a witness. Don't go simple on me, Joe."

He exploded then. "That goddamned little hot pants!" he yelled. "She would, god damn her! She would—just that!"

I leaned back and grinned at him. "Swell. I thought you had those nude photos of her."

He didn't say anything. The blonde didn't say anything. I let them chew on it. Brody's face cleared slowly, with a sort of grayish relief. He put his Colt down on the end table beside his chair but kept his right hand close to it. He knocked ash from his cigar on the carpet and stared at me with eyes that were a tight shine between narrowed lids.

"I guess you think I'm dumb," Brody said.

"Just average, for a grifter. Get the pictures."

"What pictures?"

I shook my head. "Wrong play, Joe. Innocence gets you nowhere. You were either there last night, or you got the nude photo from somebody that was there. You knew *she* was there, because you had your girl friend threaten Mrs. Regan with a police rap. The only ways you could know enough to do that would be by seeing what happened or by holding the photo and knowing where and when it was taken. Cough up and be sensible."

"I'd have to have a little dough," Brody said. He turned his head a little to look at the green-eyed blonde. Not now green-eyed and only superficially a blonde. She was as limp as a fresh-killed rabbit.

"No dough," I said.

He scowled bitterly. "How'd you get to me?"

I flicked my wallet out and let him look at my buzzer. "I was working on Geiger—for a client. I was outside last night, in the rain. I heard the shots. I crashed in. I didn't see the killer. I saw everything else."

"And kept your lip buttoned," Brody sneered.

I put my wallet away. "Yes," I admitted. "Up till now. Do I get the photos or not?"

"About these books," Brody said. "I don't get that."

"I tailed them here from Geiger's store. I have a witness."

"That punk kid?"

"What punk kid?"

He scowled again. "The kid that works at the store. He skipped out after the truck left. Agnes don't even know where he flops."

"That helps," I said, grinning at him. "That angle worried me a little. Either of you ever been in Geiger's house—before last night?"

"Not even last night," Brody said sharply. "So she says I gunned him, eh?"

"With the photos in hand I might be able to convince her she was wrong. There was a little drinking being done."

Brody sighed. "She hates my guts. I bounced her out. I got paid, sure, but I'd of had to do it anyway. She's too screwy for a simple guy like me." He cleared his throat. "How about a little dough? I'm down to nickels. Agnes and me gotta move on."

"Not from my client."

"Listen—"

"Get the pictures, Brody."

"Oh, hell," he said. "You win." He stood up and slipped the Colt into his side pocket. His left hand went up inside his coat. He was holding it there, his face twisted with disgust, when the door buzzer rang and kept on ringing.

CHAPTER FIFTEEN

HE DIDN'T LIKE that. His lower lip went in under his teeth, and his eyebrows drew down sharply at the corners. His whole face became sharp and foxy and mean.

The buzzer kept up its song. I didn't like it either. If the visitors should happen to be Eddie Mars and his boys, I might get chilled off just for being there. If it was the police, I was caught with nothing to give them but a smile and a promise. And if it was some of Brody's friends—supposing he had any—they might turn out to be tougher than he was.

The blonde didn't like it. She stood up in a surge and chipped at the air with one hand. Nerve tension made her face old and ugly.

Watching me, Brody jerked a small drawer in the desk and picked a bone-handled automatic out of it. He held it at the blonde. She slid over to him and took it, shaking.

"Sit down next to him," Brody snapped. "Hold it on him low down, away from the door. If he gets funny use your own judgment. We ain't licked yet, baby."

"Oh, Joe," the blonde wailed. She came over and sat next to me on the davenport and pointed the gun at my leg artery. I didn't like the jerky look in her eyes.

The door buzzer stopped humming and a quick impatient rapping on the wood followed it. Brody put his hand in his pocket, on his gun, and walked over to the door and opened it with his left hand. Carmen Sternwood pushed him back into the room by putting a little revolver against his lean brown lips.

Brody backed away from her with his mouth working and an expression of panic on his face. Carmen shut the door behind her and looked neither at me nor at Agnes. She stalked Brody carefully, her tongue sticking out a little between her teeth. Brody took both hands out of his pockets and gestured placatingly at her. His eyebrows designed themselves into an odd assortment of curves and angles. Agnes turned the gun away from me and swung it at Carmen. I shot my hand out and closed my fingers down hard over her hand and jammed my thumb on the safety catch. It was already on. I kept it on. There was a short silent tussle, to which neither Brody nor Carmen paid any attention whatever. I had the gun. Agnes breathed deeply and shivered the whole length of her body. Carmen's face had a bony scraped look and her breath hissed. Her voice said without tone:

"I want my pictures, Joe."

Brody swallowed and tried to grin. "Sure, kid, sure." He said it in a small flat voice that was as much like the voice he had used to me as a scooter is like a ten-ton truck.

Carmen said: "You shot Arthur Geiger. I saw you. I want my pictures." Brody turned green.

"Hey, wait a minute, Carmen," I yelped.

Blonde Agnes came to life with a rush. She ducked her head and sank her teeth in my right hand. I made more noises and shook her off.

"Listen, kid," Brody whined. "Listen a minute—"

The blonde spat at me and threw herself on my leg and tried to bite that. I cracked her on the head with the gun, not very hard, and tried to stand up. She rolled down my legs and wrapped her arms around them. I fell back on the davenport. The blonde was strong with the madness of love or fear, or a mixture of both, or maybe she was just strong.

Brody grabbed for the little revolver that was so close to his face. He missed. The gun made a sharp rapping noise that was not very loud. The bullet broke glass in a folded-back French window. Brody groaned horribly and fell down on the floor and jerked Carmen's feet from under her. She landed in a heap and the little revolver went skidding off into a corner. Brody jumped up on his knees and reached for his pocket.

I hit Agnes on the head with less delicacy than before, kicked her off my feet, and stood up. Brody flicked his eyes at me. I showed him the automatic. He stopped trying to get his hand into his pocket.

"Christ!" he whined. "Don't let her kill me!"

I began to laugh. I laughed like an idiot, without control. Blonde Agnes was sitting up on the floor with her hands flat on the carpet and her mouth wide open and a wick of metallic blond hair down over her right eye. Carmen was crawling on her hands and knees, still hissing. The metal of her little revolver glistened against the baseboard over in the corner. She crawled towards it relentlessly.

I waved my share of the guns at Brody and said: "Stay put. You're all right."

I stepped past the crawling girl and picked the gun up. She looked up at me and began to giggle. I put her gun in my pocket and patted her on the back. "Get up, angel. You look like a Pekinese."

I went over to Brody and put the automatic against his midriff and reached his Colt out of his side pocket. I now had all the guns that had been exposed to view. I stuffed them into my pockets and held my hand out to him. "Give."

He nodded, licking his lips, his eyes still scared. He took a fat envelope out of his breast pocket and gave it to me. There was a developed plate in the envelope and five glossy prints.

"Sure these are all?"

He nodded again. I put the envelope in my own breast pocket and turned away. Agnes was back on the davenport, straightening her hair. Her eyes ate Carmen with a green distillation of hate. Carmen was up on her feet too, coming towards me with her hand out, still giggling and hissing. There was a little froth at the corners of her mouth. Her small white teeth glinted close to her lips.

"Can I have them now?" she asked me with a coy smile.

"I'll take care of them for you. Go on home."

"Home?"

I went to the door and looked out. The cool night breeze was blowing peacefully down the hall. No excited neighbors hung out of doorways. A small gun had gone off and broken a pane of glass, but noises like that don't mean much any more. I held the door open and jerked my head at Carmen. She came towards me, smiling uncertainly.

"Go on home and wait for me," I said soothingly.

She put her thumb up. Then she nodded and slipped past me into the hall. She touched my cheek with her fingers as she went by. "You'll take care of Carmen, won't you?" she cooed.

"Check."

"You're cute."

"What you see is nothing," I said. "I've got a Bali dancing girl tattooed on my right thigh."

Her eyes rounded. She said: "Naughty," and wagged a finger at me. Then she whispered: "Can I have my gun?"

"Not now. Later. I'll bring it to you."

She grabbed me suddenly around the neck and kissed me on the mouth. "I like you," she said. "Carmen likes you a lot." She ran off down the hall as gay as a thrush, waved at me from the stairs and ran down the stairs out of my sight.

I went back into Brody's apartment.

CHAPTER SIXTEEN

I WENT OVER to the folded-back French window and looked at the small broken pane in the upper part of it. The bullet from Carmen's gun had smashed the glass like a blow. It had not made a hole. There was a small hole in the plaster which a keen eye would find quickly enough. I pulled the drapes over the broken pane and took Carmen's gun out of my pocket. It was a Banker's Special, .22 caliber, hollow point cartridges. It had a pearl grip, and a small round silver plate set into the butt was engraved: "Carmen from Owen." She made saps of all of them.

I put the gun back in my pocket and sat down close to Brody and stared into his bleak brown eyes. A minute passed. The blonde adjusted her face by the aid of a pocket mirror. Brody fumbled around with a cigarette and jerked: "Satisfied?"

"So far. Why did you put the bite on Mrs. Regan instead of the old man?"

"Tapped the old man once. About six, seven months ago. I figure maybe he gets sore enough to call in some law."

"What made you think Mrs. Regan wouldn't tell him about it?"

He considered that with some care, smoking his cigarette and keeping his eyes on my face. Finally he said: "How well you know her?"

"I've met her twice. You must know her a lot better to take a chance on that squeeze with the photo."

"She skates around plenty. I figure maybe she has a couple of soft spots she don't want the old man to know about. I figure she can raise five grand easy."

"A little weak," I said. "But pass it. You're broke, eh?"

"I been shaking two nickels together for a month, trying to get them to mate."

"What you do for a living?"

"Insurance. I got desk room in Puss Walgreen's office, Fulwider Building, Western and Santa Monica."

"When you open up, you open up. The books here in your apartment?"

He snapped his teeth and waved a brown hand. Confidence was oozing back into his manner. "Hell, no. In storage."

"You had a man bring them here and then you had a storage outfit come and take them away again right afterwards?"

"Sure. I don't want them moved direct from Geiger's place, do I?"

"You're smart," I said admiringly. "Anything incriminating in the joint right now?"

He looked worried again. He shook his head sharply.

"That's fine," I told him. I looked across at Agnes. She had finished fixing her face and was staring at the wall, blank-eyed, hardly listening. Her face had the drowsiness which strain and shock induce, after their first incidence.

Brody flicked his eyes warily. "Well?"

"How'd you come by the photo?"

He scowled. "Listen, you got what you came after, got it plenty cheap. You done a nice neat job. Now go peddle it to your top man. I'm clean. I don't know nothing about any photo, do I, Agnes?"

The blonde opened her eyes and looked at him with vague but uncomplimentary speculation. "A half smart guy," she said with a tired sniff. "That's all I ever draw. Never once a guy that's smart all the way around the course. Never once."

I grinned at her. "Did I hurt your head much?"

"You and every other man I ever met."

I looked back at Brody. He was pinching his cigarette between his fingers, with a sort of twitch. His hand seemed to be shaking a little. His brown poker face was still smooth.

"We've got to agree on a story," I said. "For instance, Carmen wasn't here. That's very important. She wasn't here. That was a vision you saw."

"Huh!" Brody sneered. "If you say so, pal, and if—" he put his hand out palm up and cupped the fingers and rolled the thumb gently against the index and middle fingers.

I nodded. "We'll see. There might be a small contribution. You won't count it in grands, though. Now where did you get the picture?"

"A guy slipped it to me."

"Uh-huh. A guy you just passed in the street. You wouldn't know him again. You never saw him before."

Brody yawned. "It dropped out of his pocket," he leered.

"Uh-huh. Got an alibi for last night, poker pan?"

"Sure. I was right here. Agnes was with me. Okey, Agnes?"

"I'm beginning to feel sorry for you again," I said.

His eyes flicked wide and his mouth hung loose, the cigarette balanced on his lower lip.

"You think you're smart and you're so goddamned dumb," I told him. "Even if you don't dance off up in Quentin, you have such a bleak long lonely time ahead of you."

His cigarette jerked and dropped ash on his vest.

"Thinking about how smart you are," I said.

"Take the air," he growled suddenly. "Dust. I got enough chinning with you. Beat it."

"Okey." I stood up and went over to the tall oak desk and took his two guns out of my pockets, laid them side by side on the blotter so that the barrels were exactly parallel. I reached my hat off the floor beside the davenport and started for the door.

Brody yelped: "Hey!"

I turned and waited. His cigarette was jiggling like a doll on a coiled spring. "Everything's smooth, ain't it?" he asked.

"Why, sure. This is a free country. You don't have to stay out of jail, if you don't want to. That is, if you're a citizen. Are you a citizen?"

He just stared at me, jiggling the cigarette. The blonde Agnes turned her head slowly and stared at me along the same level. Their glances contained almost the exact same blend of foxiness, doubt and frustrated anger. Agnes reached her silvery nails up abruptly and yanked a hair out of her head and broke it between her fingers, with a bitter jerk.

Brody said tightly: "You're not going to any cops, brother. Not if it's the Sternwoods you're working for. I've got too much stuff on that family. You got your pictures and you got your hush. Go and peddle your papers."

"Make your mind up," I said. "You told me to dust, I was on my way out, you hollered at me and I stopped, and now I'm on my way out again. Is that what you want?"

"You ain't got anything on me," Brody said.

"Just a couple of murders. Small change in your circle."

He didn't jump more than an inch, but it looked like a foot. The white cornea showed all around the tobacco-colored iris of his eyes. The brown skin of his face took on a greenish tinge in the lamplight.

Blonde Agnes let out a low animal wail and buried her head in a cushion on the end of the davenport. I stood there and admired the long line of her thighs.

Brody moistened his lips slowly and said: "Sit down, pal. Maybe I have a little more for you. What's that crack about two murders mean?"

I leaned against the door. "Where were you last night about seven-thirty, Joe?"

His mouth drooped sulkily and he stared down at the floor. "I was watching a guy, a guy who had a nice racket I figured he needed a partner in. Geiger. I was watching him now and then to see had he any tough connections. I figure he has friends or he don't work the racket as open as he does. But they don't go to his house. Only dames."

"You didn't watch hard enough," I said. "Go on."

"I'm there last night on the street below Geiger's house. It's raining hard and I'm buttoned up in my coupe and I don't see anything. There's a car in front of Geiger's and another car a little way up the hill. That's why I stay down below. There's a big Buick parked down where I am and after a while I go over and take a gander into it. It's registered to Vivian Regan.

Nothing happens, so I scram. That's all." He waved his cigarette. His eyes crawled up and down my face.

"Could be," I said. "Know where that Buick is now?"

"Why would I?"

"In the Sheriff's garage. It was lifted out of twelve feet of water off Lido fish pier this a.m. There was a dead man in it. He had been sapped and the car pointed out the pier and the hand throttle pulled down."

Brody was breathing hard. One of his feet tapped restlessly. "Jesus, guy, you can't pin that one on me," he said thickly.

"Why not? This Buick was down back of Geiger's according to you. Well, Mrs. Regan didn't have it out. Her chauffeur, a lad named Owen Taylor, had it out. He went over to Geiger's place to have words with him, because Owen Taylor was sweet on Carmen, and he didn't like the kind of games Geiger was playing with her. He let himself in the back way with a jimmy and a gun and he caught Geiger taking a photo of Carmen without any clothes on. So his gun went off, as guns will, and Geiger fell down dead and Owen ran away, but not without the photo negative Geiger had just taken. So you ran after him and took the photo from him. How else would you have got hold of it?"

Brody licked his lips. "Yeah," he said. "But that don't make me knock him off. Sure, I heard the shots and saw this killer come slamming down the back steps into the Buick and off. I took out after him. He hit the bottom of the canyon and went west on Sunset. Beyond Beverly Hills he skidded off the road and had to stop and I came up and played copper. He had a gun but his nerve was bad and I sapped him down. So I went through his clothes and found out who he was and I lifted the plateholder, just out of curiosity. I was wondering what it was all about and getting my neck wet when he came out of it all of a sudden and knocked me off the car. He was out of sight when I picked myself up. That's the last I saw of him."

"How did you know it was Geiger he shot?" I asked gruffly.

Brody shrugged. "I figure it was, but I can be wrong. When I had the plate developed and saw what was on it, I was pretty damn sure. And when Geiger didn't come down to the store this morning and didn't answer his phone I was plenty sure. So I figure it's a good time to move his books out and make a quick touch on the Sternwoods for travel money and blow for a while."

I nodded. "That seems reasonable. Maybe you didn't murder anybody at that. Where did you hide Geiger's body?"

He jumped his eyebrows. Then he grinned. "Nix, nix. Skip it. You think I'd go back there and handle him, not knowing when a couple carloads of law would come tearing around the corner? Nix."

"Somebody hid the body," I said.

Brody shrugged. The grin stayed on his face. He didn't believe me. While he was still not believing me the door buzzer started to ring again. Brody stood up sharply, hard-eyed. He glanced over at his guns on the desk.

"So she's back again," he growled.

"If she is, she doesn't have her gun," I comforted him. "Don't you have any other friends?"

"Just about one," he growled. "I got enough of this puss in the corner game." He marched to the desk and took the Colt. He held it down at his side and went to the door. He put his left hand to the knob and twisted it and opened the door a foot and leaned into the opening, holding the gun tight against his thigh.

A voice said: "Brody?"

Brody said something I didn't hear. The two quick reports were muffled. The gun must have been pressed tight against Brody's body. He tilted forward against the door and the weight of his body pushed it shut with a bang. He slid down the wood. His feet pushed the carpet away behind him. His left hand dropped off the knob and the arm slapped the floor with a thud. His head was wedged against the door. He didn't move. The Colt clung to his right hand.

I jumped across the room and rolled him enough to get the door open and crowd through. A woman peered out of a door almost opposite. Her face was full of fright and she pointed along the hall with a clawlike hand.

I raced down the hall and heard thumping feet going down the tile steps and went down after the sound. At the lobby level the front door was closing itself quietly and running feet slapped the sidewalk outside. I made the door before it was shut, clawed it open again and charged out.

A tall hatless figure in a leather jerkin was running diagonally across the street between the parked cars. The figure turned and flame spurted from it. Two heavy hammers hit the stucco wall beside me. The figure ran on, dodged between two cars, vanished.

A man came up beside me and barked: "What happened?"

"Shooting going on," I said.

"Jesus!" He scuttled into the apartment house.

I walked quickly down the sidewalk to my car and got in and started it. I pulled out from the curb and drove down the hill, not fast. No other car started up on the other side of the street. I thought I heard steps, but I wasn't sure about that. I rode down the hill a block and a half, turned at the intersection and started back up. The sound of a muted whistling came to me faintly along the sidewalk. Then steps. I double parked and slid out between two cars and went down low. I took Carmen's little revolver out of my pocket.

The sound of the steps grew louder, and the whistling went on cheerfully. In a moment the jerkin showed. I stepped out between the two cars and said: "Got a match, buddy?"

The boy spun towards me and his right hand darted up to go inside the jerkin. His eyes were a wet shine in the glow of the round electroliers. Moist dark eyes shaped like almonds, and a pallid handsome face with wavy black hair growing low on the forehead in two points. A very handsome boy indeed, the boy from Geiger's store.

He stood there looking at me silently, his right hand on the edge of the jerkin, but not inside it yet. I held the little revolver down at my side.

"You must have thought a lot of that queen," I said.

"Go — yourself," the boy said softly, motionless between the parked cars and the five-foot retaining wall on the inside of the sidewalk.

A siren wailed distantly coming up the long hill. The boy's head jerked towards the sound. I stepped in close and put my gun into his jerkin.

"Me or the cops?" I asked him.

His head rolled a little sideways as if I had slapped his face. "Who are you?" he snarled.

"Friend of Geiger's."

"Get away from me, you son of a bitch."

"This is a small gun, kid. I'll give it you through the navel and it will take three months to get you well enough to walk. But you'll get well. So you can walk to the nice new gas chamber up in Quentin."

He said: "Go — yourself." His hand moved inside the jerkin. I pressed harder on his stomach. He let out a long soft sigh, took his hand away from the jerkin and let it fall limp at his side. His wide shoulders sagged. "What you want?" he whispered.

I reached inside the jerkin and plucked out the automatic. "Get into my car, kid."

He stepped past me and I crowded him from behind. He got into the car.

"Under the wheel, kid. You drive."

He slid under the wheel and I got into the car beside him. I said: "Let the prowl car pass up the hill. They'll think we moved over when we heard the siren. Then turn her down hill and we'll go home."

I put Carmen's gun away and leaned the automatic against the boy's ribs. I looked back through the window. The whine of the siren was very loud now. Two red lights swelled in the middle of the street. They grew larger and blended into one and the car rushed by in a wild flurry of sound.

"Let's go," I said.

The boy swung the car and started off down the hill.

"Let's go home," I said. "To Laverne Terrace."

His smooth lips twitched. He swung the car west on Franklin. "You're a simple-minded lad. What's your name?"

"Carol Lundgren," he said lifelessly.

"You shot the wrong guy, Carol. Joe Brody didn't kill your queen."

He spoke three words to me and kept on driving.

CHAPTER SEVENTEEN

A MOON HALF GONE from the full glowed through a ring of mist among the high branches of the eucalyptus trees on Laverne Terrace. A radio sounded loudly from a house low down the hill. The boy swung the car over to the box hedge in front of Geiger's house, killed the motor and sat looking straight before him with both hands on the wheel. No light showed through Geiger's hedge.

I said: "Anybody home, son?"

"You ought to know."

"How would I know?"

"Go —— yourself."

"That's how people get false teeth."

He showed me his in a tight grin. Then he kicked the door open and got out. I scuttled out after him. He stood with his fists on his hips, looking silently at the house above the top of the hedge.

"All right," I said. "You have a key. Let's go on in."

"Who said I had a key?"

"Don't kid me, son. The fag gave you one. You've got a nice clean manly little room in there. He shooed you out and locked it up when he had lady visitors. He was like Caesar, a husband to women and a wife to men. Think I can't figure people like him and you out?"

I still held his automatic more or less pointed at him, but he swung on me just the same. It caught me flush on the chin. I backstepped fast enough to keep from falling, but I took plenty of the punch. It was meant to be a hard one, but a pansy has no iron in his bones, whatever he looks like.

I threw the gun down at the kid's feet and said: "Maybe you need this."

He stooped for it like a flash. There was nothing slow about his movements. I sank a fist in the side of his neck. He toppled over sideways, clawing for the gun and not reaching it. I picked it up again and threw it in the car. The boy came up on all fours, leering with his eyes too wide open. He coughed and shook his head.

"You don't want to fight," I told him. "You're giving away too much weight."

He wanted to fight. He shot at me like a plane from a catapult, reaching for my knees in a diving tackle. I sidestepped and reached for his neck and took it into chancery. He scraped the dirt hard and got his feet under him enough to use his hands on me where it hurt. I twisted him around and heaved him a little higher. I took hold of my right wrist with my left hand and turned my right hipbone into him and for a moment it was a balance of weights. We seemed to hang there in the misty moonlight, two grotesque creatures whose feet scraped on the road and whose breath panted with effort.

I had my right forearm against his windpipe now and all the strength of both arms in it. His feet began a frenetic shuffle and he wasn't panting any more. He was ironbound. His left foot sprawled off to one side and the knee went slack. I held on half a minute longer. He sagged on my arm, an enormous weight I could hardly hold up. Then I let go. He sprawled at my feet, out cold. I went to the car and got a pair of handcuffs out of the glove compartment and twisted his wrists behind him and snapped them on. I lifted him by the armpits and managed to drag him in behind the hedge, out of sight from the street. I went back to the car and moved it a hundred feet up the hill and locked it.

He was still out when I got back. I unlocked the door, dragged him into the house, shut the door. He was beginning to gasp now. I switched a lamp on. His eyes fluttered open and focused on me slowly.

I bent down, keeping out of the way of his knees and said: "Keep quiet or you'll get the same and more of it. Just lie quiet and hold your breath. Hold it until you can't hold it any longer and then tell yourself that you have to breathe, that you're black in the face, that your eyeballs are popping out, and that you're going to breathe right now, but that you're sitting strapped in the chair in the clean little gas chamber up in San Quentin and when you take that breath you're fighting with all your soul not to take it, it won't be air you'll get, it will be cyanide fumes. And that's what they call humane execution in our state now."

"Go — yourself," he said with a soft stricken sigh.

"You're going to cop a plea, brother, don't ever think you're not. And you're going to say just what we want you to say and nothing we don't want you to say."

"Go — yourself."

"Say that again and I'll put a pillow under your head."

His mouth twitched. I left him lying on the floor with his wrists shackled behind him and his cheek pressed into the rug and an animal brightness in his visible eye. I put on another lamp and stepped into the hallway at the back of the living room. Geiger's bedroom didn't seem to have been touched. I opened the door, not locked now, of the bedroom across the hall from it. There was a dim flickering light in the room and a smell of sandalwood. Two cones of incense ash stood side by side on a small brass tray on the bureau. The light came from the two tall black candles in the foot-high candlesticks. They were standing on straight-backed chairs, one on either side of the bed.

Geiger lay on the bed. The two missing strips of Chinese tapestry made a St. Andrew's Cross over the middle of his body, hiding the blood-smeared front of his Chinese coat. Below the cross his black-pajama'd legs lay stiff and straight. His feet were in the slippers with thick white felt soles. Above the cross his arms were crossed at the wrists and his hands lay flat against his shoulders, palms down, fingers close together and stretched out evenly. His mouth was closed and his Charlie Chan moustache was as unreal as a toupee. His broad nose was pinched and white. His eyes were almost closed, but not entirely. The faint glitter of his glass eye caught the light and winked at me.

I didn't touch him. I didn't go very near him. He would be as cold as ice and as stiff as a board.

The black candles guttered in the draft from the open door. Drops of black wax crawled down their sides. The air of the room was poisonous and unreal. I went out and shut the door again and went back to the living room. The boy hadn't moved. I stood still, listening for sirens. It was all a question of how soon Agnes talked and what she said. If she talked about Geiger, the police would be there any minute. But she might not talk for hours. She might even have got away.

I looked down at the boy. "Want to sit up, son?"

He closed his eye and pretended to go to sleep. I went over to the desk and scooped up the mulberry-colored phone and dialed Bernie Ohls' office. He had left to go home at six o'clock. I dialed the number of his home. He was there.

"This is Marlowe," I said. "Did your boys find a revolver on Owen Taylor this morning?"

I could hear him clearing his throat and then I could hear him trying to keep the surprise out of his voice. "That would come under the heading of police business," he said.

"If they did, it had three empty shells in it."

"How the hell did you know that?" Ohls asked quietly.

"Come over to 7244 Laverne Terrace, off Laurel Canyon Boulevard. I'll show you where the slugs went."

"Just like that, huh?"

"Just like that."

Ohls said: "Look out the window and you'll see me coming round the corner. I thought you acted a little cagey on that one."

"Cagey is no word for it," I said.

CHAPTER EIGHTEEN

OHLS STOOD looking down at the boy. The boy sat on the couch leaning sideways against the wall. Ohls looked at him silently, his pale eyebrows bristling and stiff and round like the little vegetable brushes the Fuller Brush man gives away.

He asked the boy: "Do you admit shooting Brody?"

The boy said his favorite three words in a muffled voice.

Ohls sighed and looked at me. I said: "He doesn't have to admit that. I have his gun."

Ohls said: "I wish to Christ I had a dollar for every time I've had that said to me. What's funny about it?"

"It's not meant to be funny," I said.

"Well, that's something," Ohls said. He turned away. "I've called Wilde. We'll go over and see him and take this punk. He can ride with me and you can follow on behind in case he tries to kick me in the face."

"How do you like what's in the bedroom?"

"I like it fine," Ohls said. "I'm kind of glad that Taylor kid went off the pier. I'd hate to have to help send him to the deathhouse for rubbing that skunk."

I went back into the small bedroom and blew out the black candles and let them smoke. When I got back to the living room Ohls had the boy up on his feet. The boy stood glaring at him with sharp black eyes in a face as hard and white as cold mutton fat.

"Let's go," Ohls said and took him by the arm as if he didn't like touching him. I put the lamps out and followed them out of the house. We got into our cars and I followed Ohls' twin tail-lights down the long curving hill. I hoped this would be my last trip to Laverne Terrace.

Taggart Wilde, the District Attorney, lived at the corner of Fourth and Lafayette Park, in a white frame house the size of a carbarn, with a red sandstone porte-cochere built on to one side and a couple of acres of soft rolling lawn in front. It was one of those solid old-fashioned houses which it used to be the thing to move bodily to new locations as the city grew westward. Wilde came of an old Los Angeles family and had probably been born in the house when it was on West Adams or Figueroa or St. James Park.

There were two cars in the driveway already, a big private sedan and a police car with a uniformed chauffeur who leaned smoking against his rear fender and admired the moon. Ohls went over and spoke to him and the chauffeur looked in at the boy in Ohls' car.

We went up to the house and rang the bell. A slick-haired blond man opened the door and led us down the hall and through a huge sunken living room crowded with heavy dark furniture and along another hall on the far side of it. He knocked at a door and stepped inside, then held the door wide and we went into a paneled study with an open French door at the end and a view of dark garden and mysterious trees. A smell of wet earth and flowers came in at the window. There were large dim oils on the walls, easy chairs, books, a smell of good cigar smoke which blended with the smell of wet earth and flowers.

Taggart Wilde sat behind a desk, a middle-aged plump man with clear blue eyes that managed to have a friendly expression without really having any expression at all. He had a cup of black coffee in front of him and he held a dappled thin cigar between the neat careful fingers of his left hand. Another man sat at the corner of the desk in a blue leather chair, a cold-eyed hatchet-faced man, as lean as a rake and as hard as the manager of a loan office. His neat well-kept face looked as if it had been shaved within the hour. He wore a well-pressed brown suit and there was a black pearl in his tie. He had the long nervous fingers of a man with a quick brain. He looked ready for a fight.

Ohls pulled a chair up and sat down and said: "Evening, Cronjager. Meet Phil Marlowe, a private eye who's in a jam." Ohls grinned.

Cronjager looked at me without nodding. He looked me over as if he was looking at a photograph. Then he nodded his chin about an inch. Wilde said: "Sit down, Marlowe. I'll try to handle Captain Cronjager, but you know how it is. This is a big city now."

I sat down and lit a cigarette. Ohls looked at Cronjager and asked: "What did you get on the Randall Place killing?"

The hatchet-faced man pulled one of his fingers until the knuckle cracked. He spoke without looking up. "A stiff, two slugs in him. Two guns that hadn't been fired. Down on the street we got a blonde trying to start a car that didn't belong to her. Hers was right next to it, the same model. She acted rattled so the boys brought her in and she spilled. She was in there when this guy Brody got it. Claims she didn't see the killer."

"That all?" Ohls asked.

Cronjager raised his eyebrows a little. "Only happened about an hour ago. What did you expect—moving pictures of the killing?"

"Maybe a description of the killer," Ohls said.

"A tall guy in a leather jerkin—if you call that a description."

"He's outside in my heap," Ohls said. "Handcuffed. Marlowe put the arm on him for you. Here's his gun." Ohls took the boy's automatic out of his pocket and laid it on a corner of Wilde's desk. Cronjager looked at the gun but didn't reach for it.

Wilde chuckled. He was leaning back and puffing his dappled cigar without letting go of it. He bent forward to sip from his coffee cup. He took a silk handkerchief from the breast pocket of the dinner jacket he was wearing and touched his lips with it and tucked it away again.

"There's a couple more deaths involved," Ohls said, pinching the soft flesh at the end of his chin.

Cronjager stiffened visibly. His surly eyes became points of steely lights.

Ohls said: "You heard about a car being lifted out of the Pacific Ocean off Lido pier this a.m. with a dead guy in it?"

Cronjager said: "No," and kept on looking nasty.

"The dead guy in the car was chauffeur to a rich family," Ohls said. "The family was being blackmailed on account of one of the daughters. Mr. Wilde recommended Marlowe to the family, through me. Marlowe played it kind of close to the vest."

"I love private dicks that play murders close to the vest," Cronjager snarled. "You don't have to be so goddamned coy about it."

"Yeah," Ohls said. "I don't have to be so goddamned coy about it. It's not so goddamned often I get a chance to be coy with a city copper. I spend most of my time telling them where to put their feet so they won't break an ankle."

Cronjager whitened around the corners of his sharp nose. His breath made a soft hissing sound in the quiet room. He said very quietly: "You haven't had to tell any of *my* men where to put their feet, smart guy."

"We'll see about that," Ohls said. "This chauffeur I spoke of that's drowned off Lido shot a guy last night in your territory. A guy named Geiger who ran a dirty book racket in a store on Hollywood Boulevard. Geiger was living with the punk I got outside in my car. I mean living with him, if you get the idea."

Cronjager was staring at him levelly now. "That sounds like it might grow up to be a dirty story," he said.

"It's my experience most police stories are," Ohls growled and turned to me, his eyebrows bristling. "You're on the air, Marlowe. Give it to him."

I gave it to him.

I left out two things, not knowing just why, at the moment, I left out one of them. I left out Carmen's visit to Brody's apartment and Eddie Mars' visit to Geiger's in the afternoon. I told the rest of it just as it happened.

Cronjager never took his eyes off my face and no expression of any kind crossed his as I talked. At the end of it he was perfectly silent for a long minute. Wilde was silent, sipping his coffee, puffing gently at his dappled cigar. Ohls stared at one of his thumbs.

Cronjager leaned slowly back in his chair and crossed one ankle over his knee and rubbed the ankle bone with his thin nervous hand. His lean face wore a harsh frown. He said with deadly politeness:

"So all you did was not report a murder that happened last night and then spend today foxing around so that this kid of Geiger's could commit a second murder this evening."

"That's all," I said. "I was in a pretty tough spot. I guess I did wrong, but I wanted to protect my client and I hadn't any reason to think the boy would go gunning for Brody."

"That kind of thinking is police business, Marlowe. If Geiger's death had been reported last night, the books could never have been moved from the store to Brody's apartment. The kid wouldn't have been led to Brody and wouldn't have killed him. Say Brody was living on borrowed time. His kind usually are. But a life is a life."

"Right," I said. "Tell that to your coppers next time they shoot down some scared petty larceny crook running away up an alley with a stolen spare."

Wilde put both his hands down on his desk with a solid smack. "That's enough of that," he snapped. "What makes you so sure, Marlowe, that this Taylor boy shot Geiger? Even if the gun that killed Geiger was found on Taylor's body or in the car, it doesn't absolutely follow that he was the killer. The gun might have been planted—say by Brody, the actual killer."

"It's physically possible," I said, "but morally impossible. It assumes too much coincidence and too much that's out of character for Brody and his girl, and out of character for what he was trying to do. I talked to Brody for a long time. He was a crook, but not a killer type. He had two guns, but he wasn't wearing either of them. He was trying to find a way to cut in on Geiger's racket, which naturally he knew all about from the girl. He says he was watching Geiger off and on to see if he had any tough backers. I believe him. To suppose he killed Geiger in order to get his books, then scrammed with the nude photo Geiger had just taken of Carmen Sternwood, then planted the gun on Owen Taylor and pushed Taylor into the ocean off Lido, is to suppose a hell of a lot too much. Taylor had the motive, jealous rage, and the opportunity to kill Geiger. He was out in one of the family cars without permission. He killed Geiger right in front of the girl, which Brody would never have done, even if he had been a killer. I can't see anybody with a purely commercial interest in Geiger doing that. But Taylor would have done it. The nude photo business was just what would have made him do it."

Wilde chuckled and looked along his eyes at Cronjager. Cronjager cleared his throat with a snort. Wilde asked: "What's this business about hiding the body? I don't see the point of that."

I said: "The kid hasn't told us, but he must have done it. Brody wouldn't have gone into the house after Geiger was shot. The boy must have got home when I was away taking Carmen to her house. He was afraid of the police, of course, being what he is, and he probably thought it a good idea to have the body hidden until he had removed his effects from the house. He dragged it out of the front door, judging by the marks on the rug, and very likely put it in the garage. Then he packed up whatever belongings he had there and took them away. And later on, sometime in the night and before the body stiffened. he had a revulsion of feeling and thought he hadn't treated his dead friend very nicely. So he went back and laid him out on the bed. That's all guessing, of course."

Wilde nodded. "Then this morning he goes down to the store as if nothing had happened and keeps his eyes open. And when Brody moved the books out he found out where they were going and assumed that whoever got them had killed Geiger just for that purpose. He may even have known more about Brody and the girl than they suspected. What do you think, Ohls?"

Ohls said: "We'll find out—but that doesn't help Cronjager's troubles. What's eating him is all this happened last night and he's only just been rung in on it."

Cronjager said sourly: "I think I can find some way to deal with that angle too." He looked at me sharply and immediately looked away again.

Wilde waved his cigar and said: "Let's see the exhibits, Marlowe."

I emptied my pockets and put the catch on his desk: the three notes and Geiger's card to General Sternwood, Carmen's photos, and the blue notebook with the code list of names and addresses. I had already given Geiger's keys to Ohls.

Wilde looked at what I gave him, puffing gently at his cigar. Ohls lit one of his own toy cigars and blew smoke peacefully at the ceiling. Cronjager leaned on the desk and looked at what I had given Wilde.

Wilde tapped the three notes signed by Carmen and said: "I guess these were just a come-on. If General Sternwood paid them, it would be through fear of something worse. Then Geiger would have tightened the screws. Do you know what he was afraid of?" He was looking at me.

I shook my head.

"Have you told your story complete in all relevant details?"

"I left out a couple of personal matters. I intend to keep on leaving them out, Mr. Wilde."

Cronjager said: "Hah!" and snorted with deep feeling.

"Why?" Wilde asked quietly.

"Because my client is entitled to that protection, short of anything but a Grand Jury. I have a license to operate as a private detective. I suppose that word 'private' has some meaning. The Hollywood Division has two murders on its hands, both solved. They have both killers. They have the motive, the instrument in each case. The blackmail angle has got to be suppressed, as far as the names of the parties are concerned."

"Why?" Wilde asked again.

"That's okey," Cronjager said dryly. "We're glad to stooge for a shamus of his standing."

I said: "I'll show you." I got up and went back out of the house to my car and got the book from Geiger's store out of it. The uniformed police driver was standing beside Ohls' car. The boy was inside it, leaning back sideways in the corner.

"Has he said anything?" I asked.

"He made a suggestion," the copper said and spat. "I'm letting it ride."

I went back into the house, put the book on Wilde's desk and opened up the wrappings. Cronjager was using a telephone on the end of the desk. He hung up and sat down as I came in.

Wilde looked through the book, wooden-faced, closed it and pushed it towards Cronjager. Cronjager opened it, looked at a page or two, shut it quickly. A couple of red spots the size of half dollars showed on his cheekbones.

I said: "Look at the stamped dates on the front endpaper."

Cronjager opened the book again and looked at them. "Well?"

"If necessary," I said, "I'll testify under oath that that book came from Geiger's store. The blonde, Agnes, will admit what kind of business the store did. It's obvious to anybody with eyes that that store is just a front for something. But the Hollywood police allowed it to operate, for their own reasons. I dare say the Grand Jury would like to know what those reasons are."

Wilde grinned. He said: "Grand Juries do ask those embarrassing questions sometimes—in a rather vain effort to find out just why cities are run as they are run."

Cronjager stood up suddenly and put his hat on. "I'm one against three here," he snapped. "I'm a homicide man. If this Geiger was running indecent literature, that's no skin off my nose. But I'm ready to admit it won't help my division any to have it washed over in the papers. What do you birds want?"

Wilde looked at Ohls. Ohls said calmly: "I want to turn a prisoner over to you. Let's go."

He stood up. Cronjager looked at him fiercely and stalked out of the room. Ohls went after him. The door closed again. Wilde tapped on his desk and stared at me with his clear blue eyes.

"You ought to understand how any copper would feel about a cover-up like this," he said. "You'll have to make statements of all of it—at least for the files. I think it may be possible to keep the two killings separate and to keep General Sternwood's name out of both of them. Do you know why I'm not tearing your ear off?"

"No. I expected to get both ears torn off."

"What are you getting for it all?"

"Twenty-five dollars a day and expenses."

"That would make fifty dollars and a little gasoline so far."

"About that."

He put his head on one side and rubbed the back of his left little finger along the lower edge of his chin.

"And for that amount of money you're willing to get yourself in Dutch with half the law enforcement of this county?"

"I don't like it," I said. "But what the hell am I to do? I'm on a case. I'm selling what I have to sell to make a living. What little guts and intelligence the Lord gave me and a willingness to get pushed around in order to protect a client. It's against my principles to tell as much as I've told tonight, without consulting the General. As for the cover-up, I've been in police business myself, as you know. They come a dime a dozen in any big city. Cops get very large and emphatic when an outsider tries to hide anything, but they do the same things themselves every other day, to oblige their friends or anybody with a little pull. And I'm not through. I'm still on the case. I'd do the same thing again, if I had to."

"Providing Cronjager doesn't get your license," Wilde grinned. "You said you held back a couple of personal matters. Of what import?"

"I'm still on the case," I said, and stared straight into his eyes.

Wilde smiled at me. He had the frank daring smile of an Irishman. "Let me tell you something, son. My father was a close friend of old Sternwood. I've done all my office permits–and maybe a good deal more–to save the old man from grief. But in the long run it can't be done. Those girls of his are bound certain to hook up with something that can't be hushed, especially that little blonde brat. They ought not to be running around loose. I blame the old man for that. I guess he doesn't realize what the world is today. And there's another thing I might mention while we're talking man to man and I don't have to growl at you. I'll bet a dollar to a Canadian dime that the General's afraid his son-in-law, the ex-bootlegger, is mixed up in this somewhere, and what he really hoped you would find out is that he isn't. What do you think of that?"

"Regan didn't sound like a blackmailer, what I heard of him. He had a soft spot where he was and he walked out on it."

Wilde snorted. "The softness of that spot neither you nor I could judge. If he was a certain sort of man, it would not have been so very soft. Did the General tell you he was looking for Regan?"

"He told me he wished he knew where he was and that he was all right. He liked Regan and was hurt the way he bounced off without telling the old man good-by."

Wilde leaned back and frowned. "I see," he said in a changed voice. His hand moved the stuff on his desk around, laid Geiger's blue notebook to one side and pushed the other exhibits toward me. "You may as well take these," he said. "I've no further use for them."

CHAPTER NINETEEN

IT WAS CLOSE to eleven when I put my car away and walked around to the front of the Hobart Arms. The plate-glass door was put on the lock at ten, so I had to get my keys out. Inside, in the square barren lobby, a man put a green evening paper down beside a potted palm and flicked a cigarette butt into the tub the palm grew in. He stood up and waved his hat at me and said: "The boss wants to talk to you. You sure keep your friends waiting, pal."

I stood still and looked at his flattened nose and club steak ear.

"What about?"

"What do you care? Just keep your nose clean and everything will be jake." His hand hovered near the upper buttonhole of his open coat.

"I smell of policemen," I said. "I'm too tired to talk, too tired to eat, too tired to think. But if you think I'm not too tired to take orders from Eddie Mars—try getting your gat out before I shoot your good ear off."

"Nuts. You ain't got no gun." He stared at me levelly. His dark wiry brows closed in together and his mouth made a downward curve.

"That was then," I told him. "I'm not always naked."

He waved his left hand. "Okey. You win. I wasn't told to blast anybody. You'll hear from him."

"Too late will be too soon," I said, and turned slowly as he passed me on his way to the door. He opened it and went out without looking back. I grinned at my own foolishness, went along to the elevator and upstairs to the apartment. I took Carmen's little gun out of my pocket and laughed at it. Then I cleaned it thoroughly, oiled it, wrapped it in a piece of canton flannel and locked it up. I made myself a drink and was drinking it when the phone rang. I sat down beside the table on which it stood.

"So you're tough tonight," Eddie Mars' voice said.

"Big, fast, tough and full of prickles. What can I do for you?"

"Cops over there—you know where. You keep me out of it?"

"Why should I?"

"I'm nice to be nice to, soldier. I'm not nice not to be nice to."

"Listen hard and you'll hear my teeth chattering."

He laughed dryly. "Did you—or did you?"

"I did. I'm damned if I know why. I guess it was just complicated enough without you."

"Thanks, soldier. Who gunned him?"

"Read it in the paper tomorrow—maybe."

"I want to know now."

"Do you get everything you want?"

"No. Is that an answer, soldier?"

"Somebody you never heard of gunned him. Let it go at that."

"If that's on the level, someday I may be able to do you a favor."

"Hang up and let me go to bed."

He laughed again. "You're looking for Rusty Regan, aren't you?"

"A lot of people seem to think I am, but I'm not."

"If you were, I could give you an idea. Drop in and see me down at the beach. Any time. Glad to see you."

"Maybe."

"Be seeing you then." The phone clicked and I sat holding it with a savage patience. Then I dialed the Sternwoods' number and heard it ring four or five times and then the butler's suave voice saying: "General Sternwood's residence."

"This is Marlowe. Remember me? I met you about a hundred years ago—or was it yesterday?"

"Yes, Mr. Marlowe. I remember, of course."

"Is Mrs. Regan home?"

"Yes, I believe so. Would you—"

I cut in on him with a sudden change of mind. "No. You give her the message. Tell her I have the pictures, all of them, and that everything is all right."

"Yes . . . yes. . . ." The voice seemed to shake a little. "You have the pictures—all of them—and everything is all right. . . . Yes, sir. I may say—thank you very much, sir."

The phone rang back in five minutes. I had finished my drink and it made me feel as if I could eat the dinner I had forgotten all about; I went out leaving the telephone ringing. It was ringing when I came back. It rang at intervals until half-past twelve. At that time I put my lights out and opened the windows up and muffled the phone bell with a piece of paper and went to bed. I had a bellyful of the Sternwood family.

I read all three of the morning papers over my eggs and bacon the next morning. Their accounts of the affair came as close to the truth as newspaper stories usually come—as close as Mars is to Saturn. None of the three connected Owen Taylor, driver of the Lido Pier Suicide Car, with the Laurel Canyon Exotic Bungalow Slaying. None of them mentioned the Sternwoods, Bernie Ohls or me. Owen Taylor was "chauffeur to a wealthy family." Captain Cronjager of the Hollywood Division got all the credit for solving the two slayings in his district, which were supposed to arise out of a dispute over the proceeds from a wire service maintained by one Geiger in the back of the bookstore on Hollywood Boulevard. Brody had shot Geiger and Carol Lundgren had shot Brody in revenge. Police were holding Carol Lundgren in custody. He had confessed. He had a bad record—probably in high school. Police were also holding one Agnes Lozelle, Geiger's secretary, as a material witness.

It was a nice write-up. It gave the impression that Geiger had been killed the night before, that Brody had been killed about an hour later, and that Captain Cronjager had solved both murders while lighting a cigarette. The suicide of Taylor made Page One of Section II. There was a photo of the sedan on the deck of the power lighter, with the license plate blacked out, and something covered with a cloth lying on the deck beside the running board. Owen Taylor had been despondent and in poor health. His family lived in Dubuque, and his body would be shipped there. There would be no inquest.

CHAPTER TWENTY

CAPTAIN GREGORY of the Missing Persons Brueau laid my card down on his wide flat desk and arranged it so that its edges exactly paralleled the edges of the desk. He studied it with his head on one side, grunted, swung around in his swivel chair and looked out of his window at the barred top floor of the Hall of Justice half a block away. He was a burly man with tired eyes and the slow deliberate movements of a night watchman. His voice was toneless, flat and uninterested.

"Private dick, eh?" he said, not looking at me at all, but looking out of his window. Smoke wisped from the blackened bowl of a briar that hung on his eye tooth. "What can I do for you?"

"I'm working for General Guy Sternwood, 3765 Alta Brea Crescent, West Hollywood."

Captain Gregory blew a little smoke from the corner of his mouth without removing the pipe. "On what?"

"Not exactly on what you're working on, but I'm interested. I thought you could help me."

"Help you on what?"

"General Sternwood's a rich man," I said. "He's an old friend of the D.A.'s father. If he wants to hire a full-time boy to run errands for him, that's no reflection on the police. It's just a luxury he is able to afford himself."

"What makes you think I'm doing anything for him?"

I didn't answer that. He swung around slowly and heavily in his swivel chair and put his large feet flat on the bare linoleum that covered his floor. His office had the musty smell of years of routine. He stared at me bleakly.

"I don't want to waste your time, Captain," I said and pushed my chair back–about four inches.

He didn't move. He kept on staring at me out of his washed-out tired eyes. "You know the D.A.?"

"I've met him. I worked for him once. I know Bernie Ohls, his chief investigator, pretty well."

Captain Gregory reached for a phone and mumbled into it: "Get me Ohls at the D.A.'s office."

He sat holding the phone down on its cradle. Moments passed. Smoke drifted from his pipe. His eyes were heavy and motionless like his hand. The bell tinkled and he reached for my card with his left hand. "Ohls? . . . Al Gregory at headquarters. A guy named Philip Marlowe is in my office.

His card says he's a private investigator. He wants information from me. . . . Yeah? What does he look like? . . . Okey, thanks."

He dropped the phone and took his pipe out of his mouth and tamped the tobacco with the brass cap of a heavy pencil. He did it carefully and solemnly, as if that was as important as anything he would have to do that day. He leaned back and stared at me some more.

"What you want?"

"An idea of what progress you're making, if any."

He thought that over. "Regan?" he asked finally.

"Sure."

"Know him?"

"I never saw him. I hear he's a good-looking Irishman in his late thirties, that he was once in the liquor racket, that he married General Sternwood's older daughter and that they didn't click. I'm told he disappeared about a month back."

"Sternwood oughta think himself lucky instead of hiring private talent to beat around in the tall grass."

"The General took a big fancy to him. Such things happen. The old man is crippled and lonely. Regan used to sit around with him and keep him company."

"What you think you can do that we can't do?"

"Nothing at all, in so far as finding Regan goes. But there's a rather mysterious blackmail angle. I want to make sure Regan isn't involved. Knowing where he is or isn't might help."

"Brother, I'd like to help you, but I don't know where he is. He pulled down the curtain and that's that."

"Pretty hard to do against your organization, isn't it, Captain?"

"Yeah—but it can be done—for a while." He touched a bell button on the side of his desk. A middle-aged woman put her head in at a side door. "Get me the file on Terence Regan, Abba."

The door closed. Captain Gregory and I looked at each other in some more heavy silence. The door opened again and the woman put a tabbed green file on his desk. Captain Gregory nodded her out, put a pair of heavy horn-rimmed glasses on his veined nose and turned the papers in the file over slowly. I rolled a cigarette around in my fingers.

"He blew on the 16th of September," he said. "The only thing important about that is it was the chauffeur's day off and nobody saw Regan take his car out. It was late afternoon, though. We found the car four days later in a garage belonging to a ritzy bungalow court place near the Sunset Towers. A garage man reported it to the stolen car detail, said it didn't belong there. The place is called the Casa de Oro. There's an angle to that I'll tell you about in a minute. We couldn't find out anything about who put the car in there. We print the car but don't find any prints that are on file anywhere. The car in that garage don't jibe with foul play, although there's a reason to suspect foul play. It jibes with something else I'll tell you about in a minute."

I said: "That jibes with Eddie Mars' wife being on the missing list."

He looked annoyed. "Yeah. We investigate the tenants and find she's living there. Left about the time Regan did, within two days anyway. A guy who sounds a bit like Regan had been seen with her, but we don't get a positive identification. It's goddamned funny in this police racket how an old woman can look out of a window and see a guy running and pick him out of a line-up six months later, but we can show hotel help a clear photo and they just can't be sure."

"That's one of the qualifications for good hotel help," I said.

"Yeah. Eddie Mars and his wife didn't live together, but they were friendly, Eddie says. Here's some of the possibilities. First off Regan carried fifteen grand, packed it in his clothes all the time. Real money, they tell me. Not just a top card and a bunch of hay. That's a lot of jack but this Regan might be the boy to have it around so he could take it out and look at it when somebody was looking at him. Then again maybe he wouldn't give a damn. His wife says he never made a nickel off of old man Sternwood except room and board and a Packard 120 his wife gave him. Tie that for an ex-legger in the rich gravy."

"It beats me," I said.

"Well, here we are with a guy who ducks out and has fifteen grand in his pants and folks know it. Well, that's money. I might duck out myself, if I had fifteen grand, and me with two kids in high school. So the first thought is somebody rolls him for it and rolls him too hard, so they have to take him out in the desert and plant him among the cactuses. But I don't like that too well. Regan carried a gat and had plenty of experience using it, and not just in a greasy-faced liquor mob. I understand he commanded a whole brigade in the Irish troubles back in 1922 or whenever it was. A guy like that wouldn't be white meat to a heister. Then, his car being in that garage makes whoever rolled him know he was sweet on Eddie Mars' wife, which he was, I guess, but it ain't something every poolroom bum would know."

"Got a photo?" I asked.

"Him, not her. That's funny too. There's a lot of funny angles to this case. Here." He pushed a shiny print across the desk and I looked at an Irish face that was more sad than merry and more reserved than brash. Not the face of a tough guy and not the face of a man who could be pushed around much by anybody. Straight dark brows with strong bone under them. A forehead wide rather than high, a mat of dark clustering hair, a thin short nose, a wide mouth. A chin that had strong lines but was small for the mouth. A face that looked a little taut, the face of a man who would move fast and play for keeps. I passed the print back. I would know that face, if I saw it.

Captain Gregory knocked his pipe out and refilled it and tamped the tobacco down with his thumb. He lit it, blew smoke and began to talk again.

"Well, there could be people who would know he was sweet on Eddie Mars' frau. Besides Eddie himself. For a wonder *he* knew it. But he don't seem to give a damn. We check him pretty thoroughly around that time.

Of course Eddie wouldn't have knocked him off out of jealousy. The set-up would point to him too obvious."

"It depends how smart he is," I said. "He might try the double bluff."

Captain Gregory shook his head. "If he's smart enough to get by in his racket, he's too smart for that. I get your idea. He pulls the dumb play because he thinks we wouldn't expect him to pull the dumb play. From a police angle that's wrong. Because he'd have us in his hair so much it would interfere with his business. *You* might think a dumb play would be smart. I might think so. The rank and file wouldn't. They'd make his life miserable. I've ruled it out. If I'm wrong, you can prove it on me and I'll eat my chair cushion. Till then I'm leaving Eddie in the clear. Jealousy is a bad motive for his type. Top-flight racketeers have business brains. They learn to do things that are good policy and let their personal feelings take care of themselves. I'm leaving that out."

"What are you leaving in?"

"The dame and Regan himself. Nobody else. She was a blonde then, but she won't be now. We don't find her car, so they probably left in it. They had a long start on us—fourteen days. Except for that car of Regan's I don't figure we'd have got the case at all. Of course I'm used to them that way, especially in good-class families. And of course everything I've done has had to be under the hat."

He leaned back and thumped the arms of his chair with the heels of his large heavy hands.

"I don't see nothing to do but wait," he said. "We've got readers out, but it's too soon to look for results. Regan had fifteen grand we know of. The girl had some, maybe a lot in rocks. But they'll run out of dough some day. Regan will cash a check, drop a marker, write a letter. They're in a strange town and they've got new names, but they've got the same old appetites. They got to get back in the fiscal system."

"What did the girl do before she married Eddie Mars?"

"Torcher."

"Can't you get any old professional photos?"

"No. Eddie must of had some, but he won't loosen up. He wants her let alone. I can't make him. He's got friends in town, or he wouldn't be what he is." He grunted. "Any of this do you any good?"

I said: "You'll never find either of them. The Pacific Ocean is too close."

"What I said about my chair cushion still goes. We'll find him. It may take time. It could take a year or two."

"General Sternwood may not live that long," I said.

"We've done all we could, brother. If he wants to put out a reward and spend some money, we might get results. The city don't give me the kind of money it takes." His large eyes peered at me and his scratchy eyebrows moved. "You serious about thinking Eddie put them both down?"

I laughed. "No. I was just kidding. I think what you think, Captain. That Regan ran away with a woman who meant more to him than a rich wife he didn't get along with. Besides, she isn't rich yet."

"You met her, I suppose?"

"Yes. She'd make a jazzy week-end, but she'd be wearing for a steady diet."

He grunted and I thanked him for his time and information and left. A gray Plymouth sedan tailed me away from the City Hall. I gave it a chance to catch up with me on a quiet street. It refused the offer, so I shook it off and went about my business.

CHAPTER TWENTY-ONE

I DIDN'T GO near the Sternwood family. I went back to the office and sat in my swivel chair and tried to catch up on my foot-dangling. There was a gusty wind blowing in at the windows and the soot from the oil burners of the hotel next door was down-drafted into the room and rolling across the top of the desk like tumbleweed drifting across a vacant lot. I was thinking about going out to lunch and that life was pretty flat and that it would probably be just as flat if I took a drink and that taking a drink all alone at that time of day wouldn't be any fun anyway. I was thinking this when Norris called up. In his carefully polite manner he said that General Sternwood was not feeling very well and that certain items in the newspaper had been read to him and he assumed that my investigation was now completed.

"Yes, as regards Geiger," I said. "I didn't shoot him, you know."

"The General didn't suppose you did, Mr. Marlowe."

"Does the General know anything about those photographs Mrs. Regan was worrying about?"

"No, sir. Decidedly not."

"Did you know what the General gave me?"

"Yes, sir. Three notes and a card, I believe."

"Right. I'll return them. As to the photos I think I'd better just destroy them."

"Very good, sir. Mrs. Regan tried to reach you a number of times last night–"

"I was out getting drunk," I said.

"Yes. Very necessary, sir, I'm sure. The General has instructed me to send you a check for five hundred dollars. Will that be satisfactory?"

"More than generous," I said.

"And I presume we may now consider the incident closed?"

"Oh sure. Tight as a vault with a busted time lock."

"Thank you, sir. I am sure we all appreciate it. When the General is feeling a little better–possibly tomorrow–he would like to thank you in person."

"Fine," I said. "I'll come out and drink some more of his brandy, maybe with champagne."

"I shall see that some is properly iced," the old boy said, almost with a smirk in his voice.

That was that. We said good-by and hung up. The coffee shop smell from next door came in at the windows with the soot but failed to make me hungry. So I got out my office bottle and took the drink and let my self-respect ride its own race.

I counted it up on my fingers. Rusty Regan had run away from a lot of money and a handsome wife to go wandering with a vague blonde who was more or less married to a racketeer named Eddie Mars. He had gone suddenly without good-bys and there might be any number of reasons for that. The General had been too proud, or, at the first interview he gave me, too careful, to tell me the Missing Persons Bureau had the matter in hand. The Missing Persons people were dead on their feet on it and evidently didn't think it was worth bothering over. Regan had done what he had done and that was his business. I agreed with Captain Gregory that Eddie Mars would have been very unlikely to involve himself in a double murder just because another man had gone to town with the blonde he was not even living with. It might have annoyed him, but business is business, and you have to hold your teeth clamped around Hollywood to keep from chewing on stray blondes. If there had been a lot of money involved, that would be different. But fifteen grand wouldn't be a lot of money to Eddie Mars. He was no two-bit chiseler like Brody.

Geiger was dead and Carmen would have to find some other shady character to drink exotic blends of hooch with. I didn't suppose she would have any trouble. All she would have to do would be to stand on the corner for five minutes and look coy. I hoped that the next grifter who dropped the hook on her would play her a little more smoothly, a little more for the long haul rather than the quick touch.

Mrs. Regan knew Eddie Mars well enough to borrow money from him. That was natural, if she played roulette and was a good loser. Any gambling house owner would lend a good client money in a pinch. Apart from this they had an added bond of interest in Regan. He was her husband and he had gone off with Eddie Mars' wife.

Carol Lundgren, the boy killer with the limited vocabulary, was out of circulation for a long, long time, even if they didn't strap him in a chair over a bucket of acid. They wouldn't, because he would take a plea and save the county money. They all do when they don't have the price of a big lawyer. Agnes Lozelle was in custody as a material witness. They wouldn't need her for that, if Carol took a plea, and if he pleaded guilty on arraignment, they would turn her loose. They wouldn't want to open up any angles on Geiger's business, apart from which they had nothing on her.

That left me. I had concealed a murder and suppressed evidence for twenty-four hours, but I was still at large and had a five-hundred-dollar check coming. The smart thing for me to do was to take another drink and forget the whole mess.

That being the obviously smart thing to do, I called Eddie Mars and told him I was coming down to Las Olindas that evening to talk to him. That was how smart I was.

I got down there about nine, under a hard high October moon that lost itself in the top layers of a beach fog. The Cypress Club was at the far end of the town, a rambling frame mansion that had once been the summer residence of a rich man named De Cazens, and later had been a hotel. It was now a big dark outwardly shabby place in a thick grove of wind-twisted Monterey cypresses, which gave it its name. It had enormous scrolled porches, turrets all over the place, stained-glass trims around the big windows, big empty stables at the back, a general air of nostalgic decay. Eddie Mars had left the outside much as he had found it, instead of making it over to look like an MGM set. I left my car on a street with sputtering arc lights and walked into the grounds along a damp gravel path to the main entrance. A doorman in a double-breasted guard's coat let me into a huge dim silent lobby from which a white oak staircase curved majestically up to the darkness of an upper floor. I checked my hat and coat and waited, listening to music and confused voices behind heavy double doors. They seemed a long way off, and not quite of the same world as the building itself. Then the slim pasty-faced blond man who had been with Eddie Mars and the pug at Geiger's place came through a door under the staircase, smiled at me bleakly and took me back with him along a carpeted hall to the boss's office.

This was a square room with a deep old bay window and a stone fireplace in which a fire of juniper logs burned lazily. It was wainscoted in walnut and had a frieze of faded damask above the paneling. The ceiling was high and remote. There was a smell of cold sea.

Eddie Mars' dark sheenless desk didn't belong in the room, but neither did anything made after 1900. His carpet had a Florida suntan. There was a bartop radio in the corner and a Sèvres china tea set on a copper tray beside a samovar. I wondered who that was for. There was a door in the corner that had a time lock on it.

Eddie Mars grinned at me sociably and shook hands and moved his chin at the vault. "I'm a pushover for a heist mob here except for that thing," he said cheerfully. "The local johns drop in every morning and watch me open it. I have an arrangement with them."

"You hinted you had something for me," I said. "What is it?"

"What's your hurry? Have a drink and sit down."

"No hurry at all. You and I haven't anything to talk about but business."

"You'll have the drink and like it," he said. He mixed a couple and put mine down beside a red leather chair and stood crosslegged against the desk himself, one hand in the side pocket of his midnight-blue dinner jacket, the thumb outside and the nail glistening. In dinner clothes he looked a little harder than in gray flannel, but he still looked like a horseman. We drank and nodded at each other.

"Ever been here before?" he asked.

"During prohibition. I don't get any kick out of gambling."

"Not with money," he smiled. "You ought to look in tonight. One of your friends is outside betting the wheels. I hear she's doing pretty well. Vivian Regan."

I sipped my drink and took one of his monogrammed cigarettes.

"I kind of liked the way you handled that yesterday," he said. "You made me sore at the time but I could see afterwards how right you were. You and I ought to get along. How much do I owe you?"

"For doing what?"

"Still careful, eh? I have my pipe line into headquarters, or I wouldn't be here. I get them the way they happen, not the way you read them in the papers." He showed me his large white teeth.

"How much have you got?" I asked.

"You're not talking money?"

"Information was the way I understood it."

"Information about what?"

"You have a short memory. Regan."

"Oh, that." He waved his glistening nails in the quiet light from one of those bronze lamps that shoot a beam at the ceiling. "I hear you got the information already. I felt I owed you a fee. I'm used to paying for nice treatment."

"I didn't drive down here to make a touch. I get paid for what I do. Not much by your standards, but I make out. One customer at a time is a good rule. You didn't bump Regan off, did you?"

"No. Did you think I did?"

"I wouldn't put it past you."

He laughed. "You're kidding."

I laughed. "Sure, I'm kidding. I never saw Regan, but I saw his photo. You haven't got the men for the work. And while we're on that subject don't send me any more gun punks with orders. I might get hysterical and blow one down."

He looked through his glass at the fire, set it down on the end of the desk and wiped his lips with a sheer lawn handkerchief.

"You talk a good game," he said. "But I dare say you can break a hundred and ten. You're not really interested in Regan, are you?"

"No, not professionally. I haven't been asked to be. But I know somebody who would like to know where he is."

"She doesn't give a damn," he said.

"I mean her father."

He wiped his lips again and looked at the handkerchief almost as if he expected to find blood on it. He drew his thick gray eyebrows close together and fingered the side of his weatherbeaten nose.

"Geiger was trying to blackmail the General," I said. "The General wouldn't say so, but I figure he was at least half scared Regan might be behind it."

Eddie Mars laughed. "Uh-uh. Geiger worked that one on everybody. It was strictly his own idea. He'd get notes from people that looked legal—were legal, I dare say, except that he wouldn't have dared sue on them. He'd present the notes, with a nice flourish, leaving himself empty-handed. If he drew an ace, he had a prospect that scared and he went to work. If he didn't draw an ace, he just dropped the whole thing."

"Clever guy," I said. "He dropped it all right. Dropped it and fell on it. How come *you* know all this?"

He shrugged impatiently. "I wish to Christ I didn't know half the stuff that's brought to me. Knowing other people's business is the worst investment a man can make in my circle. Then if it was just Geiger you were after, you're washed up on that angle."

"Washed up and paid off."

"I'm sorry about that. I wish old Sternwood would hire himself a soldier like you on a straight salary, to keep those girls of his home at least a few nights a week."

"Why?"

His mouth looked sulky. "They're plain trouble. Take the dark one. She's a pain in the neck around here. If she loses, she plunges and I end up with a fistful of paper which nobody will discount at any price. She has no money of her own except an allowance and what's in the old man's will is a secret. If she wins, she takes my money home with her."

"You get it back the next night," I said.

"I get some of it back. But over a period of time I'm loser."

He looked earnestly at me, as if that was important to me. I wondered why he thought it necessary to tell me at all. I yawned and finished my drink.

"I'm going out and look the joint over," I said.

"Yes, do." He pointed to a door near the vault door. "That leads to a door behind the tables."

"I'd rather go in the way the suckers enter."

"Okey. As you please. We're friends, aren't we, soldier?"

"Sure." I stood up and we shook hands.

"Maybe I can do you a real favor some day," he said. "You got it all from Gregory this time."

"So you own a piece of him too."

"Oh not that bad. We're just friends."

I stared at him for a moment, then went over to the door I had come in at. I looked back at him when I had it open.

"You don't have anybody tailing me around in a gray Plymouth sedan, do you?"

His eyes widened sharply. He looked jarred. "Hell, no. Why should I?"

"I couldn't imagine," I said, and went on out. I thought his surprise looked genuine enough to be believed. I thought he even looked a little worried. I couldn't think of any reason for that.

CHAPTER TWENTY-TWO

IT WAS ABOUT ten-thirty when the little yellow-sashed Mexican orchestra got tired of playing a low-voiced, prettied-up rhumba that nobody was dancing to. The gourd player rubbed his finger tips together as if they were sore and got a cigarette into his mouth almost with the same movement. The other four, with a timed simultaneous stoop, reached under their chairs for glasses from which they sipped, smacking their lips and flashing their eyes. Tequila, their manner said. It was probably mineral water. The pretense was as wasted as the music. Nobody was looking at them.

The room had been a ballroom once and Eddie Mars had changed it only as much as his business compelled him. No chromium glitter, no indirect lighting from behind angular cornices, no fused glass pictures, or chairs in violent leather and polished metal tubing, none of the pseudo-modernistic circus of the typical Hollywood night trap. The light was from heavy crystal chandeliers and the rose-damask panels of the wall were still the same rose damask, a little faded by time and darkened by dust, that had been matched long ago against the parquetry floor, of which only a small glass-smooth space in front of the little Mexican orchestra showed bare. The rest was covered by a heavy old-rose carpeting that must have cost plenty. The parquetry was made of a dozen kinds of hardwood, from Burma teak through half a dozen shades of oak and ruddy wood that looked like mahogany, and fading out to the hard pale wild lilac of the California hills, all laid in elaborate patterns, with the accuracy of a transit.

It was still a beautiful room and now there was roulette in it instead of measured, old-fashioned dancing. There were three tables close to the far wall. A low bronze railing joined them and made a fence around the croupiers. All three tables were working, but the crowd was at the middle one. I could see Vivian Regan's black head close to it, from across the room where I was leaning against the bar and turning a small glass of bacardi around on the mahogany.

The bartender leaned beside me watching the cluster of well-dressed people at the middle table. "She's pickin' 'em tonight, right on the nose," he said. "That tall blackheaded frail."

"Who is she?"

"I wouldn't know her name. She comes here a lot though."

"The hell you wouldn't know her name."

"I just work here, mister," he said without any animosity. "She's all alone too. The guy was with her passed out. They took him out to his car."

"I'll take her home," I said.

"The hell you will. Well, I wish you luck anyways. Should I gentle up that bacardi or do you like it the way it is?"

"I like it the way it is as well as I like it at all," I said.

"Me, I'd just as leave drink croup medicine," he said.

The crowd parted and two men in evening clothes pushed their way out and I saw the back of her neck and her bare shoulders in the opening. She wore a low-cut dress of dull green velvet. It looked too dressy for the occasion. The crowd closed and hid all but her black head. The two men came across the room and leaned against the bar and asked for Scotch and soda. One of them was flushed and excited. He was mopping his face with a black-bordered handkerchief. The double satin stripes down the side of his trousers were wide enough for tire tracks.

"Boy, I never saw such a run," he said in a jittery voice. "Eight wins and two stand-offs in a row on that red. That's roulette, boy, that's roulette."

"It gives me the itch," the other one said. "She's betting a grand at a crack. She can't lose." They put their beaks in their drinks, gurgled swiftly and went back.

"So wise the little men are," the barkeep drawled. "A grand a crack, huh. I saw an old horseface in Havana once–"

The noise swelled over at the middle table and a chiseled foreign voice rose above it saying: "If you will just be patient a moment, madam. The table cannot cover your bet. Mr. Mars will be here in a moment."

I left my bacardi and padded across the carpet. The little orchestra started to play a tango, rather loud. No one was dancing or intending to dance. I moved through a scattering of people in dinner clothes and full evening dress and sports clothes and business suits to the end table at the left. It had gone dead. Two croupiers stood behind it with their heads together and their eyes sideways. One moved a rake back and forth aimlessly over the empty layout. They were both staring at Vivian Regan.

Her long lashes twitched and her face looked unnaturally white. She was at the middle table, exactly opposite the wheel. There was a disordered pile of money and chips in front of her. It looked like a lot of money. She spoke to the croupier with a cool, insolent, ill-tempered drawl.

"What kind of a cheap outfit is this, I'd like to know. Get busy and spin that wheel, highpockets. I want one more play and I'm playing table stakes. You take it away fast enough I've noticed, but when it comes to dishing it out you start to whine."

The croupier smiled a cold polite smile that had looked at thousands of boors and millions of fools. His tall dark disinterested manner was flawless. He said gravely: "The table cannot cover your bet, madam. You have over sixteen thousand dollars there."

"It's your money," the girl jeered. "Don't you want it back?"

A man beside her tried to tell her something. She turned swiftly and spat something at him and he faded back into the crowd red-faced. A door opened in the paneling at the far end of the enclosed place made by the bronze railing. Eddie Mars came through the door with a set indifferent smile on his face, his hands thrust into the pockets of his dinner jacket, both thumbnails glistening outside. He seemed to like that pose. He strolled behind the croupiers and stopped at the corner of the middle table. He spoke with lazy calm, less politely than the croupier.

"Something the matter, Mrs. Regan?"

She turned her face to him with a sort of lunge. I saw the curve of her cheek stiffen, as if with an almost unbearable inner tautness. She didn't answer him.

Eddie Mars said gravely: "If you're not playing any more, you must let me send someone home with you."

The girl flushed. Her cheekbones stood out white in her face. Then she laughed off-key. She said bitterly:

"One more play, Eddie. Everything I have on the red. I like red. It's the color of blood."

Eddie Mars smiled faintly, then nodded and reached into his inner breast pocket. He drew out a large pinseal wallet with gold corners and tossed it carelessly along the table to the croupier. "Cover her bet in even thousands," he said, "if no one objects to this turn of the wheel being just for the lady."

No one objected. Vivian Regan leaned down and pushed all her winnings savagely with both hands on to the large red diamond on the layout.

The croupier leaned over the table without haste. He counted and stacked her money and chips, placed all but a few chips and bills in a neat pile and pushed the rest back off the layout with his rake. He opened Eddie Mars' wallet and drew out two flat packets of thousand-dollar bills. He broke one, counted six bills out, added them to the unbroken packet, put the four loose bills in the wallet and laid it aside as carelessly as if it had been a packet of matches. Eddie Mars didn't touch the wallet. Nobody moved except the croupier. He spun the wheel lefthanded and sent the ivory ball skittering along the upper edge with a casual flirt of his wrist. Then he drew his hands back and folded his arms.

Vivian's lips parted slowly until her teeth caught the light and glittered like knives. The ball drifted lazily down the slope of the wheel and bounced on the chromium ridges above the numbers. After a long time and then very suddenly motion left it with a dry click. The wheel slowed, carrying the ball around with it. The croupier didn't unfold his arms until the wheel had entirely ceased to revolve.

"The red wins," he said formally, without interest. The little ivory ball lay in Red 25, the third number from the Double Zero. Vivian Regan put her head back and laughed triumphantly.

The croupier lifted his rake and slowly pushed the stack of thousand-dollar bills across the layout, added them to the stake, pushed everything slowly out of the field of play.

Eddie Mars smiled, put his wallet back in his pocket, turned on his heel and left the room through the door in the paneling.

A dozen people let their breath out at the same time and broke for the bar. I broke with them and got to the far end of the room before Vivian had gathered up her winnings and turned away from the table. I went out into the large quiet lobby, got my hat and coat from the check girl, dropped a quarter in her tray and went out on the porch. The doorman loomed up beside me and said: "Can I get your car for you, sir?"

I said: "I'm just going for a walk."

The scrollwork along the edge of the porch was wet with the fog. The fog dripped from the Monterey cypresses that shadowed off into nothing towards the cliff above the ocean. You could see a scant dozen feet in any direction. I went down the porch steps and drifted off through the trees, following an indistinct path until I could hear the wash of the surf licking at the fog, low down at the bottom of the cliff. There wasn't a gleam of light anywhere. I could see a dozen trees clearly at one time, another dozen dimly, then nothing at all but the fog. I circled to the left and drifted back towards the gravel path that went around to the stables where they parked the cars. When I could make out the outlines of the house I stopped. A little in front of me I had heard a man cough.

My steps hadn't made any sound on the soft moist turf. The man coughed again, then stifled the cough with a handkerchief or a sleeve. While he was still doing that I moved forward closer to him. I made him out, a vague shadow close to the path. Something made me step behind a tree and crouch down. The man turned his head. His face should have been a white blur when he did that. It wasn't. It remained dark. There was a mask over it.

I waited, behind the tree.

CHAPTER TWENTY-THREE

LIGHT STEPS, the steps of a woman, came along the invisible pathway and the man in front of me moved forward and seemed to lean against the fog. I couldn't see the woman, then I could see her indistinctly. The arrogant carriage of her head seemed familiar. The man stepped out very quickly. The two figures blended in the fog, seemed to be part of the fog. There was dead silence for a moment. Then the man said:

"This is a gun, lady. Gentle now. Sound carries in the fog. Just hand me the bag."

The girl didn't make a sound. I moved forward a step. Quite suddenly I could see the foggy fuzz on the man's hat brim. The girl stood motionless. Then her breathing began to make a rasping sound, like a small file on soft wood.

"Yell," the man said, "and I'll cut you in half."

She didn't yell. She didn't move. There was a movement from him, and a dry chuckle. "It better be in here," he said. A catch clicked and a fumbling sound came to me. The man turned and came towards my tree. When he had taken three or four steps he chuckled again. The chuckle was something out of my own memories. I reached a pipe out of my pocket and held it like a gun.

I called out softly: "Hi, Lanny."

The man stopped dead and started to bring his hand up. I said: "No. I told you never to do that, Lanny. You're covered."

Nothing moved. The girl back on the path didn't move. I didn't move. Lanny didn't move.

"Put the bag down between your feet, kid," I told him. "Slow and easy."

He bent down. I jumped out and reached him still bent over. He straightened up against me breathing hard. His hands were empty.

"Tell me I can't get away with it," I said. I leaned against him and took the gun out of his overcoat pocket. "Somebody's always giving me guns," I told him. "I'm weighted down with them till I walk all crooked. Beat it."

Our breaths met and mingled, our eyes were like the eyes of two tomcats on a wall. I stepped back.

"On your way, Lanny. No hard feelings. You keep it quiet and I keep it quiet. Okey?"

"Okey," he said thickly.

The fog swallowed him. The faint sound of his steps and then nothing. I picked the bag up and felt in it and went towards the path. She still stood there motionless, a gray fur coat held tight around her throat with an ungloved hand on which a ring made a faint glitter. She wore no hat. Her dark parted hair was part of the darkness of the night. Her eyes too.

"Nice work, Marlowe. Are you my bodyguard now?" Her voice had a harsh note.

"Looks that way. Here's the bag."

She took it. I said: "Have you a car with you?"

She laughed. "I came with a man. What are you doing here?"

"Eddie Mars wanted to see me."

"I didn't know you knew him. Why?"

"I don't mind telling you. He thought I was looking for somebody he thought had run away with his wife."

"Were you?"

"No."

"Then what did you come for?"

"To find out why he thought I was looking for somebody he thought had run away with his wife."

"Did you find out?"

"No."

"You leak information like a radio announcer," she said. "I suppose it's none of my business—even if the man was my husband. I thought you weren't interested in that."

"People keep throwing it at me."

She clicked her teeth in annoyance. The incident of the masked man with the gun seemed to have made no impression on her at all. "Well, take me to the garage," she said. "I have to look in at my escort."

We walked along the path and around a corner of the building and there was light ahead, then around another corner and came to a bright enclosed stable yard lit with two floodlights. It was still paved with brick and still sloped down to a grating in the middle. Cars glistened and a man in a brown smock got up off a stool and came forward.

"Is my boy friend still blotto?" Vivian asked him carelessly.

"I'm afraid he is, miss. I put a rug over him and run the windows up. He's okey, I guess. Just kind of resting."

We went over to a big Cadillac and the man in the smock pulled the rear door open. On the wide back seat, loosely arranged, covered to the chin with a plaid robe, a man lay snoring with his mouth open. He seemed to be a big blond man who would hold a lot of liquor.

"Meet Mr. Larry Cobb," Vivian said. "Mister Cobb—Mister Marlowe."

I grunted.

"Mr. Cobb was my escort," she said. "Such a nice escort, Mr. Cobb. So attentive. You should see him sober. *I* should see him sober. Somebody should see him sober. I mean, just for the record. So it could become a part of history, that brief flashing moment, soon buried in time, but never forgotten —when Larry Cobb was sober."

"Yeah," I said.

"I've even thought of marrying him," she went on in a high strained voice, as if the shock of the stick-up was just beginning to get to her. "At odd times when nothing pleasant would come into my mind. We all have those spells. Lots of money, you know. A yacht, a place on Long Island, a place at Newport, a place at Bermuda, places dotted here and there all over the world probably—just a good Scotch bottle apart. And to Mr. Cobb a bottle of Scotch is not very far."

"Yeah," I said. "Does he have a driver to take him home?"

"Don't say 'yeah.' It's common." She looked at me with arched eyebrows. The man in the smock was chewing his lower lip hard. "Oh, undoubtedly a whole platoon of drivers. They probably do squads right in front of the garage every morning, buttons shining, harness gleaming, white gloves immaculate—a sort of West Point elegance about them."

"Well, where the hell is this driver?" I asked.

"He drove hisself tonight," the man in the smock said, almost apologetically. "I could call his home and have somebody come down for him."

Vivian turned around and smiled at him as if he had just presented her with a diamond tiara. "That would be lovely," she said. "Would you do that? I really wouldn't want Mr. Cobb to die like that—with his mouth open. Someone might think he had died of thirst."

The man in the smock said: "Not if they sniffed him, miss."

She opened her bag and grabbed a handful of paper money and pushed it at him. "You'll take care of him, I'm sure."

"Jeeze," the man said, pop-eyed. "I sure will, miss."

"Regan is the name," she said sweetly. "Mrs. Regan. You'll probably see me again. Haven't been here long, have you?"

"No'm." His hands were doing frantic things with the fistful of money he was holding.

"You'll get to love it here," she said. She took hold of my arm. "Let's ride in your car, Marlowe."

"It's outside on the street."

"Quite all right with me, Marlowe. I love a nice walk in the fog. You meet such interesting people."

"Oh, nuts," I said.

She held on to my arm and began to shake. She held me hard all the way to the car. She had stopped shaking by the time we reached it. I drove down a curving lane of trees on the blind side of the house. The lane opened on De Cazens Boulevard, the main drag of Las Olindas. We passed under the ancient sputtering arc lights and after a while there was a town, buildings, dead-looking stores, a service station with a light over a night bell, and at last a drugstore that was still open.

"You better have a drink," I said.

She moved her chin, a point of paleness in the corner of the seat. I turned diagonally into the curb and parked. "A little black coffee and a smattering of rye would go well," I said.

"I could get as drunk as two sailors and love it."

I held the door for her and she got out close to me, brushing my cheek with her hair. We went into the drugstore. I bought a pint of rye at the liquor counter and carried it over to the stools and set it down on the cracked marble counter.

"Two coffees," I said. "Black, strong and made this year."

"You can't drink liquor in here," the clerk said. He had a washed-out blue smock, was thin on top as to hair, had fairly honest eyes and his chin would never hit a wall before he saw it.

Vivian Regan reached into her bag for a pack of cigarettes and shook a couple loose just like a man. She held them towards me.

"It's against the law to drink liquor in here," the clerk said.

I lit the cigarettes and didn't pay any attention to him. He drew two cups of coffee from a tarnished nickel urn and set them in front of us. He looked at the bottle of rye, muttered under his breath and said wearily: "Okey, I'll watch the street while you pour it."

He went and stood at the display window with his back to us and his ears hanging out.

"My heart's in my mouth doing this," I said, and unscrewed the top of the whiskey bottle and loaded the coffee. "The law enforcement in this town is terrific. All through prohibition Eddie Mars' place was a night club and they had two uniformed men in the lobby every night—to see that the guests didn't bring their own liquor instead of buying it from the house."

The clerk turned suddenly and walked back behind the counter and went in behind the little glass window of the prescription room.

We sipped our loaded coffee. I looked at Vivian's face in the mirror back of the coffee urn. It was taut, pale, beautiful and wild. Her lips were red and harsh.

"You have wicked eyes," I said. "What's Eddie Mars got on you?"

She looked at me in the mirror. "I took plenty away from him tonight at roulette—starting with five grand I borrowed from him yesterday and didn't have to use."

"That might make him sore. You think he sent that loogan after you?"

"What's a loogan?"

"A guy with a gun."

"Are you a loogan?"

"Sure," I laughed. "But strictly speaking a loogan is on the wrong side of the fence."

"I often wonder if there is a wrong side."

"We're losing the subject. What has Eddie Mars got on you?"

"You mean a hold on me of some sort?"

"Yes."

Her lip curled. "Wittier, please, Marlowe. Much wittier."

"How's the General? I don't pretend to be witty."

"Not too well. He didn't get up today. You could at least stop questioning me."

"I remember a time when I thought the same about you. How much does the General know?"

"He probably knows everything."

"Norris would tell him?"

"No. Wilde, the District Attorney, was out to see him. Did you burn those pictures?"

"Sure. You worry about your little sister, don't you—from time to time."

"I think she's all I do worry about. I worry about Dad in a way, to keep things from him."

"He hasn't many illusions," I said, "but I suppose he still has pride."

"We're his blood. That's the hell of it." She stared at me in the mirror with deep, distant eyes. "I don't want him to die despising his own blood. It was always wild blood, but it wasn't always rotten blood."

"Is it now?"

"I guess you think so."

"Not yours. You're just playing the part."

She looked down. I sipped some more coffee and lit another cigarette for us. "So you shoot people," she said quietly. "You're a killer."

"Me? How?"

"The papers and the police fixed it up nicely. But I don't believe everything I read."

"Oh, you think I accounted for Geiger—or Brody—or both of them."

She didn't say anything. "I didn't have to," I said. "I might have, I suppose, and got away with it. Neither of them would have hesitated to throw lead at me."

"That makes you just a killer at heart, like all cops."

"Oh, nuts."

"One of those dark deadly quiet men who have no more feelings than a butcher has for slaughtered meat. I knew it the first time I saw you."

"You've got enough shady friends to know different."

"They're all soft compared to you."

"Thanks, lady. You're no English muffin yourself."

"Let's get out of this rotten little town."

I paid the check, put the bottle of rye in my pocket, and we left. The clerk still didn't like me.

We drove away from Las Olindas through a series of little dank beach towns with shack-like houses built down on the sand close to the rumble of the surf and larger houses built back on the slopes behind. A yellow window shone here and there, but most of the houses were dark. A smell of kelp came in off the water and lay on the fog. The tires sang on the moist concrete of the boulevard. The world was a wet emptiness.

We were close to Del Rey before she spoke to me for the first time since we left the drugstore. Her voice had a muffled sound, as if something was throbbing deep under it.

"Drive down by the Del Rey beach club. I want to look at the water. It's the next street on the left."

There was a winking yellow light at the intersection. I turned the car and slid down a slope with a high bluff on one side, interurban tracks to the right, a low straggle of lights far off beyond the tracks, and then very far off a glitter of pier lights and a haze in the sky over a city. That way the fog was almost gone. The road crossed the tracks where they turned to run under the bluff, then reached a paved strip of waterfront highway that bordered an open and uncluttered beach. Cars were parked along the sidewalk, facing out to sea, dark. The lights of the beach club were a few hundred yards away.

I braked the car against the curb and switched the headlights off and sat with my hands on the wheel. Under the thinning fog the surf curled and creamed, almost without sound, like a thought trying to form itself on the edge of consciousness.

"Move closer," she said almost thickly.

I moved out from under the wheel into the middle of the seat. She turned her body a little away from me as if to peer out of the window. Then she let herself fall backwards, without a sound, into my arms. Her head almost struck the wheel. Her eyes were closed, her face was dim. Then I saw that her eyes opened and flickered, the shine of them visible even in the darkness.

"Hold me close, you beast," she said.

I put my arms around her loosely at first. Her hair had a harsh feeling against my face. I tightened my arms and lifted her up. I brought her face slowly up to my face. Her eyelids were flickering rapidly, like moth wings.

I kissed her tightly and quickly. Then a long slow clinging kiss. Her lips opened under mine. Her body began to shake in my arms.

"Killer," she said softly, her breath going into my mouth.

I strained her against me until the shivering of her body was almost shaking mine. I kept on kissing her. After a long time she pulled her head away enough to say: "Where do you live?"

"Hobart Arms. Franklin near Kenmore."

"I've never seen it."

"Want to?"

"Yes," she breathed.

"What has Eddie Mars got on you?"

Her body stiffened in my arms and her breath made a harsh sound. Her head pulled back until her eyes, wide open, ringed with white, were staring at me.

"So that's the way it is," she said in a soft dull voice.

"That's the way it is. Kissing is nice, but your father didn't hire me to sleep with you."

"You son of a bitch," she said calmly, without moving.

I laughed in her face. "Don't think I'm an icicle," I said. "I'm not blind or without senses. I have warm blood like the next guy. You're easy to take —too damned easy. What has Eddie Mars got on you?"

"If you say that again, I'll scream."

"Go ahead and scream."

She jerked away and pulled herself upright, far back in the corner of the car.

"Men have been shot for little things like that, Marlowe."

"Men have been shot for practically nothing. The first time we met I told you I was a detective. Get it through your lovely head. I work at it, lady. I don't play at it."

She fumbled in her bag and got a handkerchief out and bit on it, her head turned away from me. The tearing sound of the handkerchief came to me. She tore it with her teeth, slowly, time after time.

"What makes you think he has anything on me?" she whispered, her voice muffled by the handkerchief.

"He lets you win a lot of money and sends a gunpoke around to take it back for him. You're not more than mildly surprised. You didn't even thank me for saving it for you. I think the whole thing was just some kind of an act. If I wanted to flatter myself, I'd say it was at least partly for my benefit."

"You think he can win or lose as he pleases."

"Sure. On even money bets, four times out of five."

"Do I have to tell you I loathe your guts, Mister Detective?"

"You don't owe me anything. I'm paid off."

She tossed the shredded handkerchief out of the car window. "You have a lovely way with women."

"I liked kissing you."

"You kept your head beautifully. That's so flattering. Should I congratulate you, or my father?"

"I liked kissing you."

Her voice became an icy drawl. "Take me away from here, if you will be so kind. I'm quite sure I'd like to go home."

"You won't be a sister to me?"

"If I had a razor, I'd cut your throat—just to see what ran out of it."

"Caterpillar blood," I said.

I started the car and turned it and drove back across the interurban tracks to the highway and so on into town and up to West Hollywood. She didn't speak to me. She hardly moved all the way back. I drove through the gates and up the sunken driveway to the porte-cochere of the big house. She jerked the car door open and was out of it before it had quite stopped. She didn't speak even then. I watched her back as she stood against the door after ringing the bell. The door opened and Norris looked out. She pushed past him quickly and was gone. The door banged shut and I was sitting there looking at it.

I turned back down the driveway and home.

CHAPTER TWENTY-FOUR

THE APARTMENT HOUSE lobby was empty this time. No gunman waiting under the potted palm to give me orders. I took the automatic elevator up to my floor and walked along the hallway to the tune of a muted radio behind a door. I needed a drink and was in a hurry to get one. I didn't switch the light on inside the door. I made straight for the kitchenette and brought up short in three or four feet. Something was wrong. Something on the air, a scent. The shades were down at the windows and the street light leaking in at the sides made a dim light in the room. I stood still and listened. The scent on the air was a perfume, a heavy cloying perfume.

There was no sound, no sound at all. Then my eyes adjusted themselves more to the darkness and I saw there was something across the floor in front of me that shouldn't have been there. I backed, reached the wall switch with my thumb and flicked the light on.

The bed was down. Something in it giggled. A blonde head was pressed into my pillow. Two bare arms curved up and the hands belonging to them were clasped on top of the blonde head. Carmen Sternwood lay on her back, in my bed, giggling at me. The tawny wave of her hair was spread out on the pillow as if by a careful and artificial hand. Her slaty eyes peered at me and had the effect, as usual, of peering from behind a barrel. She smiled. Her small sharp teeth glinted.

"Cute, aren't I?" she said.

I said harshly: "Cute as a Filipino on Saturday night."

I went over to a floor lamp and pulled the switch, went back to put off the ceiling light, and went across the room again to the chessboard on a card table under the lamp. There was a problem laid out on the board, a six-mover. I couldn't solve it, like a lot of my problems. I reached down and moved a knight, then pulled my hat and coat off and threw them somewhere. All this time the soft giggling went on from the bed, that sound that made me think of rats behind a wainscoting in an old house.

"I bet you can't even guess how I got in."

I dug a cigarette out and looked at her with bleak eyes. "I bet I can. You came through the keyhole, just like Peter Pan."

"Who's he?"

"Oh, a fellow I used to know around the poolroom."

She giggled. "You're cute, aren't you?" she said.

I began to say: "About that thumb–" but she was ahead of me. I didn't have to remind her. She took her right hand from behind her head and started sucking the thumb and eyeing me with very round and naughty eyes.

"I'm all undressed," she said, after I had smoked and stared at her for a minute.

"By God," I said, "it was right at the back of my mind. I was groping for it. I almost had it, when you spoke. In another minute I'd have said 'I bet you're all undressed.' I always wear my rubbers in bed myself, in case I wake up with a bad conscience and have to sneak away from it."

"You're cute." She rolled her head a little, kittenishly. Then she took her left hand from under her head and took hold of the covers, paused dramatically, and swept them aside. She was undressed all right. She lay there on the bed in the lamplight, as naked and glistening as a pearl. The Sternwood girls were giving me both barrels that night.

I pulled a shred of tobacco off the edge of my lower lip.

"That's nice," I said. "But I've already seen it all. Remember? I'm the guy that keeps finding you without any clothes on."

She giggled some more and covered herself up again. "Well, how *did* you get in?" I asked her.

"The manager let me in. I showed him your card. I'd stolen it from Vivian. I told him you told me to come here and wait for you. I was–I was mysterious." She glowed with delight.

"Neat," I said. "Managers are like that. Now I know how you got in tell me how you're going to go out."

She giggled. "Not going–not for a long time. . . . I like it here. You're cute."

"Listen," I pointed my cigarette at her. "Don't make me dress you again. I'm tired. I appreciate all you're offering me. It's just more than I could possibly take. Doghouse Reilly never let a pal down that way. I'm your friend. I won't let you down–in spite of yourself. You and I have to keep on being friends, and this isn't the way to do it. Now will you dress like a nice little girl?"

She shook her head from side to side.

"Listen," I plowed on, "you don't really care anything about me. You're just showing how naughty you can be. But you don't have to show me. I knew it already. I'm the guy that found–"

"Put the light out," she giggled.

I threw my cigarette on the floor and stamped on it. I took a handkerchief out and wiped the palms of my hands. I tried it once more.

"It isn't on account of the neighbors," I told her. "They don't really care a lot. There's a lot of stray broads in any apartment house and one more won't make the building rock. It's a question of professional pride. You know –professional pride. I'm working for your father. He's a sick man, very frail, very helpless. He sort of trusts me not to pull any stunts. Won't you please get dressed, Carmen?"

"Your name isn't Doghouse Reilly," she said. "It's Philip Marlowe. You can't fool me."

I looked down at the chessboard. The move with the knight was wrong. I put it back where I had moved it from. Knights had no meaning in this game. It wasn't a game for knights.

I looked at her again. She lay still now, her face pale against the pillow, her eyes large and dark and empty as rain barrels in a drought. One of her small five-fingered thumbless hands picked at the cover restlessly. There was a vague glimmer of doubt starting to get born in her somewhere. She didn't know about it yet. It's so hard for women—even nice women—to realize that their bodies are not irresistible.

I said: "I'm going out in the kitchen and mix a drink. Want one?"

"Uh-huh." Dark silent mystified eyes stared at me solemnly, the doubt growing larger in them, creeping into them noiselessly, like a cat in long grass stalking a young blackbird.

"If you're dressed when I get back, you'll get the drink. Okey?"

Her teeth parted and a faint hissing noise came out of her mouth. She didn't answer me. I went out to the kitchenette and got out some Scotch and fizzwater and mixed a couple of highballs. I didn't have anything really exciting to drink, like nitroglycerin or distilled tiger's breath. She hadn't moved when I got back with the glasses. The hissing had stopped. Her eyes were dead again. Her lips started to smile at me. Then she sat up suddenly and threw all the covers off her body and reached.

"Gimme."

"When you're dressed. Not *until* you're dressed."

I put the two glasses down on the card table and sat down myself and lit another cigarette. "Go ahead. I won't watch you."

I looked away. Then I was aware of the hissing noise very sudden and sharp. It startled me into looking at her again. She sat there naked, propped on her hands, her mouth open a little, her face like scraped bone. The hissing noise came tearing out of her mouth as if she had nothing to do with it. There was something behind her eyes, blank as they were, that I had never seen in a woman's eyes.

Then her lips moved very slowly and carefully, as if they were artificial lips and had to be manipulated with springs.

She called me a filthy name.

I didn't mind that. I didn't mind what she called me, what anybody called me. But this was the room I had to live in. It was all I had in the way of a home. In it was everything that was mine, that had any association for me, any past, anything that took the place of a family. Not much; a few books, pictures, radio, chessmen, old letters, stuff like that. Nothing. Such as they were they had all my memories.

I couldn't stand her in that room any longer. What she called me only reminded me of that.

I said carefully: "I'll give you three minutes to get dressed and out of here. If you're not out by then, I'll throw you out—by force. Just the way you are, naked. And I'll throw your clothes after you into the hall. Now—get started."

Her teeth chattered and the hissing noise was sharp and animal. She swung her feet to the floor and reached for her clothes on a chair beside the bed. She dressed. I watched her. She dressed with stiff awkward fingers—for a woman—but quickly at that. She was dressed in a little over two minutes. I timed it.

She stood there beside the bed, holding a green bag tight against a fur-trimmed coat. She wore a rakish green hat crooked on her head. She stood there for a moment and hissed at me, her face still like scraped bone, her eyes still empty and yet full of some jungle emotion. Then she walked quickly to the door and opened it and went out, without speaking, without looking back. I heard the elevator lurch into motion and move in the shaft.

I walked to the windows and pulled the shades up and opened the windows wide. The night air came drifting in with a kind of stale sweetness that still remembered automobile exhausts and the streets of the city. I reached for my drink and drank it slowly. The apartment house door closed itself down below me. Steps tinkled on the quiet sidewalk. A car started up not far away. It rushed off into the night with a rough clashing of gears. I went back to the bed and looked down at it. The imprint of her head was still in the pillow, of her small corrupt body still on the sheets.

I put my empty glass down and tore the bed to pieces savagely.

CHAPTER TWENTY-FIVE

IT WAS RAINING again the next morning, a slanting gray rain like a swung curtain of crystal beads. I got up feeling sluggish and tired and stood looking out of the windows, with a dark harsh taste of Sternwoods still in my mouth. I was as empty of life as a scarecrow's pockets. I went out to the kitchenette and drank two cups of black coffee. You can have a hangover from other things than alcohol. I had one from women. Women made me sick.

I shaved and showered and dressed and got my raincoat out and went downstairs and looked out of the front door. Across the street, a hundred feet up, a gray Plymouth sedan was parked. It was the same one that had tried to trail me around the day before, the same one that I had asked Eddie Mars about. There might be a cop in it, if a cop had that much time on his hands and wanted to waste it following me around. Or it might be a smoothie in the detective business trying to get a noseful of somebody else's case in order to chisel a way into it. Or it might be the Bishop of Bermuda disapproving of my night life.

I went out back and got my convertible from the garage and drove it around front past the gray Plymouth. There was a small man in it, alone. He started up after me. He worked better in the rain. He stayed close enough so that I couldn't make a short block and leave that before he entered it, and he stayed back far enough so that other cars were between us most of the time. I drove down to the boulevard and parked in the lot next to my building and came out of there with my raincoat collar up and my hat brim low and the raindrops tapping icily at my face in between. The Plymouth was across the way at a fireplug. I walked down to the intersection and crossed with the green light and walked back, close to the edge of the sidewalk and the parked cars. The Plymouth hadn't moved. Nobody got out of it. I reached it and jerked open the door on the curb side.

A small bright-eyed man was pressed back into the corner behind the wheel. I stood and looked in at him, the rain thumping my back. His eyes blinked behind the swirling smoke of a cigarette. His hands tapped restlessly on the thin wheel.

I said: "Can't you make your mind up?"

He swallowed and the cigarette bobbed between his lips. "I don't think I know you," he said, in a tight little voice.

"Marlowe's the name. The guy you've been trying to follow around for a couple of days."

"I ain't following anybody, doc."

"This jalopy is. Maybe you can't control it. Have it your own way. I'm now going to eat breakfast in the coffee shop across the street, orange juice, bacon and eggs, toast, honey, three or four cups of coffee and a toothpick. I am then going up to my office, which is on the seventh floor of the building right opposite you. If you have anything that's worrying you beyond endurance, drop up and chew it over. I'll only be oiling my machine gun."

I left him blinking and walked away. Twenty minutes later I was airing the scrubwoman's Soirée d'Amour out of my office and opening up a thick rough envelope addressed in a fine old-fashioned pointed handwriting. The envelope contained a brief formal note and a large mauve check for five hundred dollars, payable to Philip Marlowe and signed, Guy de Brisay Sternwood, by Vincent Norris. That made it a nice morning. I was making out a bank slip when the buzzer told me somebody had entered my two by four reception room. It was the little man from the Plymouth.

"Fine," I said. "Come in and shed your coat."

He slid past me carefully as I held the door, as carefully as though he feared I might plant a kick in his minute buttocks. We sat down and faced each other across the desk. He was a very small man, not more than five feet three and would hardly weigh as much as a butcher's thumb. He had tight brilliant eyes that wanted to look hard, and looked as hard as oysters on the half shell. He wore a double-breasted dark gray suit that was too wide in the shoulders and had too much lapel. Over this, open, an Irish tweed coat with some badly worn spots. A lot of foulard tie bulged out and was rain-spotted above his crossed lapels.

"Maybe you know me," he said. "I'm Harry Jones."

I said I didn't know him. I pushed a flat tin of cigarettes at him. His small neat fingers speared one like a trout taking the fly. He lit it with the desk lighter and waved his hand.

"I been around," he said. "Know the boys and such. Used to do a little liquor-running down from Hueneme Point. A tough racket, brother. Riding the scout car with a gun in your lap and a wad on your hip that would choke a coal chute. Plenty of times we paid off four sets of law before we hit Beverly Hills. A tough racket."

"Terrible," I said.

He leaned back and blew smoke at the ceiling from the small tight corner of his small tight mouth.

"Maybe you don't believe me," he said.

"Maybe I don't," I said. "And maybe I do. And then again maybe I haven't bothered to make my mind up. Just what is the build-up supposed to do to me?"

"Nothing," he said tartly.

"You've been following me around for a couple of days," I said. "Like a fellow trying to pick up a girl and lacking the last inch of nerve. Maybe you're selling insurance. Maybe you knew a fellow called Joe Brody. That's a lot of maybes, but I have a lot on hand in my business."

His eyes bulged and his lower lip almost fell in his lap. "Christ, how'd you know that?" he snapped.

"I'm psychic. Shake your business up and pour it. I haven't got all day."

The brightness of his eyes almost disappeared between the suddenly narrowed lids. There was silence. The rain pounded down on the flat tarred roof over the Mansion House lobby below my windows. His eyes opened a little, shined again, and his voice was full of thought.

"I was trying to get a line on you, sure," he said. "I've got something to sell—cheap, for a couple of C notes. How'd you tie me to Joe?"

I opened a letter and read it. It offered me a six months' correspondence course in fingerprinting at a special professional discount. I dropped it into the waste basket and looked at the little man again. "Don't mind me. I was just guessing. You're not a cop. You don't belong to Eddie Mars outfit. I asked him last night. I couldn't think of anybody else but Joe Brody's friends who would be that much interested in me."

"Jesus," he said and licked his lower lip. His face had turned white as paper when I mentioned Eddie Mars. His mouth drooped open and his cigarette hung to the corner of it by some magic, as if it had grown there. "Aw, you're kidding me," he said at last, with the sort of smile the operating room sees.

"All right. I'm kidding you." I opened another letter. This one wanted to send me a daily newsletter from Washington, all inside stuff, straight from the cookhouse. "I suppose Agnes is loose," I added.

"Yeah. She sent me. You interested?"

"Well—she's a blonde."

"Nuts. You made a crack when you were up there that night—the night Joe got squibbed off. Something about Brody must have known something good about the Sternwoods or he wouldn't have taken the chance on that picture he sent them.

"Uh-huh. So he had? What was it?"

"That's what the two hundred bucks pays for."

I dropped some more fan mail into the basket and lit myself a fresh cigarette.

"We gotta get out of town," he said. "Agnes is a nice girl. You can't hold that stuff on her. It's not so easy for a dame to get by these days."

"She's too big for you," I said. "She'll roll on you and smother you."

"That's kind of a dirty crack, brother," he said with something that was near enough to dignity to make me stare at him.

I said: "You're right. I've been meeting the wrong kind of people lately. Let's cut out the gabble and get down to cases. What have you got for the money?"

"Would you pay for it?"

"If it does what?"

"If it helps you find Rusty Regan."

"I'm not looking for Rusty Regan."

"Says you. Want to hear it or not?"

"Go ahead and chirp. I'll pay for anything I use. Two C notes buys a lot of information in my circle."

"Eddie Mars had Regan bumped off," he said calmly, and leaned back as if he had just been made a vice-president.

I waved a hand in the direction of the door. "I wouldn't even argue with you," I said. "I wouldn't waste the oxygen. On your way, small size."

He leaned across the desk, white lines at the corners of his mouth. He snubbed his cigarette out carefully, over and over again, without looking at it. From behind a communicating door came the sound of a typewriter clacking monotonously to the bell, to the shift, line after line.

"I'm not kidding," he said.

"Beat it. Don't bother me. I have work to do."

"No you don't," he said sharply. "I ain't that easy. I came here to speak my piece and I'm speaking it. I knew Rusty myself. Not well, well enough to say 'How's a boy?' and he'd answer me or he wouldn't, according to how he felt. A nice guy though. I always liked him. He was sweet on a singer named Mona Grant. Then she changed her name to Mars. Rusty got sore and married a rich dame that hung around the joints like she couldn't sleep well at home. You know all about her, tall, dark, enough looks for a Derby winner, but the type would put a lot of pressure on a guy. High-strung. Rusty wouldn't get along with her. But Jesus, he'd get along with her old man's dough, wouldn't he? That's what you think. This Regan was a cockeyed sort of buzzard. He had long-range eyes. He was looking over into the next valley all the time. He wasn't scarcely around where he was. I don't think he gave a damn about dough. And coming from me, brother, that's a compliment."

The little man wasn't so dumb after all. A three for a quarter grifter wouldn't even think such thoughts, much less know how to express them.

I said: "So he ran away."

"He started to run away, maybe. With this girl Mona. She wasn't living with Eddie Mars, didn't like his rackets. Especially the side lines, like blackmail, bent cars, hideouts for hot boys from the east, and so on. The talk was Regan told Eddie one night, right out in the open, that if he ever messed Mona up in any criminal rap, he'd be around to see him."

"Most of this is on the record, Harry," I said. "You can't expect money for that."

"I'm coming to what isn't. So Regan blew. I used to see him every afternoon in Vardi's drinking Irish whiskey and staring at the wall. He don't talk much any more. He'd give me a bet now and then, which was what I was there for, to pick up bets for Puss Walgreen."

"I thought he was in the insurance business."

"That's what it says on the door. I guess he'd sell you insurance at that, if you tramped on him. Well, about the middle of September I don't see Regan anymore. I don't notice it right away. You know how it is. A guy's there and you see him and then he ain't there and you don't see him until something makes you think of it. What makes me think about it is I hear a guy say laughing that Eddie Mars' woman lammed out with Rusty Regan and Mars is acting like he was best man, instead of being sore. So I tell Joe Brody and Joe was smart."

"Like hell he was," I said.

"Not copper smart, but still smart. He's out for the dough. He gets to figuring could he get a line somehow on the two lovebirds he could maybe collect twice—once from Eddie Mars and once from Regan's wife. Joe knew the family a little."

"Five grand worth," I said. "He nicked them for that a while back."

"Yeah?" Harry Jones looked mildly surprised. "Agnes ought to of told me that. There's a frail for you. Always holding out. Well, Joe and me watch the papers and we don't see anything, so we know old Sternwood has a blanket on it. Then one day I see Lash Canino in Vardi's. Know him?"

I shook my head.

"There's a boy that is tough like some guys think they are tough. He does a job for Eddie Mars when Mars needs him—trouble-shooting. He'd bump a guy off between drinks. When Mars don't need him he don't go near him. And he don't stay in L.A. Well it might be something and it might not. Maybe they got a line on Regan and Mars has just been sitting back with a smile on his puss, waiting for the chance. Then again it might be something else entirely. Anyway I tell Joe and Joe gets on Canino's tail. He can tail. Me, I'm no good at it. I'm giving that one away. No charge. And Joe tails Canino out to the Sternwood place and Canino parks outside the estate and a car come up beside him with a girl in it. They talk for a while and Joe thinks the girl passes something over, like maybe dough. The girl beats it. It's Regan's wife. Okey, she knows Canino and Canino knows Mars. So Joe figures Canino knows something about Regan and is trying to squeeze a little on the side for himself. Canino blows and Joe loses him. End of Act One."

"What does this Canino look like?"

"Short, heavy set, brown hair, brown eyes, and always wears brown clothes and a brown hat. Even wears a brown suede raincoat. Drives a brown coupe. Everything brown for Mr. Canino."

"Let's have Act Two," I said.

"Without some dough that's all."

"I don't see two hundred bucks in it. Mrs. Regan married an ex-bootlegger out of the joints. She'd know other people of his sort. She knows Eddie Mars well. If she thought anything had happened to Regan, Eddie would be the very man she'd go to, and Canino might be the man Eddie would pick to handle the assignment. Is that all you have?"

"Would you give the two hundred to know where Eddie's wife is?" the little man asked calmly.

He had all my attention now. I almost cracked the arms of my chair leaning on them.

"Even if she was alone?" Harry Jones added in a soft, rather sinister tone. "Even if she never run away with Regan at all, and was being kept now about forty miles from L.A. in a hideout—so the law would keep on thinking she had dusted with him? Would you pay two hundred bucks for that, shamus?"

I licked my lips. They tasted dry and salty. "I think I would," I said. "Where?"

"Agnes found her," he said grimly. "Just by a lucky break. Saw her out riding and managed to tail her home. Agnes will tell you where that is—when she's holding the money in her hand."

I made a hard face at him. "You could tell the coppers for nothing, Harry. They have some good wreckers down at Central these days. If they killed you trying, they still have Agnes."

"Let 'em try," he said. "I ain't so brittle."

"Agnes must have something I didn't notice."

"She's a grifter, shamus. I'm a grifter. We're all grifters. So we sell each other out for a nickel. Okey. See can you make me." He reached for another of my cigarettes, placed it neatly between his lips and lit it with a match the way I do myself, missing twice on his thumbnail and then using his foot. He puffed evenly and stared at me level-eyed, a funny little hard guy I could have thrown from home plate to second base. A small man in a big man's world. There was something I liked about him.

"I haven't pulled anything in here," he said steadily. "I come in talking two C's. That's still the price. I come because I thought I'd get a take it or leave it, one right gee to another. Now you're waving cops at me. You oughta be ashamed of yourself."

I said: "You'll get the two hundred—for that information. I have to get the money myself first."

He stood up and nodded and pulled his worn little Irish tweed coat tight around his chest. "That's okey. After dark is better anyway. It's a leery job—buckin' guys like Eddie Mars. But a guy has to eat. The book's been pretty dull lately. I think the big boys have told Puss Walgreen to move on. Suppose you come over there to the office, Fulwider Building, Western and Santa Monica, four-twenty-eight at the back. You bring the money, I'll take you to Agnes."

"Can't you tell me yourself? I've seen Agnes."

"I promised her," he said simply. He buttoned his overcoat, cocked his hat jauntily, nodded again and strolled to the door. He went out. His steps died along the hall.

I went down to the bank and deposited my five-hundred-dollar check and drew out two hundred in currency. I went upstairs again and sat in my chair thinking about Harry Jones and his story. It seemed a little too pat. It had the austere simplicity of fiction rather than the tangled woof of fact. Captain Gregory ought to have been able to find Mona Mars, if she was that close to his beat. Supposing, that is, he had tried.

I thought about it most of the day. Nobody came into the office. Nobody called me on the phone. It kept on raining.

CHAPTER TWENTY-SIX

AT SEVEN the rain had stopped for a breathing spell, but the gutters were still flooded. On Santa Monica the water was level with the sidewalk and a thin film of it washed over the top of the curbing. A traffic cop in shining black rubber from boots to cap sloshed through the flood on his way from the shelter of a sodden awning. My rubber heels slithered on the sidewalk as I turned into the narrow lobby of the Fulwider Building. A single drop light burned far back, beyond an open, once gilt elevator. There was a tarnished and well-missed spittoon on a gnawed rubber mat. A case of false teeth hung on the mustard-colored wall like a fuse box in a screen porch. I shook the rain off my hat and looked at the building directory beside the case of teeth. Numbers with names and numbers without names. Plenty of vacancies or plenty of tenants who wished to remain anonymous. Painless dentists, shyster detective agencies, small sick businesses that had crawled there to die, mail order schools that would teach you how to become a railroad clerk or a radio technician or a screen writer—if the postal inspectors didn't catch up with them first. A nasty building. A building in which the smell of stale cigar butts would be the cleanest odor.

An old man dozed in the elevator, on a ramshackle stool, with a burst-out cushion under him. His mouth was open, his veined temples glistened in the weak light. He wore a blue uniform coat that fitted him the way a stall fits a horse. Under that gray trousers with frayed cuffs, white cotton socks and black kid shoes, one of which was slit across a bunion. On the stool he slept miserably, waiting for a customer. I went past him softly, the clandestine air of the building prompting me, found the fire door and pulled it open. The fire stairs hadn't been swept in a month. Bums had slept on them, eaten on them, left crusts and fragments of greasy newspaper, matches, a gutted imitation-leather pocketbook. In a shadowy angle against the scribbled wall a pouched ring of pale rubber had fallen and had not been disturbed. A very nice building.

I came out at the fourth floor sniffing for air. The hallway had the same dirty spittoon and frayed mat, the same mustard walls, the same memories of low tide. I went down the line and turned a corner. The name: "L. D. Walgreen—Insurance," showed on a dark pebbled glass door, on a second dark door, on a third behind which there was a light. One of the dark doors said: "Entrance."

A glass transom was open above the lighted door. Through it the sharp birdlike voice of Harry Jones spoke, saying:

"Canino? . . . Yeah, I've seen you around somewhere. Sure."

I froze. The other voice spoke. It had a heavy purr, like a small dynamo behind a brick wall. It said: "I thought you would." There was a vaguely sinister note in that voice.

A chair scraped on linoleum, steps sounded, the transom above me squeaked shut. A shadow melted from behind the pebbled glass.

I went back to the first of the three doors marked with the name Walgreen. I tried it cautiously. It was locked. It moved in a loose frame, an old door fitted many years past, made of half-seasoned wood and shrunken now. I reached my wallet out and slipped the thick hard window of celluloid from over my driver's license. A burglar's tool the law had forgotten to proscribe. I put my gloves on, leaned softly and lovingly against the door and pushed the knob hard away from the frame. I pushed the celluloid plate into the wide crack and felt for the slope of the spring lock. There was a dry click, like a small icicle breaking. I hung there motionless, like a lazy fish in the water. Nothing happened inside. I turned the knob and pushed the door back into darkness. I shut it behind me as carefully as I had opened it.

The lighted oblong of an uncurtained window faced me, cut by the angle of a desk. On the desk a hooded typewriter took form, then the metal knob of a communicating door. This was unlocked. I passed into the second of the three offices. Rain rattled suddenly against the closed window. Under its noise I crossed the room. A tight fan of light spread from an inch opening of the door into the lighted office. Everything very convenient. I walked like a cat on a mantel and reached the hinged side of the door, put an eye to the crack and saw nothing but light against the angle of the wood.

The purring voice was now saying quite pleasantly: "Sure, a guy could sit on his fanny and crab what another guy done if he knows what it's all about. So you go to see this peeper. Well, that was your mistake. Eddie don't like it. The peeper told Eddie some guy in a gray Plymouth was tailing him. Eddie naturally wants to know who and why, see."

Harry Jones laughed lightly. "What makes it his business?"

"That don't get you no place."

"You know why I went to the peeper. I already told you. Account of Joe

Brody's girl. She has to blow and she's shatting on her uppers. She figures the peeper can get her some dough. I don't have any."

The purring voice said gently: "Dough for what? Peepers don't give that stuff out to punks."

"He could raise it. He knows rich people." Harry Jones laughed, a brave little laugh.

"Don't fuss with me, little man." The purring voice had an edge, like sand in the bearings.

"Okey, okey. You know the dope on Brody's bump-off. That screwy kid done it all right, but the night it happened this Marlowe was right there in the room."

"That's known, little man. He told it to the law."

"Yeah—here's what isn't. Brody was trying to peddle a nudist photo of the young Sternwood girl. Marlowe got wise to him. While they were arguing about it the young Sternwood girl dropped around herself—with a gat. She took a shot at Brody. She lets one fly and breaks a window. Only the peeper didn't tell the coppers about that. And Agnes didn't neither. She figures it's railroad fare for her not to."

"This ain't got anything to do with Eddie?"

"Show me how."

"Where's this Agnes at?"

"Nothing doing."

"You tell me, little man. Here, or in the back room where the boys pitch dimes against the wall."

"She's my girl now, Canino. I don't put my girl in the middle for anybody."

A silence followed. I listened to the rain lashing the windows. The smell of cigarette smoke came through the crack of the door. I wanted to cough. I bit hard on a handkerchief.

The purring voice said, still gentle: "From what I hear this blonde broad was just a shill for Geiger. I'll talk it over with Eddie. How much you tap the peeper for?"

"Two centuries."

"Get it?"

Harry Jones laughed again. "I'm seeing him tomorrow. I have hopes."

"Where's Agnes?"

"Listen—"

"Where's Agnes?"

Silence.

"Look at it, little man."

I didn't move. I wasn't wearing a gun. I didn't have to see through the crack of the door to know that a gun was what the purring voice was inviting Harry Jones to look at. But I didn't think Mr. Canino would do anything with his gun beyond showing it. I waited.

"I'm looking at it," Harry Jones said, his voice squeezed tight as if it could hardly get past his teeth. "And I don't see anything I didn't see before. Go ahead and blast and see what it gets you."

"A Chicago overcoat is what it would get *you*, little man."

Silence.

"Where's Agnes?"

Harry Jones sighed. "Okey," he said wearily. "She's in an apartment house at 28 Court Street, up on Bunker Hill. Apartment 301. I guess I'm yellow all right. Why should I front for that twist?"

"No reason. You got good sense. You and me'll go out and talk to her. All I want is to find out is she dummying up on you, kid. If it's the way you say it is, everything is jakeloo. You can put the bite on the peeper and be on your way. No hard feelings?"

"No," Harry Jones said. "No hard feelings, Canino."

"Fine. Let's dip the bill. Got a glass?" The purring voice was now as false as an usherette's eyelashes and as slippery as a watermelon seed. A drawer was pulled open. Something jarred on wood. A chair squeaked. A scuffing sound on the floor. "This is bond stuff," the purring voice said.

There was a gurgling sound. "Moths in your ermine, as the ladies say."

Harry Jones said softly: "Success."

I heard a short sharp cough. Then a violent retching. There was a small thud on the floor, as if a thick glass had fallen. My fingers curled against my raincoat.

The purring voice said gently: "You ain't sick from just one drink, are you, pal?"

Harry Jones didn't answer. There was labored breathing for a short moment. Then thick silence folded down. Then a chair scraped.

"So long, little man," said Mr. Canino.

Steps, a click, the wedge of light died at my feet, a door opened and closed quietly. The steps faded, leisurely and assured.

I stirred around the edge of the door and pulled it wide and looked into blackness relieved by the dim shine of a window. The corner of a desk glittered faintly. A hunched shape took form in a chair behind it. In the close air there was a heavy clogged smell, almost a perfume. I went across to the corridor door and listened. I heard the distant clang of the elevator.

I found the light switch and light glowed in a dusty glass bowl hanging from the ceiling by three brass chains. Harry Jones looked at me across the desk, his eyes wide open, his face frozen in a tight spasm, the skin bluish. His small dark head was tilted to one side. He sat upright against the back of the chair.

A street-car bell clanged at an almost infinite distance and the sound came buffeted by innumerable walls. A brown half pint of whiskey stood on the desk with the cap off. Harry Jones' glass glinted against a castor of the desk. The second glass was gone.

I breathed shallowly, from the top of my lungs, and bent above the bottle. Behind the charred smell of the bourbon another odor lurked, faintly, the odor of bitter almonds. Harry Jones dying had vomited on his coat. That made it cyanide.

I walked around him carefully and lifted a phone book from a hook on the wooden frame of the window. I let it fall again, reached the telephone as far as it would go from the little dead man. I dialed information. The voice answered.

"Can you give me the phone number of Apartment 301, 28 Court Street?"

"One moment, please." The voice came to me borne on the smell of bitter almonds. A silence. "The number is Wentworth 2528. It is listed under Glendower Apartments."

I thanked the voice and dialed the number. The bell rang three times, then the line opened. A radio blared along the wire and was muted. A burly male voice said: "Hello."

"Is Agnes there?"

"No Agnes here, buddy. What number you want?"

"Wentworth two-five-two-eight."

"Right number, wrong gal. Ain't that a shame?" The voice cackled.

I hung up and reached for the phone book again and looked up the Wentworth Apartments. I dialed the manager's number. I had a blurred vision of Mr. Canino driving fast through rain to another appointment with death.

"Glendower Apartments. Mr. Schiff speaking."

"This is Wallis, Police Identification Bureau. Is there a girl named Agnes Lozelle registered in your place?"

"Who did you say you were?"

I told him again.

"If you give me your number, I'll—"

"Cut the comedy," I said sharply, "I'm in a hurry. Is there or isn't there?"

"No. There isn't." The voice was as stiff as a breadstick.

"Is there a tall blonde with green eyes registered in the flop?"

"Say, this isn't any flop—"

"Oh, can it, *can it!*" I rapped at him in a police voice. "You want me to send the vice squad over there and shake the joint down? I know all about Bunker Hill apartment houses, mister. Especially the ones that have phone numbers listed for each apartment."

"Hey, take it easy, officer. I'll co-operate. There's a couple of blondes here, sure. Where isn't there? I hadn't noticed their eyes much. Would yours be alone?"

"Alone, or with a little chap about five feet three, a hundred and ten, sharp black eyes, wears double-breasted dark gray suit and Irish tweed overcoat, gray hat. My information is Apartment 301, but all I get there is the big razzoo."

"Oh, she ain't there. There's a couple of car salesmen living in three-o-one."

"Thanks, I'll drop around."

"Make it quiet, won't you? Come to my place, direct?"

"Much obliged, Mr. Schiff." I hung up.

I wiped sweat off my face. I walked to the far corner of the office and stood with my face to the wall, patted it with a hand. I turned around slowly and looked across at little Harry Jones grimacing in his chair.

"Well, you fooled him, Harry," I said out loud, in a voice that sounded queer to me. "You lied to him and you drank your cyanide like a little gentleman. You died like a poisoned rat, Harry, but you're no rat to me."

I had to search him. It was a nasty job. His pockets yielded nothing about Agnes, nothing that I wanted at all. I didn't think they would, but I had to be sure. Mr. Canino might be back. Mr. Canino would be the kind of self-confident gentleman who would not mind returning to the scene of his crime.

I put the light out and started to open the door. The phone bell rang jarringly down on the baseboard. I listened to it, my jaw muscles drawn into a knot, aching. Then I shut the door and put the light on again and went across to it.

"Yeah?"

A woman's voice. Her voice. "Is Harry around?"

"Not for a minute, Agnes."

She waited a while on that. Then she said slowly: "Who's talking?"

"Marlowe, the guy that's trouble to you."

"Where is he?" sharply.

"I came over to give him two hundred bucks in return for certain information. The offer holds. I have the money. Where are you?"

"Didn't he tell you?"

"No."

"Perhaps you'd better ask him. Where is he?"

"I can't ask him. Do you know a man named Canino?"

Her gasp came as clearly as though she had been beside me.

"Do you want the two C's or not?" I asked.

"I–I want it pretty bad, mister."

"All right then. Tell me where to bring it."

"I–I–" Her voice trailed off and came back with a panic rush. "Where's Harry?"

"Got scared and blew. Meet me somewhere–anywhere at all–I have the money."

"I don't believe you–about Harry. It's a trap."

"Oh stuff. I could have had Harry hauled in long ago. There isn't anything to make a trap for. Canino got a line on Harry somehow and he blew. I want quiet, you want quiet, Harry wants quiet." Harry already had it. Nobody could take it away from him. "You don't think I'd stooge for Eddie Mars, do you, angel?"

"No-o, I guess not. Not that. I'll meet you in half an hour. Beside Bullocks Wilshire, the east entrance to the parking lot."

"Right," I said.

I dropped the phone in its cradle. The wave of almond odor flooded me again, and the sour smell of vomit. The little dead man sat silent in his chair, beyond fear, beyond change.

I left the office. Nothing moved in the dingy corridor. No pebbled glass door had light behind it. I went down the fire stairs to the second floor and from there looked down at the lighted roof of the elevator cage. I pressed the button. Slowly the car lurched into motion. I ran down the stairs again. The car was above me when I walked out of the building.

It was raining hard again. I walked into it with the heavy drops slapping my face. When one of them touched my tongue I knew that my mouth was open and the ache at the side of my jaws told me it was open wide and strained back, mimicking the rictus of death carved upon the face of Harry Jones.

CHAPTER TWENTY-SEVEN

"GIVE ME the money."

The motor of the gray Plymouth throbbed under her voice and the rain pounded above it. The violet light at the top of Bullocks green-tinged tower was far above us, serene and withdrawn from the dark, dripping city. Her black-gloved hand reached out and I put the bills in it. She bent over to count them under the dim light of the dash. A bag clicked open, clicked shut. She let a spent breath die on her lips. She leaned towards me.

"I'm leaving, copper. I'm on my way. This is a get-away stake and God how I need it. What happened to Harry?"

"I told you he ran away. Canino got wise to him somehow. Forget Harry. I've paid and I want my information."

"You'll get it. Joe and I were out riding Foothill Boulevard Sunday before last. It was late and the lights coming up and the usual mess of cars. We passed a brown coupe and I saw the girl who was driving it. There was a man beside her, a dark short man. The girl was a blonde. I'd seen her before. She was Eddie Mars' wife. The guy was Canino. You wouldn't forget either of them, if you ever saw them. Joe tailed the coupe from in front. He was good at that. Canino, the watchdog, was taking her out for air. A mile or so east of Realito a road turns towards the foothills. That's orange country to the south but to the north it's as bare as hell's back yard and smack up against the hills there's a cyanide plant where they make the stuff for fumagation. Just off the highway there's a small garage and paintshop run by a gee named Art Huck. Hot car drop, likely. There's a frame house beyond this, and beyond the house nothing but the foothills and the bare stone outcrop and the cyanide plant a couple of miles on. That's the place where she's holed up. They turned off on this road and Joe swung around and went back and we saw the car turn off the road where the frame house was. We sat there half an hour looking through the cars going by. Nobody came back out. When it was quite dark Joe sneaked up there and took a look. He said there were lights in the house and a radio was going and just the one car out in front, the coupe. So we beat it."

She stopped talking and I listened to the swish of tires on Wilshire. I said: "They might have shifted quarters since then but that's what you have to sell—that's what you have to sell. Sure you knew her?"

"If you ever see her, you won't make a mistake the second time. Good-by, copper, and wish me luck. I got a raw deal."

"Like hell you did," I said, and walked away across the street to my own car.

The gray Plymouth moved forward, gathered speed, and darted around the corner on to Sunset Place. The sound of its motor died, and with it blonde Agnes wiped herself off the slate for good, so far as I was concerned. Three men dead, Geiger, Brody and Harry Jones, and the woman went riding off in the rain with my two hundred in her bag and not a mark on her. I kicked my starter and drove on downtown to eat. I ate a good dinner. Forty miles in the rain is a hike, and I hoped to make it a round trip.

I drove north across the river, on into Pasadena, through Pasadena and almost at once I was in orange groves. The tumbling rain was solid white spray in the headlights. The windshield wiper could hardly keep the glass clear enough to see through. But not even the drenched darkness could hide the flawless lines of the orange trees wheeling away like endless spokes into the night.

Cars passed with a tearing hiss and a wave of dirty spray. The highway jerked through a little town that was all packing houses and sheds, and railway sidings nuzzling them. The groves thinned out and dropped away to the south and the road climbed and it was cold and to the north the black foothills crouched closer and sent a bitter wind whipping down their flanks. Then faintly out of the dark two yellow vapor lights glowed high up in the air and a neon sign between them said: "Welcome to Realito."

Frame houses were spaced far back from a wide main street, then a sudden knot of stores, the lights of a drugstore behind fogged glass, the fly-cluster of cars in front of the movie theater, a dark bank on a corner with a clock sticking out over the sidewalk and a group of people standing in the rain looking at its windows, as if they were some kind of a show. I went on. Empty fields closed in again.

Fate stage-managed the whole thing. Beyond Realito, just about a mile beyond, the highway took a curve and the rain fooled me and I went too close to the shoulder. My right front tire let go with an angry hiss. Before I could stop the right rear went with it. I jammed the car to a stop, half on the pavement, half on the shoulder, got out and flashed a spotlight around. I had two flats and one spare. The flat butt of a heavy galvanized tack stared at me from the front tire.

The edge of the pavement was littered with them. They had been swept off, but not far enough off.

I snapped the flash off and stood there breathing rain and looking up a side road at a yellow light. It seemed to come from a skylight. The skylight could belong to a garage, the garage could be run by a man named Art Huck, and there could be a frame house next door to it. I tucked my chin down in my collar and started towards it, then went back to unstrap the license holder from the steering post and put it in my pocket. I leaned lower under the wheel. Behind a weighted flap, directly under my right leg as I sat in the car, there was a hidden compartment. There were two guns in it. One belonged to Eddie Mars' boy Lanny and one belonged to me. I took Lanny's. It would have had more practice than mine. I stuck it nose down in an inside pocket and started up the side road.

The garage was a hundred yards from the highway. It showed the highway a blank side wall. I played the flash on it quickly. "Art Huck—Auto Repairs and Painting." I chuckled, then Harry Jones' face rose up in front of me, and I stopped chuckling. The garage doors were shut, but there was an edge of light under them and a thread of light where the halves met. I went on past. The frame house was there, light in two front windows, shades down. It was set well back from the road, behind a thin clump of trees. A car stood on the gravel drive in front. It was dark, indistinct, but it would be a brown coupe and it would belong to Mr. Canino. It squatted there peacefully in front of the narrow wooden porch.

He would let her take it out for a spin once in a while, and sit beside her, probably with a gun handy. The girl Rusty Regan ought to have married, that Eddie Mars couldn't keep, the girl that hadn't run away with Regan. Nice Mr. Canino.

I trudged back to the garage and banged on the wooden door with the butt of my flash. There was a hung instant of silence, as heavy as thunder. The light inside went out. I stood there grinning and licking the rain off my lip. I clicked the spot on the middle of the doors. I grinned at the circle of white. I was where I wanted to be.

A voice spoke through the door, a surly voice: "What you want?"

"Open up. I've got two flats back on the highway and only one spare. I need help."

"Sorry, mister. We're closed up. Realito's a mile west. Better try there."

I didn't like that. I kicked the door hard. I kept on kicking it. Another voice made itself heard, a purring voice, like a small dynamo behind a wall. I liked this voice. It said: "A wise guy, huh? Open up, Art."

A bolt squealed and half of the door bent inward. My flash burned briefly on a gaunt face. Then something that glittered swept down and knocked the flash out of my hand. A gun had peaked at me. I dropped low where the flash burned on the wet ground and picked it up.

The surly voice said: "Kill that spot, bo. Folks get hurt that way."

I snapped the flash off and straightened. Light went on inside the garage, outlined a tall man in coveralls. He backed away from the open door and kept a gun leveled at me.

"Step inside and shut the door, stranger. We'll see what we can do."

I stepped inside, and shut the door behind my back. I looked at the gaunt man, but not at the other man who was shadowy over by a workbench, silent. The breath of the garage was sweet and sinister with the smell of hot pyroxylin paint.

"Ain't you got no sense?" the gaunt man chided me. "A bank job was pulled at Realito this noon."

"Pardon," I said, remembering the people staring at the bank in the rain. "I didn't pull it. I'm a stranger here."

"Well, there was," he said morosely. "Some say it was a couple of punk kids and they got 'em cornered back here in the hills."

"It's a nice night for hiding," I said. "I suppose they threw tacks out. I got some of them. I thought you just needed the business."

"You didn't ever get socked in the kisser, did you?" the gaunt man asked me briefly.

"Not by anybody your weight."

The purring voice from over in the shadows said: "Cut out the heavy menace, Art. This guy's in a jam. You run a garage, don't you?"

"Thanks," I said, and didn't look at him even then.

"Okey, okey," the man in the coveralls grumbled. He tucked his gun through a flap in his clothes and bit a knuckle, staring at me moodily over it. The smell of the pyroxylin paint was as sickening as ether. Over in the corner, under a drop light, there was a big new-looking sedan with a paint gun lying on its fender.

I looked at the man by the workbench now. He was short and thick-bodied with strong shoulders. He had a cool face and cool dark eyes. He wore a belted brown suede raincoat that was heavily spotted with rain. His brown hat was tilted rakishly. He leaned his back against the workbench and looked me over without haste, without interest, as if he was looking at a slab of cold meat. Perhaps he thought of people that way.

He moved his dark eyes up and down slowly and then glanced at his fingernails one by one, holding them up against the light and studying them with care, as Hollywood has taught it should be done. He spoke around a cigarette.

"Got two flats, huh? That's tough. They swept them tacks, I thought."

"I skidded a little on the curve."

"Stranger in town you said?"

"Traveling through. On the way to L.A. How far is it?"

"Forty miles. Seems longer this weather. Where from, stranger?"

"Santa Rosa."

"Come the long way, eh? Tahoe and Lone Pine?"

"Not Tahoe. Reno and Carson City."

"Still the long way." A fleeting smile curved his lips.

"Any law against it?" I asked him.

"Huh? No, sure not. Guess you think we're nosey. Just on account of that heist back there. Take a jack and get his flats, Art."

"I'm busy," the gaunt man growled. "I've got work to do. I got this spray job. And it's raining, you might have noticed."

The man in brown said pleasantly: "Too damp for a good spray job, Art. Get moving."

I said: "They're front and rear, on the right side. You could use the spare for one spot, if you're busy."

"Take two jacks, Art," the brown man said.

"Now, listen—" Art began to bluster.

The brown man moved his eyes, looked at Art with a soft quiet-eyed stare, lowered them again almost shyly. He didn't speak. Art rocked as if a gust of wind had hit him. He stamped over to the corner and put a rubber coat over his coveralls, a sou'wester on his head. He grabbed a socket wrench and a hand jack and wheeled a dolly jack over to the doors.

He went out silently, leaving the door yawning. The rain blustered in. The man in brown strolled over and shut it and strolled back to the workbench and put his hips exactly where they had been before. I could have taken him then. We were alone. He didn't know who I was. He looked at me lightly and threw his cigarette on the cement floor and stamped on it without looking down.

"I bet you could use a drink," he said. "Wet the inside and even up." He reached a bottle from the workbench behind him and set it on the edge and set two glasses beside it. He poured a stiff jolt into each and held one out.

Walking like a dummy I went over and took it. The memory of the rain was still cold on my face. The smell of hot paint drugged the close air of the garage.

"That Art," the brown man said. "He's like all mechanics. Always got his face in a job he ought to have done last week. Business trip?"

I sniffed my drink delicately. It had the right smell. I watched him drink some of his before I swallowed mine. I rolled it around on my tongue. There was no cyanide in it. I emptied the little glass and put it down beside him and moved away.

"Partly," I said. I walked over to the half-painted sedan with the big metal paint gun lying along its fender. The rain hit the flat roof hard. Art was out in it, cursing.

The brown man looked at the big car. "Just a panel job, to start with," he said casually, his purring voice still softer from the drink. "But the guy had dough and his driver needed a few bucks. You know the racket."

I said: "There's only one that's older." My lips felt dry. I didn't want to talk. I lit a cigarette. I wanted my tires fixed. The minutes passed on tiptoe. The brown man and I were two strangers chance-met, looking at each other across a little dead man named Harry Jones. Only the brown man didn't know that yet.

Feet crunched outside and the door was pushed open. The light hit pencils of rain and made silver wires of them. Art trundled two muddy flats in sullenly, kicked the door shut, let one of the flats fall over on its side. He looked at me savagely.

"You sure pick spots for a jack to stand on," he snarled.

The brown man laughed and took a rolled cylinder of nickels out of his pocket and tossed it up and down on the palm of his hand.

"Don't crab so much," he said dryly. "Fix those flats."

"I'm fixin' them, ain't I?"

"Well, don't make a song about it."

"Yah!" Art peeled his rubber coat and sou'wester off and threw them away from him. He heaved one tire up on a spreader and tore the rim loose viciously. He had the tube out and cold-patched in nothing flat. Still scowling, he strode over to the wall beside me and grabbed an air hose, put enough air into the tube to give it body and let the nozzle of the air hose smack against the whitewashed wall.

I stood watching the roll of wrapped coins dance in Canino's hand. The moment of crouched intensity had left me. I turned my head and watched the gaunt mechanic beside me toss the air-stiffened tube up and catch it with his hands wide, one on each side of the tube. He looked it over sourly, glanced at a big galvanized tub of dirty water in the corner and grunted.

The teamwork must have been very nice. I saw no signal, no glance of meaning, no gesture that might have a special import. The gaunt man had the stiffened tube high in the air, staring at it. He half turned his body, took one long quick step, and slammed it down over my head and shoulders, a perfect ringer.

He jumped behind me and leaned hard on the rubber. His weight dragged on my chest, pinned my upper arms tight to my sides. I could move my hands, but I couldn't reach the gun in my pocket.

The brown man came almost dancing towards me across the floor. His hand tightened over the roll of nickels. He came up to me without sound, without expression. I bent forward and tried to heave Art off his feet.

The fist with the weighted tube inside it went through my spread hands like a stone through a cloud of dust. I had the stunned moment of shock when the lights danced and the visible world went out of focus but was still there. He hit me again. There was no sensation in my head. The bright glare got brighter. There was nothing but hard aching white light. Then there was darkness in which something red wriggled like a germ under a microscope. Then there was nothing bright or wriggling, just darkness and emptiness and a rushing wind and a falling as of great trees.

CHAPTER TWENTY-EIGHT

IT SEEMED there was a woman and she was sitting near a lamp, which was where she belonged, in a good light. Another light shone hard on my face, so I closed my eyes again and tried to look at her through the lashes. She was so platinumed that her hair shone like a silver fruit bowl. She wore a green knitted dress with a broad white collar turned over it. There was a sharp-angled glossy bag at her feet. She was smoking and a glass of amber fluid was tall and pale at her elbow.

I moved my head a little, carefully. It hurt, but not more than I expected. I was trussed like a turkey ready for the oven. Handcuffs held my wrists behind me and a rope went from them to my ankles and then over the end of the brown davenport on which I was sprawled. The rope dropped out of sight over the davenport. I moved enough to make sure it was tied down.

I stopped these furtive movements and opened my eyes again and said: "Hello."

The woman withdrew her gaze from some distant mountain peak. Her small firm chin turned slowly. Her eyes were the blue of mountain lakes. Overhead the rain still pounded, with a remote sound, as if it was somebody else's rain.

"How do you feel?" It was a smooth silvery voice that matched her hair. It had a tiny tinkle in it, like bells in a doll's house. I thought that was silly as soon as I thought of it.

"Great," I said. "Somebody built a filling station on my jaw."

"What did you expect, Mr. Marlowe—orchids?"

"Just a plain pine box," I said. "Don't bother with bronze or silver handles. And don't scatter my ashes over the blue Pacific. I like the worms better. Did you know that worms are of both sexes and that any worm can love any other worm?"

"You're a little light-headed," she said, with a grave stare.

"Would you mind moving this light?"

She got up and went behind the davenport. The light went off. The dimness was a benison.

"I don't think you're so dangerous," she said. She was tall rather than short, but no bean-pole. She was slim, but not a dried crust. She went back to her chair.

"So you know my name."

"You slept well. They had plenty of time to go through your pockets. They did everything but embalm you. So you're a detective."

"Is that all they have on me?"

She was silent. Smoke floated dimly from the cigarette. She moved it in the air. Her hand was small and had shape, not the usual bony garden tool you see on women nowadays.

"What time is it?" I asked.

She looked sideways at her wrist, beyond the spiral of smoke, at the edge of the grave luster of the lamplight. "Ten-seventeen. You have a date?"

"I wouldn't be surprised. Is this the house next to Art Huck's garage?"

"Yes."

"What are the boys doing—digging a grave?"

"They had to go somewhere."

"You mean they left you here alone?"

Her head turned slowly again. She smiled. "You don't look dangerous."

"I thought they were keeping you a prisoner."

It didn't seem to startle her. It even slightly amused her. "What made you think that?"

"I know who you are."

Her very blue eyes flashed so sharply that I could almost see the sweep of their glance, like the sweep of a sword. Her mouth tightened. But her voice didn't change.

"Then I'm afraid you're in a bad spot. And I hate killing."

"And you Eddie Mars' wife? Shame on you."

She didn't like that. She glared at me. I grinned. "Unless you can unlock these bracelets, which I'd advise you not to do, you might spare me a little of that drink you're neglecting."

She brought the glass over. Bubbles rose in it like false hopes. She bent over me. Her breath was as delicate as the eyes of a fawn. I gulped from the glass. She took it away from my mouth and watched some of the liquid run down my neck.

She bent over me again. Blood began to move around in me, like a prospective tenant looking over a house.

"Your face looks like a collision mat," she said.

"Make the most of it. It won't last long even this good."

She swung her head sharply and listened. For an instant her face was pale. The sounds were only the rain drifting against the walls. She went back across the room and stood with her side to me, bent forward a little, looking down at the floor.

"Why did you come here and stick your neck out?" she asked quietly. "Eddie wasn't doing you any harm. You know perfectly well that if I hadn't hid out here, the police would have been certain Eddie murdered Rusty Regan."

"He did," I said.

She didn't move, didn't change position an inch. Her breath made a harsh quick sound. I looked around the room. Two doors, both in the same wall, one half open. A carpet of red and tan squares, blue curtains at the windows, a wallpaper with bright green pine trees on it. The furniture looked as if it had come from one of those places that advertise on bus benches. Gay, but full of resistance.

She said softly: "Eddie didn't do anything to him. I haven't seen Rusty in months. Eddie's not that sort of man."

"You left his bed and board. You were living alone. People at the place where you lived identified Regan's photo."

"That's a lie," she said coldly.

I tried to remember whether Captain Gregory had said that or not. My head was too fuzzy. I couldn't be sure.

"And it's none of your business," she added.

"The whole thing is my business. I'm hired to find out."

"Eddie's not that sort of man."

"Oh, you like racketeers."

"As long as people will gamble there will be places for them to gamble."

"That's just protective thinking. Once outside the law you're all the way outside. You think he's just a gambler. I think he's a pornographer, a blackmailer, a hot car broker, a killer by remote control, and a suborner of crooked cops. He's whatever looks good to him, whatever has the cabbage pinned to it. Don't try to sell me on any high-souled racketeers. They don't come in that pattern."

"He's not a killer." Her nostrils flared.

"Not personally. He has Canino. Canino killed a man tonight, a harmless little guy who was trying to help somebody out. I almost saw him killed."

She laughed wearily.

"All right," I growled. "Don't believe it. If Eddie is such a nice guy, I'd like to get to talk to him without Canino around. You know what Canino will do—beat my teeth out and then kick me in the stomach for mumbling."

She put her head back and stood there thoughtful and withdrawn, thinking something out.

"I thought platinum hair was out of style," I bored on, just to keep sound alive in the room, just to keep from listening.

"It's a wig, silly. While mine grows out." She reached up and yanked it off. Her own hair was clipped short all over, like a boy's. She put the wig back on.

"Who did that to you?"

She looked surprised. "I had it done. Why?"

"Yes. Why?"

"Why, to show Eddie I was willing to do what he wanted me to do—hide out. That he didn't need to have me guarded. I wouldn't let him down. I love him."

"Good grief," I groaned. "And you have me right here in the room with you."

She turned a hand over and stared at it. Then abruptly she walked out of the room. She came back with a kitchen knife. She bent and sawed at my rope.

"Canino has the key to the handcuffs," she breathed. "I can't do anything about those."

She stepped back, breathing rapidly. She had cut the rope at every knot.

"You're a kick," she said. "Kidding with every breath—the spot you're in."

"I thought Eddie wasn't a killer."

She turned away quickly and went back to her chair by the lamp and sat down and put her face in her hands. I swung my feet to the floor and stood up. I tottered around, stiff-legged. The nerve on the left side of my face was jumping in all its branches. I took a step. I could still walk. I could run, if I had to.

"I guess you mean me to go," I said.

She nodded without lifting her head.

"You'd better go with me—if you want to keep on living."

"Don't waste time. He'll be back any minute."

"Light a cigarette for me."

I stood beside her, touching her knees. She came to her feet with a sudden lurch. Our eyes were only inches apart.

"Hello, Silver-Wig," I said softly.

She stepped back, around the chair, and swept a package of cigarettes up off the table. She jabbed one loose and pushed it roughly into my mouth. Her hand was shaking. She snapped a small green leather lighter and held it to the cigarette. I drew in the smoke, staring into her lake-blue eyes. While she was still close to me I said:

"A little bird named Harry Jones led me to you. A little bird that used to hop in and out of cocktail bars picking up horse bets for crumbs. Picking up information too. This little bird picked up an idea about Canino. One way and another he and his friends found out where you were. He came to me to sell the information because he knew—how he knew is a long story—that I was working for General Sternwood. I got his information, but Canino got the little bird. He's a dead little bird now, with his feathers ruffled and his neck limp and a pearl of blood on his beak. Canino killed him. But Eddie Mars wouldn't do that, would he, Silver-Wig? He never killed anybody. He just hires it done."

"Get out," she said harshly. "Get out of here quick."

Her hand clutched in midair on the green lighter. The fingers strained. The knuckles were as white as snow.

"But Canino doesn't know I know that," I said. "About the little bird. All he knows is I'm nosing around."

Then she laughed. It was almost a racking laugh. It shook her as the wind shakes a tree. I thought there was puzzlement in it, not exactly surprise, but as if a new idea had been added to something already known and it didn't fit. Then I thought that was too much to get out of a laugh.

"It's very funny," she said breathlessly. "Very funny, because, you see—I still love him. Women—" She began to laugh again.

I listened hard, my head throbbing. Just the rain still. "Let's go," I said. "Fast."

She took two steps back and her face set hard. "Get out, you! Get out! You can walk to Realito. You can make it—and you can keep your mouth shut—for an hour or two at least. You owe me that much."

"Let's go," I said. "Got a gun, Silver-Wig?"

"You know I'm not going. You know that. Please, please get out of here quickly."

I stepped up close to her, almost pressing against her. "You're going to stay here after turning me loose? Wait for that killer to come back so you can say so sorry? A man who kills like swatting a fly. Not much. You're going with me, Silver-Wig."

"No."

"Suppose," I said thinly, "your handsome husband *did* kill Regan? Or suppose Canino did, without Eddie's knowing it. Just suppose. How long will *you* last, after turning me loose?"

"I'm not afraid of Canino. I'm still his boss's wife."

"Eddie's a handful of mush," I snarled. "Canino would take him with a teaspoon. He'll take him the way the cat took the canary. A handful of mush. The only time a girl like you goes for a wrong gee is when he's a handful of mush."

"Get out!" she almost spit at me.

"Okey." I turned away from her and moved out through the half-open door into a dark hallway. Then she rushed after me and pushed past to the front door and opened it. She peered out into the wet blackness and listened. She motioned me forward.

"Good-by," she said under her breath. "Good luck in everything but one thing. Eddie didn't kill Rusty Regan. You'll find him alive and well somewhere, when he wants to be found."

I leaned against her and pressed her against the wall with my body. I pushed my mouth against her face. I talked to her that way.

"There's no hurry. All this was arranged in advance, rehearsed to the last detail, timed to the split second. Just like a radio program. No hurry at all. Kiss me, Silver-Wig."

Her face under my mouth was like ice. She put her hands up and took hold of my head and kissed me hard on the lips. Her lips were like ice, too.

I went out through the door and it closed behind me, without sound, and the rain blew in under the porch, not as cold as her lips.

CHAPTER TWENTY-NINE

THE GARAGE next door was dark. I crossed the gravel drive and a patch of sodden lawn. The road ran with small rivulets of water. It gurgled down a ditch on the far side. I had no hat. That must have fallen in the garage. Canino hadn't bothered to give it back to me. He hadn't thought I would need it anymore. I imagined him driving back jauntily through the rain, alone, having left the gaunt and sulky Art and the probably stolen sedan in a safe place. She loved Eddie Mars and she was hiding to protect him. So he would find her there when he came back, calm beside the light and the untasted drink, and me tied up on the davenport. He would carry her stuff out to the car and go through the house carefully to make sure nothing incriminating was left. He would tell her to go out and wait. She wouldn't hear a shot. A blackjack is just as effective at short range. He would tell her he had left me tied up and I would get loose after a while. He would think she was that dumb. Nice Mr. Canino.

The raincoat was open in front and I couldn't button it, being handcuffed. The skirts flapped against my legs like the wings of a large and tired bird. I came to the highway. Cars went by in a wide swirl of water illuminated by headlights. The tearing noise of their tires died swiftly. I found my convertible where I had left it, both tires fixed and mounted, so it could be driven away, if necessary. They thought of everything. I got into it and leaned down sideways under the wheel and fumbled aside the flap of leather that covered the pocket. I got the other gun, stuffed it up under my coat and started back. The world was small, shut in, black. A private world for Canino and me.

Halfway there the headlights nearly caught me. They turned swiftly off the highway and I slid down the bank into the wet ditch and flopped there breathing water. The car hummed by without slowing. I lifted my head, heard the rasp of its tires as it left the road and took the gravel of the driveway. The motor died, the lights died, a door slammed. I didn't hear the house door shut, but a fringe of light trickled through the clump of trees, as though a shade had been moved aside from a window, or the light had been put on in the hall.

I came back to the soggy grass plot and sloshed across it. The car was between me and the house, the gun was down at my side, pulled as far around as I could get it, without pulling my left arm out by the roots. The car was dark, empty, warm. Water gurgled pleasantly in the radiator. I peered in at the door. The keys hung on the dash. Canino was very sure of himself. I went around the car and walked carefully across the gravel to the window and listened. I couldn't hear any voices, any sound but the swift bong-bong of the raindrops hitting the metal elbows at the bottom of the rain gutters.

I kept on listening. No loud voices, everything quiet and refined. He would be purring at her and she would be telling him she had let me go and I had promised to let them get away. He wouldn't believe me, as I wouldn't believe him. So he wouldn't be in there long. He would be on his way and take her with him. All I had to do was wait for him to come out.

I couldn't do it. I shifted the gun to my left hand and leaned down to scoop up a handful of gravel. I tossed it against the screen of the window. It was a feeble effort. Very little of it reached the glass above the screen, but the loose rattle of that little was like a dam bursting.

I ran back to the car and got on the running board behind it. The house had already gone dark. That was all. I dropped quietly on the running board and waited. No soap. Canino was too cagey.

I straightened up and got into the car backwards, fumbled around for the ignition key and turned it. I reached with my foot, but the starter button had to be on the dash. I found it at last, pulled it and the starter ground. The warm motor caught at once. It purred softly, contentedly. I got out of the car again and crouched down by the rear wheels.

I was shivering now but I knew Canino wouldn't like that last effect. He needed that car badly. A darkened window slid down inch by inch, only some shifting of light on the glass showing it moved. Flame spouted from it abruptly, the blended roar of three swift shots. Glass starred in the coupe. I yelled with agony. The yell went off into a wailing groan. The groan became a wet gurgle, choked with blood. I let the gurgle die sickeningly, on choked gasp. It was nice work. I liked it. Canino liked it very much. I heard him laugh. It was a large booming laugh, not at all like the purr of his speaking voice.

Then silence for a little while, except for the rain and the quietly throbbing motor of the car. Then the house door crawled open, a deeper blackness in the black night. A figure showed in it cautiously, something white around the neck. It was her collar. She came out on the porch stiffly, a wooden woman. I caught the pale shine of her silver wig. Canino came crouched methodically behind her. It was so deadly it was almost funny.

She came down the steps. Now I could see the white stiffness of her face. She started towards the car. A bulwark of defense for Canino, in case I could still spit in his eye. Her voice spoke through the lisp of the rain, saying slowly, without any tone: "I can't see a thing, Lash. The windows are misted."

He grunted something and the girl's body jerked hard, as though he had jammed a gun into her back. She came on again and drew near the lightless car. I could see him behind her now, his hat, a side of his face, the bulk of his shoulder. The girl stopped rigid and screamed. A beautiful thin tearing scream that rocked me like a left hook.

"I can see him!" she screamed. "Through the window. Behind the wheel, Lash!"

He fell for it like a bucket of lead. He knocked her roughly to one side and jumped forward, throwing his hand up. Three more spurts of flame cut the darkness. More glass scarred. One bullet went on through and smacked into a tree on my side. A ricochet whined off into the distance. But the motor went quietly on.

He was low down, crouched against the gloom, his face a grayness without form that seemed to come back slowly after the glare of the shots. If it was a revolver he had, it might be empty. It might not. He had fired six times, but he might have reloaded inside the house. I hoped he had. I didn't want him with an empty gun. But it might be an automatic.

I said: "Finished?"

He whirled at me. Perhaps it would have been nice to allow him another shot or two, just like a gentleman of the old school. But his gun was still up and I couldn't wait any longer. Not long enough to be a gentleman of the old school. I shot him four times, the Colt straining against my ribs. The gun jumped out of his hand as if it had been kicked. He reached both his hands for his stomach. I could hear them smack hard against his body. He fell like that, straight forward, holding himself together with his broad hands. He fell face down in the wet gravel. And after that there wasn't a sound from him.

Silver-Wig didn't make a sound either. She stood rigid, with the rain swirling at her. I walked around Canino and kicked his gun, without any purpose. Then I walked after it and bent over sideways and picked it up. That put me close beside her. She spoke moodily, as if she was talking to herself. "I–I was afraid you'd come back."

I said: "We had a date. I told you it was all arranged." I began to laugh like a loon.

Then she was bending down over him, touching him. And after a little while she stood up with a small key on a thin chain.

She said bitterly: "Did you have to kill him?"

I stopped laughing as suddenly as I had started. She went behind me and unlocked the handcuffs.

"Yes," she said softly. "I suppose you did."

CHAPTER THIRTY

THIS WAS another day and the sun was shining again.

Captain Gregory of the Missing Persons Bureau looked heavily out of his office window at the barred upper floor of the Hall of Justice, white and clean after the rain. Then he turned ponderously in his swivel chair and tamped his pipe with a heat-scarred thumb and stared at me bleakly.

"So you got yourself in another jam."

"Oh, you heard about it."

"Brother, I sit here all day on my fanny and I don't look as if I had a brain in my head. But you'd be surprised what I hear. Shooting this Canino was all right I guess, but I don't figure the homicide boys pinned any medals on you."

"There's been a lot of killing going on around me," I said. "I haven't been getting my share of it."

He smiled patiently. "Who told you this girl out there was Eddie Mars' wife?"

I told him. He listened carefully and yawned. He tapped his gold-studded mouth with a palm like a tray. "I guess you figure I ought to of found her."

"That's a fair deduction."

"Maybe I knew," he said. "Maybe I thought if Eddie and his woman wanted to play a little game like that, it would be smart—or as smart as I ever get—to let them think they were getting away with it. And then again maybe you think I was letting Eddie get away with it for more personal reasons." He held his big hand out and revolved the thumb against the index and second fingers.

"No," I said. "I didn't really think that. Not even when Eddie seemed to know all about our talk here the other day."

He raised his eyebrows as if raising them was an effort, a trick he was out of practice on. It furrowed his whole forehead and when it smoothed out it was full of white lines that turned reddish as I watched them.

"I'm a copper," he said. "Just a plain ordinary copper. Reasonably honest. As honest as you could expect a man to be in a world where it's out of style. That's mainly why I asked you to come in this morning. I'd like you to believe that. Being a copper I like to see the law win. I'd like to see the flashy well-dressed muggs like Eddie Mars spoiling their manicures in the rock quarry at Folsom, alongside of the poor little slum-bred hard guys that got knocked over on their first caper and never had a break since. That's what I'd like. You and me both lived too long to think I'm likely to see it happen. Not in this town, not in any town half this size, in any part of this wide, green and beautiful U.S.A. We just don't run our country that way."

I didn't say anything. He blew smoke with a backward jerk of his head, looked at the mouthpiece of his pipe and went on:

"But that don't mean I think Eddie Mars bumped off Regan or had any reason to or would have done it if he had. I just figured maybe he knows something about it, and maybe sooner or later something will sneak out into the open. Hiding his wife out at Realito was childish, but it's the kind of childishness a smart monkey thinks is smart. I had him in here last night, after the D.A. got through with him. He admitted the whole thing. He said he knew Canino as a reliable protection guy and that's what he had him for. He didn't know anything about his hobbies or want to. He didn't know Harry Jones. He didn't know Joe Brody. He did know Geiger, of course, but claims he didn't know about his racket. I guess you heard all that."

"Yes."

"You played it smart down there at Realito, brother. Not trying to cover up. We keep a file on unidentified bullets nowadays. Someday you might use that gun again. Then you'd be over a barrel."

"I played it smart," I said, and leered at him.

He knocked his pipe out and stared down at it broodingly. "What happened to the girl?" he asked, not looking up.

"I don't know. They didn't hold her. We made statements, three sets of them, for Wilde, for the Sheriff's office, for the Homicide Bureau. They turned her loose. I haven't seen her since. I don't expect to."

"Kind of a nice girl, they say. Wouldn't be one to play dirty games."

"Kind of a nice girl," I said.

Captain Gregory sighed and rumpled his mousy hair. "There's just one more thing," he said almost gently. "You look like a nice guy, but you play too rough. If you really want to help the Sternwood family—leave 'em alone."

"I think you're right, Captain."

"How you feel?"

"Swell," I said. "I was standing on various pieces of carpet most of the night, being balled out. Before that I got soaked to the skin and beaten up. I'm in perfect condition."

"What the hell did you expect, brother?"

"Nothing else." I stood up and grinned at him and started for the door. When I had almost reached it he cleared his throat suddenly and said in a harsh voice: "I'm wasting my breath, huh? You still think you can find Regan."

I turned around and looked him straight in the eyes. "No, I don't think I can find Regan. I'm not even going to try. Does that suit you?"

He nodded slowly. Then he shrugged. "I don't know what the hell I even said that for. Good luck, Marlowe. Drop around any time."

"Thanks, Captain."

I went down out of the City Hall and got my car from the parking lot and drove home to the Hobart Arms. I lay down on the bed with my coat off and stared at the ceiling and listened to the traffic sounds on the street outside and watched the sun move slowly across a corner of the ceiling. I tried to go to sleep, but sleep didn't come. I got up and took a drink, although it was the wrong time of day, and lay down again. I still couldn't go to sleep.

My brain ticked like a clock. I sat up on the side of the bed and stuffed a pipe and said out loud:

"That old buzzard knows something."

The pipe tasted as bitter as lye. I put it aside and lay down again. My mind drifted through waves of false memory, in which I seemed to do the same thing over and over again, go to the same places, meet the same people, say the same words to them, over and over again, and yet each time it seemed real, like something actually happening, and for the first time. I was driving hard along the highway through the rain, with Silver-Wig in the corner of the car, saying nothing, so that by the time we reached Los Angeles we seemed to be utter strangers again. I was getting out at an all night drugstore and phoning Bernie Ohls that I had killed a man at Realito and was on my way over to Wilde's house with Eddie Mars' wife, who had seen me do it. I was pushing the car along the silent, rain-polished streets to Lafayette Park and up under the porte-cochere of Wilde's big frame house and the porch light was already on, Ohls having telephoned ahead that I was coming. I was in Wilde's study and he was behind his desk in a flowered dressing-gown and a tight hard face and a dappled cigar moved in his fingers and up to the bitter smile on his lips. Ohls was there and a slim gray scholarly man from the Sheriff's office who looked and talked more like a professor of economics than a cop. I was telling the story and they were listening quietly and Silver-Wig sat in a shadow with her hands folded in her lap, looking at nobody. There was a lot of telephoning. There were two men from the Homicide Bureau who looked at me as if I was some kind of strange beast escaped from a traveling circus. I was driving again, with one of them beside me, to the Fulwider Building. We were there in the room where Harry Jones was still in the chair behind the desk, the twisted stiffness of his dead face and the sour-sweet smell in the room. There was a medical examiner, very young and husky, with red bristles on his neck. There was a fingerprint man fussing around and I was telling him not to forget the latch of the transom. (He found Canino's thumb print on it, the only print the brown man had left to back up my story.)

I was back again at Wilde's house, signing a typewritten statement his secretary had run off in another room. Then the door opened and Eddie Mars came in and an abrupt smile flashed to his face when he saw Silver-Wig, and he said: "Hello, sugar," and she didn't look at him or answer him. Eddie Mars fresh and cheerful, in a dark business suit, with a fringed white scarf hanging outside his tweed overcoat. Then they were gone, everybody was gone out of the room but myself and Wilde, and Wilde was saying in a cold, angry voice: "This is the last time, Marlowe. The next fast one you pull I'll throw you to the lions, no matter whose heart it breaks."

It was like that, over and over again, lying on the bed and watching the patch of sunlight slide down the corner of the wall. Then the phone rang, and it was Norris, the Sternwood butler, with his usual untouchable voice.

"Mr. Marlowe? I telephoned your office without success, so I took the liberty of trying to reach you at home."

"I was out most of the night," I said. "I haven't been down."

"Yes, sir. The General would like to see you this morning, Mr. Marlowe, if it's convenient."

"Half an hour or so," I said. "How is he?"

"He's in bed, sir, but not doing badly."

"Wait till he sees me," I said, and hung up.

I shaved, changed clothes and started for the door. Then I went back and got Carmen's little pearl-handled revolver and dropped it into my pocket. The sunlight was so bright that it danced. I got to the Sternwood place in twenty minutes and drove up under the arch at the side door. It was eleven-fifteen. The birds in the ornamental trees were crazy with song after the rain, the terraced lawns were as green as the Irish flag, and the whole estate looked as though it had been made about ten minutes before. I rang the bell. It was five days since I had rung it for the first time. It felt like a year.

A maid opened the door and led me along a side hall to the main hallway and left me there, saying Mr. Norris would be down in a moment. The main hallway looked just the same. The portrait over the mantel had the same hot black eyes and the knight in the stained-glass window still wasn't getting anywhere untying the naked damsel from the tree.

In a few minutes Norris appeared, and he hadn't changed either. His acid-blue eyes were as remote as ever, his grayish-pink skin looked healthy and rested, and he moved as if he was twenty years younger than he really was. I was the one who felt the weight of the years.

We went up the tiled staircase and turned the opposite way from Vivian's room. With each step the house seemed to grow larger and more silent. We reached a massive old door that looked as if it had come out of a church. Norris opened it softly and looked in. Then he stood aside and I went in past him across what seemed to be about a quarter of a mile of carpet to a huge canopied bed like the one Henry the Eighth died in.

General Sternwood was propped up on pillows. His bloodless hands were clasped on top of the sheet. They looked gray against it. His black eyes were still full of fight and the rest of his face still looked like the face of a corpse.

"Sit down, Mr. Marlowe." His voice sounded weary and a little stiff.

I pulled a chair close to him and sat down. All the windows were shut tight. The room was sunless at that hour. Awnings cut off what glare there might be from the sky. The air had the faint sweetish smell of old age.

He stared at me silently for a long minute. He moved a hand, as if to prove to himself that he could still move it, then folded it back over the other. He said lifelessly:

"I didn't ask you to look for my son-in-law, Mr. Marlowe."

"You wanted me to, though."

"I didn't ask you to. You assume a great deal. I usually ask for what I want."

I didn't say anything.

"You have been paid," he went on coldly. "The money is of no consequence one way or the other. I merely feel that you have, no doubt unintentionally, betrayed a trust."

He closed his eyes on that. I said: "Is that all you wanted to see me about?"

He opened his eyes again, very slowly, as though the lids were made of lead. "I suppose you are angry at that remark," he said.

I shook my head. "You have an advantage over me, General. It's an advantage I wouldn't want to take away from you, not a hair of it. It's not much, considering what you have to put up with. You can say anything you like to me and I wouldn't think of getting angry. I'd like to offer you your money back. It may mean nothing to you. It might mean something to me."

"What does it mean to you?"

"It means I have refused payment for an unsatisfactory job. That's all."

"Do you do many unsatisfactory jobs?"

"A few. Everyone does."

"Why did you go to see Captain Gregory?"

I leaned back and hung an arm over the back of the chair. I studied his face. It told me nothing. I didn't know the answer to his question—no satisfactory answer.

I said: "I was convinced you put those Geiger notes up to me chiefly as a test, and that you were a little afraid Regan might somehow be involved in an attempt to blackmail you. I didn't know anything about Regan then. It wasn't until I talked to Captain Gregory that I realized Regan wasn't that sort of guy in all probability."

"That is scarcely answering my question."

I nodded. "No. That is scarcely answering your question. I guess I just don't like to admit that I played a hunch. The morning I was here, after I left you out in the orchid house, Mrs. Regan sent for me. She seemed to assume I was hired to look for her husband and she didn't seem to like it. She let drop however that 'they' had found his car in a certain garage. The 'they' could only be the police. Consequently the police must know something about it. If they did, the Missing Persons Bureau would be the department that would have the case. I didn't know whether you had reported it, of course, or somebody else, or whether they had found the car through somebody reporting it abandoned in a garage. But I know cops, and I knew that if they got that much, they would get a little more—especially as your driver happened to have a police record. I didn't know how much more they would get. That started me thinking about the Missing Persons Bureau. What convinced me was something in Mr. Wilde's manner the night we had the conference over at his house about Geiger and so on. We were alone for a minute and he asked me whether you had told me you were looking for Regan. I said you had told me you wished you knew where he was and that he was all right. Wilde pulled his lip in and looked funny. I knew just as plainly as though he had said it that by 'looking for Regan' he meant using the machinery of the law to look for him. Even then I tried to go up against Captain Gregory in such a way that I wouldn't tell him anything he didn't know already."

"And you allowed Captain Gregory to think I had employed you to find Rusty?"

"Yeah. I guess I did—when I was sure he had the case."

He closed his eyes. They twitched a little. He spoke with them closed. "And do you consider that ethical?"

"Yes," I said. "I do."

The eyes opened again. The piercing blackness of them was startling coming suddenly out of that dead face. "Perhaps I don't understand," he said.

"Maybe you don't. The head of a Missing Persons Bureau isn't a talker. He wouldn't be in that office if he was. This one is a very smart cagey guy who tries, with a lot of success at first, to give the impression he's a middle-aged hack fed up with his job. The game I play is not spillikins. There's always a large element of bluff connected with it. Whatever I might say to a cop, he would be apt to discount it. And to *that* cop it wouldn't make much difference what I said. When you hire a boy in my line of work it isn't like hiring a window-washer and showing him eight windows and saying: 'Wash those and you're through.' *You* don't know what I have to go through or over or under to do your job for you. I do it my way. I do my best to protect you and I may break a few rules, but I break them in your favor. The client comes first, unless he's crooked. Even then all I do is hand the job back to him and keep my mouth shut. After all you didn't tell me *not* to go to Captain Gregory."

"That would have been rather difficult," he said with a faint smile.

"Well, what have I done wrong? Your man Norris seemed to think when Geiger was eliminated the case was over. I don't see it that way. Geiger's method of approach puzzled me and still does. I'm not Sherlock Holmes or Philo Vance. I don't expect to go over ground the police have covered and pick up a broken pen point and build a case from it. If you think there is anybody in the detective business making a living doing that sort of thing, you don't know much about cops. It's not things like that they overlook, if they overlook anything. I'm not saying they often overlook anything when they're really allowed to work. But if they do, it's apt to be something looser and vaguer, like a man of Geiger's type sending you his evidence of debt and asking you to pay like a gentleman—Geiger, a man in a shady racket, in a vulnerable position, protected by a racketeer and having at least some negative protection from some of the police. Why did he do that? Because he wanted to find out if there was anything putting pressure on you. If there was, you would pay him. If not, you would ignore him and wait for his next move. But there was something putting a pressure on you. Regan. You were afraid he was not what he had appeared to be, that he had stayed around and been nice to you just long enough to find out how to play games with your bank account."

He started to say something but I interrupted him. "Even at that it wasn't your money you cared about. It wasn't even your daughters. You've more or less written them off. It's that you're still too proud to be played for a sucker —and you really liked Regan."

There was a silence. Then the General said quietly: "You talk too damn much, Marlowe. Am I to understand you are still trying to solve that puzzle?"

"No. I've quit. I've been warned off. The boys think I play too rough. That's why I thought I should give you back your money—because it isn't a completed job by my standards."

He smiled. "Quit, nothing," he said. "I'll pay you another thousand dollars to find Rusty. He doesn't have to come back. I don't even have to know where he is. A man has a right to live his own life. I don't blame him for walking out on my daughter, nor even for going so abruptly. It was probably a sudden impulse. I want to know that he is all right wherever he is. I want to know it from him directly, and if he should happen to need money, I should want him to have that also. Am I clear?"

I said: "Yes, General."

He rested a little while, lax on the bed, his eyes closed and dark-lidded, his mouth tight and bloodless. He was used up. He was pretty nearly licked. He opened his eyes again and tried to grin at me.

"I guess I'm a sentimental old goat," he said. "And no soldier at all. I took a fancy to that boy. He seemed pretty clean to me. I must be a little too vain about my judgment of character. Find him for me, Marlowe. Just find him."

"I'll try," I said. "You'd better rest now. I've talked your arm off."

I got up quickly and walked across the wide floor and out. He had his eyes shut again before I opened the door. His hands lay limp on the sheet. He looked a lot more like a dead man than most dead men look. I shut the door quietly and went back along the upper hall and down the stairs.

CHAPTER THIRTY-ONE

THE BUTLER appeared with my hat. I put it on and said: "What do you think of him?"

"He's not as weak as he looks, sir."

"If he was, he'd be ready for burial. What did this Regan fellow have that bored into him so?"

The butler looked at me levelly and yet with a queer lack of expression. "Youth, sir," he said. "And the soldier's eye."

"Like yours," I said.

"If I may say so, sir, not unlike yours."

"Thanks. How are the ladies this morning?"

He shrugged politely.

"Just what I thought," I said, and he opened the door for me.

I stood outside on the step and looked down the vistas of grassed terraces and trimmed trees and flowerbeds to the tall metal railing at the bottom of the gardens. I saw Carmen about halfway down, sitting on a stone bench, with her head between her hands, looking forlorn and alone.

I went down the red brick steps that led from terrace to terrace. I was quite close before she heard me. She jumped up and whirled like a cat. She wore the light blue slacks she had worn the first time I saw her. Her blonde hair was the same loose tawny wave. Her face was white. Red spots flared in her cheeks as she looked at me. Her eyes were slaty.

"Bored?" I said.

She smiled slowly, rather shyly, then nodded quickly. Then she whispered: "You're not mad at me?"

"I thought you were mad at me."

She put her thumb up and giggled. "I'm not." When she giggled I didn't like her any more. I looked around. A target hung on a tree about thirty feet away, with some darts sticking to it. There were three or four more on the stone bench where she had been sitting.

"For people with money you and your sister don't seem to have much fun," I said.

She looked at me under her long lashes. This was the look that was supposed to make me roll over on my back. I said: "You like throwing those darts?"

"Uh-huh."

"That reminds me of something." I looked back towards the house. By moving about three feet I made a tree hide me from it. I took her little pearl-handled gun out of my pocket. "I brought you back your artillery. I cleaned it and loaded it up. Take my tip—don't shoot it at people, unless you get to be a better shot. Remember?"

Her face went paler and her thin thumb dropped. She looked at me, then at the gun I was holding. There was a fascination in her eyes. "Yes," she said, and nodded. Then suddenly: "Teach me to shoot."

"Huh?"

"Teach me how to shoot. I'd like that."

"Here? It's against the law."

She came close to me and took the gun out of my hand, cuddled her hand around the butt. Then she tucked it quickly inside her slacks, almost with a furtive movement, and looked around.

"I know where," she said in a secret voice. "Down by some of the old wells." She pointed off down the hill. "Teach me?"

I looked into her slaty blue eyes. I might as well have looked at a couple of bottle-tops. "All right. Give me back the gun until I see if the place looks all right."

She smiled and made a mouth, then handed it back with a secret naughty air, as if she was giving me a key to her room. We walked up the steps and around to my car. The gardens seemed deserted. The sunshine was as empty as a headwaiter's smile. We got into the car and I drove down the sunken driveway and out through the gates.

"Where's Vivian?" I asked.

"Not up yet." She giggled.

I drove on down the hill through the quiet opulent streets with their faces washed by the rain, bore east to La Brea, then south. We reached the place she meant in about ten minutes.

"In there." She leaned out of the window and pointed.

It was a narrow dirt road, not much more than a track, like the entrance to some foothill ranch. A wide five-barred gate was folded back against a stump and looked as if it hadn't been shut in years. The road was fringed with tall eucalyptus trees and deeply rutted. Trucks had used it. It was empty and sunny now, but not yet dusty. The rain had been too hard and too recent. I followed the ruts along and the noise of city traffic grew curiously and quickly faint, as if this were not in the city at all, but far away in a daydream land. Then the oil-stained, motionless walking-beam of a squat wooden derrick stuck up over a branch. I could see the rusty old steel cable that connected this walking-beam with half a dozen others. The beams didn't move, probably hadn't moved for a year. The wells were no longer pumping. There was a pile of rusted pipe, a loading platform that sagged at one end, half a dozen empty oil drums lying in a ragged pile. There was the stagnant, oil-scummed water of an old sump iridescent in the sunlight.

"Are they going to make a park of all this?" I asked.

She dipped her chin down and gleamed at me.

"It's about time. The smell of that sump would poison a herd of goats. This the place you had in mind?"

"Uh-huh. Like it?"

"It's beautiful." I pulled up beside the loading platform. We got out. I listened. The hum of the traffic was a distant web of sound, like the buzzing of bees. The place was as lonely as a churchyard. Even after the rain the tall eucalyptus trees still looked dusty. They always look dusty. A branch broken off by the wind had fallen over the edge of the sump and the flat leathery leaves dangled in the water.

I walked around the sump and looked into the pumphouse. There was some junk in it, nothing that looked like recent activity. Outside a big wooden bull wheel was tilted against the wall. It looked like a good place all right.

I went back to the car. The girl stood beside it preening her hair and holding it out in the sun. "Gimme," she said, and held her hand out.

I took the gun out and put it in her palm. I bent down and picked up a rusty can.

"Take it easy now," I said. "It's loaded in all five. I'll go over and set this can in that square opening in the middle of that big wooden wheel. See?" I pointed. She ducked her head, delighted. "That's about thirty feet. Don't start shooting until I get back beside you. Okey?"

"Okey," she giggled.

I went back around the sump and set the can up in the middle of the bull wheel. It made a swell target. If she missed the can, which she was certain to do, she would probably hit the wheel. That would stop a small slug completely. However, she wasn't going to hit even that.

I went back towards her around the sump. When I was about ten feet from her, at the edge of the sump, she showed me all her sharp little teeth and brought the gun up and started to hiss.

I stopped dead, the sump water stagnant and stinking at my back.

"Stand there, you son of a bitch," she said.

The gun pointed at my chest. Her hand seemed to be quite steady. The hissing sound grew louder and her face had the scraped bone look. Aged, deteriorated, become animal, and not a nice animal.

I laughed at her. I started to walk towards her. I saw her small finger tighten on the trigger and grow white at the tip. I was about six feet away from her when she started to shoot.

The sound of the gun made a sharp slap, without body, a brittle crack in the sunlight. I didn't see any smoke. I stopped again and grinned at her.

She fired twice more, very quickly. I don't think any of the shots would have missed. There were five in the little gun. She had fired four. I rushed her.

I didn't want the last one in my face, so I swerved to one side. She gave it to me quite carefully, not worried at all. I think I felt the hot breath of the powder blast a little.

I straightened up. "My, but you're cute," I said.

Her hand holding the empty gun began to shake violently. The gun fell out of it. Her mouth began to shake. Her whole face went to pieces. Then her head screwed up towards her left ear and froth showed on her lips. Her breath made a whining sound. She swayed.

I caught her as she fell. She was already unconscious. I pried her teeth open with both hands and stuffed a wadded handkerchief in between them. It took all my strength to do it. I lifted her up and got her into the car, then went back for the gun and dropped it into my pocket. I climbed in under the wheel, backed the car and drove back the way we had come along the rutted road, out of the gateway, back up the hill and so home.

Carmen lay crumpled in the corner of the car, without motion. I was halfway up the drive to the house before she stirred. Then her eyes suddenly opened wide and wild. She sat up.

"What happened?" she gasped.

"Nothing. Why?"

"Oh, yes it did," she giggled. "I wet myself."

"They always do," I said.

She looked at me with a sudden sick speculation and began to moan.

CHAPTER THIRTY-TWO

THE GENTLE-EYED, horse-faced maid let me into the long gray and white upstairs sitting room with the ivory drapes tumbled extravagantly on the floor and the white carpet from wall to wall. A screen star's boudoir, a place of charm and seduction, artificial as a wooden leg. It was empty at the moment. The door closed behind me with the unnatural softness of a hospital door. A breakfast table on wheels stood by the chaise-longue. Its silver glittered. There were cigarette ashes in the coffee cup. I sat down and waited.

It seemed a long time before the door opened again and Vivian came in. She was in oyster-white lounging pajamas trimmed with white fur, cut as flowingly as a summer sea frothing on the beach of some small and exclusive island.

She went past me in long smooth strides and sat down on the edge of the chaise-longue. There was a cigarette in her lips, at the corner of her mouth. Her nails today were copper red from quick to tip, without half moons.

"So you're just a brute after all," she said quietly, staring at me. "An utter callous brute. You killed a man last night. Never mind how I heard it. I heard it. And now you have to come out here and frighten my kid sister into a fit."

I didn't say a word. She began to fidget. She moved over to a slipper chair and put her head back against a white cushion that lay along the back of the chair against the wall. She blew pale gray smoke upwards and watched it float towards the ceiling and come apart in wisps that were for a little while distinguishable from the air and then melted and were nothing. Then very slowly she lowered her eyes and gave me a cool hard glance.

"I don't understand you," she said. "I'm thankful as hell one of us kept his head the night before last. It's bad enough to have a bootlegger in my past. Why don't you for Christ's sake say something?"

"How is she?"

"Oh, she's all right, I suppose. Fast asleep. She always goes to sleep. What did you do to her?"

"Not a thing. I came out of the house after seeing your father and she was out in front. She had been throwing darts at a target on a tree. I went down to speak to her because I had something that belonged to her. A little revolver Owen Taylor gave her once. She took it over to Brody's place the other evening, the evening he was killed. I had to take it away from her there. I didn't mention it, so perhaps you didn't know it."

The black Sternwood eyes got large and empty. It was her turn not to say anything.

"She was pleased to get her little gun back and she wanted me to teach her how to shoot and she wanted to show me the old oil wells down the hill where your family made some of its money. So we went down there and the place was pretty creepy, all rusted metal and old wood and silent wells and greasy scummy sumps. Maybe that upset her. I guess you've been there yourself. It was kind of eerie."

"Yes–it is." It was a small breathless voice now.

"So we went in there and I stuck a can up in a bull wheel for her to pop at. She threw a wingding. Looked like a mild epileptic fit to me."

"Yes." The same minute voice. "She has them once in a while. Is that all you wanted to see me about?"

"I guess you still wouldn't tell me what Eddie Mars has on you."

"Nothing at all. And I'm getting a little tired of that question," she said coldly.

"Do you know a man named Canino?"

She drew her fine black brows together in thought. "Vaguely. I seem to remember the name."

"Eddie Mars' trigger man. A tough hombre, they said. I guess he was. Without a little help from a lady I'd be where he is—in the morgue."

"The ladies seem to—" She stopped dead and whitened. "I can't joke about it," she said simply.

"I'm not joking, and if I seem to talk in circles, it just seems that way. It all ties together—everything. Geiger and his cute little blackmail tricks, Brody and his pictures, Eddie Mars and his roulette tables, Canino and the girl Rusty Regan didn't run away with. It all ties together."

"I'm afraid I don't even know what you're talking about."

"Suppose you did—it would be something like this. Geiger got his hooks into your sister, which isn't very difficult, and got some notes from her and tried to blackmail your father with them, in a nice way. Eddie Mars was behind Geiger, protecting him and using him for a cat's-paw. Your father sent for me instead of paying up, which showed he wasn't scared about anything. Eddie Mars wanted to know that. He had something on you and he wanted to know if he had it on the General too. If he had, he could collect a lot of money in a hurry. If not, he would have to wait until you got your share of the family fortune, and in the meantime be satisfied with whatever spare cash he could take away from you across the roulette table. Geiger was killed by Owen Taylor, who was in love with your silly little sister and didn't like the kind of games Geiger played with her. That didn't mean anything to Eddie. He was playing a deeper game than Geiger knew anything about, or than Brody knew anything about, or anybody except you and Eddie and a tough guy named Canino. Your husband disappeared and Eddie, knowing everybody knew there had been bad blood between him and Regan, hid his wife out at Realito and put Canino to guard her, so that it would look as if she had run away with Regan. He even got Regan's car into the garage of the place where Mona Mars had been living. But that sounds a little silly taken merely as an attempt to divert suspicion that Eddie had killed your husband or had him killed. It isn't so silly, really. He had another motive. He was playing for a million or so. He knew where Regan had gone and why and he didn't want the police to have to find out. He wanted them to have an explanation of the disappearance that would keep them satisfied. Am I boring you?"

"You tire me," she said in a dead, exhausted voice. "God, how you tire me!"

"I'm sorry. I'm not just fooling around trying to be clever. Your father offered me a thousand dollars this morning to find Regan. That's a lot of money to me, but I can't do it."

Her mouth jumped open. Her breath was suddenly strained and harsh. "Give me a cigarette," she said thickly. "Why?" The pulse in her throat had begun to throb.

I gave her a cigarette and lit a match and held it for her. She drew in a lungful of smoke and let it out raggedly and then the cigarette seemed to be forgotten between her fingers. She never drew on it again.

"Well, the Missing Persons Bureau can't find him," I said. "It's not so easy. What they can't do it's not likely that I can do."

"Oh." There was a shade of relief in her voice.

"That's one reason. The Missing Persons people think he just disappeared on purpose, pulled down the curtain, as they call it. They don't think Eddie Mars did away with him."

"Who said anybody did away with him?"

"We're coming to it," I said.

For a brief instant her face seemed to come to pieces, to become merely a set of features without form or control. Her mouth looked like the prelude to a scream. But only for an instant. The Sternwood blood had to be good for something more than her black eyes and her recklessness.

I stood up and took the smoking cigarette from between her fingers and killed it in an ashtray. Then I took Carmen's little gun out of my pocket and laid it carefully, with exaggerated care, on her white satin knee. I balanced it there, and stepped back with my head on one side like a window-dresser getting the effect of a new twist of a scarf around a dummy's neck.

I sat down again. She didn't move. Her eyes came down millimeter by millimeter and looked at the gun.

"It's harmless," I said. "All five chambers empty. She fired them all. She fired them all at me."

The pulse jumped wildly in her throat. Her voice tried to say something and couldn't. She swallowed.

"From a distance of five or six feet," I said. "Cute little thing, isn't she? Too bad I had loaded the gun with blanks." I grinned nastily. "I had a hunch about what she would do—if she got the chance."

She brought her voice back from a long way off. "You're a horrible man," she said. "Horrible."

"Yeah. You're her big sister. What are you going to do about it?"

"You can't prove a word of it."

"Can't prove what?"

"That she fired at you. You said you were down there around the wells with her, alone. You can't prove a word of what you say."

"Oh that," I said. "I wasn't thinking of trying. I was thinking of another time—when the shells in the little gun had bullets in them."

Her eyes were pools of darkness, much emptier than darkness.

"I was thinking of the day Regan disappeared," I said. "Late in the afternoon. When he took her down to those old wells to teach her to shoot and put up a can somewhere and told her to pop at it and stood near her while she shot. And she didn't shoot at the can. She turned the gun and shot him, just the way she tried to shoot me today, and for the same reason."

She moved a little and the gun slid off her knee and fell to the floor. It was one of the loudest sounds I ever heard. Her eyes were riveted on my face. Her voice was a stretched whisper of agony. "Carmen! . . . Merciful God, Carmen! . . . Why?"

"Do I really have to tell you why she shot at me?"

"Yes." Her eyes were still terrible. "I'm—I'm afraid you do."

"Night before last when I got home she was in my apartment. She'd kidded the manager into letting her in to wait for me. She was in my bed—naked. I threw her out on her ear. I guess maybe Regan did the same thing to her sometime. But you can't do that to Carmen."

She drew her lips back and made a half-hearted attempt to lick them. It made her, for a brief instant, look like a frightened child. The lines of her cheeks sharpened and her hand went up slowly like an artificial hand worked by wires and its fingers closed slowly and stiffly around the white fur at her collar. They drew the fur tight against her throat. After that she just sat staring.

"Money," she croaked. "I suppose you want money."

"How much money?" I tried not to sneer.

"Fifteen thousand dollars?"

I nodded. "That would be about right. That would be the established fee. That was what he had in his pockets when she shot him. That would be what Mr. Canino got for disposing of the body when you went to Eddie Mars for help. But that would be small change to what Eddie expects to collect one of these days, wouldn't it?"

"You son of a bitch!" she said.

"Uh-uh. I'm a very smart guy. I haven't a feeling or a scruple in the world. All I have the itch for is money. I am so money greedy that for twenty-five bucks a day and expenses, mostly gasoline and whiskey, I do my thinking myself, what there is of it; I risk my whole future, the hatred of the cops and of Eddie Mars and his pals, I dodge bullets and eat saps, and say thank you very much, if you have any more trouble, I hope you'll think of me, I'll just leave one of my cards in case anything comes up. I do all this for twenty-five bucks a day—and maybe just a little to protect what little pride a broken and sick old man has left in his blood, in the thought that his blood is not poison, and that although his two little girls are a trifle wild, as many nice girls are these days, they are not perverts or killers. And that makes me a son of a bitch. All right. I don't care anything about that. I've been called that by people of all sizes and shapes, including your little sister. She called me worse than that for not getting into bed with her. I got five hundred dollars from your father, which I didn't ask for, but he can afford to give it to me. I can get another thousand for finding Mr. Rusty Regan, if I could find him. Now you offer me fifteen grand. That makes me a big shot. With fifteen grand I could own a home and a new car and four suits of clothes. I might even take a vacation without worrying about losing a case. That's fine. What are you offering it to me for? Can I go on being a son of a bitch, or do I have to become a gentleman, like that lush that passed out in his car the other night?"

She was as silent as a stone woman.

"All right," I went on heavily. "Will you take her away? Somewhere far off from here where they can handle her type, where they will keep guns and knives and fancy drinks away from her? Hell, she might even get herself cured, you know. It's been done."

She got up and walked slowly to the windows. The drapes lay in heavy ivory folds beside her feet. She stood among the folds and looked out, towards the quiet darkish foothills. She stood motionless, almost blending into the drapes. Her hands hung loose at her sides. Utterly motionless hands. She turned and came back along the room and walked past me blindly. When she was behind me she caught her breath sharply and spoke.

"He's in the sump," she said. "A horrible decayed thing. I did it. I did just what you said. I went to Eddie Mars. She came home and told me about it, just like a child. She's not normal. I knew the police would get it all out of her. In a little while she would even brag about it. And if dad knew, he would call them instantly and tell them the whole story. And sometime in that night he would die. It's not his dying—it's what he would be thinking just before he died. Rusty wasn't a bad fellow. I didn't love him. He was all right, I guess. He just didn't mean anything to me, one way or another, alive or dead, compared with keeping it from dad."

"So you let her run around loose," I said, "getting into other jams."

"I was playing for time. Just for time. I played the wrong way, of course. I thought she might even forget it herself. I've heard they do forget what happens in those fits. Maybe she has forgotten it. I knew Eddie Mars would bleed me white, but I didn't care. I had to have help and I could only get it from somebody like him. . . . There have been times when I hardly believed it all myself. And other times when I had to get drunk quickly—whatever time of day it was. Awfully damn quickly."

"You'll take her away," I said. "And do that awfully damn quickly."

She still had her back to me. She said softly now: "What about you?"

"Nothing about me. I'm leaving. I'll give you three days. If you're gone by then—okey. If you're not, out it comes. And don't think I don't mean that."

She turned suddenly. "I don't know what to say to you. I don't know how to begin."

"Yeah. Get her out of here and see that she's watched every minute. Promise?"

"I promise. Eddie—"

"Forget Eddie. I'll go see him after I get some rest. I'll handle Eddie."

"He'll try to kill you."

"Yeah," I said. "His best boy couldn't. I'll take a chance on the others. Does Norris know?"

"He'll never tell."

"I thought he knew."

I went quickly away from her down the room and out and down the tiled staircase to the front hall. I didn't see anybody when I left. I found my hat alone this time. Outside the bright gardens had a haunted look, as though small wild eyes were watching me from behind the bushes, as though the sunshine itself had a mysterious something in its light. I got into my car and drove off down the hill.

What did it matter where you lay once you were dead? In a dirty sump or in a marble tower on top of a high hill? You were dead, you were sleeping the big sleep, you were not bothered by things like that. Oil and water were the same as wind and air to you. You just slept the big sleep, not caring about the nastiness of how you died or where you fell. Me, I was part of the nastiness now. Far more a part of it than Rusty Regan was. But the old man didn't have to be. He could lie quiet in his canopied bed, with his bloodless hands folded on the sheet, waiting. His heart was a brief, uncertain murmur. His thoughts were as gray as ashes. And in a little while he too, like Rusty Regan, would be sleeping the big sleep.

On the way downtown I stopped at a bar and had a couple of double Scotches. They didn't do me any good. All they did was make me think of Silver-Wig, and I never saw her again.

THE BONE OF CONTENTION

by Dorothy L. Sayers

"I AM AFRAID you have brought shocking weather with you, Lord Peter," said Mrs. Frobisher-Pym, with playful reproof. "If it goes on like this they will have a bad day for the funeral."

Lord Peter Wimsey glanced out of the morning-room window to the soaked green lawn and the shrubbery, where the rain streamed down remorselessly over the laurel leaves, stiff and shiny like mackintoshes.

"Nasty exposed business, standing round at funerals," he agreed.

"Yes, I always think it's such a shame for the old people. In a tiny village like this it's about the only pleasure they get during the winter. It makes something for them to talk about for weeks."

"Is it anybody's funeral in particular?"

"My dear Wimsey," said his host, "it is plain that you, coming from your little village of London, are quite out of the swim. There has never been a funeral like it in Little Doddering before. It's an event."

"Really?"

"Oh dear, yes. You may possibly remember old Burdock?"

"Burdock? Let me see. Isn't he a sort of local squire, or something?"

"He was," corrected Mr. Frobisher-Pym. "He's dead—died in New York about three weeks ago, and they're sending him over to be buried. The Burdocks have lived in the big house for hundreds of years, and they're all buried in the churchyard, except, of course, the one who was killed in the War. Burdock's secretary cabled the news of his death across, and said the body was following as soon as the embalmers had finished with it. The boat gets in to Southampton this morning, I believe. At any rate, the body will arrive here by the 6.30 from town."

"Are you going down to meet it, Tom?"

"No, my dear. I don't think that is called for. There will be a grand turn-out of the village, of course. Joliffe's people are having the time of their lives; they borrowed an extra pair of horses from young Mortimer for the occasion. I only hope they don't kick over the traces and upset the hearse. Mortimer's horseflesh is generally on the spirited side."

"But, Tom, we must show some respect to the Burdocks."

"We're attending the funeral to-morrow, and that's quite enough. We must do that, I suppose, out of consideration for the family, though, as far as the old man himself goes, respect is the very last thing anybody would think of paying him."

From *Lord Peter Views the Body*

"Oh, Tom, he's dead."

"And quite time too. No, Agatha, it's no use pretending that old Burdock was anything but a spiteful, bad-tempered, dirty-living old blackguard that the world's well rid of. The last scandal he stirred up made the place too hot to hold him. He had to leave the country and go to the States, and, even so, if he hadn't had the money to pay the people off, he'd probably have been put in gaol. That's why I'm so annoyed with Hancock. I don't mind his calling himself a priest, though clergyman was always good enough for dear old Weeks—who, after all, was a canon—and I don't mind his vestments. He can wrap himself up in a Union Jack if he likes—it doesn't worry *me*. But when it comes to having old Burdock put on trestles in the south aisle, with candles round him, and Hubbard from the 'Red Cow' and Duggin's boy praying over him half the night, I think it's time to draw the line. The people don't like it, you know—at least, the older generation don't. It's all right for the young ones, I dare say; they must have their amusement; but it gives offence to a lot of the farmers. After all, they knew Burdock a bit too well. Simpson—he's people's warden, you know—came up quite in distress to speak to me about it last night. You couldn't have a sounder man than Simpson. I said I would speak to Hancock. I did speak to him this morning, as a matter of fact, but you might as well talk to the west door of the church."

"Mr. Hancock is one of those young men who fancy they know everything," said his wife. "A sensible man would have listened to you, Tom. You're a magistrate and have lived here all your life, and it stands to reason you know considerably more about the parish than he does."

"He took up the ridiculous position," said Mr. Frobisher-Pym, "that the more sinful the old man had been the more he needed praying for. I said, 'I think it would need more praying than you or I could do to help old Burdock out of the place he's in now.' Ha, ha! So he said, 'I agree with you, Mr. Frobisher-Pym; that is why I am having eight watchers to pray all through the night for him.' I admit he had me there."

"Eight people?" exclaimed Mrs. Frobisher-Pym.

"Not all at once, I understand; in relays, two at a time. 'Well,' I said, 'I think you ought to consider that you will be giving a handle to the Nonconformists.' Of course, he couldn't deny that."

Wimsey helped himself to marmalade. Nonconformists, it seemed, were always searching for handles. Though what kind—whether door-handles, teapot handles, pump-handles, or starting-handles—was never explained, nor what the handles were to be used for when found. However, having been brought up in the odour of the Establishment, he was familiar with this odd dissenting peculiarity, and merely said:

"Pity to be extreme in a small parish like this. Disturbs the ideas of the simple fathers of the hamlet and the village blacksmith, with his daughter singin' in the choir and the Old Hundreth and all the rest of it. Don't Burdock's family have anything to say to it? There are some sons, aren't there?"

"Only the two, now. Aldine was the one that was killed, of course, and

Martin is somewhere abroad. He went off after that row with his father, and I don't think he has been back in England since."

"What was the row about?"

"Oh, that was a disgraceful business. Martin got a girl into trouble—a film actress or a typist or somebody of that sort—and insisted on marrying her."

"Oh?"

"Yes, so dreadful of him," said the lady, taking up the tale, "when he was practically engaged to the Delaprime girl—the one with glasses, you know. It made a terrible scandal. Some horribly vulgar people came down and pushed their way into the house and insisted on seeing old Mr. Burdock. I will say for him he stood up to them—he wasn't the sort of person you could intimidate. He told them the girl had only herself to blame, and they could sue Martin if they liked—*he* wouldn't be blackmailed on his son's account. The butler was listening at the door, naturally, and told the whole village about it. And then Martin Burdock came home and had a quarrel with his father you could have heard for miles. He said that the whole thing was a lie, and he meant to marry the girl, anyway. I cannot understand how anybody could marry into a blackmailing family like that."

"My dear," said Mr. Frobisher-Pym gently, "I don't think you're being quite fair to Martin, or his wife's parents, either. From what Martin told me, they were quite decent people, only not his class, of course, and they came in a well-meaning way to find out what Martin's 'intentions' were. You would want to do the same yourself, if it were a daughter of ours. Old Burdock, naturally, thought they meant blackmail. He was the kind of man who thinks everything can be paid for; and he considered a son of his had a perfect right to seduce a young woman who worked for a living. I don't say Martin was altogether in the right——"

"Martin is a chip off the old block, I'm afraid," retorted the lady. "He married the girl, anyway, and why should he do that, unless he had to?"

"Well, they've never had any children, you know," said Mr. Frobisher-Pym.

"That's as may be. I've no doubt the girl was in league with her parents. And you know the Martin Burdocks have lived in Paris ever since."

"That's true," admitted her husband. "It was an unfortunate affair altogether. They've had some difficulty in tracing Martin's address, too, but no doubt he'll be coming back shortly. He is engaged in producing some film play, they tell me, so possibly he can't get away in time for the funeral."

"If he had any natural feeling, he would not let a film play stand in his way," said Mrs. Frobisher-Pym.

"My dear, there are such things as contracts, with very heavy monetary penalties for breaking them. And I don't suppose Martin could afford to lose a big sum of money. It's not likely that his father will have left him anything."

"Martin is the younger son, then?" asked Wimsey, politely showing more interest than he felt in the rather well-worn plot of this village melodrama.

"No, he is the eldest of the lot. The house is entailed, of course, and so is the estate, such as it is. But there's no money in the land. Old Burdock made his fortune in rubber shares during the boom, and the money will go as he leaves it—wherever that may be, for they haven't found any will yet. He's probably left it all to Haviland."

"The younger son?"

"Yes. He's something in the City—a director of a company—connected with silk stockings, I believe. Nobody has seen very much of him. He came down as soon as he heard of his father's death. He's staying with the Hancocks. The big house has been shut up since old Burdock went to the States four years ago. I suppose Haviland thought it wasn't worth while opening it up till they knew what Martin was going to do about it. That's why the body is being taken to the church."

"Much less trouble, certainly," said Wimsey.

"Oh, yes—though, mind you, I think Haviland ought to take a more neighbourly view of it. Considering the position the Burdock's have always held in the place, the people had a right to expect a proper reception after the funeral. It's usual. But these business people think less of tradition than we do down here. And, naturally, since the Hancocks are putting Haviland up, he can't raise much objection to the candles and the prayers and things."

"Perhaps not," said Mrs. Frobisher-Pym, "but it would have been more suitable if Haviland had come to us, rather than to the Hancocks, whom he doesn't even know."

"My dear, you forget the very unpleasant dispute I had with Haviland Burdock about shooting over my land. After the correspondence that passed between us, last time he was down here, I could scarcely offer him hospitality. His father took a perfectly proper view of it, I will say that for him, but Haviland was exceedingly discourteous to me, and things were said which I could not possibly overlook. However, we mustn't bore you, Lord Peter, with our local small talk. If you've finished your breakfast, what do you say to a walk round the place? It's a pity it's raining so hard—and you don't see the garden at its best this time of year, of course—but I've got some cocker spaniels you might like to have a look at."

Lord Peter expressed eager anxiety to see the spaniels, and in a few minutes' time found himself squelching down the gravel path which led to the kennels.

"Nothing like a healthy country life," said Mr. Frobisher-Pym. "I always think London is so depressing in the winter. Nothing to do with one's self. All right to run up for a day or two and see a theatre now and again, but how you people stick it week in and week out beats me. I must speak to Plunkett about this archway," he added. "It's getting out of trim."

He broke off a dangling branch of ivy as he spoke. The plant shuddered revengefully, tipping a small shower of water down Wimsey's neck.

The cocker spaniel and her family occupied a comfortable and airy stall in the stable buildings. A youngish man in breeches and leggings emerged to greet the visitors, and produced the little bundles of puppyhood for their inspection. Wimsey sat down on an upturned bucket and examined them gravely one by one. The bitch, after cautiously reviewing his boots and grumbling a little, decided that he was trustworthy and slobbered genially over his knees.

"Let me see," said Mr. Frobisher-Pym, "how old are they?"

"Thirteen days, sir."

"Is she feeding them all right?"

"Fine, sir. She's having some of the malt food. Seems to suit her very well, sir."

"Ah, yes. Plunkett was a little doubtful about it, but I heard it spoken very well of. Plunkett doesn't care for experiments, and, in a general way, I agree with him. Where is Plunkett, by the way?"

"He's not very well this morning, sir."

"Sorry to hear that, Merridew. The rheumatics again?"

"No, sir. From what Mrs. Plunkett tells me, he's had a bit of a shock."

"A shock? What sort of a shock? Nothing wrong with Alf or Elsie, I hope?"

"No, sir. The fact is—I understand he's seen something, sir."

"What do you mean, seen something?"

"Well, sir—something in the nature of a warning, from what he says."

"A warning? Good heavens, Merridew, he mustn't get those sort of ideas in his head. I'm surprised at Plunkett; I always thought he was a very level-headed man. What sort of warning did he say it was?"

"I couldn't say, sir."

"Surely he mentioned what he thought he'd seen."

Merridew's face took on a slightly obstinate look.

"I can't say, I'm sure, sir."

"This will never do. I must go and see Plunkett. Is he at the cottage?"

"Yes, sir."

"We'll go down there at once. You don't mind, do you, Wimsey? I can't allow Plunkett to make himself ill. If he's had a shock he'd better see a doctor. Well, carry on, Merridew, and be sure you keep her warm and comfortable. The damp is apt to come up through these brick floors. I'm thinking of having the whole place re-set with concrete, but it takes money, of course. I can't imagine," he went on, as he led the way past the greenhouse towards a trim cottage set in its own square of kitchen-garden, "what can have happened to have upset Plunkett. I hope it's nothing serious. He's getting elderly, of course, but he ought to be above believing in warnings. You wouldn't believe the extraordinary ideas these people get hold of. Fact is, I expect he's been round at the 'Weary Traveller,' and caught sight of somebody's washing hung out on the way home."

"Not washing," corrected Wimsey mechanically. He had a deductive turn of mind which exposed the folly of the suggestion even while irritably admitting that the matter was of no importance. "It poured with rain last night, and, besides, it's Thursday. But Tuesday and Wednesday were fine, so the drying would have all been done then. No washing."

"Well, well—something else then—a post, or old Mrs. Giddens's white donkey. Plunkett does occasionally take a drop too much, I'm sorry to say, but he's a very good kennel-man, so one overlooks it. They're superstitious round about these parts, and they can tell some queer tales if once you get into their confidence. You'd be surprised how far off the main track we are as regards civilisation. Why, not here, but at Abbotts Bolton, fifteen miles off, it's as much as one's life's worth to shoot a hare. Witches, you know, and that sort of thing."

"I shouldn't be a bit surprised. They'll still tell you about werewolves in some parts of Germany."

"Yes, I dare say. Well, here we are." Mr. Frobisher-Pym rapped loudly with his walking-stick on the door of the cottage and turned the handle without waiting for permission.

"You there, Mrs. Plunkett? May we come in? Ah! good morning. Hope we're not disturbing you, but Merridew told me Plunkett was not so well. This is Lord Peter Wimsey—a very old friend of mine; that is to say, I'm a very old friend of *his;* ha, ha!"

"Good morning, sir; good morning, your lordship. I'm sure Plunkett will be very pleased to see you. Please step in. Plunkett, here's Mr. Pym to see you."

The elderly man who sat crouching over the fire turned a mournful face towards them, and half rose, touching his forehead.

"Well, now, Plunkett, what's the trouble?" enquired Mr. Frobisher-Pym, with the hearty bedside manner adopted by country gentlefolk visiting their dependents. "Sorry not to see you out and about. Touch of the old complaint, eh?"

"No, sir; no, sir. Thank you, sir. I'm well enough in myself. But I've had a warning, and I'm not long for this world."

"Not long for this world? Oh, nonsense, Plunkett. You mustn't talk like that. A touch of indigestion, that's what you've got, I expect. Gives one the blues, I know. I'm sure I often feel like nothing on earth when I've got one of my bilious attacks. Try a dose of castor-oil, or a good old-fashioned blue pill and black draught. Nothing like it. Then you won't talk about warnings and dying."

"No medicine won't do no good to *my* complaint, sir. Nobody as see what I've seed ever got the better of it. But as you and the gentleman are here, sir, I'm wondering if you'll do me a favour."

"Of course, Plunkett, anything you like. What is it?"

"Why, just to draw up my will, sir. Old Parson, he used to do it. But I don't fancy this new young man, with his candles and bits of things. It don't seem as if he'd make it good and legal, sir, and I wouldn't like it if there was any dispute after I was gone. So as there ain't much time left me, I'd be grateful if you'd put it down clear for me in pen and ink that I wants my little bit all to go to Sarah here, and after her to Alf and Elsie, divided up equal."

"Of course I'll do that for you, Plunkett, any time you like. But it's all nonsense to be talking about wills. Bless my soul, I shouldn't be surprised if you were to see us all underground."

"No, sir. I've been a hale and hearty man, I'm not denying. But I've been called, sir, and I've got to go. It must come to all of us, I know that. But it's a fearful thing to see the death-coach come for one, and know that the dead are in it, that cannot rest in the grave."

"Come now, Plunkett, you don't mean to tell me you believe in that old foolishness about the death-coach. I thought you were an educated man. What would Alf say if he heard you talking such nonsense?"

"Ah, sir, young people don't know everything, and there's many more things in God's creation than what you'll find in the printed books."

"Oh, well," said Mr. Frobisher-Pym, finding this opening irresistible, "we know there are more things in heaven and earth, Horatio, than are dreamt of in your philosophy. Quite so. But that doesn't apply nowadays," he added contradictorily. "There are no ghosts in the twentieth century. Just you think the matter out quietly, and you'll find you've made a mistake. There's probably some quite simple explanation. Dear me! I remember Mrs. Frobisher-Pym waking up one night and having a terrible fright, because she thought somebody'd been and hanged himself on our bedroom door. Such a silly idea, because I was safe in bed beside her—snoring, *she* said, ha, ha!—and, if anybody was feeling like hanging himself, he wouldn't come into our bedroom to do it. Well, she clutched my arm in a great state of mind, and when I went to see what had alarmed her, what do you think it was? My trousers, which I'd hung up by the braces, with the socks still in the legs! My word! and didn't I get a wigging for not having put my things away tidy!"

Mr. Frobisher-Pym laughed, and Mrs. Plunkett said dutifully, "There now!" Her husband shook his head.

"That may be, sir, but I see the death-coach last night with my own eyes. Just striking midnight it was, by the church clock, and I see it come up the lane by the old priory wall."

"And what were you doing out of bed at midnight, eh?"

"Well, sir, I'd been round to my sister's, that's got her boy home on leaf off of his ship."

"And you'd been drinking his health, I dare say, Plunkett." Mr. Frobisher-Pym wagged an admonitory forefinger.

"No, sir, I don't deny I'd had a glass or two of ale, but not to fuddle me. My wife can tell you I was sober enough when I got home."

"That's right, sir. Plunkett hadn't taken too much last night, that I'll swear to."

"Well, what was it you saw, Plunkett?"

"I see the death-coach, same as I'm telling you, sir. It come up the lane, all ghostly white, sir, and never making no more sound than the dead—which it were, sir."

"A waggon or something going through to Lymptree or Herriotting."

"No, sir—'tweren't a waggon. I counted the horses—four white horses, and they went by with never a sound of hoof or bridle. And that weren't——"

"Four horses! Come, Plunkett, you must have been seeing double. There's nobody about here would be driving four horses, unless it was Mr. Mortimer from Abbotts Bolton, and he wouldn't be taking his horseflesh out at midnight."

"Four horses they was, sir. I see them plain. And it weren't Mr. Mortimer, neither, for he drives a drag, and this were a big, heavy coach, with no lights on it, but shinin' all of itself, with a colour like moonshine."

"Oh, nonsense, man! You couldn't see the moon last night. It was pitch-dark."

"No, sir, but the coach shone all moony-like, all the same."

"And no lights? I wonder what the police would say to that."

"No mortal police could stop that coach," said Plunkett contemptuously, "nor no mortal man could abide the sight on it. I tell you, sir, that ain't the worst of it. The horses——"

"Was it going slowly?"

"No, sir. It were going at a gallop, only the hoofs didn't touch the ground. There weren't no sound, and I see the black road and the white hoofs half a foot off of it. And the horses had no heads."

"No heads?"

"No, sir."

Mr. Frobisher-Pym laughed.

"Come, come, Plunkett, you don't expect us to swallow that. No heads? How could even a ghost drive horses with no heads? How about the reins, eh?"

"You may laugh, sir, but we know that with God all things are possible. Four white horses they was. I see them clearly, but there was neither head nor neck beyond the collar, sir. I see the reins, shining like silver, and they ran up to the rings of the hames, and they didn't go no further. If I was to drop down dead this minute, sir, that's what I see."

"Was there a driver to this wonderful turn-out?"

"Yes, sir, there was a driver."

"Headless too, I suppose?"

"Yes, sir, headless too. At least, I couldn't see nothing of him beyond his coat, which had them old-fashioned capes at the shoulders."

"Well, I must say, Plunkett, you're very circumstantial. How far off was this—er—apparition when you saw it?"

"I was passing by the War Memorial, sir, when I see it come up the lane. It wouldn't be above twenty or thirty yards from where I stood. It went by at a gallop, and turned off to the left round the churchyard wall."

"Well, well, it sounds odd, certainly, but it was a dark night, and at that distance your eyes may have deceived you. Now, if you'll take my advice you'll think no more about it."

"Ah, sir, it's all very well saying that, but everybody knows the man who sees the death-coach of the Burdocks is doomed to die within the week. There's no use rebelling against it, sir; it is so. And if you'll be so good as to oblige me over that matter of a will, I'd die happier for knowing as Sarah and the children was sure of their bit of money."

Mr. Frobisher-Pym obliged over the will, though much against the grain, exhorting and scolding as he wrote. Wimsey added his own signature as one of the witnesses, and contributed his own bit of comfort.

"I shouldn't worry too much about the coach, if I were you," he said. "Depend upon it, if it's the Burdock coach it'll just have come for the soul of the old squire. It couldn't be expected to go to New York for him, don't you see? It's just gettin' ready for the funeral to-morrow."

"That's likely enough," agreed Plunkett. "Often and often it's been seen in these parts when one of the Burdocks was taken. But it's terrible unlucky to see it."

The thought of the funeral seemed, however, to cheer him a little. The visitors again begged him not to think about it, and took their departure.

"Isn't it wonderful," said Mr. Frobisher-Pym, "what imagination will do with these people? And they're obstinate. You could argue with them till you were black in the face."

"Yes. I say, let's go down to the church and have a look at the place. I'd like to know how much he could really have seen from where he was standing."

The parish church of Little Doddering stands, like so many country churches, at some distance from the houses. The main road from Herriotting, Abbotts Bolton, and Frimpton runs past the west gate of the churchyard—a wide God's acre, crowded with ancient stones. On the south side is a narrow and gloomy lane, heavily overhung with old elm-trees, dividing the church from the still more ancient ruins of Doddering Priory. On the main road, a little beyond the point where Old Priory Lane enters, stands the War Memorial, and from here the road runs straight on into Little Doddering. Round the remaining two sides of the churchyard winds another lane, known to the village simply as the Back Lane. This branches out from the Herriotting road about a hundred yards north of the church, connects with the far end of Priory Lane, and thence proceeds deviously to Shootering Underwood, Hamsey, Thripsey, and Wyck.

"Whatever it was Plunkett thinks he saw," said Mr. Frobisher-Pym, "it must have come from Shootering. The Back Lane only leads round by some fields and a cottage or two, and it stands to reason anybody coming from Frimpton would have taken the main road, going and coming. The lane is in a very bad state with all this rain. I'm afraid even your detective ability, my dear Wimsey, would not avail to find wheel-marks on this modern tarmac."

"Hardly," said Wimsey, "especially in the case of a ghostly chariot which gets along without touching the ground. But your reasoning seems perfectly sound, sir."

"It was probably a couple of belated waggons going to market," pursued Mr. Frobisher-Pym, "and the rest of it is superstition and, I am afraid, the local beer. Plunkett couldn't have seen all those details about drivers and hames and so on at this distance. And, if it was making no noise, how did he come to notice it at all, since he'd got past the turn and was walking in the other direction? Depend upon it, he heard the wheels and imagined the rest."

"Probably," said Wimsey.

"Of course," went on his host, "if the waggons really were going about without lights, it ought to be looked into. It is a very dangerous thing, with all these motor vehicles about, and I've had to speak severely about it before now. I fined a man only the other day for the very same thing. Do you care to see the church while we're here?"

Knowing that in country places it is always considered proper to see the church, Lord Peter expressed his eagerness to do so.

"It's always open nowadays," said the magistrate, leading the way to the west entrance. "The vicar has an idea that churches should be always open for private prayer. He comes from a town living, of course. Round about here the people are always out on the land, and you can't expect them to come into church in their working clothes and muddy boots. They wouldn't think it respectful, and they've other things to do. Besides, I said to him, consider the opportunity it gives for undesirable conduct. But he's a young man, and he'll have to learn by experience."

He pushed the door open. A curious, stuffy waft of stale incense, damp, and stoves rushed out at them as they entered—a kind of concentrated extract of Church of England. The two altars, bright with flowers and gilding, and showing as garish splashes among the heavy shadows and oppressive architecture of the little Norman building, sounded the same note of contradiction; it was the warm and human that seemed exotic and unfamiliar; the cold and unwelcoming that seemed native to the place and people.

"This Lady-chapel, as Hancock calls it, in the south aisle, is new, of course," said Mr. Frobisher-Pym. "It aroused a good deal of opposition, but the Bishop is lenient with the High Church party—too lenient, some people think—but, after all, what does it matter? I'm sure I can say my prayers just as well with two communion-tables as with one. And, I will say for Hancock, he is very good with the young men and the girls. In these days of motor-cycles, it's something to get them interested in religion at all. Those trestles in the chapel are for old Burdock's coffin, I suppose. Ah! Here is the vicar."

A thin man in a cassock emerged from a door beside the high altar and came down towards them, carrying a tall, oaken candlestick in his hand. He greeted them with a slightly professional smile of welcome. Wimsey diagnosed him promptly as earnest, nervous, and not highly intellectual.

"The candlesticks have only just come," he observed after the usual introductions had been made. "I was afraid they would not be here in time. However, all is now well."

He set the candlestick beside the coffin-trestles, and proceeded to decorate its brass spike with a long candle of unbleached wax, which he took from a parcel in a neighbouring pew.

Mr. Frobisher-Pym said nothing. Wimsey felt it incumbent of him to express his interest, and did so.

"It is very gratifying," said Mr. Hancock, thus encouraged, "to see the people beginning to take a real interest in their church. I have really had very little difficulty in finding watchers for to-night. We are having eight watchers, two by two, from 10 o'clock this evening—till which time I shall be myself on duty—till six in the morning, when I come in to say Mass. The men will carry on till 2 o'clock, then my wife and daughter will relieve them, and Mr. Hubbard and young Rawlinson have kindly consented to take the hours from four till six."

"What Rawlinson is that?" demanded Mr. Frobisher-Pym.

"Mr. Graham's clerk from Herriotting. It is true he is not a member of the parish, but he was born here, and was good enough to wish to take his turn in watching. He is coming over on his motor-cycle. After all, Mr. Graham has had charge of Burdock's family affairs for very many years, and no doubt they wished to show their respect in some way."

"Well, I only hope he'll be awake enough to do his work in the morning, after gadding about all night," said Mr. Frobisher-Pym gruffly. "As for Hubbard, that's his own look-out, though I must say it seems an odd occupation for a publican. Still, if he's pleased, and you're pleased, there's no more to be said about it."

"You've got a very beautiful old church here, Mr. Hancock," said Wimsey, seeing that controversy seemed imminent.

"Very beautiful indeed," said the vicar. "Have you noticed that apse? It is rare for a village church to possess such a perfect Norman apse. Perhaps you would like to come and look at it." He genuflected as they passed a hanging lamp which burned before a niche. "You see, we are permitted Reservation. The Bishop——" He prattled cheerfully as they wandered up the chancel, digressing from time to time to draw attention to the handsome miserere seats ("Of course, this was the original Priory Church"), and a beautifully carved piscina and aumbry ("It is rare to find them so well preserved"). Wimsey assisted him to carry down the remaining candlesticks from the vestry, and, when these had been put in position, joined Mr. Frobisher-Pym at the door.

. . . .

"I think you said you were dining with the Lumsdens to-night," said the magistrate, as they sat smoking after lunch. "How are you going? Will you have the car?"

"I'd rather you'd lend me one of the saddle-horses," said Wimsey. "I get few opportunities of riding in town."

"Certainly, my dear boy, certainly. Only I'm afraid you'll have rather a wet ride. Take Polly Flinders; it will do her good to get some exercise. You are quite sure you would prefer it? Have you got your kit with you?"

"Yes—I brought an old pair of bags down with me, and, with this raincoat, I shan't come to any harm. They won't expect me to dress. How far is it to Frimpton, by the way?"

"Nine miles by the main road, and tarmac all the way, I'm afraid, but there's a good wide piece of grass each side. And, of course, you can cut off a mile or so by going across the common. What time will you want to start?"

"Oh, about seven o'clock, I should think. And, I say, sir—will Mrs. Frobisher-Pym think it very rude if I'm rather late back? Old Lumsden and I went through the war together, and if we get yarning over old times we may go on into the small hours. I don't want to feel I'm treating your house like a hotel, but—"

"Of course not, of course not! That's absolutely all right. My wife won't mind in the very least. We want you to enjoy your visit and do exactly what you like. I'll give you the key, and I'll remember not to put the chain up. Perhaps you wouldn't mind doing that yourself when you come in?"

"Rather not. And how about the mare?"

"I'll tell Merridew to look out for you; he sleeps over the stables. I only wish it were going to be a better night for you. I'm afraid the glass is going back. Yes. Dear, dear! It's a bad look-out for to-morrow. By the way, you'll probably pass the funeral procession at the church. It should be along by about then, if the train is punctual."

The train, presumably, was punctual, for as Lord Peter cantered up to the west gate of the church he saw a hearse of great funereal pomp drawn up before it, surrounded by a little crowd of people. Two mourning coaches were in attendance; the driver of the second seemed to be having some difficulty with the horses, and Wimsey rightly inferred that this was the pair which had been borrowed from Mr. Mortimer. Restraining Polly Flinders as best he might, he sidled into a respectful position on the edge of the crowd, and watched the coffin taken from the hearse and carried through the gate, where it was met by Mr. Hancock, in full pontificals, attended by a thurifer and two torchbearers. The effect was a little marred by the rain, which had extinguished the candles, but the village seemed to look upon it as an excellent show nevertheless. A massive man, dressed with great correctness in a black frock coat and tall hat, and accompanied by a woman in handsome mourning and furs, was sympathetically commented on. This was Haviland Burdock of silk-stocking fame, the younger son of the deceased. A vast number of white wreaths were then handed out, and greeted with murmurs of admiration and approval. The choir struck up a hymn, rather raggedly, and the procession filed away into the church. Polly Flinders shook her head vigorously, and Wimsey, taking this as a signal to be gone, replaced his hat and ambled gently away towards Frimpton.

He followed the main road for about four miles, winding up through finely wooded country to the edge of Frimpton Common. Here the road made a wide sweep, skirting the common and curving gently down into Frimpton village. Wimsey hesitated for a moment, considering that it was growing dark and that both the way and the animal he rode were strange to him. There seemed, however, to be a well-defined bridle-path across the common, and eventually he decided to take it. Polly Flinders seemed to know it well enough, and cantered along without hesitation. A ride of about a mile and a half brought them without adventure into the main road again. Here a fork in the road presented itself confusingly; an electric torch, however, and a signpost solved the problem; after which ten minutes' ride brought the traveller to his goal.

Major Lumsden was a large, cheerful man—none the less cheerful for having lost a leg in the War. He had a large, cheerful wife, a large, cheerful house, and a large, cheerful family. Wimsey soon found himself seated before a fire as large and cheerful as the rest of the establishment, exchanging gossip with his hosts over a whisky-and-soda. He described the Burdock funeral with irreverent gusto, and went on to tell the story of the phantom coach. Major Lumsden laughed.

"It's a quaint part of the country," he said. "The policeman is just as bad as the rest of them. Do you remember, dear, the time I had to go out and lay a ghost, down at Pogson's farm?"

"I do, indeed," said his wife emphatically. "The maids had a wonderful time. Trivett—that's our local constable—came rushing in here and fainted in the kitchen, and they all sat round howling and sustaining him with our best brandy, while Dan went down and investigated."

"Did you find the ghost?"

"Well, not the ghost, exactly, but we found a pair of boots and half a pork-pie in the empty house, so we put it all down to a tramp. Still, I must say odd things do happen about here. There were those fires on the common last year. They were never explained."

"Gipsies, Dan."

"Maybe; but nobody ever saw them, and the fires would start in the most unexpected way, sometimes in the pouring rain; and, before you could get near one, it would be out, and only a sodden wet black mark left behind it. And there's another bit of the common that animals don't like—near what they call the Dead Man's Post. My dogs won't go near it. Funny brutes. I've never seen anything there, but even in broad daylight they don't seem to fancy it. The common's not got a good reputation. It used to be a great place for highwaymen."

"Is the Burdock coach anything to do with highwaymen?"

"No. I fancy it was some rakehelly dead-and-gone Burdock. Belonged to the Hell-fire Club or something. The usual sort of story. All the people round here believe in it, of course. It's rather a good thing. Keeps the servants indoors at night. Well, let's go and have some grub, shall we?"

. . . .

"Do you remember," said Major Lumsden, "that damned old mill, and the three elms by the pig-sty?"

"Good Lord, yes! You very obligingly blew them out of the landscape for us, I remember. They made us a damned sight too conspicuous."

"We rather missed them when they were gone."

"Thank heaven you didn't miss them when they were there. I'll tell you what you did miss, though."

"What's that?"

"The old sow."

"By Jove, yes. Do you remember old Piper fetching her in?"

"I'll say I do. That reminds me. You knew Bunthorne . . ."

"I'll say good night," said Mrs. Lumsden, "and leave you people to it."

"Do you remember," said Lord Peter Wimsey, "that awkward moment when Popham went off his rocker?"

"No. I'd been sent back with a batch of prisoners. I heard about it, though. I never knew what became of him."

"I got him sent home. He's married now and living in Lincolnshire."

"Is he? Well, he couldn't help himself, I suppose. He was only a kid. What's happened to Philpotts?"

"Oh, Philpotts . . ."

"Where's your glass, old man?"

"Oh, rot, old man. The night is still young . . ."

"Really? Well, but look here, why not stay the night? My wife will be delighted. I can fix you up in no time."

"No, thanks most awfully. I must be rolling off home. I said I'd be back; and I'm booked to put the chain on the door."

"As you like, of course, but it's still raining. Not a good night for a ride on an open horse."

"I'll bring a saloon next time. We shan't hurt. Rain's good for the complexion—makes the roses grow. Don't wake your man up. I can saddle her myself."

"My dear man, it's no trouble."

"No, really, old man."

"Well, I'll come along and lend you a hand."

A gust of rain and wind blew in through the hall door as they struggled out into the night. It was past one in the morning and pitch-dark. Major Lumsden again pressed Wimsey to stay.

"No, thanks, really. The old lady's feelings might be hurt. It's not so bad, really—wet, but not cold. Come up, Polly, stand over, old lady."

He put the saddle on and girthed it, while Lumsden held the lantern. The mare, fed and rested, came delicately dancing out of the warm loose-box, head well stretched forward, and nostrils snuffing at the rain.

"Well, so long, old lad. Come and look us up again. It's been great."

"Rather! By Jove, yes. Best respects to madame. Is the gate open?"

"Yes."

"Well, cheerio!"

"Cheerio!"

Polly Flinders, with her nose turned homewards, settled down to make short work of the nine miles of high-road. Once outside the gates, the night seemed lighter, though the rain poured heavily. Somewhere buried behind the thronging clouds there was a moon, which now and again showed as a pale stain on the sky, a paler reflection on the black road. Wimsey, with a mind full of memories and a skin full of whisky, hummed to himself as he rode.

As he passed the fork, he hesitated for a moment. Should he take the path over the common or stick to the road? On consideration, he decided to give the common a miss—not because of its sinister reputation, but because of ruts and rabbit-holes. He shook the reins, bestowed a word of encouragement on his mount, and continued by the road, having the common on his right hand, and, on the left, fields bounded by high hedges, which gave some shelter from the driving rain.

He had topped the rise, and passed the spot where the bridle-path again joined the high-road, when a slight start and stumble drew his attention unpleasantly to Polly Flinders.

"Hold up, mare," he said disapprovingly.

Polly shook her head, moved forward, tried to pick up her easy pace again. "Hullo!" said Wimsey, alarmed. He pulled her to a standstill.

"Lame in the near fore," he said, dismounting. "If you've been and gone and strained anything, my girl, four miles from home, father *will* be pleased." It occurred to him for the first time how curiously lonely the road was. He had not seen a single car. They might have been in the wilds of Africa.

He ran an exploratory hand down the near foreleg. The mare stood quietly enough, without shrinking or wincing. Wimsey was puzzled.

"If these had been the good old days," he said, "I'd have thought she'd picked up a stone. But what—"

He lifted the mare's foot, and explored it carefully with fingers and pocket-torch. His diagnosis had been right, after all. A steel nut, evidently dropped from a passing car, had wedged itself firmly between the shoe and the frog. He grunted and felt for his knife. Happily, it was one of that excellent old-fashioned kind which includes, besides blades and corkscrews, an ingenious apparatus for removing foreign bodies from horses' feet.

The mare nuzzled him gently as he stooped over his task. It was a little awkward getting to work; he had to wedge the torch under his arm, so as to leave one hand free for the tool and the other to hold the hoof. He was swearing gently at these difficulties when, happening to glance down the road ahead, he fancied he caught the gleam of something moving. It was not easy to see, for at this point the tall trees stood up on both sides of the road, which dipped abruptly from the edge of the common. It was not a car; the light was too faint. A waggon, probably, with a dim lantern. Yet it seemed to move fast. He puzzled for a moment, then bent to work again.

The nut resisted his efforts, and the mare, touched in a tender spot, pulled away, trying to get her foot down. He soothed her with his voice and patted her neck. The torch slipped from his arm. He cursed it impatiently, set down the hoof, and picked up the torch from the edge of the grass, into which it had rolled. As he straightened himself again, he looked along the road and saw.

Up from under the dripping dark of the trees it came, shining with a thin, moony radiance. There was no clatter of hoofs, no rumble of wheels, no ringing of bit or bridle. He saw the white, sleek, shining shoulders with the collar that lay on each, like a faint fiery ring, enclosing nothing. He saw the gleaming reins, their cut ends slipping back and forward unsupported through the ring of the hames. The feet, that never touched earth, ran swiftly—four times four noiseless hoofs, bearing the pale bodies by like smoke. The driver leaned forward, brandishing his whip. He was faceless and headless, but his whole attitude bespoke desperate haste. The coach was barely visible through the driving rain, but Wimsey saw the dimly spinning wheels and a faint whiteness, still and stiff, at the window. It went past at a gallop—headless driver and headless horses and silent coach. Its passing left a stir, a sound that was less a sound than a vibration—and the wind roared suddenly after it, with a great sheet of water blown up out of the south.

"Good God!" said Wimsey. And then: "How many whiskies did we have?"

He turned and looked back along the road, straining his eyes. Then suddenly he remembered the mare, and, without troubling further about the torch, picked up her foot and went to work by touch. The nut gave no more trouble, but dropped out into his hand almost immediately. Polly Flinders sighed gratefully and blew into his ear.

Wimsey led her forward a few steps. She put her feet down firmly and strongly. The nut, removed without delay, had left no tenderness. Wimsey mounted, let her go—then pulled her head round suddenly.

"I'm going to see," he said resolutely. "Come up, mare! We won't let any headless horses get the better of *us*. Perfectly indecent, goin' about without heads. Get on, old lady. Over the common with you. We'll catch 'em at the cross-roads."

Without the slightest consideration for his host or his host's property, he put the mare to the bridle-path again, and urged her into a gallop.

At first he thought he could make out a pale, fluttering whiteness, moving away ahead of him on the road. Presently, as high-road and bridle-path diverged, he lost it altogether. But he knew there was no side-road. Bar any accident to his mount, he was bound to catch it before it came to the fork. Polly Flinders, answering easily to the touch of his heel, skimmed over the rough track with the indifference born of familiarity. In less than ten minutes her feet rang out again on the tarmac. He pulled her up, faced round in the direction of Little Doddering, and stared down the road. He could see nothing yet. Either he was well ahead of the coach, or it had already passed at unbelievable speed, or else——

He waited. Nothing. The violent rain had ceased, and the moon was struggling out again. The road appeared completely deserted. He glanced over his shoulder. A small beam of light near the ground moved, turned, flashed green, and red, and white again, and came towards him. Presently he made out that it was a policeman wheeling a bicycle.

"A bad night, sir," said the man civilly, but with a faint note of enquiry in his voice.

"Rotten," said Wimsey.

"Just had to mend a puncture, to make it all the pleasanter," added the policeman.

Wimsey expressed sympathy. "Have you been here long?" he added.

"Best part o' twenty minutes."

"Did you see anything pass along this way from Little Doddering?"

"Ain't been nothing along while I've been here. What sort of thing did you mean, sir?"

"I thought I saw—" Wimsey hesitated. He did not care about the idea of making a fool of himself. "A carriage with four horses," he said hesitatingly. "It passed me on this road not a quarter of an hour ago—down at the other end of the common. I—I came back to see. It seemed unusual—" He became aware that his story sounded very lame.

The policeman spoke rather sharply and rapidly.

"There ain't been nothing past here."

"You're sure?"

"Yes, sir; and, if you don't mind me sayin' so, you'd best be getting home. It's a lonesome bit o' road."

"Yes, isn't it?" said Wimsey. "Well, good night, sergeant."

He turned the mare's head back along the Little Doddering road, going very quietly. He saw nothing, heard nothing, and passed nothing. The night was brighter now, and, as he rode back, he verified the entire absence of side-roads. Whatever the thing was which he had seen, it had vanished somewhere along the edge of the common; it had not gone by the main road, nor by any other.

. . . .

Wimsey came down rather late for breakfast in the morning, to find his hosts in a state of some excitement.

"The most extraordinary thing has happened," said Mrs. Frobisher-Pym.

"Outrageous!" added her husband. "I warned Hancock—he can't say I didn't warn him. Still, however much one may disapprove of his goings-on, there is no excuse whatever for such abominable conduct. Once let me get hold of the beggars, whoever they are—"

"What's up?" said Wimsey, helping himself to broiled kidneys at the sideboard.

"A most scandalous thing," said Mrs. Frobisher-Pym. "The vicar came up to Tom at once—I hope we didn't disturb you, by the way, with all the excitement. It appears that when Mr. Hancock got to the church this morning at 6 o'clock to take the early service—"

"No, no, my dear, you've got it wrong. Let *me* tell it. When Joe Grinch—that's the sexton, you know, and he has to get there first to ring the bell—when he arrived, he found the south door wide open and nobody in the chapel, where they should have been, beside the coffin. He was very much perplexed, of course, but he supposed that Hubbard and young Rawlinson had got sick of it and gone off home. So he went on to the vestry to get the vestments and things ready, and to his amazement he heard women's voices, calling out to him from inside. He was so astonished, didn't know where he was, but he went on and unlocked the door—"

"With his own key?" put in Wimsey.

"The key was in the door. As a rule it's kept hanging up on a nail under a curtain near the organ, but it was in the lock—where it ought not to have been. And inside the vestry he found Mrs. Hancock and her daughter, nearly dead with fright and annoyance."

"Great Scott!"

"Yes, indeed. They had a most extraordinary story to tell. They'd taken over at 2 o'clock from the other pair of watchers, and had knelt down by the coffin in the Lady-chapel, according to plan, to say the proper sort of prayers, whatever they are. They'd been there, to the best of their calculation, about ten minutes, when they heard a noise up by the High Altar, as though somebody was creeping stealthily about. Miss Hancock is a very plucky girl, and she got up and walked up the aisle in the dark, with Mrs. Hancock following on behind because, as she said, she didn't want to be left alone. When they'd got as far as the rood-screen, Miss Hancock called out aloud, 'Who's there?' At that they heard a sort of rustling sound, and a noise like something being knocked over. Miss Hancock most courageously snatched up one of the churchwarden's staffs, which was clipped on to the choir-stalls, and ran forward, thinking, she says, that somebody was trying to steal the ornaments off the altar. There's a very fine fifteenth-century cross——"

"Never mind the cross, Tom. That hasn't been taken, at any rate."

"No, it hasn't, but she thought it might be. Anyhow, just as she got up to the sanctuary steps, with Mrs. Hancock coming close after her and begging her to be careful, somebody seemed to rush out of the choir-stalls, and caught her by the arms and frog's-marched her—that's her expression—into the vestry. And before she could get breath even to shriek, Mrs. Hancock was pushed in beside her, and the door locked on them."

"By Jove! You do have exciting times in your village."

"Well," said Mr. Frobisher-Pym, "of course they were dreadfully frightened, because they didn't know but what these wretches would come back and murder them, and, in any case, they thought the church was being robbed. But the vestry windows are very narrow and barred, and they couldn't do anything except wait. They tried to listen, but they couldn't hear much. Their only hope was that the four-o'clock watchers might come early and catch the thieves at work. But they waited and they waited, and they heard four strike, and five, and nobody came."

"What had happened to what's-his-name and Rawlinson then?"

"They couldn't make out, and nor could Grinch. However, they had a good look round the church, and nothing seemed to be taken or disturbed in any way. Just then the vicar came along, and they told him all about it. He was very much shocked, naturally, and his first thought—when he found the ornaments were safe and the poor-box all right—was that some Kensitite people had been stealing the wafers from the what d'you call it."

"The tabernacle," suggested Wimsey.

"Yes, that's his name for it. That worried him very much, and he unlocked it and had a look, but the wafers were all there all right, and, as there's only one key, and that was on his own watch-chain, it wasn't a case of anyone substituting unconsecrated wafers for consecrated ones, or any practical joke of that kind. So he sent Mrs. and Miss Hancock home, and had a look round the church outside, and the first thing he saw, lying in the bushes near the south door, was young Rawlinson's motor-cycle."

"Oho!"

"So his next idea was to hunt for Rawlinson and Hubbard. However, he didn't have to look far. He'd got round the church as far as the furnace-house on the north side, when he heard a terrific hullabaloo going on, and people shouting and thumping on the door. So he called Grinch, and they looked in through the little window, and there, if you please, were Hubbard and young Rawlinson, bawling and going on and using the most shocking language. It seems they were set upon in exactly the same way, only before they got inside the church. Rawlinson had been passing the evening with Hubbard, I understand, and they had a bit of a sleep downstairs in the back bar, to avoid disturbing the house early—or so they say, though I dare say if the truth was known they were having drinks; and if that's Hancock's idea of a suitable preparation for going to church and saying prayers, all I can say is, it isn't mine. Anyway, they started off just before four, Hubbard going down on the carrier of Rawlinson's bicycle. They had to get off at the south gate, which was pushed to, and while Rawlinson was wheeling the machine up the path two or three men—they couldn't see exactly—jumped out from the trees. There was a bit of a scuffle, but what with the bicycle, and it's being so unexpected, they couldn't put up a very good fight, and the men dropped blankets over their heads, or something. I don't know all the details. At any rate, they were bundled into the furnace-house and left there. They may be there still, for all I know, if they haven't found the key. There should be a spare key, but I don't know what's become of it. They sent up for it this morning, but I haven't seen it about for a long time."

"It wasn't left in the lock this time, then?"

"No, it wasn't. They've had to send for the locksmith. I'm going down now to see what's to be done about it. Like to come, if you're ready?"

Wimsey said he would. Anything in the nature of a problem always fascinated him.

"You were back pretty late, by the way," said Mr. Frobisher-Pym jovially, as they left the house. "Yarning over old times, I suppose."

"We were, indeed," said Wimsey.

"Hope the old girl carried you all right. Lonely bit of road, isn't it? I don't suppose you saw anybody worse than yourself, as the saying goes?"

"Only a policeman," said Wimsey untruthfully. He had not yet quite decided about the phantom coach. No doubt Plunkett would be relieved to know that he was not the only person to whom the "warning" had come. But, then, had it really been the phantom coach, or merely a delusion, begotten by whisky upon reminiscence? Wimsey, in the cold light of day, was none too certain.

On arriving at the church, the magistrate and his guest found quite a little crowd collected, conspicuous among whom were the vicar, in cassock and biretta, gesticulating freely, and the local policeman, his tunic buttoned awry and his dignity much impaired by the small fry of the village, who clustered round his legs. He had just finished taking down the statements of the two men who had been released from the stoke-hole. The younger of these, a fresh-faced, impudent-looking fellow of twenty-five or so, was in the act of starting up his motor-cycle. He greeted Mr. Frobisher-Pym pleasantly. "Afraid they've made us look a bit small, sir. You'll excuse me, won't you? I'll have to be getting back to Herriotting. Mr. Graham won't be any too pleased if I'm late for the office. I think some of the bright lads have been having a joke with us." He grinned as he pushed the throttle-lever over and departed in a smother of unnecessary smoke that made Mr. Frobisher-Pym sneeze. His fellow-victim, a large, fat man, who looked the sporting publican that he was, grinned shamefacedly at the magistrate.

"Well, Hubbard," said the latter, "I hope you've enjoyed your experience. I must say I'm surprised at a man of your size letting himself be shut up in a coal-hole like a naughty urchin."

"Yes, sir, I was surprised myself at the time," retorted the publican, good-humoredly enough. "When that there blanket came down on my head, I was the most surprised man in this here county. I gave 'em a hack or two on the shins, though, to remember me by," he added, with a reminiscent chuckle.

"How many of them were there?" asked Wimsey.

"Three or four, I should say, sir. But not 'avin' seen 'em, I can only tell from 'earin' 'em talk. There was two laid 'old of me, I'm pretty sure, and young Rawlinson thinks there was only one 'ad 'old of 'im, but 'e was a wonderful strong 'un."

"We must leave no stone unturned to find out who these people were," said the vicar excitedly. "Ah, Mr. Frobisher-Pym, come and see what they have done in the church. It is as I thought—an anti-Catholic protest. We must be most thankful that they have done no more than they have."

He led the way in. Somebody had lit two or three hanging lamps in the gloomy little chancel. By their light Wimsey was able to see that the neck of the eagle lectern was decorated with an enormous red-white-and-blue bow, and bore a large placard—obviously pinched from the local newspaper offices—"VATICAN BANS IMMODEST DRESS." In each of the choir-stalls a teddy-bear sat, lumpishly amiable, apparently absorbed in reading the choir-books upside-down, while on the ledge before them copies of the *Pink 'Un* were obtrusively displayed. In the pulpit, a waggish hand had set up a pantomime ass's head, elegantly arrayed in a nightgown, and crowned with a handsome nimbus, cut from gold paper.

"Disgraceful, isn't it?" said the vicar.

"Well, Hancock," replied Mr. Frobisher-Pym, "I must say I think you have brought it upon yourself—though I quite agree, of course, that this sort of thing cannot possibly be allowed, and the offenders must be discovered and severely punished. But you must see that many of your practices appear to these people to be papistical nonsense at best, and while that is no excuse . . ."

His reprimanding voice barked on.

". . . what I really can only look upon as this sacrilegious business with old Burdock—a man whose life . . ."

The policeman had by this time shoved away the attendant villagers and was standing beside Lord Peter at the entrance of the rood-screen.

"Was that you was out on the road this morning, sir? Ah! I thought I reckernised your voice. Did you get home all right, sir? Didn't meet nothing?"

There seemed to be a shade more than idle questioning in the tone of his voice. Wimsey turned quickly.

"No, I met nothing—more. Who is it drives a coach with four white horses about this village of a night, sergeant?"

"Not sergeant, sir—I ain't due for promotion yet awhile. Well, sir, as to white horses, I don't altogether like to say. Mr. Mortimer over at Abbotts Bolton has some nice greys, and he's the biggest horse-breeder about these parts—but, well, there, sir, he wouldn't be driving out in all that rain, sir, would he?"

"It doesn't seem a sensible thing to do, certainly."

"No, sir. And"—the constable leaned close to Wimsey and spoke into his ear—"and Mr. Mortimer is a man that's got a head on his shoulders—*and, what's more, so have his horses.*"

"Why," said Wimsey, a little startled by the aptness of this remark, "did you ever know a horse that hadn't?"

"No, sir," said the policeman, with emphasis, "I never knew no *livin'* horse that hadn't. But that's neether here nor there, as the sayin' goes. But as to this church business, that's just a bit of a lark got up among the boys, that's what that is. They don't mean no harm, you know, sir; they likes to be up to their tricks. It's all very well for the vicar to talk, sir, but this ain't no Kensitites nor anythink of that, as you can see with half an eye. Just a bit of fun, that's all it is."

"I'd come to the same conclusion myself," said Wimsey, interested, "but I'd rather like to know what makes you think so."

"Lord bless you, sir, ain't it plain as the nose on your face? If it had a-bin these Kensitites, wouldn't they have gone for the crosses and the images and the lights and—that there?" He extended a horny finger in the direction of the tabernacle. "No, sir, these lads what did this ain't laid a finger on the things what you might call sacred images—and they ain't done no harm neether to the communion-table. So I says as it ain't a case of con*trou*versy, but more a bit of fun, like. And they've treated Mr. Burdock's corpse respectful, sir, you see, too. That shows they wasn't meaning anything wrong at heart, don't you see?"

"I agree absolutely," said Wimsey. "In fact, they've taken particular care not to touch anything that a church-man holds really sacred. How long have you been on this job, officer?"

"Three year, sir, come February."

"Ever had any idea of going to town or taking up the detective side of the business?"

"Well, sir—I have—but it isn't just ask and have, as you might say."

Wimsey took a card from his note-case.

"If ever you think seriously about it," he said, "give this card to Chief Inspector Parker, and have a chat with him. Tell him I think you haven't got opportunities enough down here. He's a great friend of mine, and he'll give you a good chance, I know."

"I've heard of you, my lord," said the constable, gratified, "and I'm sure it's very kind of your lordship. Well, I suppose I'd best be getting along now. You leave it to me, Mr. Frobisher-Pym, sir; we'll soon get at the bottom of this here."

"I hope you do," said the magistrate. "Meanwhile, Mr. Hancock, I trust you will realise the inadvisability of leaving the church doors open at night. Well, come along, Wimsey; we'll leave them to get the church straight for the funeral. What have you found there?"

"Nothing," said Wimsey, who had been peering at the floor of the Lady-chapel. "I was afraid you'd got the worm in here, but I see it's only sawdust." He dusted his fingers as he spoke, and followed Mr. Frobisher-Pym out of the building.

. . . .

When you are staying in a village, you are expected to take part in the interests and amusements of the community. Accordingly, Lord Peter duly attended the funeral of Squire Burdock, and beheld the coffin safely committed to the ground, in a drizzle, certainly, but not without the attendance of a large and reverent congregation. After this ceremony, he was formally introduced to Mr. and Mrs. Haviland Burdock, and was able to confirm his previous impression that the lady was well, not to say too well, dressed, as might be expected from one whose wardrobe was based upon silk stockings. She was a handsome woman, in a large, bold style, and the hand that clasped Wimsey's was quite painfully encrusted with diamonds. Haviland was disposed to be friendly—and, indeed, silk manufacturers have no reason to be otherwise to rich men of noble birth. He seemed to be aware of Wimsey's reputation as an antiquarian and book-collector, and extended a hearty invitation to him to come and see the old house.

"My brother Martin is still abroad," he said, "but I'm sure he would be delighted to have you come and look at the place. I'm told there are some very fine old books in the library. We shall be staying here till Monday—if Mrs. Hancock will be good enough to have us. Suppose you come along to-morrow afternoon."

Wimsey said he would be delighted.

Mrs. Hancock interposed and said, wouldn't Lord Peter come to tea at the vicarage first.

Wimsey said it was very good of her.

"Then that's settled," said Mrs. Burdock. "You and Mr. Pym come to tea, and then we'll all go over the house together. I've hardly seen it myself yet."

"It's very well worth seeing," said Mr. Frobisher-Pym. "Fine old place, but takes some money to keep up. Has nothing been seen of the will yet, Mr. Burdock?"

"Nothing whatever," said Haviland. "It's curious, because Mr. Graham—the solicitor, you know, Lord Peter—certainly drew one up, just after poor Martin's unfortunate difference with our father. He remembers it perfectly."

"Can't he remember what's in it?"

"He could, of course, but he doesn't think it etiquette to say. He's one of the crusted old type. Poor Martin always called him an old scoundrel—but then, of course, he never approved of Martin, so Martin was not altogether unprejudiced. Besides, as Mr. Graham says, all that was some years ago, and it's quite possible that the governor destroyed the will later, or made a new one in America."

"'Poor Martin' doesn't seem to have been popular hereabouts," said Wimsey to Mr. Frobisher-Pym, as they parted from the Burdocks and turned homewards.

"N-no," said the magistrate. "Not with Graham, anyway. Personally, I rather liked the lad, though he was a bit harum-scarum. I dare say he's sobered up with time—and marriage. It's odd that they can't find the will. But, if it was made at the time of the rumpus, it's bound to be in Haviland's favour."

"I think Haviland thinks so," said Wimsey. "His manner seemed to convey a chastened satisfaction. I expect the discreet Graham made it fairly clear that the advantage was not with the unspeakable Martin."

The following morning turned out fine, and Wimsey, who was supposed to be enjoying a rest-and-fresh-air cure in Little Doddering, petitioned for a further loan of Polly Flinders. His host consented with pleasure, and only regretted that he could not accompany his guest, being booked to attend a Board of Guardians meeting in connection with the work-house.

"But you could go up and get a good blow on the common," he suggested. "Why not go round by Petering Friars, turn off across the common till you get to Dead Man's Post, and come back by the Frimpton road? It makes a very pleasant round—about nineteen miles. You'll be back in nice time for lunch if you take it easy."

Wimsey fell in with the plan—the more readily that it exactly coincided with his own inward purpose. He had a reason for wishing to ride over the Frimpton road by daylight.

"You'll be careful about Dead Man's Post," said Mrs. Frobisher-Pym a little anxiously. "The horses have a way of shying at it. I don't know why. People say, of course——"

"All nonsense," said her husband. "The villagers dislike the place and that makes the horses nervous. It's remarkable how a rider's feelings communicate themselves to his mount. *I've* never had any trouble at Dead Man's Post."

It was a quiet and pretty road, even on a November day, that led to Petering Friars. Jogging down the winding Essex lanes in the wintry sunshine, Wimsey felt soothed and happy. A good burst across the common raised his spirits to exhilaration pitch. He had entirely forgotten Dead Man's Post and its uncanny reputation, when a violent start and swerve, so sudden that it nearly unseated him, recalled him to what he was doing. With some difficulty, he controlled Polly Flinders, and brought her to a standstill.

He was at the highest point of the common, following a bridle-path which was bordered on each side by gorse and dead bracken. A little way ahead of him another bridle-path seemed to run into it, and at the junction of the two was something which he had vaguely imagined to be a decayed sign-post. Certainly it was short and thick for a sign-post, and had no arms. It appeared, however, to bear some sort of inscription on the face that was turned towards him.

He soothed the mare, and urged her gently towards the post. She took a few hesitating steps, and plunged sideways, snorting and shivering.

"Queer!" said Wimsey. "If this is my state of mind communicating itself to my mount, I'd better see a doctor. My nerves must be in a rotten state. Come up, old lady? What's the matter with you?"

Polly Flinders, apologetic but determined, refused to budge. He urged her gently with his heel. She sidled away, with ears laid back, and he saw the white of a protesting eye. He slipped from the saddle, and, putting his hand through the bridle, endeavoured to lead her forward. After a little persuasion, the mare followed him, with stretched neck and treading as though on egg-shells. After a dozen hesitating paces, she stopped again, trembling in all her limbs. He put his hand on her neck and found it wet with sweat.

"Damn it all!" said Wimsey. "Look here, I'm jolly well going to read what's on that post. If you won't come, will you stand still?"

He dropped the bridle. The mare stood quietly, with hanging head. He left her and went forward, glancing back from time to time to see that she showed no disposition to bolt. She stood quietly enough, however, only shifting her feet uneasily.

Wimsey walked up to the post. It was a stout pillar of ancient oak, newly painted white. The inscription, too, had been recently blacked in. It read:

ON THIS SPOT
GEORGE WINTER
WAS FOULLY MURTHERED
IN DEFENSE OF
HIS MASTER'S GOODS
BY BLACK RALPH
OF HERRIOTTING
WHO WAS AFTERWARD
HANGED IN CHAINS
ON THE PLACE OF HIS CRIME
9 NOVEMBER 1674

FEAR JUSTICE

"And very nice, too," said Wimsey. "Dead Man's Post without a doubt. Polly Flinders seems to share the local feeling about the place. Well, Polly, if them's your sentiments, I won't do violence to them. But may I ask why, if you're so sensitive about a mere post, you should swallow a death-coach and four headless horses with such hardened equanimity?"

The mare took the shoulder of his jacket gently between her lips and mumbled at it.

"Just so," said Wimsey. "I perfectly understand. You would if you could, but you really can't. But those horses, Polly—did they bring with them no brimstone blast from the nethermost pit? Can it be that they really exuded nothing but an honest and familiar smell of stables?"

He mounted, and, turning Polly's head to the right, guided her in a circle, so as to give Dead Man's Post a wide berth before striking the path again.

"The supernatural explanation is, I think, excluded. Not on *a priori* grounds, which would be unsound, but on the evidence of Polly's senses. There remain the alternatives of whisky and jiggery-pokery. Further investigation seems called for."

He continued to muse as the mare moved quietly forward.

"Supposing I wanted, for some reason, to scare the neighbourhood with the apparition of a coach and headless horses, I should choose a dark, rainy night. Good! It was that kind of night. Now, if I took black horses and painted their bodies white—poor devils! what a state they'd be in. No. How do they do these Maskelyne-and-Devant stunts where they cut off people's heads? White horses, of course—and black felt clothing over their heads. Right! And luminous paint on the harness, with a touch here and there on their bodies, to make good contrast and ensure that the whole show wasn't invisible. No difficulty about that. But they must go silently. Well, why not? Four stout black cloth bags filled with bran, drawn well up and tied round the fetlocks would make any horse go quietly enough, especially if there was a bit of a wind going. Rags round the bridle-rings to prevent clinking, and round the ends of the traces to keep 'em from squeaking. Give 'em a coachman in a white coat and a black mask, hitch 'em to a rubber-tyred fly, picked out with phosphorus and well-oiled at the joints—and I swear I'd make something quite ghostly enough to startle a rather well-irrigated gentleman on a lonely road at half-past two in the morning."

He was pleased with his thought, and tapped his boot cheerfully with his whip.

"But damn it all! They never passed me again. Where did they go to? A coach-and-horses can't vanish into thin air, you know. There must be a side-road after all—or else, Polly Flinders, you've been pulling my leg all the time."

The bridle-path eventually debouched upon the highway at the now familiar fork where Wimsey had met the policeman. As he slowly ambled homewards, his lordship scanned the left-hand hedgerow, looking for the lane which surely must exist. But nothing rewarded his search. Enclosed fields with padlocked gates presented the only breaks in the hedge, till he again found himself looking down the avenue of trees up which the death-coach had come galloping two nights before.

"Damn!" said Wimsey.

It occurred to him for the first time that the coach might perhaps have turned round and gone back through Little Doddering. Certainly it had been seen by Little Doddering Church on Wednesday. But on that occasion, also, it had galloped off in the direction of Frimpton. In fact, thinking it over, Wimsey concluded that it had approached from Frimpton, gone round the church—widdershins, naturally—by the Back Lane, and returned by the high-road whence it came. But in that case——

"Turn again, Whittington," said Wimsey, and Polly Flinders rotated obediently in the road. "Through one of those fields it went, or I'm a Dutchman."

He pulled Polly into a slow walk, and passed along the strip of grass at the right-hand side, staring at the ground as though he were an Aberdonian who had lost a sixpence.

The first gate led into a ploughed field, harrowed smooth and sown with autumn wheat. It was clear that no wheeled thing had been across it for many weeks. The second gate looked more promising. It gave upon fallow ground, and the entrance was seamed with innumerable wheel-ruts. On further examination, however, it was clear that this was the one and only gate. It seemed unlikely that the mysterious coach should have been taken into a field from which there was no way out. Wimsey decided to seek further.

The third gate was in bad repair. It sagged heavily from its hinges; the hasp was gone, and gate and post had been secured with elaborate twists of wire. Wimsey dismounted and examined these, convincing himself that their rusty surface had not been recently disturbed.

There remained only two more gates before he came to the cross-roads. One led into plough again, where the dark ridge-and-furrow showed no sign of disturbance, but at sight of the last gate Wimsey's heart gave a leap. There was plough-land here also, but round the edge of the field ran a wide, beaten path, rutted and water-logged. The gate was not locked, but opened simply with a spring catch. Wimsey examined the approach. Among the wide ruts made by farm-waggons was the track of four narrow wheels—the unmistakable prints of rubber tyres. He pushed the gate open and passed through.

The path skirted two sides of the plough; then came another gate and another field, containing a long barrow of mangold wurzels and a couple of barns. At the sound of Polly's hoofs, a man emerged from the nearest barn, with a paint-brush in his hand, and stood watching Wimsey's approach.

"'Morning!" said the latter genially.

"'Morning, sir."

"Fine day after the rain."

"Yes, it is, sir."

"I hope I'm not trespassing?"

"Where was you wanting to go, sir?"

"I thought, as a matter of fact—hullo!"

"Anything wrong, sir?"

Wimsey shifted in the saddle.

"I fancy this girth's slipped a bit. It's a new one." (This was a fact.) "Better have a look."

The man advanced to investigate, but Wimsey had dismounted and was tugging at the strap, with his head under the mare's belly.

"Yes, it wants taking up a trifle. Oh! Thanks most awfully. Is this a short cut to Abbotts Bolton, by the way?"

"Not to the village, sir, though you can get through this way. It comes out by Mr. Mortimer's stables."

"Ah, yes. This his land?"

"No, sir, it's Mr. Topham's land, but Mr. Mortimer rents this field and the next for fodder."

"Oh, yes." Wimsey peered across the hedge. "Lucerne, I suppose. Or clover."

"Clover, sir. And the mangolds is for the cattle."

"Oh–Mr. Mortimer keeps cattle as well as horses?"

"Yes, sir."

"Very jolly. Have a gasper?" Wimsey had sidled across to the barn in his interest, and was gazing absently into its dark interior. It contained a number of farm implements and a black fly of antique construction, which seemed to be undergoing renovation with black varnish. Wimsey pulled some vestas from his pocket. The box was apparently damp, for, after one or two vain attempts he abandoned it, and struck a match on the wall of the barn. The flame, lighting up the ancient fly, showed it to be incongruously fitted with rubber tyres.

"Very fine stud, Mr. Mortimer's, I understand," said Wimsey carelessly.

"Yes, sir, very fine indeed."

"I suppose he hasn't any greys, by any chance. My mother–queenly woman, Victorian ideas, and all that–is rather keen on greys. Sports a carriage and pay-ah, don't you know."

"Yes, sir? Well, Mr. Mortimer would be able to suit the lady, I think, sir. He has several greys."

"No? has he though? I must really go over and see him. Is it far?"

"Matter of five or six mile by the fields, sir."

Wimsey looked at his watch.

"Oh, dear! I'm really afraid it's too far for this morning. I absolutely promised to get back to lunch. I must come over another day. Thanks *so* much. Is that girth right now? Oh, really, I'm immensely obliged. Get yourself a drink, won't you–and tell Mr. Mortimer not to sell his greys till I've seen them. Well, *good* morning, and many thanks."

He set Polly Flinders on the homeward path and trotted gently away. Not till he was out of sight of the barn did he pull up and, stooping from the saddle, thoughtfully examined his boots. They were liberally plastered with bran.

"I must have picked it up in the barn," said Wimsey. "Curious, if true. Why should Mr. Mortimer be lashing the stuffing out of his greys in an old fly at dead of night–and with muffled hoofs and no heads, to boot? It's not a kind thing to do. It frightened Plunkett very much. It made me think I was drunk–a thought I hate to think. Ought I to tell the police? Are Mr.

Mortimer's jokes any business of mine? What do *you* think, Polly?"

The mare, hearing her name, energetically shook her head.

"You think not? Perhaps you are right. Let us say that Mr. Mortimer did it for a wager. Who am I to interfere with his amusements? All the same," added his lordship, "I'm glad to know it wasn't Lumsden's whisky."

. . . .

"This is the library," said Haviland, ushering in his guests. "A fine room—and a fine collection of books, I'm told, though literature isn't much in my line. It wasn't much in the governor's line, either, I'm afraid. The place wants doing up, as you see. I don't know whether Martin will take it in hand. It's a job that'll cost money, of course."

Wimsey shivered a little as he gazed round—more from sympathy than from cold, though a white November fog lay curled against the tall windows and filtered damply through the frames.

A long, mouldering room, in the frigid neo-classical style, the library was melancholy enough in the sunless grey afternoon, even without the signs of neglect which wrung the book-collector's heart. The walls, panelled to half their height with book-cases, ran up in plaster to the moulded ceiling. Damp had blotched them into grotesque shapes, and here and there were ugly cracks and squamous patches, from which the plaster had fallen in yellowish flakes. A wet chill seemed to ooze from the books, from the calf bindings peeling and perishing, from the stains of greenish mildew which spread horridly from volume to volume. The curious musty odour of decayed leather and damp paper added to the general cheerlessness of the atmosphere.

"Oh, dear, dear!" said Wimsey, peering dismally into this sepulchre of forgotten learning. With his shoulders hunched like the neck-feathers of a chilly bird, with his long nose and half-shut eyes, he resembled a dilapidated heron, brooding over the stagnation of a wintry pool.

"What a freezing-cold place," exclaimed Mrs. Hancock. "You really ought to scold Mrs. Lovall, Mr. Burdock. When she was put in here as caretaker, I said to my husband—didn't I, Philip?—that your father had chosen the laziest woman in Little Doddering. She ought to have kept up big fires here, *at least* twice a week! It's really shameful, the way she has let things go."

"Yes, isn't it?" agreed Haviland.

Wimsey said nothing. He was nosing along the shelves, every now and then taking a volume down and glancing at it.

"It was always rather a depressing room," went on Haviland. "I remember, when I was a kid, it used to over-awe me rather. Martin and I used to browse about among the books, you know, but I think we were always afraid that something or somebody would stalk out upon us from the dark corners. What's that you've got there, Lord Peter? Oh, *Foxe's Book of Martyrs*. Dear me! How those pictures did terrify me in the old days! And there was a *Pilgrim's Progress*, with a most alarming picture of Apollyon straddling over the whole breadth of the way, which gave me many nightmares. Let me see. It used to live over in this bay, I think. Yes, here it is. How it does bring it all back to be sure! Is it valuable, by the way?"

"No, not really. But this first edition of Burton is worth money; badly spotted, though—you'd better send it to be cleaned. And this is an extremely fine Boccaccio; take care of it."

"John Boccace—*The Dance of Machabree*. It's a good title, anyhow. Is that the same Boccaccio that wrote the naughty stories?"

"Yes," said Wimsey, a little shortly. He resented this attitude towards Boccaccio.

"Never read them," said Haviland, with a wink at his wife, "but I've seen 'em in the windows of those surgical shops—so I suppose they're naughty, eh? The vicar's looking shocked."

"Oh, not at all," said Mr. Hancock, with a conscientious assumption of broad-mindedness. "*Et ego in Arcadia*—that is to say, one doesn't enter the Church without undergoing a classical education, and making the acquaintance of much more worldly authors even than Boccaccio. Those woodcuts are very fine, to my uninstructed eye."

"Very fine indeed," said Wimsey.

"There's another old book I remember, with jolly pictures," said Haviland. "A chronicle of some sort—what's 'is name—place in Germany—*you* know—where that hangman came from. They published his diary the other day. I read it, but it wasn't really exciting; not half as gruesome as old Harrison Ainsworth. What's the name of the place?"

"Nüremberg?" suggested Wimsey.

"That's it, of course—the *Nüremberg Chronicle*. I wonder if that's still in its old place. It was over here by the window, if I remember rightly."

He led the way to the end of one of the bays, which ran up close against a window. Here the damp seemed to have done its worst. A pane of glass was broken, and rain had blown in.

"Now where has it gone to? A big book, it was, with a stamped leather binding. I'd like to see the old *Chronicle* again. I haven't set eyes on it for donkey's years."

His glance roamed vaguely over the shelves. Wimsey, with the book-lover's instinct, was the first to spot the *Chronicle*, wedged at the extreme end of the shelf, against the outer wall. He hitched his finger into the top edge of the spine, but finding that the rotting leather was ready to crumble at a touch, he dislodged a neighbouring book and drew the *Chronicle* gently out, using his whole hand.

"Here he is—in pretty bad condition, I'm afraid. Hullo!"

As he drew the book away from the wall, a piece of folded parchment came away with it and fell at his feet. He stooped and picked it up.

"I say, Burdock—isn't this what you've been looking for?"

Haviland Burdock, who had been rooting about on one of the lower shelves, straightened himself quickly, his face red from stooping.

"By Jove!" he said, turning first redder and then pale with excitement. "Look at this, Winnie. It's the governor's will. What an extraordinary thing! Whoever would have thought of looking for it here, of all places?"

"Is it really the will?" cried Mrs. Hancock.

"No doubt about it, I should say," observed Wimsey coolly. "Last Will and Testament of Simon Burdock." He stood, turning the grimy document over and over in his hands, looking from the endorsement to the plain side of the folded parchment.

"Well, well!" said Mr. Hancock. "How strange! It seems almost providential that you should have taken that book down."

"What does the will say?" demanded Mrs. Burdock, in some excitement.

"I beg your pardon," said Wimsey, handing it over to her. "Yes, as you say, Mr. Hancock, it does almost seem as if I was meant to find it." He glanced down again at the *Chronicle*, mournfully tracing with his finger the outline of a damp stain which had rotted the cover and spread to the inner pages, almost obliterating the colophon.

Haviland Burdock meanwhile had spread the will out on the nearest table. His wife leaned over his shoulder. The Hancocks, barely controlling their curiosity, stood near, awaiting the result. Wimsey, with an elaborate pretence of non-interference in this family matter, examined the wall against which the *Chronicle* had stood, feeling its moist surface and examining the damp-stains. They had assumed the appearance of a grinning face. He compared them with the corresponding mark on the book, and shook his head desolately over the damage.

Mr. Frobisher-Pym, who had wandered away some time before and was absorbed in an ancient book of Farriery, now approached, and enquired what the excitement was about.

"Listen to this!" cried Haviland. His voice was quiet, but a suppressed triumph throbbed in it and glittered from his eyes.

" 'I bequeath everything of which I die possessed'—there's a lot of enumeration of properties here, which doesn't matter—'to my eldest son, Martin'—"

Mr. Frobisher-Pym whistled.

"Listen! 'To my eldest son Martin, for so long as my body shall remain above ground. But so soon as I am buried, I direct that the whole of this property shall revert to my younger son Haviland absolutely'—"

"Good God!" said Mr. Frobisher-Pym.

"There's a lot more," said Haviland, "but that's the gist of it."

"Let me see," said the magistrate.

He took the will from Haviland, and read it through with a frowning face.

"That's right," he said. "No possible doubt about it. Martin has had his property and lost it again. How very curious. Up till yesterday everything belonged to him, though nobody knew it. Now it is all yours, Burdock. This certainly is the strangest will I ever saw. Just fancy that. Martin the heir, up to the time of the funeral. And now—well, Burdock, I must congratulate you."

"Thank you," said Haviland. "It is very unexpected." He laughed unsteadily.

"But what a queer idea!" cried Mrs. Burdock. "Suppose Martin had been at home. It almost seems a mercy that he wasn't, doesn't it? I mean, it would all have been so awkward. What would have happened if he had tried to stop the funeral, for instance?"

"Yes," said Mrs. Hancock. "Could he have done anything? Who decides about funerals?"

"The executors, as a rule," said Mr. Frobisher-Pym.

"Who are the executors in this case?" enquired Wimsey.

"I don't know. Let me see." Mr. Frobisher-Pym examined the document again. "Ah, yes! Here we are. 'I appoint my two sons, Martin and Haviland, joint executors of this my will.' What an extraordinary arrangement."

"I call it a wicked, un-Christian arrangement," cried Mrs. Hancock. "It might have caused dreadful mischief if the will hadn't been—quite providentially—lost!"

"Hush, my dear!" said her husband.

"I'm afraid," said Haviland grimly, "that that was my father's idea. It's no use my pretending he wasn't spiteful; he was, and I believe he hated both Martin and me like poison."

"Don't say that," pleaded the vicar.

"I do say it. He made our lives a burden to us, and he obviously wanted to go on making them a burden after he was dead. If he'd seen us cutting each other's throats, he'd only have been too pleased. Come, vicar, it's no use pretending. He hated our mother and was jealous of us. Everybody knows that. It probably pleased his unpleasant sense of humour to think of us squabbling over his body. Fortunately, he overreached himself when he hid the will here. He's buried now, and the problem settles itself."

"Are you quite sure of that?" said Wimsey.

"Why, of course," said the magistrate. "The property goes to Mr. Haviland Burdock as soon as his father's body is underground. Well, his father was buried yesterday."

"But are you sure of *that?*" repeated Wimsey. He looked from one to the other quizzically, his long lips curling into something like a grin.

"Sure of that?" exclaimed the vicar. "My dear Lord Peter, you were present at the funeral. You saw him buried yourself."

"I saw his coffin buried," said Wimsey mildly. "That the body was in it is merely an unverified inference."

"I think," said Mr. Frobisher-Pym, "this is rather an unseemly kind of jest. There is no reason to imagine that the body was not in the coffin."

"I saw it in the coffin," said Haviland, "and so did my wife."

"And so did I," said the vicar. "I was present when it was transferred from the temporary shell in which it crossed over from the States to a permanent lead-and-oak coffin provided by Joliffe. And, if further witnesses are necessary, you can easily get Joliffe himself and his men, who put the body in and screwed it down."

"Just so," said Wimsey. "I'm not denying that the body was in the coffin when the coffin was placed in the chapel. I only doubt whether it was there when it was put in the ground."

"That is a most unheard-of suggestion to make, Lord Peter," said Mr. Frobisher-Pym, with severity. "May I ask if you have anything to go upon? And, if the body is not in the grave, perhaps you wouldn't mind telling us where you imagine it to be?"

"Not at all," said Wimsey. He perched himself on the edge of the table and sat, swinging his legs and looking down at his own hands, as he ticked his points off on his fingers.

"I think," he said, "that this story begins with young Rawlinson. He is a clerk in the office of Mr. Graham, who drew up this will, and I fancy he knows something about its conditions. So, of course, does Mr. Graham, but I don't somehow suspect *him* of being mixed up in this. From what I can hear, he is not a man to take sides—or not Mr. Martin's side at any rate.

"When the news of Mr. Burdock's death was cabled over from the States, I think young Rawlinson remembered the terms of the will, and considered that Mr. Martin—being abroad and all that—would be rather at a disadvantage. Rawlinson must be rather attached to your brother, by the way——"

"Martin always had a way of picking up good-for-nothing youths and wasting his time with them," agreed Haviland sulkily.

The vicar seemed to feel that this statement needed some amendment, and murmured that he had always heard how good Martin was with the village lads.

"Quite so," said Wimsey. "Well, I think young Rawlinson wanted to give Martin an equal chance of securing the legacy, don't you see. He didn't like to say anything about the will—which might or might not turn up—and possibly he thought that even if it did turn up there might be difficulties. Well, anyway, he decided that the best thing to do was to steal the body and keep it above-ground till Martin came home to see to things himself."

"This is an extraordinary accusation," began Mr. Frobisher-Pym.

"I dare say I'm mistaken," said Wimsey, "but it's just my idea. It makes a damn good story, anyhow—you see! Well, then, young Rawlinson saw that this was too big a job to carry out alone, so he looked round for somebody to help him. And he pitched on Mr. Mortimer."

"Mortimer?"

"I don't know Mr. Mortimer personally, but he seems to be a sportin' sort of customer from what I can hear, with certain facilities which everybody hasn't got. Young Rawlinson and Mortimer put their heads together and worked out a plan of action. Of course, Mr. Hancock, you helped them enormously with this lying-in-state idea of yours. Without that, I don't know if they could have worked it."

Mr. Hancock made an embarrassed clucking sound.

"The idea was this. Mortimer was to provide an antique fly and four white horses, made up with luminous paint and black cloth to represent the Burdock death-coach. The advantage of that idea was that nobody would feel inclined to inspect the turn-out too closely if they saw it hangin' round the churchyard at unearthly hours. Meanwhile, young Rawlinson had to get himself accepted as a watcher for the chapel, and to find a sporting companion to watch with him and take a hand in the game. He fixed things up with the publican-fellow, and spun a tale for Mr. Hancock, so as to get the vigil from four to six. Didn't it strike you as odd, Mr. Hancock, that he should be so keen to come all the way from Herriotting?"

"I am accustomed to find keenness in my congregation," said Mr. Hancock stiffly.

"Yes, but Rawlinson didn't belong to your congregation. Anyway it was all worked out, and there was a dress-rehersal on the Wednesday night, which frightened your man Plunkett into fits, sir."

"If I thought this was true——" said Mr. Frobisher-Pym.

"On Thursday night," pursued Wimsey, "the conspirators were ready, hidden in the chancel at two in the morning. They waited till Mrs. and Miss Hancock had taken their places, and then made a row to attract their attention. When the ladies courageously advanced to find out what was up, they popped out and bundled 'em into the vestry."

"Good gracious!" said Mrs. Hancock.

"That was when the death-coach affair was timed to drive up to the south door. It came round the Back Lane, I fancy, though I can't be sure. Then Mortimer and the other two took the embalmed body out of the coffin and filled its place up with bags of sawdust. I know it was sawdust, because I found the remains of it on the Lady-chapel floor in the morning. They put the body in the fly, and Mortimer drove off with it. They passed me on the Herriotting road at half-past two, so they can't have wasted much time over the job. Mortimer may have been alone, or possibly he had someone with him to see to the body while he himself did the headless coachman business in a black mask. I'm not certain about that. They drove through the last gate before you come to the fork at Frimpton, and went across the fields to Mortimer's barn. They left the fly there—I know that, because I saw it, and I saw the bran they used to muffle the horses' hoofs, too. I expect they took it on from there in a car, and fetched the horses up next day—but that's a detail. I don't know, either, where they took the body to, but I expect, if you went and asked Mortimer about it, he would be able to assure you that it was still above ground."

Wimsey paused. Mr. Frobisher-Pym and the Hancocks were looking only puzzled and angry, but Haviland's face was green. Mrs. Haviland showed a red, painted spot on each cheek, and her mouth was haggard. Wimsey picked up the *Nüremberg Chronicle* and caressed its covers thoughtfully as he went on.

"Meanwhile, of course, young Rawlinson and his companion were doing the camouflage in the church, to give the idea of a Protestant outrage. Having fixed everything up neat and pretty, all they had to do was to lock themselves up in the furnace-house and chuck the key through the window. You'll probably find it there, Mr. Hancock, if you care to look. Didn't you think that story of an assault by two or three men was a bit thin? Hubbard is a hefty great fellow, and Rawlinson's a sturdy lad—and yet, on their own showing, they were bundled into a coal-hole like helpless infants, without a scratch on either of 'em. Look for the men in buckram, my dear sir, look for the men in buckram!"

"Look here, Wimsey, are you sure you're not romancing?" said Mr. Frobisher-Pym. "One would need some very clear proof before—"

"Certainly," said Wimsey. "Get a Home Office order. Open the grave. You'll soon see whether it's true or whether it's just my diseased imagination."

"I think this whole conversation is disgusting," cried Mrs. Burdock. "Don't listen to it, Haviland. Anything more heartless on the day after father's funeral than sitting here and inventing such a revolting story I simply can't imagine. It is not worth paying a moment's attention to. You will certainly not permit your father's body to be disturbed. It's horrible. It's a desecration."

"It is very unpleasant indeed," said Mr. Frobisher-Pym gravely, "but if Lord Peter is seriously putting forward this astonishing theory, which I can scarcely credit—"

Wimsey shrugged his shoulders.

"—then I feel bound to remind you, Mr. Burdock, that your brother, when he returns, may insist on having the matter investigated."

"But he can't, can he?" said Mrs. Burdock.

"Of course he can, Winnie," snapped her husband savagely. "He's an executor. He has as much right to have the governor dug up as I have to forbid it. Don't be a fool."

"If Martin had any decency, he would forbid it, too," said Mrs. Burdock.

"Oh, well!" said Mrs. Hancock, "shocking as it may seem, there's the money to be considered. Mr. Martin might think it a duty to his wife, and his family, if he should ever have any—"

"The whole thing is preposterous," said Haviland decidedly. "I don't believe a word of it. If I did, naturally I should be the first person to take action in the matter—not only in justice to Martin, but on my own account. But if you ask me to believe that a responsible man like Mortimer would purloin a corpse and desecrate a church—the thing only has to be put into plain words to show how absurd and unthinkable it is. I suppose Lord Peter Wimsey, who consorts, as I understand, with criminals and police officers, finds the idea conceivable. I can only say that I do not. I am sorry that his mind should have become so blunted to all decent feeling. That's all. Good afternoon."

Mr. Frobisher-Pym jumped up.

"Come, come, Burdock, don't take that attitude. I am sure Lord Peter intended no discourtesy. I must say I think he's all wrong, but, 'pon my soul, things have been so disturbed in the village these last few days, I'm not surprised anybody should think there was something behind it. Now, let's forget about it—and hadn't we better be moving out of this terribly cold room? It's nearly dinner-time. Bless me, what will Agatha think of us?"

Wimsey held out his hand to Burdock, who took it reluctantly.

"I'm sorry," said Wimsey. "I suffer from hypertrophy of the imagination, y'know. Over-stimulation of the thyroid probably. Don't mind me. I apologise, and all that."

"I don't think, Lord Peter," said Mrs. Burdock acidly, "you ought to exercise your imagination at the expense of good taste."

Wimsey followed her from the room in some confusion. Indeed, he was so disturbed that he carried away the *Nüremberg Chronicle* beneath his arm, which was an odd thing for him to do under the circumstances.

• • • • • • •

"I am gravely distressed," said Mr. Hancock.

He had come over, after Sunday evening service, to call upon the Frobisher-Pyms. He sat upright on his chair, his thin face flushed with anxiety.

"I could never have believed such a thing of Hubbard. It has been a grievous shock to me. It is not only the great wickedness of stealing a dead body from the very precincts of the church, though that is grave enough. It is the sad hypocrisy of his behaviour—the mockery of sacred things—the making use of the holy services of his religion to further worldly ends. He actually attended the funeral, Mr. Frobisher-Pym, and exhibited every sign of grief and respect. Even now he hardly seems to realise the sinfulness of his conduct. I feel it very much, as a priest and as a pastor—very much indeed."

"Oh, well, Hancock," said Mr. Frobisher-Pym, "you must make allowances, you know. Hubbard's not a bad fellow, but you can't expect refinement of feeling from a man of his class. The point is, what are we to do about it? Mr. Burdock must be told, of course. It's a most awkward situation. Dear me! Hubbard confessed the whole conspiracy, you say? How did he come to do that?"

"I taxed him with it," said the parson. "When I came to think over Lord Peter Wimsey's remarks, I was troubled in my mind. It seemed to me—I cannot say why—that there might be some truth in the story, wild as it appeared. I was so worried about it that I swept the floor of the Lady-chapel myself last night, and I found quite a quantity of sawdust among the sweepings. That led me to search for the key of the furnace-house, and I discovered it in some bushes at a little distance—in fact, within a stone's throw—of the furnace-house window. I sought guidance in prayer—and from my wife, whose judgment I greatly respect—and I made up my mind to speak to Hubbard after Mass. It was a great relief to me that he did not present himself at Early Celebration. Feeling as I did, I should have had scruples."

"Just so, just so," said the magistrate, a little impatiently. "Well, you taxed him with it, and he confessed?"

"He did. I am sorry to say he showed no remorse at all. He even laughed. It was a most painful interview."

"I am sure it must have been," said Mrs. Frobisher-Pym sympathetically.

"We must go and see Mr. Burdock," said the magistrate, rising. "Whatever old Burdock may or may not have intended by that iniquitous will of his, it's quite evident that Hubbard and Mortimer and Rawlinson were entirely in the wrong. Upon my word, I've no idea whether it's an indictable offence to steal a body. I must look it up. But I should say it was. If there is any property in a corpse, it must belong to the family or the executors. And in any case, it's sacrilege, to say nothing of the scandal in the parish. I must say,

Hancock, it won't do us any good in the eyes of the Nonconformists. However, no doubt you realise that. Well, it's an unpleasant job, and the sooner we tackle it the better. I'll run over to the vicarage with you and help you to break it to the Burdocks. How about you, Wimsey? You were right, after all, and I think Burdock owes you an apology."

"Oh, I'll keep out of it," said Wimsey. "I shan't be exactly *persona grata*, don't you know. It's going to mean a deuce of a big financial loss to the Haviland Burdocks."

"So it is. Most unpleasant. Well, perhaps you're right. Come along, vicar."

Wimsey and his hostess sat discussing the matter by the fire for half an hour or so, when Mr. Frobisher-Pym suddenly put his head in and said: "I say, Wimsey—we're all going over to Mortimer's. I wish you'd come and drive the car. Merridew always has the day off on Sunday, and I don't care about driving at night, particularly in this fog."

"Right you are," said Wimsey. He ran upstairs and came down in a few moments wearing a heavy leather flying-coat, and with a parcel under his arm. He greeted the Burdocks briefly, climbed into the driving-seat, and was soon steering cautiously through the mist along the Herriotting Road.

He smiled a little grimly to himself as they came up under the trees to the spot where the phantom coach had passed him. As they passed the gate through which the ingenious apparition had vanished, he indulged himself by pointing it out, and was rewarded by hearing a snarl from Haviland. At the well-remembered fork, he took the right-hand turning into Frimpton and drove steadily for six miles or so, till a warning shout from Mr. Frobisher-Pym summoned him to look out for the turning up to Mortimer's.

Mr. Mortimer's house, with its extensive stabling and farm buildings, stood about two miles back from the main road. In the darkness Wimsey could see little of it; but he noticed that the ground-floor windows were all lit up, and, when the door opened to the magistrate's imperative ring, a loud burst of laughter from the interior gave evidence that Mr. Mortimer was not taking his misdoings too seriously.

"Is Mr. Mortimer at home?" demanded Mr. Frobisher-Pym, in the tone of a man not to be trifled with.

"Yes, sir. Will you come in, please?"

They stepped into a large, old-fashioned hall, brilliantly lit, and made cosy with a heavy oak screen across the door. As Wimsey advanced, blinking, from the darkness, he saw a large, thick-set man, with a ruddy face, advancing with hand outstretched in welcome.

"Frobisher-Pym! By Jove! how decent of you to come over! We've got some old friends of yours here. Oh!" (in a slightly altered tone) "Burdock! Well, well—"

"Damn you!" said Haviland Burdock, thrusting furiously past the magistrate, who was trying to hold him back. "Damn you, you swine! Chuck this bloody farce. What have you done with the body?"

"The body, eh?" said Mr. Mortimer, retreating in some confusion.

"Yes, curse you! Your friend Hubbard's split. It's no good denying it.

What the devil do you mean by it? You've got the body here somewhere. Where is it? Hand it over!"

He strode threateningly round the screen into the lamplight. A tall, thin man rose up unexpectedly from the depths of an armchair and confronted him.

"Hold hard, old man!"

"Good God!" said Haviland, stepping heavily back on Wimsey's toes. "Martin!"

"Sure," said the other. "Here I am. Come back like a bad halfpenny. How are you?"

"So *you're* at the bottom of this!" stormed Haviland. "I might have known it. You damned, dirty hound! I suppose you think it's decent to drag your father out of his coffin and tote him about the country like a circus. It's degrading. It's disgusting. It's abominable. You must be perfectly dead to all decent feeling. You don't deny it, I suppose?"

"I say, Burdock!" expostulated Mortimer.

"Shut up, curse you!" said Haviland. "I'll deal with you in a minute. Now, look here, Martin, I'm not going to stand any more of this disgraceful behaviour. You'll give up that body, and——"

"Just a moment, just a moment," said Martin. He stood, smiling a little, his hands thrust into the pockets of his dinner-jacket. "This *éclaircissement* seems to be rather public. Who are all these people? Oh, it's the vicar, I see. I'm afraid we owe you a little explanation, vicar. And, er——"

"This is Lord Peter Wimsey," put in Mr. Frobisher-Pym, "who discovered your—I'm afraid, Burdock, I must agree with your brother in calling it your disgraceful plot."

"Oh, Lord!" said Martin. "I say, Mortimer, you didn't know you were up against Lord Peter Wimsey, did you? No wonder the cat got out of the bag. The man's known to be a perfect Sherlock. However, I seem to have got home at the crucial moment, so there's no harm done. Diana, this is Lord Peter Wimsey—my wife."

A young and pretty woman in a black evening dress greeted Wimsey with a shy smile, and turned deprecatingly to her brother-in-law.

"Haviland, we want to explain——"

He paid no attention to her.

"Now then, Martin, the game's up."

"I think it is, Haviland. But why make all this racket?"

"Racket! I like that. You take your own father's body out of its coffin——"

"No, no, Haviland. I knew nothing of it. I swear that. I only got the news of his death a few days ago. We were right out in the wilds, filming a show in the Pyrenees, and I came straight back as soon as I could get away. Mortimer here, with Rawlinson and Hubbard, staged the whole show by themselves. I never heard a word about it till yesterday morning in Paris, when I found his letter waiting at my old digs. Honestly, Haviland, I had nothing to do with it. Why should I? I didn't need to."

"Well, if I'd been here, I should only have had to speak to stop the funeral altogether. Why on earth should I have gone to the trouble of stealing the body? Quite apart from the irreverence and all that. As it is, when Mortimer told me about it, I must say I was a bit revolted at the idea, though I appreciated the kindness and the trouble they'd been to on my account. I think Mr. Hancock has most cause for wrath, really. But Mortimer has been as careful as possible, sir—really he has. He has placed the old governor quite reverently and decently in what used to be the chapel, and put flowers round him and so on. You will be quite satisfied, I'm sure."

"What do you mean?"

"Yes, yes," said Mortimer. "No disrespect intended, don't you know. Come and see him."

"This is dreadful," said the vicar helplessly.

"They had to do the best they could, don't you see, in my absence," said Martin. "As soon as I can, I'll make proper arrangements for a suitable tomb—above ground, of course. Or possibly cremation would fit the case."

"What!" gasped Haviland. "Do you mean to say you imagine I'm going to let my father stay unburied, simply because of your disgusting greed about money?"

"My dear chap, do you think I'm going to let you put him underground, simply to enable you to grab my property?"

"I'm the executor of his will, and I say he shall be buried, whether you like it or not!"

"And *I'm* an executor too—and I say he shan't be buried. He can be kept absolutely decently above ground, and he shall be."

"But hear me," said the vicar, distracted between these two disagreeable and angry young men.

"I'll see what Graham says about you," bawled Haviland.

"Oh, yes—the honest lawyer, Graham," sneered Martin. "*He* knew what was in the will, didn't he? I suppose he didn't mention it to *you*, by any chance?"

"He did not," retorted Haviland. "He knew too well the sort of skunk *you* were to say anything about it. Not content with disgracing us with your miserable, blackmailing marriage——"

"Mr. Burdock, Mr. Burdock——"

"Take care, Haviland!"

"You have no more decency——"

"Stop it!"

"Than to steal your father's body and my money so that you and your damned wife can carry on your loose-living, beastly ways with a parcel of film-actors and chorus-girls——"

"Now then, Haviland. Keep your tongue off my wife and my friends. How about your own? Somebody told me Winnie'd been going the pace pretty well—next door to bankruptcy, aren't you, with the gees and the tables and God knows what! No wonder you want to do your brother out of his money. I never thought much of you, Haviland, but by God——"

"One moment!"

Mr. Frobisher-Pym at last succeeded in asserting himself, partly through the habit of authority, and partly because the brothers had shouted themselves breathless.

"One moment, Martin. I will call you so, because I have known you a long time, and your father too. I understand your anger at the things Haviland has said. They were unpardonable, as I am sure he will realise when he comes to his right mind. But you must remember that he has been greatly shocked and upset—as we all have been—by this very very painful business. And it is not fair to say that Haviland has tried to 'do you out' of anything. He knew nothing about this iniquitous will, and he naturally saw to it that the funeral arrangements were carried out in the usual way. You must settle the future amicably between you, just as you would have done had the will not been accidentally mislaid. Now, Martin—and Haviland too—think it over. My dear boys, this scene is simply appalling. It really must not happen. Surely the estate can be divided up in a friendly manner between you. It is horrible that an old man's body should be a bone of contention between his own sons, just over a matter of money."

"I'm sorry," said Martin. "I forgot myself. You're quite right, sir. Look here, Haviland, forget it. I'll let you have half the money——"

"Half the money! But it's all mine. *You'll* let me have half? How damned generous! My own money!"

"No, old man. It's mine at the moment. The governor's not buried yet, you know. That's right, isn't it, Mr. Frobisher-Pym?"

"Yes; the money is yours, legally, at this moment. You must see that, Haviland. But your brother offers you half, and——"

"Half! I'm damned if I'll take half. The man's tried to swindle me out of it. I'll send for the police, and have him put in gaol for robbing the Church. You see if I don't. Give me the telephone."

"Excuse me," said Wimsey. "I don't want to butt in on your family affairs any more than I have already, but I really don't advise you to send for the police."

"*You* don't, eh? What the hell's it got to do with you?"

"Well," said Wimsey deprecatingly, "if this will business comes into court, I shall probably have to give evidence, because I was the bird who found the thing, don't you see?"

"Well, then?"

"Well, then. They might ask how long the will was supposed to have been where I found it."

Haviland appeared to swallow something which obstructed his speech.

"What about it, curse you!"

"Yes. Well, you see, it's rather odd when you come to think of it. I mean, your late father must have hidden that will in the bookcase before he went abroad. That was—how long ago? Three years? Five years?"

"About four years."

"Quite. And since then your bright caretaker has let the damp get into the library, hasn't she? No fires, and the window getting broken, and so on.

Ruinous to the books. Very distressin' to anybody like myself, you know. Yes. Well, supposin' they asked that question about the will—and you said it had been there in the damp for four years. Wouldn't they think it a bit funny if I told 'em that there was a big damp stain like a grinning face on the end of the bookshelf, and a big, damp, grinning face on the jolly old *Nüremberg Chronicle* to correspond with it, and no stain on the will which had been sittin' for four years between the two?"

Mrs. Haviland screamed suddenly. "Haviland! You fool! You utter fool!"

"Shut up!"

Haviland snapped round at his wife with a cry of rage, and she collapsed into a chair, with her hand snatched to her mouth.

"Thank you, Winnie," said Martin. "No, Haviland—don't trouble to explain. Winnie's given the show away. So you knew—you *knew* about the will, and you deliberately hid it away and let the funeral go on. I'm immensely obliged to you—nearly as obliged as I am to the discreet Graham. Is it fraud or conspiracy or what, to conceal wills? Mr. Frobisher-Pym will know."

"Dear, dear!" said the magistrate. "Are you certain of your facts, Wimsey?"

"Positive," said Wimsey, producing the *Nüremberg Chronicle* from under his arm. "Here's the stain—you can see it yourself. Forgive me for having borrowed your property, Mr. Burdock. I was rather afraid Mr. Haviland might think this little discrepancy over in the still watches of the night, and decide to sell the *Chronicle*, or give it away, or even think it looked better without its back pages and cover. Allow me to return it to you, Mr. Martin—intact. You will perhaps excuse my saying that I don't very much admire any of the rôles in this melodrama. It throws, as Mr. Pecksniff would say, a sad light on human nature. But I resent extremely the way in which I was wangled up to that bookshelf and made to be the bright little independent witness who found the will. I may be an ass, Mr. Haviland Burdock, but I'm not a bloody ass. Good night. I will wait in the car till you are all ready."

Wimsey stalked out with some dignity.

Presently he was followed by the vicar and by Mr. Frobisher-Pym.

"Mortimer's taking Haviland and his wife to the station," said the magistrate. "They're going back to town at once. You can send their traps off in the morning, Hancock. We'd better make ourselves scarce."

Wimsey pressed the self-starter.

As he did so, a man ran hastily down the steps and came up to him. It was Martin.

"I say," he muttered. "You've done me a good turn—more than I deserve, I'm afraid. You must think I'm a damned swine. But I'll see the old man decently put away, and I'll share with Haviland. You mustn't judge him too hardly, either. That wife of his is an awful woman. Run him over head and ears in debt. Bust up his business. I'll see it's all squared up. See? Don't want you to think us too awful."

"Oh, right-ho!" said Wimsey.

He slipped in the clutch, and faded away into the wet, white fog.

THE ARROW OF GOD

by Leslie Charteris

CHAPTER ONE

ONE OF Simon Templar's stock criticisms of the classic type of detective story is that the victim of the murder, the reluctant spark-plug of all the entertaining mystery and strife, is usually a mere nonentity who wanders vaguely through the first few pages with the sole purpose of becoming a convenient body in the library by the end of Chapter One. But what his own feelings and problems may have been, the personality which has to provide so many people with adequate motives for desiring him to drop dead, is largely a matter of hearsay, retrospectively brought out in the conventional process of drawing attention to one suspect after another.

"You could almost," Simon has said, "call him a *corpus derelicti*. . . . Actually, the physical murder should only be the mid-point of the story: the things that led up to it are at least as interesting as the mechanical solution of who done it. . . . Personally, I've killed very few people that I didn't know plenty about first."

Coming from a man who is generally regarded as almost a detective-story character himself, this comment is at least worth recording for reference; but it certainly did not apply to the shuffling off of Mr Floyd Vosper, which caused a brief commotion on the island of New Providence in the early spring of that year.

CHAPTER TWO

WHY SIMON TEMPLAR should have been in Nassau (which, for the benefit of the untraveled, is the city of New Providence, which is an island in the Bahamas) at the time is one of those questions which always arise in stories about him, and which can only be answered by repeating that he liked to travel and was just as likely to show up there as in Nova Zembla or Namaqualand. As for why he should have been invited to the house of Mrs Herbert H Wexall, that is another irrelevancy which is hardly covered by the fact that he could just as well have shown up at the house of Joe Wallenski (of the arsonist Wallenskis) or the White House—he had friends in many places, legitimate and otherwise. But Mrs Wexall had some international renown as a lion hunter, even if her stalking had been confined to the variety which roars loudest in plush drawing rooms; and it was not to be expected that the advent of such a creature as Simon Templar would have escaped the attention of her salon safari.

Thus one noontime Simon found himself strolling up the driveway and into what little was left of the life of Floyd Vosper. Naturally he did not know this at the time; nor did he know Floyd Vosper, except by name. In this he was no different from at least fifty million other people in that hemisphere; for Floyd Vosper was not only one of the most widely syndicated pundits of the day, but his books (*Feet of Clay; As I Saw Them;* and *The Twenty Worst Men in the World*) had all been the selections of one book club or another and still sold by the million in reprints. For Mr Vosper specialized in the ever-popular sport of shattering reputations. In his journalistic years he had met, and apparently had unique opportunities to study, practically every great name in the national and international scene, and could unerringly remember everything in their biographies that they would prefer forgotten, and could impale and epitomize all their weaknesses with devastatingly pinpoint precision, leaving them naked and squirming on the operating table of his vocabulary. But what this merciless professional iconoclast was like as a person, Simon had never heard or bothered much to wonder about.

So the first impression that Vosper made on him was a voice, a still unidentified voice, a dry and deliberate and peculiarly needling voice, which came from behind a bank of riotous hibiscus and oleander.

"My dear Janet," it said, "you must not let your innocent admiration for Reggie's bulging biceps color your estimate of his perspicacity in world affairs. The title of All-American, I hate to disillusion you, has no reference to statesmanship."

There was a rather strained laugh that must have come from Reggie, and a girl's clear young voice said: "That isn't fair, Mr Vosper. Reggie doesn't pretend to be a genius, but he's bright enough to have a wonderful job waiting for him on Wall Street."

"I don't doubt that he will make an excellent contact man for the more stupid clients," conceded the voice with the measured nasal gripe. "And I'm sure that his education can cope with the simple arithmetic of the Stock Exchange, just as I'm sure it can grasp the basic figures of your father's Dun and Bradstreet. This should not dazzle you with his brilliance, any more than it should make you believe that you have some spiritual fascination that lured him to your feet."

At this point Simon rounded a curve in the driveway and caught his first sight of the speakers, all of whom looked up at him with reserved curiosity and two-thirds of them with a certain hint of relief.

There was no difficulty in assigning them to their lines—the young redheaded giant with the pleasantly rugged face and the slim pretty blonde girl, who sat at a wrought-iron table on the terrace in front of the house with a broken deck of cards in front of them which established an interrupted game of gin rummy, and the thin stringy man reclining in a long cane chair with a cigarette-holder in one hand and a highball glass in the other.

Simon smiled and said: "Hello. This is Mrs Wexall's house, is it?"

The girl said "Yes," and he said: "My name's Templar, and I was invited here."

The girl jumped up and said: "Oh, yes. Lucy told me. I'm her sister, Janet Blaise. This is my fiancé, Reg Herrick. And Mr Vosper."

Simon shook hands with the two men, and Janet said: "I think Lucy's on the beach. I'll take you around."

Vosper unwound his bony length from the long chair, looking like a slightly dissolute and acidulated mahatma in his white shorts and burnt chocolate tan.

"Let me do it," he said. "I'm sure you two ingénues would rather be alone together. And I need another drink."

He led the way, not into the house but around it, by a flagged path which struck off to the side and meandered through a bower of scarlet poinciana. A breeze rustled in the leaves and mixed flower scents with the sweetness of the sea. Vosper smoothed down his sparse gray hair; and Simon was aware that the man's beady eyes and sharp thin nose were cocked towards him with brash speculation, as if he were already measuring another target for his tongue.

"Templar," he said. "Of course, you must be the Saint—the fellow they call the Robin Hood of modern crime."

"I see you read the right papers," said the Saint pleasantly.

"I read all the papers," Vosper said, "in order to keep in touch with the vagaries of vulgar taste. I've often wondered why the Robin Hood legend should have so much romantic appeal. Robin Hood, as I understand it, was a bandit who indulged in some well-publicized charity—but not, as I recall, at the expense of his own stomach. A good many unscrupulous promoters have also become generous—and with as much shrewd publicity—when their ill-gotten gains exceeded their personal spending capacity, but I don't remember that they succeeded in being glamorized for it."

"There may be some difference," Simon suggested, "in who was robbed to provide the surplus spoils."

"Then," Vosper said challengingly, "you consider yourself an infallible judge of who should be penalized and who should be rewarded."

"Oh, no," said the Saint modestly. "Not at all. No more, I'm sure, than you would call yourself the infallible judge of all the people that you dissect so definitively in print."

He felt the other's probing glance stab at him suspiciously and almost with puzzled incredulity, as if Vosper couldn't quite accept the idea that anyone had actually dared to cross swords with him, and moreover might have scored at least even on the riposte—or if it had happened at all, that it had been anything but a semantic accident. But the Saint's easily inscrutable poise gave no clue to the answer at all; and before anything further could develop there was a paragraphic distraction.

This took the form of a man seated on top of a truncated column which for reasons best known to the architect had been incorporated into the design of a wall which curved out from the house to encircle a portion of the shore like a possessive arm. The man had long curly hair that fell to his shoulders, which with his delicate ascetic features would have made him look more like a woman if it had not been complemented with an equally curly and silken beard. He sat cross-legged and upright, his hands folded symmetrically in his lap, staring straight out into the blue sky a little above the horizon, so motionless and almost rigid that he might easily have been taken for a tinted statue except for the fluttering of the long flowing white robe he wore.

After rolling with the first reasonable shock of the apparition, Simon would have passed on politely without comment, but the opportunity was irresistible for Vosper to display his virtuosity again, and perhaps also to recover from his momentary confusion.

"That fugitive from a Turkish bath," Vosper said, in the manner of a tired guide to a geek show, "calls himself Astron. He's a nature boy from the Dardanelles who just concluded a very successful season in Hollywood. He wears a beard to cover a receding chin, and long hair to cover a hole in the head. He purifies his soul with a diet of boiled grass and prune juice. Whenever this diet lets him off the pot, he meditates. After he was brought to the attention of the Western world by some engineers of the Anglo-Mongolian Oil Company, whom he cures of stomach ulcers by persuading them not to spike their ration of sacramental wine with rubbing alcohol, he began to meditate about the evils of earthly riches."

"Another member of our club?" Simon prompted innocuously.

"Astron maintains," Vosper said, leaning against the pillar and giving out as oracularly as if the object of his dissertation were not sitting on it at all, "that the only way for the holders of worldly wealth to purify themselves is to get rid of as much of it as they can spare. Being himself so pure that it hurts, he is unselfishly ready to become the custodian of as much corrupting cabbage as they would like to get rid of. Of course, he would have no part of it himself, but he will take the responsibility of parking it in a shrine in the Sea of Marmora which he plans to build as soon as there is enough kraut in the kitty."

The figure on the column finally moved. Without any waste motion, it simply expanded its crossed legs like a lazy tongs until it towered at its full height over them.

"You have heard the blasphemer," it said. "But I say to you that his words are dust in the wind, as he himself is dust among the stars that I see."

"I'm a blasphemer," Vosper repeated to the Saint, with a sort of derisive pride combined with the ponderous bonhomie of a vaudeville old-timer in a routine with a talking dog. He looked back up at the figure of the white-robed mystic towering above him, and said: "So if you have this direct pipeline to the Almighty, why don't you strike me dead?"

"Life and death are not in my hands," Astron said, in a calm and confident voice. "Death can only come from the hands of the Giver of all Life. In His own good time He will strike you down, and the arrow of God will silence your mockeries. This I have seen in the stars."

"Quaint, isn't he?" Vosper said, and opened the gate between the wall and the beach.

Beyond the wall a few steps led down to a kind of Grecian courtyard open on the seaward side, where the paving merged directly into the white sand of the beach. The courtyard was furnished with gaily colored lounging chairs and a well-stocked pushcart bar, to which Vosper immediately directed himself.

"You have visitors, Lucy," he said, without letting it interfere with the important work of reviving his highball.

Out on the sand, on a towel spread under an enormous beach umbrella, Mrs Herbert Wexall rolled over and said: "Oh, Mr Templar."

Simon went over and shook hands with her as she stood up. It was hard to think of her as Janet Blaise's sister, for there were at least twenty years between them and hardly any physical resemblances. She was a big woman with an open homely face and patchily sun-bleached hair and a sloppy figure, but she made a virtue of those disadvantages by the cheerfulness with which she ignored them. She was what is rather inadequately known as "a person," which means that she had the personality to dispense with appearances and the money to back it up.

"Good to see you," she said, and turned to the man who had been sitting beside her, as he struggled to his feet. "Do you know Arthur Gresson?"

Mr Gresson was a full head shorter than the Saint's six foot two, but he weighed a good deal more. Unlike anyone else that Simon had encountered on the premises so far, his skin looked as if it was unaccustomed to exposure. His round body and his round balding brow, under a liberal sheen of oil, had the hot rosy blush which the kiss of the sun evokes in virgin epidermis.

"Glad to meet you, Mr Templar." His hand was soft and earnestly adhesive.

"I expect you'd like a drink," Lucy Wexall said. "Let's keep Floyd working."

They joined Vosper at the bar wagon, and after he had started to work on the orders she turned back to the Saint and said: "After this formal service, just make yourself at home. I'm so glad you could come."

"I'm sure Mr Templar will be happy," Vosper said. "He's a man of the world like I am. We enjoy Lucy's food and liquor, and in return we give her the pleasure of hitting the society columns with our names. A perfectly businesslike exchange."

"That's progress for you," Lucy Wexall said breezily. "In the old days I'd have had a court jester. Now all I get is a professional stinker."

"That's no way to refer to Arthur," Vosper said, handing Simon a long cold glass. "For your information, Templar, Mr Gresson–Mr Arthur *Granville* Gresson–is a promoter. He has a long history of selling phony oil stock behind him. He is just about to take Herb Wexall for another sucker; but since Herb married Lucy he can afford it. Unless you're sure you can take Janet away from Reggie, I advise you not to listen to him."

Arthur Gresson's elbow nudged Simon's ribs.

"What a character!" he said, almost proudly.

"I only give out with facts," Vosper said. "My advice to you, Templar, is, never be an elephant. Resist all inducements. Because when you reach back into that memory, you will only be laughed at, and the people who should thank you will call you a stinker."

Gresson giggled, deep from his round pink stomach.

"Would you like to get in a swim before lunch?" Lucy Wexall said. "Floyd, show him where he can change."

"A pleasure," Vosper said. "And probably a legitimate part of the bargain."

He thoughtfully refilled his glass before he steered Simon by way of the verandah into the beachward side of the house, and into a bedroom. He sat on the bed and watched unblinkingly while Simon stripped down and pulled on the trunks he had brought with him.

"It must be nice to have the Body Beautiful," he observed. "Of course, in your business it almost ranks with plant and machinery, doesn't it?"

The Saint's blue eyes twinkled.

"The main difference," he agreed goodhumoredly, "is that if I get a screw loose it may not be so noticeable."

As they were starting back through the living room, a small birdlike man in a dark and (for the setting outside the broad picture window) incongruous business suit bustled in by another door. He had the bright baggy eyes behind rimless glasses, the slack but fleshless jowls, and the wide tight mouth which may not be common to all lawyers, bankers, and business executives, but which is certainly found in very few other vocations; and he was followed by a statuesque brunette whose severe tailoring failed to disguise an outstanding combination of curves, who carried a notebook and a sheaf of papers.

"Herb!" Vosper said. "I want you to meet Lucy's latest addition to the menagerie which already contains Astron and me–Mr Simon Templar, known as the Saint. Templar–your host, Mr Wexall."

"Pleased to meet you," said Herbert Wexall, shaking hands briskly.

"And this is Pauline Stone," Vosper went on, indicating the nubile brunette. "The tired business man's consolation. Whatever Lucy can't supply, she can."

"How do you do," said the girl stoically.

Her dark eyes lingered momentarily on the Saint's torso, and he noticed that her mouth was very full and soft.

"Going for a swim?" Wexall said, as if he had heard nothing. "Good. Then I'll see you at lunch, in a few minutes."

He trotted busily on his way, and Vosper ushered the Saint to the beach by another flight of steps that led directly down from the verandah. The house commanded a small half-moon bay, and both ends of the crescent of sand were naturally guarded by abrupt rises of jagged coral rock.

"Herbert is the living example of how really stupid a successful business man can be," Vosper said tirelessly. "He was just an office-boy of some kind in the Blaise outfit when he got smart enough to woo and win the boss's daughter. And from that flying start, he was clever enough to really pay his way by making Blaise Industries twice as big as even the old man himself had been able to do. And yet he's dumb enough to think that Lucy won't catch on to the extracurricular functions of that busty secretary sooner or later—or that when she does he won't be out on a cold doorstep in the rain. . . . No, I'm not going in. I'll hold your drink for you."

Simon ran down into the surf and churned seawards for a couple of hundred yards, then turned over and paddled lazily back, co-ordinating his impressions with idle amusement. The balmy water was still refreshing after the heat of the morning, and when he came out the breeze had become brisk enough to give him the luxury of a fleeting shiver as the wetness started to evaporate from his tanned skin.

He crossed the sand to the Greek patio, where Floyd Vosper was on duty again at the bar in a strategic position to keep his own needs supplied with a minimum of effort. Discreet servants were setting up a buffet table. Janet Blaise and Reg Herrick had transferred their gin rummy game and were playing at a table right under the column where Astron had resumed his seat and his cataleptic meditations—a weird juxtaposition of which the three members all seemed equally unconscious.

Simon took Lucy Wexall a Martini and said with another glance at the tableau: "Where did you find him?"

"The people who brought him to California sent him to me when he had to leave the States. They gave me such a good time when I was out there, I couldn't refuse to do something for them. He's writing a book, you know, and of course he can't go back to that dreadful place he came from, wherever it is, before he has a chance to finish it in reasonable comfort."

Simon avoided discussing this assumption, but he said: "What's it like, having a resident prophet in the house?"

"He's very interesting. And quite as drastic as Floyd, in his own way, in summing up people. You ought to talk to him."

Arthur Gresson came over with an hors d'oeuvre plate of smoked salmon and stuffed eggs from the buffet. He said: "Anyone you meet at Lucy's is interesting, Mr Templar. But if you don't mind my saying so, you have it all over the rest of 'em. Who'd ever think we'd find the Saint looking for crime in the Bahamas?"

"I hope no one will think I'm looking for crime," Simon said deprecatingly, "any more than I take it for granted that you're looking for oil."

"That's where you'd be wrong," Gresson said. "As a matter of fact, I am."

The Saint raised an eyebrow.

"Well, I can always learn something. I'd never heard of oil in the Bahamas."

"I'm not a bit surprised. But you will, Mr Templar, you will." Gresson sat down, pillowing his round stomach on his thighs. "Just think for a moment about some of the places you have heard of, where there is certainly oil. Let me mention them in a certain order. Mexico, Texas, Louisiana, and the recent strike in the Florida Everglades. We might even include Venezuela in the south. Does that suggest anything to you?"

"Hm-mm," said the Saint thoughtfully.

"A pattern," Gresson said. "A vast central pool of oil somewhere under the Gulf of Mexico, with oil wells dipping into it from the edges of the bowl, where the geological strata have also been forced up. Now think of the islands of the Caribbean as the eastern edge of the same bowl. Why not?"

"It's a hell of an interesting theory," said the Saint.

"Mr Wexall thinks so too, and I hope he's going into partnership with me."

"Herbert can afford it," intruded the metallic sneering voice of Floyd Vosper. "But before you decide to buy in, Templar, you'd better check with New York about the time when Mr Gresson thought he could dig gold in the Catskills."

"Shut up, Floyd," said Mrs Wexall, "and get me another Martini."

Arthur Granville Gresson chuckled in his paunch like a happy Buddha. "What a guy!" he said. "What a ribber. And he gets everyone mad. He kills me!"

Herbert Wexall came down from the verandah and beamed around. As a sort of tacit announcement that he had put aside his work for the day, he had changed into a sport shirt on which various exotic animals were depicted wandering through an idealized jungle, but he retained his business trousers and business shoes and business face.

"Well," he said, inspecting the buffet and addressing the world at large. "Let's come and get it whenever we're hungry."

As if a spell had been snapped, Astron removed himself from the contemplation of the infinite, descended from his pillar, and began to help himself to cottage cheese and caviar on a foundation of lettuce leaves.

Simon drifted in the same direction, and found Pauline Stone beside him, saying: "What do you feel like, Mr Templar?"

Her indication of having come off duty was a good deal more radical than her employer's. In fact, the bathing suit which she had changed into seemed to be based more on the French minimums of the period than on any British tradition. There was no doubt that she filled it opulently; and her question amplified its suggestiveness with undertones which the Saint felt it wiser not to challenge at that moment.

"There's so much to drool over," he said, referring studiously to the buffet table. "But that green turtle aspic looks pretty good to me."

She stayed with him when he carried his plate to a table as thoughtfully diametric as possible from the berth chosen by Floyd Vosper, even though

Astron had already settled there in temporary solitude. They were promptly joined by Reg Herrick and Janet Blaise, and slipped at once into an easy exchange of banalities.

But even then it was impossible to escape Vosper's tongue. It was not many minutes before his saw-edged voice whined across the patio above the general level of harmless chatter:

"When are you going to tell the Saint's fortune, Astron? That ought to be worth hearing."

There was a slightly embarrassed lull, and then everyone went on talking again; but Astron looked at the Saint with a gentle smile and said quietly: "You are a seeker after truth, Mr Templar, as I am. But when instead of truth you find falsehood, you will destroy it with a sword. I only say 'This is falsehood, and God will destroy it. Do not come too close, lest you be destroyed with it.'"

"Okay," Herrick growled, just as quietly. "But if you're talking about Vosper, it's about time someone destroyed it."

"Sometimes," Astron said, "God places His arrow in the hand of a man."

For a few moments that seemed unconscionably long nobody said anything; and then before the silence spread beyond their small group the Saint said casually: "Talking of arrows—I hear that the sport this season is to go hunting sharks with a bow and arrow."

Herrick nodded with a healthy grin.

"It's a lot of fun. Would you like to try it?"

"Reggie's terrific," Janet Blaise said. "He shoots like a regular Howard Hill, but of course he uses a bow that nobody else can pull."

"I'd like to try," said the Saint, and the conversation slid harmlessly along the tangent he had provided.

After lunch everyone went back to the beach, with the exception of Astron, who retired to put his morning's meditations on paper. Chatter surrendered to an afternoon torpor which even subdued Vosper.

An indefinite while later, Herrick aroused with a yell and plunged roaring into the sea, followed by Janet Blaise. They were followed by others, including the Saint. An interlude of aquatic brawling developed somehow into a pick-up game of touch football on the beach, which was delightfully confused by recurrent arguments about who was supposed to be on which of the unequal sides. This boisterous nonsense churned up so much sand for the still freshening breeze to spray over Floyd Vosper, who by that time had drunk enough to be trying to sleep under the big beach umbrella, that the misanthropic oracle finally got back on his feet.

"Perhaps," he said witheringly, "I had better get out of the way of you perennial juveniles before you convert me into a dune."

He stalked off along the beach and lay down again about a hundred yards away. Simon noticed him still there, flat on his face and presumably unconscious, when the game eventually broke up through a confused water-polo phase to leave everyone gasping and laughing and dripping on the patio with no immediate resurge of inspiration. It was the last time he saw the unpopular Mr Vosper alive.

"Well," Arthur Gresson observed, mopping his short round body with a towel, "at least one of us seems to have enough sense to know when to lie down."

"And to choose the only partner who'd do it with him," Pauline added vaguely.

Herbert Wexall glanced along the beach in the direction that they both referred to, then glanced for further inspiration at the waterproof watch he was still wearing.

"It's almost cocktail time," he said. "How about it, anyone?"

His wife shivered, and said: "I'm starting to freeze my tail off. It's going to blow like a son-of-a-gun any minute. Let's all go in and get some clothes on first—then we'll be set for the evening. You'll stay for supper of course, Mr Templar?"

"I hadn't planned to make a day of it," Simon protested diffidently, and was promptly overwhelmed from all quarters.

He found his way back to the room where he had left his clothes without the benefit of Floyd Vosper's chatty courier service, and made leisured and satisfactory use of the fresh-water shower and monogrammed towels. Even so, when he sauntered back into the living room, he almost had the feeling of being lost in a strange and empty house, for all the varied individuals who had peopled the stage so vividly and vigorously a short time before had vanished into other and unknown seclusions and had not yet returned.

He lighted a cigarette and strolled idly towards the picture window that overlooked the verandah and the sea. Everything around his solitude was so still, excepting the subsonic suggestion of distant movements within the house, that he was tempted to walk on tiptoe; and yet outside the broad pane of plate glass the fronds of coconut palms were fluttering in a thin febrile frenzy, and there were lacings of white cream on the incredible jade of the short waves simmering on the beach.

He noticed, first, in what should have been a lazily sensual survey of the panorama, that the big beach umbrella was no longer where he had first seen it, down to his right outside the pseudo-Grecian patio. He saw, as his eye wandered on, that it had been moved a hundred yards or so to his left—in fact, to the very place where Floyd Vosper was still lying. It occurred to him first that Vosper must have moved it himself, except that no shade was needed in the brief and darkening twilight. After that he noticed that Vosper seemed to have turned over on his back; and then at last as the Saint focused his eyes he saw with a weird thrill that the shaft of the umbrella stood straight up out of the left side of Vosper's scrawny brown chest, not in the sand beside him at all, but like a gigantic pin that had impaled a strange and inelegant insect—or, in a fantastic phrase that was not Simon's at all, like the arrow of God.

CHAPTER THREE

MAJOR RUPERT FANSHIRE, the senior Superintendent of Police, which made him third in the local hierarchy after the Commissioner and Deputy Commissioner, paid tribute to the importance of the case by taking personal charge of it. He was a slight pinkish blond man with rather large and very bright blue eyes and such a discreetly modulated voice that it commanded rapt attention through the basic effort of trying to hear what it was saying. He sat at an ordinary writing desk in the living room, with a Bahamian sergeant standing stiffly beside him, and contrived to turn the whole room into an office in which seven previously happy-go-lucky adults wriggled like guilty schoolchildren whose teacher has been found libelously caricatured on their blackboard.

He said, with wholly impersonal conciseness: "Of course, you all know by now that Mr Vosper was found on the beach with the steel spike of an umbrella through his chest. My job is to find out how it happened. So to start with, if anyone did it to him, the topography suggests that that person came from, or through, this house. I've heard all your statements, and all they seem to amount to is that each of you was going about his own business at the time when this might have happened."

"All I know," Herbert Wexall said, "is that I was in my study, reading and signing the letters that I dictated this morning."

"And I was getting dressed," said his wife.

"So was I," said Janet Blaise.

"I guess I was in the shower," said Reginald Herrick.

"I was having a bubble bath," said Pauline Stone.

"I was still working," said Astron. "This morning I started a new chapter of my book—in my mind, you understand. I do not write by putting everything on paper. For me it is necessary to meditate, to feel, to open floodgates in my mind, so that I can receive the wisdom that comes from beyond the——"

"Quite," Major Fanshire assented politely. "The point is that none of you have alibis, if you need them. You were all going about your own business, in your own rooms. Mr Templar was changing in the late Mr Vosper's room——"

"I wasn't here," Arthur Gresson said recklessly. "I drove back to my own place—I'm staying at the Fort Montagu Beach Hotel. I wanted a clean shirt. I drove back there, and when I came back here all this had happened."

"There's not much difference," Major Fanshire said. "Dr Horan tells me we couldn't establish the time of death within an hour or two, anyway. . . . So the next thing we come to is the question of motive. Did anyone here," Fanshire said almost innocently, "have any really serious trouble with Mr Vosper?"

There was an uncomfortable silence, which the Saint finally broke by saying: "I'm on the outside here, so I'll take the rap. I'll answer for everyone."

The Superintendent cocked his bright eyes.

"Very well, sir. What would you say?"

"My answer," said the Saint, "is—everybody."

There was another silence, but a very different one, in which it seemed, surprisingly, as if all of them relaxed as unanimously as they had stiffened before. And yet, in its own way, this relaxation was as self-conscious and uncomfortable as the preceding tension had been. Only the Saint, who had every attitude of the completely careless onlooker, and Major Fanshire, whose deferential patience was impregnably correct, seemed immune to the interplay of hidden strains.

"Would you care to go any further?" Fanshire asked.

"Certainly," said the Saint. "I'll go anywhere. I can say what I like, and I don't have to care whether anyone is on speaking terms with me tomorrow. I'll go on record with my opinion that the late Mr Vosper was one of the most unpleasant characters I've ever met. I'll make the statement, if it isn't already general knowledge, that he made a specialty of needling everyone he spoke to or about. He goaded everyone with nasty little things that he knew, or thought he knew, about them. I wouldn't blame anyone here for wanting, at least theoretically, to kill him."

"I'm not exactly concerned with your interpretation of blame," Fanshire said detachedly. "But if you have any facts, I'd like to hear them."

"I have no facts," said the Saint coolly. "I only know that in the few hours I've been here, Vosper made statements to me, a stranger, about everyone here, any one of which could be called fighting words."

"You will have to be more specific," Fanshire said.

"Okay," said the Saint. "I apologize in advance to anyone it hurts. Remember, I'm only repeating the kind of thing that made Vosper a good murder candidate. . . . I am now specific. In my hearing, he called Reg Herrick a dumb athlete who was trying to marry Janet Blaise for her money. He suggested that Janet was a stupid juvenile for taking him seriously. He called Astron a commercial charlatan. He implied that Lucy Wexall was a dope and a snob. He inferred that Herb Wexall had more use for his secretary's sex than for her stenography, and he thought out loud that Pauline was amenable. He called Mr Gresson a crook to his face."

"And during all this," Fanshire said, with an inoffensiveness that had to be heard to be believed, "he said nothing about you?"

"He did indeed," said the Saint. "He analyzed me, more or less, as a flamboyant phony."

"And you didn't object to that?"

"I hardly could," Simon replied blandly, "after I'd hinted to him that I thought he was even phonier."

It was a line on which a stage audience could have tittered, but the tensions of the moment let it sink with a slow thud.

Fanshire drew down his upper lip with one forefinger and nibbled it inscrutably.

"I expect this bores you as much as it does me, but this is the job I'm paid for. I've got to say that all of you had the opportunity, and from what Mr Templar says you could all have had some sort of motive. Well, now I've got to look into what you might call the problem of physical possibility."

Simon Templar lighted a cigarette. It was the only movement that anyone made, and after that he was the most intent listener of them all as Fanshire went on: "Dr Horan says, and I must say I agree with him, that to drive that umbrella shaft clean through a man's chest must have taken quite exceptional strength. It seems to be something that no woman, and probably no ordinary man, could have done."

His pale bright eyes came to rest on Herrick as he finished speaking, and the Saint found his own eyes following others in the same direction.

The picture formed in his mind, the young giant towering over a prostrate Vosper, the umbrella raised in his mighty arms like a fantastic spear and the setting sun flaming on his red head, like an avenging angel, and the thrust downwards with all the power of those Herculean shoulders . . . and then, as Herrick's face began to flush under the awareness of so many stares, Janet Blaise suddenly cried out: "No! No—it couldn't have been Reggie!"

Fanshire's gaze transferred itself to her curiously, and she said in a stammering rush: "You see, it's silly, but we didn't quite tell the truth, I mean about being in our own rooms. As a matter of fact, Reggie was in my room most of the time. We were—talking."

The Superintendent cleared his throat and continued to gaze at her stolidly for a while. He didn't make any comment. But presently he looked at the Saint in the same dispassionately thoughtful way that he had first looked at Herrick.

Simon said calmly: "Yes, I was just wondering myself whether I could have done it. And I had a rather interesting thought."

"Yes, Mr Templar?"

"Certainly it must take quite a lot of strength to drive a spike through a man's chest with one blow. But now remember that this wasn't just a spike, or a spear. It had an enormous great umbrella on top of it. Now think what would happen if you were stabbing down with a thing like that?"

"Well, what would happen?"

"The umbrella would be like a parachute. It would be like a sort of sky anchor holding the shaft back. The air resistance would be so great that I'm wondering how anyone, even a very strong man, could get much momentum into the thrust. And the more force he put into it, the more likely he'd be to lift himself off the ground, rather than drive the spike down."

Fanshire digested this, blinking, and took his full time to do it.

"That certainly is a thought," he admitted. "But damn it," he exploded, "we know it was done. So it must have been possible."

"There's something entirely backwards about that logic," said the Saint. "Suppose we say, if it was impossible, maybe it wasn't done."

"Now you're being a little ridiculous," Fanshire snapped. "We saw——"

"We saw a man with the sharp iron-tipped shaft of a beach umbrella through his chest. We jumped to the natural conclusion that somebody stuck it into him like a sword. And that may be just what a clever murderer meant us to think."

Then it was Arthur Gresson who shattered the fragile silence by leaping out of his chair like a bouncing ball.

"I've got it!" he yelped. "Believe me, everybody, I've got it! This'll kill you!"

"I hope not," Major Fanshire said dryly. "But what is it?"

"Listen," Gresson said. "I knew something rang a bell somewhere, but I couldn't place it. Now it all comes back to me. This is something I only heard at the hotel the other day, but some of you must have heard it before. It happened about a year ago, when Gregory Peck was visiting here. He stayed at the same hotel where I am, and one afternoon he was on the beach, and the wind came up, just like it did today, and it picked up one of those beach umbrellas and carried it right to where he was lying, and the point just grazed his ribs and gave him a nasty gash, but what the people who saw it happen were saying was that if it'd been just a few inches the other way, it could have gone smack into his heart, and you'd've had a film star killed in the most sensational way that ever was. Didn't you ever hear about that, Major?"

"Now you mention it," Fanshire said slowly, "I think I did hear something about it."

"Well," Gresson said, "*what if it happened again this afternoon, to someone who wasn't as lucky as Peck?*"

There was another of those electric silences of assimilation, out of which Lucy Wexall said: "Yes, I heard about that." And Janet said: "Remember, I told you about it! I was visiting some friends at the hotel that day, and I didn't see it happen, but I was there for the commotion."

Gresson spread out his arms, his round face gleaming with excitement and perspiration.

"That's got to be it!" he said. "You remember how Vosper was lying under the umbrella outside the patio when we started playing touch football, and he got sore because we were kicking sand over him, and he went off to the other end of the beach? But he didn't take the umbrella with him. The wind did that, after we all went off to change. And this time it didn't miss!"

Suddenly Astron stood up beside him; but where Gresson had risen like a jumping bean, this was like the growth and unfolding of a tree.

"I have heard many words," Astron said, in his firm gentle voice, "but now at last I think I am hearing truth. No man struck the blasphemer down. The arrow of God smote him, in his wickedness and his pride, as it was written long ago in the stars."

"You can say that again," Gresson proclaimed triumphantly. "He sure had it coming."

Again the Saint drew at his cigarette and created his own vision behind half-closed eyes. He saw the huge umbrella plucked from the sand by the invisible fingers of the wind, picked up and hurled spinning along the deserted twilight beach, its great mushroom spread of gaudy canvas no longer a drag now but a sail for the wind to get behind, the whole thing transformed into a huge unearthly dart flung with literally superhuman power, the arrow of God indeed. A fantastic, an almost unimaginable solution; and yet it did not have to be imagined because there were witnesses that it had actually almost happened once before. . . .

Fanshire was saying: "By Jove, that's the best suggestion I've heard yet—without any religious implication, of course. It sounds as if it could be the right answer!"

Simon's eyes opened on him fully for an instant, almost pityingly, and then closed completely as the true and right and complete answer rolled through the Saint's mind like a long peaceful wave.

"I have one question to ask," said the Saint.

"What's that?" Fanshire said, too politely to be irritable, yet with a trace of impatience, as if he hated the inconvenience of even defending such a divinely tailored theory.

"Does anyone here have a gun?" asked the Saint.

There was an almost audible creaking of knitted brows, and Fanshire said: "Really, Mr Templar, I don't quite follow you."

"I only asked," said the Saint imperturbably, "if anyone here had a gun. I'd sort of like to know the answer before I explain why."

"I have a revolver," Wexall said with some perplexity. "What about it?"

"Could we see it, please?" said the Saint.

"I'll get it," said Pauline Stone.

She got up and left the room.

"You know I have a gun, Fanshire," Wexall said. "You gave me my permit. But I don't see——"

"Neither do I," Fanshire said.

The Saint said nothing. He devoted himself to his cigarette, with impregnable detachment, until the voluptuous secretary came back. Then he put out the cigarette and extended his hand.

Pauline looked at Wexall, hesitantly, and at Fanshire. The Superintendent nodded a sort of grudging acquiescence. Simon took the gun and broke it expertly.

"A Colt .38 Detective Special," he said. "Unloaded." He sniffed the barrel. "But fired quite recently," he said, and handed the gun to Fanshire.

"I used it myself this morning," Lucy Wexall said cheerfully. "Janet and Reg and I were shooting at the Portuguese men-of-war. There were quite a lot of them around before the breeze came up."

"I wondered what the noise was," Wexall said vaguely.

"I was coming up the drive when I heard it first," Gresson said, "and I thought the next war had started."

"This is all very int'resting," Fanshire said, removing the revolver barrel from the proximity of his nostrils with a trace of exasperation, "but I don't see what it has to do with the case. Nobody has been shot——"

"Major Fanshire," said the Saint quietly, "may I have a word with you, outside? And will you keep that gun in your pocket so that at least we can hope there will be no more shooting?"

The Superintendent stared at him for several seconds, and at last unwillingly got up.

"Very well, Mr Templar." He stuffed the revolver into the side pocket of his rumpled white jacket, and glanced back at his impassive chocolate sentinel. "Sergeant, see that nobody leaves here, will you?"

He followed Simon out on to the verandah and said almost peremptorily: "Come on now, what's this all about?"

It was so much like a flash of a faraway Scotland Yard Inspector that the Saint had to control a smile. But he took Fanshire's arm and led him persuasively down the front steps to the beach. Off to their left a tiny red glowworm blinked low down under the silver stars.

"You still have somebody watching the place where the body was found," Simon said.

"Of course," Fanshire grumbled. "As a matter of routine. But the sand's much too soft to show any footprints, and——"

"Will you walk over there with me?"

Fanshire sighed briefly, and trudged beside him. His politeness was dogged but unfailing. He was a type that had been schooled from adolescence never to give up, even to the ultimate in ennui. In the interests of total fairness, he would be game to the last yawn.

He did go so far as to say: "I don't know what you're getting at, but why *couldn't* it have been an accident?"

"I never heard a better theory in my life," said the Saint equably, "with one insuperable flaw."

"What's that?"

"Only," said the Saint, very gently, "that the wind wasn't blowing the right way."

Major Fanshire kept his face straight ahead to the wind and said nothing more after that until they reached the glowworm that they were making for and it became a cigarette-end that a constable dropped as he came to attention.

The place where Floyd Vosper had been lying was marked off in a square of tape, but there was nothing out of the ordinary about it except some small stains that showed almost black under the flashlight which the constable produced.

"May I mess up the scene a bit?" Simon asked.

"I don't see why not," Fanshire said doubtfully. "It doesn't show anything, really."

Simon went down on his knees and began to dig with his hands, around and under the place where the stains were. Minutes later he stood up, with sand trickling through his fingers, and showed Fanshire the mushroomed scrap of metal that he had found.

"A .38 bullet," Fanshire said, and whistled.

"And I think you'll be able to prove it was fired from the gun you have in your pocket," said the Saint. "Also you'd better have a sack of sand picked up from where I was digging. I think a laboratory examination will find that it also contains fragments of bone and human flesh."

"You'll have to explain this to me," Fanshire said quite humbly.

Simon dusted his hands and lighted a cigarette.

"Vosper was lying on his face when I last saw him," he said, "and I think he was as much passed out as sleeping. With the wind and the surf and the soft sand, it was easy for the murderer to creep up on him and shoot him in the back where he lay. But the murderer didn't want you looking for guns and comparing bullets. The umbrella was the inspiration. I don't have to remind you that the exit hole of a bullet is much larger than the entrance. By turning Vosper's body over, the murderer found a hole in his chest that it can't have been too difficult to force the umbrella shaft through—obliterating the original wound and confusing everybody in one simple operation."

"Let's get back to the house," said the Superintendent abruptly.

After a while, as they walked, Fanshire said: "It's going to feel awfully funny, having to arrest Herbert Wexall."

"Good God!" said the Saint, in honest astonishment. "You weren't thinking of doing that?"

Fanshire stopped and blinked at him under the still distant light of the uncurtained windows.

"Why not?"

"Did Herbert seem at all guilty when he admitted he had a gun? Did he seem at all uncomfortable—I don't mean just puzzled, like you were—about having it produced? Was he ready with the explanation of why it still smelled of being fired?"

"But if anyone else used Wexall's gun," Fanshire pondered laboriously, "why should they go to such lengths to make it look as if no gun was used at all, when Wexall would obviously have been suspected?"

"Because it was somebody who didn't want Wexall to take the rap," said the Saint. "Because Wexall is the goose who could still lay golden eggs—but he wouldn't do much laying on the end of a rope, or whatever you do to murderers here."

The Superintendent pulled out a handkerchief and wiped his face.

"My God," he said, "you mean you think Lucy——"

"I think we have to go all the way back to the prime question of motive," said the Saint. "Floyd Vosper was a nasty man who made dirty cracks about everyone here. But his cracks were dirtiest because he always had a wickedly good idea what he was talking about. Nevertheless, very few people become murderers because of a dirty crack. Very few people except me kill other people on points of principle. Vosper called us all variously dupes, phonies, cheaters and fools. But since he had roughly the same description for all of us, we could all laugh it off. There was only one person about whom he made the unforgivable accusation. . . . Now shall we rejoin the mob?"

"You'd better do this your own way," Fanshire muttered.

Simon Templar took him up the steps to the verandah and back through the french doors into the living room, where all eyes turned to them in deathly silence.

"A paraffin test will prove who fired that revolver in the last twenty-four hours, aside from those who have already admitted it," Simon said, as if there had been no interruption. "And you'll remember, I'm sure, who supplied that very handy theory about the arrow of God."

"Astron!" Fanshire gasped.

"Oh, no," said the Saint, a little tiredly. "He only said that God sometimes places His arrow in the hands of a man. And I feel quite sure that a wire to New York will establish that there is actually a criminal file under the name of Granville, with fingerprints and photos that should match Mr Gresson's—as Vosper's fatally elephantine memory remembered. . . . That was the one crack he shouldn't have made, because it was the only one that was more than gossip or shrewd insult, the only one that could be easily proved, and the only one that had a chance of upsetting an operation which was all set—if you'll excuse the phrase—to make a big killing."

Major Fanshire fingered his upper lip.

"I don't know," he began; and then, as Arthur Granville Gresson began to rise like a floating balloon from his chair, and the ebony-faced sergeant moved to intercept him like a well-disciplined automaton, he knew.

I CAN FIND MY WAY OUT

by Ngaio Marsh

AT HALF-PAST SIX on the night in question, Anthony Gill, unable to eat, keep still, think, speak or act coherently, walked from his rooms to the Jupiter Theatre. He knew that there would be nobody backstage, that there was nothing for him to do in the theatre, that he ought to stay quietly in his rooms and presently dress, dine and arrive at, say, a quarter to eight. But it was as if something shoved him into his clothes, thrust him into the street and compelled him to hurry through the West End to the Jupiter. His mind was overlaid with a thin film of inertia. Odd lines from the play occurred to him, but without any particular significance. He found himself busily reiterating a completely irrelevant sentence: "She has a way of laughing that would make a man's heart turn over."

Piccadilly, Shaftesbury Avenue. "Here I go," he thought, turning into Hawke Street, "towards my play. It's one hour and twenty-nine minutes away. A step a second. It's rushing towards me. Tony's first play. Poor young Tony Gill. Never mind. Try again."

The Jupiter. Neon lights: I CAN FIND MY WAY OUT—*by Anthony Gill.* And in the entrance the bills and photographs. *Coralie Bourne with H. J. Bannington, Barry George and Canning Cumberland.*

Canning Cumberland. The film across his mind split and there was the Thing itself and he would have to think about it. How bad would Canning Cumberland be if he came down drunk? Brilliantly bad, they said. He would bring out all the tricks. Clever actor stuff, scoring off everybody, making a fool of the dramatic balance. "In Mr. Canning Cumberland's hands indifferent dialogue and unconvincing situations seemed almost real." What can you do with a drunken actor?

He stood in the entrance feeling his heart pound and his inside deflate and sicken.

Because, of course, it was a bad play. He was at this moment and for the first time really convinced of it. It was terrible. Only one virtue in it and that was not his doing. It had been suggested to him by Coralie Bourne: "I don't think the play you have sent me will do as it is but it has occurred to me—" It was a brilliant idea. He had rewritten the play round it and almost immediately and quite innocently he had begun to think of it as his own although he had said shyly to Coralie Bourne: "You should appear as joint author." She had quickly, over-emphatically, refused. "It was nothing at all," she said. "If you're to become a dramatist you will learn to get ideas from everywhere. A single situation is nothing. Think of Shakespeare," she added lightly. "Entire plots! Don't be silly." She had said later, and still with the same hurried, nervous air: "Don't go talking to everyone about it. They will think there is more, instead of less, than meets the eye in my small suggestion. Please promise." He promised, thinking he'd made an error in taste when he suggested that Coralie Bourne, so famous an actress, should appear as joint author with an unknown youth. And how right she was, he thought, because, of course, it's going to be a ghastly flop. She'll be sorry she consented to play in it.

Standing in front of the theatre he contemplated nightmare possibilities. What did audiences do when a first play flopped? Did they clap a little, enough to let the curtain rise and quickly fall again on a discomforted group of players? How scanty must the applause be for them to let him off his own appearance? And they were to go on to the Chelsea Arts Ball. A hideous prospect. Thinking he would give anything in the world if he could stop his play, he turned into the foyer. There were lights in the offices and he paused, irresolute, before a board of photographs. Among them, much smaller than the leading players, was Dendra Gay with the eyes looking straight into his. *She had a way of laughing that would make a man's heart turn over*. "Well," he thought, "so I'm in love with her." He turned away from the photograph. A man came out of the office. "Mr. Gill? Telegrams for you."

Anthony took them and as he went out he heard the man call after him: "Very good luck for tonight, sir."

There were queues of people waiting in the side street for the early doors.

At six-thirty Coralie Bourne dialled Canning Cumberland's number and waited.

She heard his voice. "It's me," she said.

"O, God! darling, I've been thinking about you." He spoke rapidly, too loudly. "Coral, I've been thinking about Ben. You oughtn't to have given that situation to the boy."

"We've been over it a dozen times, Cann. Why not give it to Tony? Ben will never know." She waited and then said nervously, "Ben's gone, Cann. We'll never see him again."

"I've got a 'Thing' about it. After all, he's your husband."

"No, Cann, no."

"Suppose he turns up. It'd be like him to turn up."

"He won't turn up."

She heard him laugh. "I'm sick of all this," she thought suddenly. "I've had it once too often. I can't stand any more. . . . Cann," she said into the telephone. But he had hung up.

At twenty to seven, Barry George looked at himself in his bathroom mirror. "I've got a better appearance." he thought, "than Cann Cumberland. My head's a good shape, my eyes are bigger and my jaw line's cleaner. I never let a show down. I don't drink. I'm a better actor." He turned his head a little, slewing his eyes to watch the effect. "In the big scene," he thought, "I'm the star. He's the feed. That's the way it's been produced and that's what the author wants. I ought to get the notices."

Past notices came up in his memory. He saw the print, the size of the paragraphs; a long paragraph about Canning Cumberland, a line tacked on the end of it. "Is it unkind to add that Mr. Barry George trotted in the wake of Mr. Cumberland's virtuosity with an air of breathless dependability?" And again: "It is a little hard on Mr. Barry George that he should be obliged to act as foil to this brilliant performance." Worst of all: "Mr. Barry George succeeded in looking tolerably unlike a stooge, an achievement that evidently exhausted his resources."

"Monstrous!" he said loudly to his own image, watching the fine glow of indignation in the eyes. Alcohol, he told himself, did two things to Cann Cumberland. He raised his finger. Nice, expressive hand. An actor's hand. Alcohol destroyed Cumberland's artistic integrity. It also invested him with devilish cunning. Drunk, he would burst the seams of a play, destroy its balance, ruin its form and himself emerge blazing with a showmanship that the audience mistook for genius. "While I," he said aloud, "merely pay my author the compliment of faithful interpretation. Psha!"

He returned to his bedroom, completed his dressing and pulled his hat to the right angle. Once more he thrust his face close to the mirror and looked searchingly at its image. "By God!" he told himself, "he's done it once too often, old boy. Tonight we'll even the score, won't we? By God, we will."

Partly satisfied, and partly ashamed, for the scene, after all, had smacked a little of ham, he took his stick in one hand and a case holding his costume for the Arts Ball in the other, and went down to the theatre.

At ten minutes to seven, H. J. Bannington passed through the gallery queue on his way to the stage door alley, raising his hat and saying: "Thanks so much," to the gratified ladies who let him through. He heard them murmur his name. He walked briskly along the alley, greeted the stage-doorkeeper, passed under a dingy lamp, through an entry and so to the stage. Only working lights were up. The walls of an interior set rose dimly into shadow. Bob Reynolds, the stage-manager, came out through the prompt-entrance. "Hello, old boy," he said, "I've changed the dressing-rooms. You're third on the right: they've moved your things in. Suit you?"

"Better, at least, than a black-hole the size of a W.C. but without its appointments," H.J. said acidly. "I suppose the great Mr. Cumberland still has the star-room?"

"Well, yes, old boy."

"And who pray, is next to him? In the room with the other gas fire?"

"We've put Barry George there, old boy. You know what he's like."

"Only too well, old boy, and the public, I fear, is beginning to find out." H.J. turned into the dressing-room passage. The stage-manager returned to the set where he encountered his assistant. "What's biting *him?*" asked the assistant. "He wanted a dressing-room with a fire." "Only natural," said the A.S.M. nastily. "He started life reading gas meters."

On the right and left of the passage, nearest the stage end, were two doors, each with its star in tarnished paint. The door on the left was open. H.J. looked in and was greeted with the smell of greasepaint, powder, wet-white, and flowers. A gas fire droned comfortably. Coralie Bourne's dresser was spreading out towels. "Good evening, Katie, my jewel," said H.J. "La Belle not down yet?" "We're on our way," she said.

H.J. hummed stylishly: *"Bella filia del amore,"* and returned to the passage. The star-room on the right was closed but he could hear Cumberland's dresser moving about inside. He went on to the next door, paused, read the card, "Mr. Barry George," warbled a high derisive note, turned in at the third door and switched on the light.

Definitely not a second lead's room. No fire. A wash-basin, however, and opposite mirrors. A stack of telegrams had been placed on the dressing-table. Still singing he reached for them, disclosing a number of bills that had been tactfully laid underneath and a letter, addressed in a flamboyant script.

His voice might have been mechanically produced and arbitrarily switched off, so abruptly did his song end in the middle of a roulade. He let the telegrams fall on the table, took up the letter and tore it open. His face, wretchedly pale, was reflected and endlessly re-reflected in the mirrors.

At nine o'clock the telephone rang. Roderick Alleyn answered it. "This is Sloane 84405. No, you're on the wrong number. *No.*" He hung up and returned to his wife and guest. "That's the fifth time in two hours."

"Do let's ask for a new number."

"We might get next door to something worse."

The telephone rang again. "This is not 84406," Alleyn warned it. "No, I cannot take three large trunks to Victoria Station. No, I am not the Instant All Night Delivery. No."

"They're 84406," Mrs. Alleyn explained to Lord Michael Lamprey. "I suppose it's just faulty dialing, but you can't imagine how angry everyone gets. Why do you want to be a policeman?"

"It's a dull hard job, you know—" Alleyn began.

"Oh," Lord Mike said, stretching his legs and looking critically at his shoes, "I don't for a moment imagine I'll leap immediately into false whiskers and plainclothes. No, no. But I'm revoltingly healthy, sir. Strong as a horse. And I don't think I'm as stupid as you might feel inclined to imagine—"

The telephone rang.

"I say, do let me answer it," Mike suggested and did so.

"Hullo?" he said winningly. He listened, smiling at his hostess. "I'm afraid—" he began. "Here, wait a bit—Yes, but—" His expression became blank and complacent. "May I," he said presently, "repeat your order, sir? Can't be too sure, can we? Call at 11 Harrow Gardens, Sloane Square, for one suitcase to be delivered immediately at the Jupiter Theatre to Mr. Anthony Gill. Very good, sir. Thank you, sir. Collect. Quite."

He replaced the receiver and beamed at the Alleyns.

"What the devil have you been up to?" Alleyn said.

"He just simply wouldn't listen to reason. I tried to tell him."

"But it may be urgent," Mrs. Alleyn ejaculated.

"It couldn't be more urgent, really. It's a suitcase for Tony Gill at the Jupiter."

"Well, then—"

"I was at Eton with the chap," said Mike reminiscently. "He's four years older than I am so of course he was madly important while I was less than the dust. This'll learn him."

"I think you'd better put that order through at once," said Alleyn firmly.

"I rather thought of executing it myself, do you know, sir. It'd be a frightfully neat way of gate-crashing the show, wouldn't it? I did try to get a ticket but the house was sold out."

"If you're going to deliver this case you'd better get a bend on."

"It's clearly an occasion for dressing up though, isn't it? I say," said Mike modestly, "would you think it most frightful cheek if I—well I'd promise to come back and return everything. I mean—"

"Are you suggesting that my clothes look more like a vanman's than yours?"

"I thought you'd have things—"

"For Heaven's sake, Rory," said Mrs. Alleyn, "dress him up and let him go. The great thing is to get that wretched man's suitcase to him."

"I know," said Mike earnestly. "It's most frightfully sweet of you. That's how I feel about it."

Alleyn took him away and shoved him into an old and begrimed raincoat, a cloth cap and a muffler. "You wouldn't deceive a village idiot in a total eclipse," he said, "but out you go."

He watched Mike drive away and returned to his wife.

"What'll happen?" she asked.

"Knowing Mike, I should say he will end up in the front stalls and go on to supper with the leading lady. She, by the way, is Coralie Bourne. Very lovely and twenty years his senior so he'll probably fall in love with her." Alleyn reached for his tobacco jar and paused. "I wonder what's happened to her husband," he said.

"Who was he?"

"An extraordinary chap. Benjamin Vlasnoff. Violent temper. Looked like a bandit. Wrote two very good plays and got run in three times for common assault. She tried to divorce him but it didn't go through. I think he afterwards lit off to Russia." Alleyn yawned. "I believe she had a hell of a time with him," he said.

"All Night Delivery," said Mike in a hoarse voice, touching his cap.

"Suitcase. One." "Here you are," said the woman who had answered the door. "Carry it carefully, now, it's not locked and the catch springs out."

"Fanks," said Mike. "Much obliged. Chilly, ain't it?"

He took the suitcase out to the car.

It was a fresh spring night. Sloane Square was threaded with mist and all the lamps had halos round them. It was the kind of night when individual sounds separate themselves from the conglomerate voice of London; hollow sirens spoke imperatively down on the river and a bugle rang out over in Chelsea Barracks; a night, Mike thought, for adventure.

He opened the rear door of the car and heaved the case in. The catch flew open, the lid dropped back and the contents fell out. "Damn!" said Mike and switched on the inside light.

Lying on the floor of the car was a false beard.

It was flaming red and bushy and was mounted on a chin-piece. With it was incorporated a stiffened mustache. There were wire hooks to attach the whole thing behind the ears. Mike laid it carefully on the seat. Next he picked up a wide black hat, then a vast overcoat with a fur collar, finally a pair of black gloves.

Mike whistled meditatively and thrust his hands into the pockets of Alleyn's mackintosh. His right-hand fingers closed on a card. He pulled it out. "Chief Detective-Inspector Alleyn," he read, "C.I.D. New Scotland Yard."

"Honestly," thought Mike exultantly, "this is a gift."

Ten minutes later a car pulled into the curb at the nearest parking place to the Jupiter Theatre. From it emerged a figure carrying a suitcase. It strode rapidly along Hawke Street and turned into the stage-door alley. As it passed under the dirty lamp it paused, and thus murkily lit, resembled an illustration from some Edwardian spy-story. The face was completely shadowed, a black cavern from which there projected a square of scarlet beard, which was the only note of color.

The doorkeeper who was taking the air with a member of stage-staff, moved forward, peering at the stranger.

"Was you wanting something?"

"I'm taking this case in for Mr. Gill."

"He's in front. You can leave it with me."

"I'm so sorry," said the voice behind the beard, "but I promised I'd leave it backstage myself."

"So you will be leaving it. Sorry, sir, but no one's admitted be'ind without a card."

"A card? Very well. Here is a card."

He held it out in his black-gloved hand. The stage-doorkeeper, unwillingly removing his gaze from the beard, took the card and examined it under the light. "Coo!" he said, "what's up, governor?"

"No matter. Say nothing of this."

The figure waved its hand and passed through the door. " 'Ere!" said the doorkeeper excitedly to the stage-hand, "take a slant at this. That's a plain-clothes flattie, that was."

"*Plain* clothes!" said the stage-hand. "Them!"

"'E's disguised," said the doorkeeper. "That's what it is. 'E's disguised 'isself."

"'E's bloody well lorst 'isself be'ind them whiskers if you arst me."

Out on the stage someone was saying in a pitched and beautifully articulate voice: *"I've always loathed the view from these windows. However if that's the sort of thing you admire. Turn off the lights, damn you. Look at it."*

"Watch it, now, watch it," whispered a voice so close to Mike that he jumped. "O.K.," said a second voice somewhere above his head. The lights on the set turned blue. "Kill that working light." "Working light gone."

Curtains in the set were wrenched aside and a window flung open. An actor appeared, leaning out quite close to Mike, seeming to look into his face and saying very distinctly: "God: it's frightful!" Mike backed away towards a passage, lit only from an open door. A great volume of sound broke out beyond the stage. "House lights," said the sharp voice. Mike turned into the passage. As he did so, someone came through the door. He found himself face to face with Coralie Bourne, beautifully dressed and heavily painted.

For a moment she stood quite still; then she made a curious gesture with her right hand, gave a small breathy sound and fell forward at his feet.

Anthony was tearing his program into long strips and dropping them on the floor of the O.P. box. On his right hand, above and below, was the audience; sometimes laughing, sometimes still, sometimes as one corporate being, raising its hands and striking them together. As now; when down on the stage, Canning Cumberland, using a strange voice, and inspired by some inward devil, flung back the window and said: "God: it's frightful!"

"Wrong! Wrong!" Anthony cried inwardly, hating Cumberland, hating Barry George because he let one speech of three words over-ride him, hating the audience because they liked it. The curtain descended with a long sigh on the second act and a sound like heavy rain filled the theatre, swelled prodigiously and continued after the house lights welled up.

"They seem," said a voice behind him, "to be liking your play."

It was Gosset, who owned the Jupiter and had backed the show. Anthony turned on him stammering: "He's destroying it. It should be the other man's scene. He's stealing."

"My boy," said Gosset, "he's an actor."

"He's drunk. It's intolerable."

He felt Gosset's hand on his shoulder.

"People are watching us. You're on show. This is a big thing for you; a first play, and going enormously. Come and have a drink, old boy. I want to introduce you–"

Anthony got up and Gosset, with his arm across his shoulders, flashing smiles, patting him, led him to the back of the box.

"I'm sorry," Anthony said, "I can't. Please let me off. I'm going backstage."

"Much better not, old son." The hand tightened on his shoulder. "Listen, old son—" But Anthony had freed himself and slipped through the pass-door from the box to the stage.

At the foot of the breakneck stairs Dendra Gay stood waiting. "I thought you'd come," she said.

Anthony said: "He's drunk. He's murdering the play."

"It's only one scene, Tony. He finishes early in the next act. It's going colossally."

"But don't you understand—"

"I do. You *know* I do. But your success, Tony darling! You can hear it and smell it and feel it in your bones."

"Dendra—" he said uncertainly.

Someone came up and shook his hand and went on shaking it. Flats were being laced together with a slap of rope on canvas. A chandelier ascended into darkness. "Lights," said the stage-manager, and the set was flooded with them. A distant voice began chanting. "Last act, please. Last act."

"Miss Bourne all right?" the stage-manager suddenly demanded.

"She'll be all right. She's not on for ten minutes," said a woman's voice.

"What's the matter with Miss Bourne?" Anthony asked.

"Tony, I must go and so must you. Tony, it's going to be grand. *Please* think so. *Please.*"

"Dendra—" Tony began, but she had gone.

Beyond the curtain, horns and flutes announced the last act.

"Clear please."

The stage hands came off.

"House lights."

"House lights gone."

"Stand by."

And while Anthony still hesitated in the O.P. corner, the curtain rose. Canning Cumberland and H. J. Bannington opened the last act.

As Mike knelt by Coralie Bourne he heard someone enter the passage behind him. He turned and saw, silhouetted against the lighted stage, the actor who had looked at him through a window in the set. The silhouette seemed to repeat the gesture Coralie Bourne had used, and to flatten itself against the wall.

A woman in an apron came out of the open door.

"I say—here!" Mike said.

Three things happened almost simultaneously. The woman cried out and knelt beside him. The man disappeared through a door on the right.

The woman, holding Coralie Bourne in her arms, said violently: "Why have you come back?" Then the passage lights came on. Mike said: "Look here, I'm most frightfully sorry," and took off the broad black hat. The dresser gaped at him, Coralie Bourne made a crescendo sound in her throat and opened her eyes. "Katie?" she said.

"It's all right, my lamb. It's not him, dear. You're all right." The dresser jerked her head at Mike: "Get out of it," she said.

"Yes, of course, I'm most frightfully—" He backed out of the passage, colliding with a youth who said: "Five minutes, please." The dresser called out: "Tell them she's not well. Tell them to hold the curtain."

"No," said Coralie Bourne strongly. "I'm all right, Katie. Don't say anything. Katie, what was it?"

They disappeared into the room on the left.

Mike stood in the shadow of a stack of scenic flats by the entry into the passage. There was great activity on the stage. He caught a glimpse of Anthony Gill on the far side talking to a girl. The call-boy was speaking to the stage-manager who now shouted into space: "Miss Bourne all right?" The dresser came into the passage and called: "She'll be all right. She's not on for ten minutes." The youth began chanting: "Last act, please." The stage-manager gave a series of orders. A man with an eyeglass and a florid beard came from further down the passage and stood outside the set, bracing his figure and giving little tweaks to his clothes. There was a sound of horns and flutes. Canning Cumberland emerged from the room on the right and on his way to the stage, passed close to Mike, leaving a strong smell of alcohol behind him. The curtain rose.

Behind his shelter, Mike stealthily removed his beard and stuffed it into the pocket of his overcoat.

A group of stage-hands stood nearby. One of them said in a hoarse whisper: "'E's squiffy." "Garn, 'e's going good." "So 'e may be going good. And for why? *Becos* 'e's squiffy."

Ten minutes passed. Mike thought: "This affair has definitely not gone according to plan." He listened. Some kind of tension seemed to be building up on the stage. Canning Cumberland's voice rose on a loud but blurred note. A door in the set opened. "Don't bother to come," Cumberland said. "Goodbye. I can find my way out." The door slammed. Cumberland was standing near Mike. Then, very close, there was a loud explosion. The scenic flats vibrated, Mike's flesh leapt on his bones and Cumberland went into his dressing-rooms. Mike heard the key turn in the door. The smell of alcohol mingled with the smell of gunpowder. A stage-hand moved to a trestle table and laid a pistol on it. The actor with the eyeglass made an exit. He spoke for a moment to the stage-manager, passed Mike and disappeared in the passage.

Smells. There were all sorts of smells. Subconsciously, still listening to the play, he began to sort them out. Glue. Canvas. Greasepaint. The call-boy tapped on doors. "Mr. George, please." "Miss Bourne, please." They came out, Coralie Bourne with her dresser. Mike heard her turn a door handle and say something. An indistinguishable voice answered her. Then she and her dresser passed him. The others spoke to her and she nodded and then seemed to withdraw into herself, waiting with her head bent, ready to make her entrance. Presently she drew back, walked swiftly to the door in the set, flung it open and swept on, followed a minute later by Barry George.

Smells. Dust, stale paint, cloth. Gas. Increasingly, the smell of gas.

The group of stage-hands moved away behind the set to the side of the stage. Mike edged out of cover. He could see the prompt-corner. The stage-manager stood there with folded arms, watching the action. Behind him were grouped the players who were not on. Two dressers stood apart, watching. The light from the set caught their faces. Coralie Bourne's voice sent phrases flying like birds into the auditorium.

Mike began peering at the floor. Had he kicked some gas fitting adrift? The call-boy passed him, stared at him over his shoulder and went down the passage, tapping. "Five minutes to the curtain, please. Five minutes." The actor with the elderly make-up followed the call-boy out. "God, what a stink of gas," he whispered. "Chronic, ain't it?" said the call-boy. They stared at Mike and then crossed to the waiting group. The man said something to the stage-manager who tipped his head up, sniffing. He made an impatient gesture and turned back to the prompt-box, reaching over the prompter's head. A bell rang somewhere up in the flies and Mike saw a stage-hand climb to the curtain platform.

The little group near the prompt corner was agitated. They looked back towards the passage entrance. The call-boy nodded and came running back. He knocked on the first door on the right. "*Mr. Cumberland! Mr. Cumberland!* You're on for the call." He rattled the door handle. "*Mr. Cumberland! You're on.*"

Mike ran into the passage. The call-boy coughed retchingly and jerked his hand at the door. "Gas!" he said, "Gas!"

"Break it in."

"I'll get Mr. Reynolds."

He was gone. It was a narrow passage. From halfway across the opposite room Mike took a run, head down, shoulder forward, at the door. It gave a little and a sickening increase in the smell caught him in the lungs. A vast storm of noise had broken out and as he took another run he thought: "It's hailing outside."

"Just a minute if *you* please sir."

It was a stage-hand. He'd got a hammer and screwdriver. He wedged the point of the screwdriver between the lock and the doorpost, drove it home and wrenched. The screws squeaked, the wood splintered and gas poured into the passage. "No winders," coughed the stage-hand.

Mike wound Alleyn's scarf over his mouth and nose. Half-forgotten instructions from anti-gas drill occurred to him. The room looked queer but he could see the man slumped down in the chair quite clearly. He stooped low and ran in.

He was knocking against things as he backed out, lugging the dead weight. His arms tingled. A high insistent voice hummed in his brain. He floated a short distance and came to earth on a concrete floor among several pairs of legs. A long way off, someone said loudly: "I can only thank you for being so kind to what I know, too well, is a very imperfect play." Then the sound of hail began again. There was a heavenly stream of clear air flowing into his mouth and nostrils. "I could eat it," he thought and sat up.

The telephone rang. "Suppose," Mrs. Alleyn suggested, "that this time you ignore it."

"It might be the Yard," Alleyn said, and answered it.

"Is that Chief Detective-Inspector Alleyn's flat? I'm speaking from the Jupiter Theatre. I've rung up to say that the Chief Inspector is here and that he's had a slight mishap. He's all right, but I think it might be as well for someone to drive him home. No need to worry."

"What sort of mishap?" Alleyn asked.

"Er—well—er, he's been a bit gassed."

"*Gassed!* All right. Thanks, I'll come."

"*What* a bore for you, darling," said Mrs. Alleyn. "What sort of case is it? Suicide?"

"Masquerading within the meaning of the act, by the sound of it. Mike's in trouble."

"What trouble, for Heaven's sake?"

"Got himself gassed. He's all right. Good-night darling. Don't wait up."

When he reached the theatre, the front of the house was in darkness. He made his way down the side alley to the stage-door where he was held up.

"Yard," he said, and produced his official card.

" 'Ere," said the stage-doorkeeper. " 'Ow many more of you?"

"The man inside was working for me," said Alleyn and walked in. The doorkeeper followed, protesting.

To the right of the entrance was a large scenic dock from which the double doors had been rolled back. Here Mike was sitting in an armchair, very white about the lips. Three men and two women, all with painted faces, stood near him and behind them a group of stage-hands with Reynolds, the stage-manager, and, apart from these, three men in evening dress. The men looked woodenly shocked. The women had been weeping.

"I'm most frightfully sorry, sir," Mike said. "I've tried to explain. This," he added generally, "is Inspector Alleyn."

"I can't understand all this," said the oldest of the men in evening dress irritably. He turned on the doorkeeper. "You said—"

"I seen 'is card—"

"I know," said Mike, "but you see—"

"This is Lord Michael Lamprey," Alleyn said. "A recruit to the Police Department. What's happened here?"

"Doctor Rankin, would you—?"

The second of the men in evening dress came forward. "All right, Gosset. It's a bad business, Inspector. I've just been saying the police would have to be informed. If you'll come with me—"

Alleyn followed him through a door onto the stage proper. It was dimly lit. A trestle table had been set up in the centre and on it, covered with a sheet, was an unmistakable shape. The smell of gas, strong everywhere, hung heavily about the table.

"Who is it?"

"Canning Cumberland. He'd locked the door of his dressing-room. There's a gas fire. Your young friend dragged him out, very pluckily, but it was no go. I was in front. Gosset, the manager, had asked me to supper. It's a perfectly clear case of suicide as you'll see."

"I'd better look at the room. Anybody been in?"

"God, no. It was a job to clear it. They turned the gas off at the main. There's no window. They had to open the double doors at the back of the stage and a small outside door at the end of the passage. It may be possible to get in now."

He led the way to the dressing-room passage. "Pretty thick, still," he said. "It's the first room on the right. They burst the lock. You'd better keep down near the floor."

The powerful lights over the mirror were on and the room still had its look of occupation. The gas fire was against the left hand wall. Alleyn squatted down by it. The tap was still turned on, its face lying parallel with the floor. The top of the heater, the tap itself, and the carpet near it, were covered with a creamish powder. On the end of the dressing-table shelf nearest to the stove was a box of this powder. Further along the shelf, greasepaints were set out in a row beneath the mirror. Then came a wash basin and in front of this an overturned chair. Alleyn could see the track of heels, across the pile of the carpet, to the door immediately opposite. Beside the wash basin was a quart bottle of whiskey, three parts empty, and a tumbler. Alleyn had had about enough and returned to the passage.

"Perfectly clear," the hovering doctor said again, "isn't it?"

"I'll see the other rooms, I think."

The one next to Cumberland's was like his in reverse, but smaller. The heater was back to back with Cumberland's. The dressing-shelf was set out with much the same assortment of greasepaints. The tap of this heater, too, was turned on. It was of precisely the same make as the other and Alleyn, less embarrassed here by fumes, was able to make a longer examination. It was a common enough type of gas fire. The lead-in was from a pipe through a flexible metallic tube with a rubber connection. There were two taps, one in the pipe and one at the junction of the tube with the heater itself. Alleyn disconnected the tube and examined the connection. It was perfectly sound, a close fit and stained red at the end. Alleyn noticed a wiry thread of some reddish stuff resembling packing that still clung to it. The nozzle and tap were brass, the tap pulling over when it was turned on, to lie in a parallel plane with the floor. No powder had been scattered about here.

He glanced round the room, returned to the door and read the card: "Mr. Barry George."

The doctor followed him into the rooms opposite these, on the left-hand side of the passage. They were a repetition in design of the two he had already seen but were hung with women's clothes and had a more elaborate assortment of greasepaint and cosmetics.

There was a mass of flowers in the star-room. Alleyn read the cards. One in particular caught his eye: "From Anthony Gill to say a most inadequate 'thank you' for the great idea." A vase of red roses stood before the mirror:

"To your greatest triumph, Coralie darling. C.C." In Miss Gay's room there were only two bouquets, one from the management and one "from Anthony, with love."

Again in each room he pulled off the lead-in to the heater and looked at the connection.

"All right, aren't they?" said the doctor.

"Quite all right. Tight fit. Good solid grey rubber."

"Well, then–"

Next on the left was an unused room, and opposite it, "Mr. H. J. Bannington." Neither of these rooms had gas fires. Mr. Bannington's dressing-table was littered with the usual array of greasepaint, the materials for his beard, a number of telegrams and letters, and several bills.

"About the body," the doctor began.

"We'll get a mortuary van from the Yard."

"But–Surely in a case of suicide–"

"I don't think this is suicide."

"But, good God!–D'you mean there's been an accident?"

"No accident," said Alleyn.

At midnight, the dressing-room lights in the Jupiter Theatre were brilliant, and men were busy there with the tools of their trade. A constable stood at the stage-door and a van waited in the yard. The front of the house was dimly lit and there, among the shrouded stalls, sat Coralie Bourne, Basil Gosset, H. J. Bannington, Dendra Gay, Anthony Gill, Reynolds, Katie the dresser, and the call-boy. A constable sat behind them and another stood by the doors into the foyer. They stared across the backs of seats at the fire curtain. Spirals of smoke rose from their cigarettes and about their feet were discarded programs. "Basil Gosset presents I CAN FIND MY WAY OUT by Anthony Gill."

In the manager's office Alleyn said: "You're sure of your facts, Mike?"

"Yes, sir. Honestly. I was right up against the entrance into the passage. They didn't see me because I was in the shadow. It was very dark off-stage."

"You'll have to swear to it."

"I know."

"Good. All right, Thompson. Miss Gay and Mr. Gosset may go home. Ask Miss Bourne to come in."

When Sergeant Thompson had gone Mike said: "I haven't had a chance to say I know I've made a perfect fool of myself. Using your card and everything."

"Irresponsible gaiety doesn't go down very well in the service, Mike. You behaved like a clown."

"I *am* a fool," said Mike wretchedly.

The red beard was lying in front of Alleyn on Gosset's desk. He picked it up and held it out. "Put it on," he said.

"She might do another faint."

"I think not. Now the hat: yes–yes, I see. Come in."

Sergeant Thompson showed Coralie Bourne in and then sat at the end of the desk with his notebook.

Tears had traced their course through the powder on her face, carrying black cosmetic with them and leaving the greasepaint shining like snail-tracks. She stood near the doorway looking dully at Michael. "Is he back in England?" she said. "Did he tell you to do this?" She made an impatient movement. "Do take it off," she said, "it's a very bad beard. If Cann had only looked—" Her lips trembled. "Who told you to do it?"

"Nobody," Mike stammered, pocketing the beard. "I mean— As a matter of fact, Tony Gill—"

"*Tony?* But *he* didn't know. Tony wouldn't do it. Unless—"

"Unless?" Alleyn said.

She said frowning: "Tony didn't want Cann to play the part that way. He was furious."

"He says it was his dress for the Chelsea Arts Ball," Mike mumbled. "I brought it here. I just thought I'd put it on—it was idiotic, I know—for fun. I'd no idea you and Mr. Cumberland would mind."

"Ask Mr. Gill to come in," Alleyn said.

Anthony was white and seemed bewildered and helpless. "I've told Mike," he said. "It was my dress for the ball. They sent it round from the costume-hiring place this afternoon but I forgot it. Dendra reminded me and rang up the Delivery people—or Mike, as it turns out—in the interval."

"Why," Alleyn asked, "did you choose that particular disguise?"

"I didn't. I didn't know what to wear and I was too rattled to think. They said they were hiring things for themselves and would get something for me. They said we'd all be characters out of a Russian melodrama."

"Who said this?"

"Well—well, it was Barry George, actually."

"*Barry,*" Coralie Bourne said. "*It was Barry.*"

"I don't understand," Anthony said. "Why should a fancy dress upset everybody?"

"It happened," Alleyn said, "to be a replica of the dress usually worn by Miss Bourne's husband who also had a red beard. That was it, wasn't it, Miss Bourne? I remember seeing him—"

"Oh, yes," she said, "you would. He was known to the police." Suddenly she broke down completely. She was in an armchair near the desk but out of the range of its shaded lamp. She twisted and writhed, beating her hand against the padded arm of the chair. Sergeant Thompson sat with his head bent and his hand over his notes. Mike, after an agonized glance at Alleyn, turned his back. Anthony Gill leant over her: "Don't," he said violently. "Don't! For God's sake, stop."

She twisted away from him and gripping the edge of the desk, began to speak to Alleyn; little by little gaining mastery of herself. "I want to tell you. I want you to understand. Listen." Her husband had been fantastically cruel, she said. "It was a kind of slavery." But when she sued for divorce he brought evidence of adultery with Cumberland. They had thought he knew nothing.

"There was an abominable scene. He told us he was going away. He said he'd keep track of us and if I tried again for divorce, he'd come home. He was very friendly with Barry in those days." He had left behind him the first draft of a play he had meant to write for her and Cumberland. It had a wonderful scene for them. "And now you will never have it," he had said, "because there is no other playwright who could make this play for you but I." He was, she said, a melodramatic man but he was never ridiculous. He returned to the Ukraine where he was born and they had heard no more of him. In a little while she would have been able to presume death. But years of waiting did not agree with Canning Cumberland. He drank consistently and at his worst used to imagine her husband was about to return. "He was really terrified of Ben," she said. "He seemed like a creature in a nightmare."

Anthony Gill said: "This play—was it—?"

"Yes. There was an extraordinary similarity between your play and his. I saw at once that Ben's central scene would enormously strengthen your piece. Cann didn't want me to give it to you. Barry knew. He said: 'Why not?' He wanted Cann's part and was furious when he didn't get it. So you see, when he suggested you should dress and make-up like Ben—" She turned to Alleyn. "You see?"

"What did Cumberland do when he saw you?" Alleyn asked Mike.

"He made a queer movement with his hands as if—well, as if he expected me to go for him. Then he just bolted into his room."

"He thought Ben had come back," she said.

"Were you alone at any time after you fainted?" Alleyn asked.

"I? No. No, I wasn't. Katie took me into my dressing-room and stayed with me until I went on for the last scene."

"One other question. Can you, by any chance, remember if the heater in you room behaved at all oddly?"

She looked wearily at him. "Yes, it did give a sort of plop, I think. It made me jump. I was nervy."

"You went straight from your room to the stage?"

"Yes. With Katie. I wanted to go to Cann. I tried the door when we came out. It was locked. He said: 'Don't come in.' I said: 'It's all right. It wasn't Ben,' and went on to the stage."

"I heard Miss Bourne," Mike said.

"He must have made up his mind by then. He was terribly drunk when he played his last scene." She pushed her hair back from her forehead. "May I go?" she asked Alleyn.

"I've sent for a taxi. Mr. Gill, will you see if it's there? In the meantime, Miss Bourne, would you like to wait in the foyer?"

"May I take Katie home with me?"

"Certainly. Thompson will find her. Is there anyone else we can get?"

"No, thank you. Just old Katie."

Alleyn opened the door for her and watched her walk into the foyer. "Check up with the dresser, Thompson," he murmured, "and get Mr. H. J. Bannington."

He saw Coralie Bourne sit on the lower step of the dress-circle stairway and lean her head against the wall. Nearby, on a gilt easel, a huge photograph of Canning Cumberland smiled handsomely at her.

H. J. Bannington looked pretty ghastly. He had rubbed his hand across his face and smeared his make-up. Florid red paint from his lips had stained the crêpe hair that had been gummed on and shaped into a beard. His monocle was still in his left eye and gave him an extraordinarily rakish look. "See here," he complained, "I've about *had* this party. When do we go home?"

Alleyn uttered placatory phrases and got him to sit down. He checked over H.J.'s movements after Cumberland left the stage and found that his account tallied with Mike's. He asked if H.J. had visited any of the other dressing-rooms and was told acidly that H.J. knew his place in the company. "I remained in my unheated and squalid kennel, thank you very much."

"Do you know if Mr. Barry George followed your example?"

"Couldn't say, old boy. He didn't come near *me*."

"Have you any theories at all about this unhappy business, Mr. Bannington?"

"Do you mean, why did Cann do it? Well, speak no ill of the dead, but I'd have thought it was pretty obvious he was morbid-drunk. Tight as an owl when we finished the second act. Ask the great Mr. Barry George. Cann took the big scene away from Barry with both hands and left him looking pathetic. All wrong artistically, but that's how Cann was in his cups." H.J.'s wicked little eyes narrowed. "The great Mr. George," he said, "must be feeling very unpleasant by now. You might say he'd got a suicide on his mind, mightn't you? Or don't you know about that?"

"It was not suicide."

The glass dropped from H.J.'s eye. "God!" he said. "God, I told Bob Reynolds! I told him the whole plant wanted overhauling."

"The gas plant, you mean?"

"Certainly. I was in the gas business years ago. Might say I'm in it still with a difference, ha-ha!"

"Ha-ha!" Alleyn agreed politely. He leaned forward. "Look here," he said: "We can't dig up a gas man at this time of night and may very likely need an expert opinion. You can help us."

"Well, old boy, I was rather pining for a spot of shut-eye. But, of course—"

"I shan't keep you very long."

"God, I hope not!" said H.J. earnestly.

Barry George had been made up pale for the last act. Colorless lips and shadows under his cheek bones and eyes had skilfully underlined his character as a repatriated but broken prisoner-of-war. Now, in the glare of the office lamp, he looked like a grossly exaggerated figure of mourning. He began at once to tell Alleyn how grieved and horrified he was. Everybody, he said, had their faults, and poor old Cann was no exception but wasn't it terrible to think what could happen to a man who let himself go downhill? He, Barry

George, was abnormally sensitive and he didn't think he'd ever really get over the awful shock this had been to him. What, he wondered, could be at the bottom of it? Why had poor old Cann decided to end it all?

"Miss Bourne's theory," Alleyn began. Mr. George laughed. "Coralie?" he said. "So she's got a theory! Oh, well. Never mind."

"Her theory is this. Cumberland saw a man whom he mistook for her husband and, having a morbid dread of his return, drank the greater part of a bottle of whiskey and gassed himself. The clothes and beard that deceived him had, I understand, been ordered by you for Mr. Anthony Gill."

This statement produced startling results. Barry George broke into a spate of expostulation and apology. There had been no thought in his mind of resurrecting poor old Ben, who was no doubt dead but had been, mind you, in many ways one of the best. They were all to go to the Ball as exaggerated characters from melodrama. Not for the world—He gesticulated and protested. A line of sweat broke out along the margin of his hair. "I don't know what you're getting at," he shouted. "What are you suggesting?"

"I'm suggesting, among other things, that Cumberland was murdered."

"You're mad! He'd locked himself in. They had to break down the door. There's no window. You're crazy!"

"Don't," Alleyn said wearily, "let us have any nonsense about sealed rooms. Now, Mr. George, you knew Benjamin Vlasnoff pretty well. Are you going to tell us that when you suggested Mr. Gill should wear a coat with a fur collar, a black sombrero, black gloves and a red beard, it never occurred to you that his appearance might be a shock to Miss Bourne and to Cumberland?"

"I wasn't the only one," he blustered. "H.J. knew. And if it had scared him off, *she* wouldn't have been so sorry. She'd had about enough of him. Anyway if this is murder, the costume's got nothing to do with it."

"That," Alleyn said, getting up, "is what we hope to find out."

In Barry George's room, Detective-Sergeant Bailey, a fingerprint expert, stood by the gas heater. Sergeant Gibson, a police photographer, and a uniformed constable were near the door. In the centre of the room stood Barry George, looking from one man to another and picking at his lips.

"I don't know why he wants me to watch all this," he said. "I'm exhausted. I'm emotionally used up. What's he doing? Where is he?"

Alleyn was next door in Cumberland's dressing-room, with H.J., Mike and Sergeant Thompson. It was pretty clear now of fumes and the gas fire was burning comfortably. Sergeant Thompson sprawled in the armchair near the heater, his head sunk and his eyes shut.

"This is the theory, Mr. Bannington," Alleyn said. "You and Cumberland have made your final exits; Miss Bourne and Mr. George and Miss Gay are all on the stage. Lord Michael is standing just outside the entrance to the passage. The dressers and stage-staff are watching the play from the side. Cumberland has locked himself in this room. There he is, dead drunk and sound asleep. The gas fire is burning, full pressure. Earlier in the evening he powdered himself and a thick layer of the powder lies undisturbed on the tap. Now."

He tapped on the wall.

The fire blew out with a sharp explosion. This was followed by the hiss of escaping gas. Alleyn turned the taps off. "You see," he said, "I've left an excellent print on the powdered surface. Now, come next door."

Next door, Barry George appealed to him stammering: "But I didn't know. I don't know anything about it. I don't *know*."

"Just show Mr. Bannington, will you, Bailey?"

Bailey knelt down. The lead-in was disconnected from the tap on the heater. He turned on the tap in the pipe and blew down the tube.

"An air lock, you see. It works perfectly."

H.J. was staring at Barry George. "But I don't know about gas, H.J. H.J., tell them—"

"One moment." Alleyn removed the towels that had been spread over the dressing-shelf, revealing a sheet of clean paper on which lay the rubber push-on connection.

"Will you take this lens, Bannington, and look at it. You'll see that it's stained a florid red. It's a very slight stain but it's unmistakably greasepaint. And just above the stain you'll see a wiry hair. Rather like some sort of packing material, but it's not that. It's crêpe hair, isn't it?"

The lens wavered above the paper.

"Let me hold it for you," Alleyn said. He put his hand over H.J.'s shoulder and, with a swift movement, plucked a tuft from his false moustache and dropped it on the paper. "Identical, you see. Ginger. It seems to be stuck to the connection with spirit-gum."

The lens fell. H.J. twisted round, faced Alleyn for a second, and then struck him full in the face. He was a small man but it took three of them to hold him.

"In a way, sir, it's handy when they have a smack at you," said Detective-Sergeant Thompson half an hour later. "You can pull them in nice and straightforward without any 'will you come to the station and make a statement' business."

"Quite," said Alleyn, nursing his jaw.

Mike said: "He must have gone to the room after Barry George and Miss Bourne were called."

"That's it. He had to be quick. The call-boy would be round in a minute and he had to be back in his own room."

"But look here—what about motive?"

"That, my good Mike, is precisely why, at half-past one in the morning, we're still in this miserable theatre. You're getting a view of the duller aspect of homicide. Want to go home?"

"No. Give me another job."

"Very well. About ten feet from the prompt-entrance, there's a sort of garbage tin. Go through it."

At seventeen minutes to two, when the dressing-rooms and passage had been combed clean and Alleyn had called a spell, Mike came to him with filthy hands. "*Eureka*," he said, "I hope."

They all went into Bannington's room. Alleyn spread out on the dressing-table the fragments of paper that Mike had given him.

"They'd been pushed down to the bottom of the tin," Mike said.

Alleyn moved the fragments about. Thompson whistled through his teeth. Bailey and Gibson mumbled together.

"There you are," Alleyn said at last.

They collected round him. The letter that H. J. Bannington had opened at this same table six hours and forty-five minutes earlier, was pieced together like a jig-saw puzzle.

"Dear H.J.
Having seen the monthly statement of my account, I called at my bank this morning and was shown a check that is undoubtedly a forgery. Your histrionic versatility, my dear H.J., is only equalled by your audacity as a calligraphist. But fame has its disadvantages. The teller recognized you. I propose to take action."

"Unsigned," said Bailey.

"Look at the card on the red roses in Miss Bourne's room, signed C.C. It's a very distinctive hand." Alleyn turned to Mike. "Do you still want to be a policeman?"

"Yes."

"Lord help you. Come and talk to me at the office tomorrow."

"Thank you, sir."

They went out, leaving a constable on duty. It was a cold morning. Mike looked up at the façade of the Jupiter. He could just make out the shape of the neon sign: I CAN FIND MY WAY OUT—*by Anthony Gill.*

[illegible] Way Out

At [illegible] minutes [illegible] and [illegible] back [illegible] clean and [illegible] a [illegible]

[illegible] up the [illegible] pieces of paper [illegible]

[illegible] the fragments [illegible]

[illegible]

"There you [illegible]"

[illegible]

The [illegible]

[illegible]

"Night," [illegible]

[illegible]

"Yes."

[illegible]

They went [illegible]

INSTEAD OF EVIDENCE

by Rex Stout

AMONG THE KINDS of men I have a prejudice against are the ones named Eugene. There's no use asking me why, because I admit it's a prejudice. It may be that when I was in kindergarten out in Ohio a man named Eugene stole candy from me, but, if so, I have forgotten all about it. For all practical purposes, it is merely one facet of my complex character that I do not like men named Eugene.

That, and that alone, accounted for my offish attitude when Mr. and Mrs. Eugene R. Poor called at Nero Wolfe's office that Tuesday afternoon in October, because I had never seen or heard of the guy before, and neither had Wolfe.

The appointment had been made by phone that morning, so I was prejudiced before I ever got a look at him. The look hadn't swayed me much one way or the other. He wasn't too old to remember what his wife had given him on his fortieth birthday, but neither was he young enough to be still looking forward to it. Nothing about him stood out. His face was taken at random out of stock, with no alterations. Gray herringbone suits like his were that afternoon being bought in stores from San Diego to Bangor. Really, his only distinction was that they had named him Eugene.

In spite of which I was regarding him with polite curiosity, for he had just told Nero Wolfe that he was going to be murdered by his partner, a man named Conroy Blaney.

I was sitting at my desk in the room Nero Wolfe used for an office in his home on West 35th Street, and Wolfe was behind his desk, arranged in a chair that had been especially constructed to support up to a quarter of a ton, which was not utterly beyond the limits of possibility. Eugene R. Poor was in the red leather chair a short distance beyond Wolfe's desk, with a little table smack against its right arm for the convenience of clients in writing checks. Mrs. Poor was on a spare between her husband and me.

I might mention that I was not aware of any prejudice against Mrs. Poor. For one thing, there was no reason to suppose that her name was Eugene. For another, there were several reasons to suppose that her fortieth birthday would not come before mine, though she was good and mature. She had by no means struck me dumb, but there are people who seem to improve a room just by being in it.

Naturally, Wolfe was scowling. He shook his head, moving it a full half-inch right and left, which was, for him, a frenzy of negation.

"No, sir," he said emphatically. "I suppose two hundred men and women have sat in that chair, Mr. Poor, and tried to hire me to keep someone from killing them." His eyes switched to me. "How many, Archie?"

I said, to oblige him, "Two hundred and nine."

"Have I taken the jobs?"

"No, sir. Never."

He wiggled a finger at Eugene. "For two million dollars a year you can make it fairly difficult for a man to kill you. That's about what it costs to protect a president or a king, and even so, consider the record. Of course, if you give up all other activity it can be done more cheaply, say, forty thousand a year. A cave in a mountainside, never emerging, with six guards you can trust and a staff to suit—"

Eugene was trying to get something in. He finally did: "I don't expect you to keep him from killing me. That's not what I came for."

"Then what the deuce did you come for?"

"To keep him from getting away with it." Eugene cleared his throat. "I was trying to tell you. I agree that you can't stop him; I don't see how anybody can. Sooner or later. He's a clever man." His voice took on bitterness: "Too damn clever for me, and I wish I'd never met him. Sure, I know a man can kill a man if he once decides to, but Con Blaney is so damn clever that it isn't a question whether he can kill me or not; the question is whether he can manage it so that he is in the clear. I'm afraid he can. I would bet he can. And I don't want him to."

His wife made a little noise, and he stopped to look at her. Then he shook his head at her as if she had said something, took a cigar from his vest pocket, removed the band, inspected first one end and then the other to decide which was which, got a gadget from another vest pocket and snipped one of the ends, and lit up. He no sooner had it lit than it slipped out of his mouth, bounced on his thigh, and landed on the rug. He retrieved it and got his teeth sunk in it.

"So," I thought to myself, "you're not so doggone calm about getting murdered as you were making out to be."

"So I came," he told Wolfe, "to give you the facts, to get the facts down, and to pay you five thousand dollars to see that he doesn't manage it that way." The cigar between his teeth interfered with his talking, and he took it out of his mouth. "If he kills me I'll be dead. I want someone to know about it."

Wolfe's eyes had gone half shut. "But why pay me five thousand dollars in advance? Wouldn't someone know about it? Your wife, for instance?"

Eugene nodded. "I've thought about that. I've thought it all out. What if he kills her, too? I have no idea how he'll try to work it, or when, and who is there besides my wife whom I can absolutely trust? I'm not taking any chances. Of course, I thought of the police, but judging from my own experience, a couple of burglaries down at the shop, and, you know, the experiences of a businessman, I'm not sure they'd even remember I'd been there if it happened in a year or maybe two years." He stuck his cigar in his mouth, puffed twice, and took it out again. "What's the matter—don't you want five thousand dollars?"

Wolfe said gruffly, "I wouldn't get five thousand. This is October. As my 1945 income now stands, I'll keep about ten per cent of any additional receipts after paying taxes. Out of five thousand, five hundred would be mine. If Mr. Blaney is as clever as you think he is, I wouldn't consider trying to uncover him on a murder for five hundred dollars." He stopped and opened his eyes to glare at the wife. "May I ask, madam, what you are looking so pleased about?"

Wolfe couldn't stand to see a woman look pleased.

Mrs. Poor was regarding him with a little smile of obvious approval. "Because," she said, in a voice that was pleased too, and a nice voice, "I need help, and I think you're going to help me. I don't approve of this. I didn't want my husband to come here."

"Indeed. Where did you want him to go—to the Atlantic Detective Agency?"

"Oh, no; if I had been in favor of his going to any detective at all, of course it would have been Nero Wolfe. But—May I explain?"

Wolfe glanced at the clock on the wall. Three-forty. In twenty minutes he would be leaving for the plant-rooms on the roof, to indulge in his favorite hobby—monkeying around with orchids. Besides being a champion eater and drinker, Wolfe is the best orchid grower in New York. He said curtly, "I have eighteen minutes."

Eugene put in, with a determined voice, "Then I'm going to use them—" But his wife smiled him out of it. She went on to Wolfe: "It won't take that long. My husband and Mr. Blaney have been business partners for ten years. They own the firm of Blaney & Poor, manufacturers of novelties—you know—they make things like matches that won't strike and chairs with rubber legs and bottled drinks that taste like soap—"

"Good God," Wolfe muttered in horror.

She ignored it. "It's the biggest firm in the business. Mr. Blaney gets the ideas and handles the production—he's a genius at it—and my husband handles the business part, sales and so on. But Mr. Blaney is really just about too conceited to live, and now that the business is a big success he thinks my husband isn't needed, and he wants him to get out and take twenty thousand dollars for his half. Of course, it's worth a great deal more than that—at least ten times as much—and my husband won't do it. Mr. Blaney is very conceited, and also he will not let anything stand in his way. The argument has gone on and on, until now my husband is convinced that Mr. Blaney is capable of doing anything to get rid of him."

"Of killing him. And you don't agree."

"Oh, no. I do agree. I think Mr. Blaney would stop at nothing."

"Has he made threats?"

She shook her head. "He isn't that kind. He doesn't make threats; he just goes ahead."

"Then why didn't you want your husband to come to me?"

"Because he's simply too stubborn to live." She smiled at Eugene to take out any sting, and back at Wolfe. "There's a clause in the partnership agreement—they signed it when they started the business—that says if either one of them dies, the other one owns the whole thing. That's another reason why my husband thinks Mr. Blaney will kill him, and I think so, too. But what my husband wants is to make sure Mr. Blaney gets caught—that's how stubborn he is—and what I want is for my husband to stay alive."

"Now, Martha," Eugene put in, "I came here to—"

So her name was Martha. I had no prejudice against women named Martha.

She kept the floor. "It's like this," she appealed to Wolfe. "My husband thinks that Mr. Blaney is determined to kill him if he can't get what he wants any other way, and I think so, too. You, yourself, think that if a man is determined to kill another man nothing can stop him. So isn't it perfectly obvious? My husband has over two hundred thousand dollars saved up outside the business, about half of it in war bonds. He can get another twenty thousand from Mr. Blaney for his half of the business—"

"It's worth twenty times that," Eugene said savagely, showing real emotion for the first time.

"Not to you if you're dead," she snapped back at him, and went on to Wolfe: "With the income from that we could live more than comfortably—and happily. I hope my husband loves me—I *hope* he does—and I know I love him." She leaned forward in her chair. "That's why I came along today—I thought maybe you would help me persuade him. It isn't as if I wouldn't stand by my husband in a fight if there was any chance of his winning. But is there any sense in being so stubborn if you can't possibly win? If, instead of winning, you will probably die? Now, does that make sense? I ask you, Mr. Wolfe—you are a wise and clever and able man—what would you do if you were in my husband's position?"

Wolfe muttered, "You put that as a question?"

"Yes, I do."

"Well. Granting that you have described the situation correctly, I would kill Mr. Blaney."

She looked startled. "But that's silly." She frowned. "Of course you're joking, and it's no joke."

"I'd kill him in a second," Eugene told Wolfe, "if I thought I could get away with it. I suppose *you* could, but I couldn't."

"And I'm afraid," Wolfe said politely, "you couldn't hire me for that." He glanced at the clock. "I would advise against your consulting even your wife. An undetected murder is strictly a one-man job. Her advice, sir, is sound. Are you going to take it?"

"No." Eugene sounded as stubborn as she said he was.

"Are you going to kill Mr. Blaney?"

"No."

"Do you still want to pay me five thousand dollars?"

"Yes, I do."

Mrs. Poor, who was rapidly becoming Martha to me, tried to horn in, but bigger and louder people than she had failed at that when orchid time was at hand. Wolfe ignored her and went on to Mr. Poor:

"I advise you against that, too, under the circumstances. Here are the circumstances—Archie, take your notebook. Make a receipt reading, 'Received from Eugene R. Poor five thousand dollars, in return for which I agree, in case he dies within one year, to give the police the information he has given me today, and to take any further action that may seem to me advisable.' Sign my name and initial it as usual. Get all details from Mr. Poor." Wolfe pushed back his chair and got the levers of his muscles in position to hoist the bulk.

Eugene's eyes were moist with tears, but they came, not from emotion, but from smoke from his second cigar. In fact, throughout the interview his nervousness seemed to concentrate on his cigar. He had dropped it twice, and the smoke seemed determined to go down the wrong way and make him cough. But he was able to speak, all right.

"That's no good," he objected. "You don't even say what kind of action. At least, you ought to say—"

"I advised you against it under the circumstances." Wolfe was on his feet. "Those, sir, are the circumstances. That's all I'll undertake. Suit yourself." He started to move.

But Eugene had another round to fire. His hand went in a pocket and came out full of folded money. "I hadn't mentioned," he said, displaying the pretty objects, "that I brought it in cash. Speaking of income tax, if you're up to the ninety per cent bracket, getting it in cash would make it a lot more—"

Wolfe's look stopped him. "Pfui," Wolfe said. He hadn't had as good a chance to show off for a month. "I am not a common cheat, Mr. Poor. Not that I am a saint. Given adequate provocation, I might conceivably cheat a man—or a woman, or even a child. But you are suggesting that I cheat, not a man or woman or child, but a hundred and forty million of my fellow citizens. Bah."

We stared at his back as he left, as he knew we would, and in a moment we heard the sound of his elevator door opening.

I flipped to a fresh page in my notebook and turned to Eugene and Martha. "To refresh your memory," I said, "the name is Archie Goodwin. Among other things, I'm Wolfe's assistant, and I'm the one that has been doing the work around here for fifty years, more or less. I am also, Mr. Poor, an admirer of your wife."

He nearly dropped his cigar again. "You're what?"

"I admire your wife as an advice giver. She has learned one of the most important rules—that, far as life falls short of perfection, it is more fun outside the grave than in it. With over two hundred thousand bucks—"

"I've had enough advice," he said as if he meant it. "My mind is made up."

"Okay." I got the notebook in position. "Give me everything you think we'll need. First, basic facts. Home and business addresses?"

It took close to an hour, so it was nearly five o'clock when they left. I found Eugene irritating and therefore kept my prejudice intact. I wondered later what difference it would have made in my attitude if I had known that in a few hours he would be dead. Even if you take the line that he had it coming to him, which would be easy to justify, at least it would have made the situation more interesting. But during that hour, as far as I knew, they were just a couple of white-livers, scared stiff by a false alarm named Blaney, so it was merely another job.

I was still typing from my notes when, at six o'clock, after the regulation two hours in the plant-rooms, Wolfe came down to the office. He got fixed in his chair, rang for Fritz to bring beer, and demanded, "Did you take that man's money?"

I grinned at him. Up to his old tricks. I had been a civilian again for only a week, and here he was, already treating me like a hireling, just as he had for years, acting as if I had never been a colonel, as, in fact, I hadn't, but anyway I had been a major.

I asked him, "What do you think? If I say I took it you'll claim that your attitude as you left plainly indicated that he had insulted you and you wouldn't play. If I say I refused it you'll claim I've done you out of a fee. Which do you prefer?"

He abandoned it. "Do your typing. I like to hear you typing. If you are typing you can't talk."

To humor him I typed, which as it turned out, was just as well, since that neat list of facts was going to be needed before bedtime. It was finished when Fritz entered at eight o'clock to announce dinner.

Back in the office, where the clock said 9:42, I was just announcing my intention of catching a movie by the tail at the Rialto, when the phone rang. It was our old friend, Inspector Cramer, whose voice I hadn't heard for weeks, asking for Wolfe. Wolfe picked up his receiver, and I stuck to mine so as to get it firsthand.

"Wolfe? . . . Cramer. I've got a paper here, taken from the pocket of a dead man, a receipt for five thousand dollars, signed by you, dated today. It says you have information to give the police if he dies. All right, he's dead. I don't ask you to come up here, because I know you wouldn't, and I'm too busy to go down there. What's the information?"

Wolfe grunted. "What killed him?"

"An explosion. Just give—"

"Did it kill his wife too?"

"Naw, she's okay, only overcome, you know. Just give–"

"I haven't got the information. Mr. Goodwin has it. Archie?"

I spoke up: "It would take quite a while, Inspector, and I've got it all typed. I can run up there–"

"All right; come ahead. The Poor apartment on Eighty-fourth Street. The number is–"

"I know the number. I know everything. Sit down and rest till I get there. . . ."

In the living-room of an apartment on the sixth floor, on 84th Street near Amsterdam Avenue, I stood and looked down at what was left of Eugene Poor. All I really recognized was the gray herringbone suit and the shirt and tie, on account of what the explosion had done to his face, and also on that account I didn't look much, for while I may not be a softy, I see no point in prolonged staring at a face that has entirely stopped being a face.

I asked Sergeant Purley Stebbins, who was sticking close by me, apparently to see that I didn't swipe Eugene's shoes, "You say a cigar did that to him?"

Purley nodded. "Yeah; so the wife says. He lit a cigar, and it blew up."

"Huh. I don't believe it. . . . Yes, I guess I do, too, if she says so. They make novelties. Now, that's a novelty."

I looked around. The room was full of what you would expect–assorted snoops, all doing the chores, from print collectors up to inspectors, or at least one inspector, namely, Cramer himself, who sat at a table near a wall reading the script I had brought him. Most of them I knew, at least by sight, but there was one complete stranger. She was in a chair in a far corner, being questioned by a homicide dick named Rowcliff. Being trained to observe details even when under a strain, I had caught at a glance some of her outstanding characteristics, such as youth, shapeliness, and shallow depressions at the temples, which happen to appeal to me.

I aimed a thumb in her direction and asked Purley, "Bystander, wife's sister, or what?"

He shook his head. "God knows. She came to call just after we got here, and we want to know what for."

I strolled over to the corner and stopped against them, and the girl and the dick looked up. "Excuse me," I told her; "when you get through here will you kindly call on Nero Wolfe at this address?" I handed her a card. The temples were even better close up. "Mr. Wolfe is going to solve this murder."

Rowcliff snarled. He always snarled. "Get away from here, and stay away."

Actually, he was helpless, because the inspector had sent for me, and he knew it. I ignored him and told the temples, "If this person takes that card away from you, it's in the phone book–Nero Wolfe," left them, and crossed over to Cramer at the table, dodging photographers and other scientists on the way.

Cramer didn't look up, so I asked the top of his head, "Where's Mrs. Poor?"

He growled, "Bedroom."

"I want to see her."

"The hell you do." He jiggled the sheets I had brought him. "Sit down."

I sat down and said, "I want to see our client."

"So you've got a client?"

"Sure, we have. Didn't you see that receipt?"

He grunted. "Give her a chance. I am. Let her get herself together. . . . Don't touch that!"

I was only moving a hand to point at a box of cigars there on the table, with the lid closed. I grinned at him. "The more the merrier. I mean, fingerprints. But if that's the box the loaded one came from, you ought to satisfy my curiosity. He smoked two cigars this afternoon at the office."

Cramer shot me a glance, then got out his penknife and opened the lid and lifted the paper flap. It was a box of 25, and 24 of them were still there. Only one gone. I inspected at close range, sat back, and nodded. "They're the same. They not only look it, but the bands say Alta Vista. There would be two of those bands still in the ash tray down at the office if Fritz wasn't so neat." I squinted again at the array in the box. "They certainly look kosher. Do you suppose they're all loaded?"

"I don't know. The laboratory can answer that one." He closed the box with the tip of his knife. "Damn murders, anyhow." He tapped the papers with his finger. "This is awful pat. The wife let out a hint or two, and I've sent for Blaney. I hope to God it's a wrap-up, and maybe it is. How did Poor seem this afternoon, scared, nervous, what?"

"Mostly stubborn. Mind made up."

"What about the wife?"

"Stubborn too. She wanted him to get out from under and go on breathing. She thought they could be as happy as larks on the income from a measly quarter of a million."

The next twenty minutes was a record—Inspector Cramer and me conversing without a single ugly remark. It lasted that long only because of various interruptions from his army. The last one, toward the end, was from Rowcliff walking up to the table to say, "Do you want to talk to this young woman, Inspector?"

"How do I know? What about her?"

"Her name is Helen Vardis. She's an employee of Poor's firm, Blaney & Poor—been with them four years. At first she showed signs of hysteria and then calmed down. First she said she just happened to come here. Then she saw what that was worth and said she came to see Poor by appointment, at his request, on a confidential matter, and wants us to promise not to tell Blaney, because she would lose her job."

"What confidential matter?"

"She won't say. That's what I've been working on."

"Work on it some more."

There was a commotion at the outer door, and it came on through the foyer into the living-room in the shape of a municipal criminologist gripping the arm of a wild-eyed young man who apparently didn't want to be gripped. They were both talking, or at least making noises. It was hard to tell whether they were being propelled by the young man pulling or the cop pushing.

Cramer boomed, "Doyle! What the hell? Who is that?"

The young man goggled around, declaiming, "I have a right—Oh! There you are."

She said, as if she didn't need any information from snakes or rats, "You didn't lose any time, did you? Now you think you can have her, don't you?"

He held the stare, showing no reaction except clamping his jaw, and their audience sat tight. In a moment he seemed to realize it was rather a public performance, and his head started to pivot, doing a slow circle, taking in the surroundings. It was a good, thorough job of looking, without any waver or pause, so far as I could see, even when it hit the most sensational item, namely, the corpse. During the process his eyes lost their wild look entirely, and when he spoke his voice was cool and controlled. It was evident that his mental operations were enough in order for him to pick the most intelligent face in the bunch, since it was to me he put the question:

"Are you in charge here?"

I replied, "No. This one. Inspector Cramer."

He strode across and looked Cramer in the eye and made a speech: "My name is Joe Groll. I work for Blaney & Poor, factory foreman. I followed that girl, Helen Vardis, when she left home tonight, because I wanted to know where she was going, and she came here. The police cars and cops going in and out made me want to ask questions, and finally I got the answer that a man named Poor had been murdered, so I wanted to find out. Where is Blaney? Conroy Blaney, the partner—"

"I know," Cramer said, looking disgusted. Naturally he was disgusted, since what he had hoped would be a wrap-up was spilling out in various directions. "We've sent for Blaney. Why were you following—?"

"That isn't true!"

More diversions. Helen Vardis had busted out of her corner to join the table group, close enough to Joe Groll to touch him, but they weren't touching. Instead of resuming their staring match, they were both intent on Cramer.

Looking even more disgusted, Cramer asked her, "What isn't true?"

"That he was following me!" Helen was mad clear to her temples and pretty as a picture. "Why should he follow me? He came here to—" She bit it off sharp.

"Yeah," Cramer said encouragingly. "To what?"

"I don't know! But I do know who killed Mr. Poor! It was Martha Davis!"

"That helps. Who is Martha Davis?"

Joe Groll said, giving information again, "She means Mrs. Poor. That was her name when she worked in the factory, before she got married. She means Mrs. Poor killed her husband. That's on account of jealousy. She's crazy."

A quiet but energetic voice came from a new direction: "She certainly is." It was Martha, who emerged from a door at the far end and approached the table. She was pale and didn't seem any too sure of her leg action, but she made her objective all right. She spoke to the girl, with no sign of violent emotion that I could detect, not even resentment: "Helen, you ought to be ashamed of yourself. I think you will be when you have calmed down and thought things over. You have no right or reason to talk like that. You accuse me of killing my husband? Why?"

Very likely Helen would have proceeded to tell her why, but at that moment a cop entered from the foyer escorting a stranger. Cramer motioned with his hand for them to back out.

But the stranger was not a backer-out. He came on straight to the table and, since the arrangement showed plainly that Cramer was it, addressed the inspector: "I'm Conroy Blaney. Where's Gene Poor?"

Not that he was aggressive or in any way overwhelming. His voice was a tenor squeak and it fitted his looks. I could have picked him up and set him down again without grunting, he had an undersized nose and not much chin, and he was going bald. In spite of all those handicaps his sudden appearance had a remarkable effect. Martha Poor simply turned and left the room. The expressions on the faces of Helen Vardis and Joe Groll changed completely; they went deadpan in one second flat. I saw at once that there would be no more blurting, and so did Cramer.

As for Blaney, he looked around, saw the body of his partner on the floor, stepped toward it and gazed down at it, and squeaked, "Good heavens! Good heavens! Who did it?" . . .

Next morning at eleven o'clock, when Wolfe came down to the office after his two-hour session up in the plant-rooms, I made my report. He took it, as usual, leaning back in his chair with his eyes closed, with no visible sign of consciousness. The final chapter was the details given me by Martha Poor, with whom I had managed to have a talk around midnight by pressing Cramer on the client angle and wearing him down. I gave it to Wolfe:

"They came here yesterday in their own car. When they left here, a little before five, they drove to Madison Square Garden and got a program of the afternoon rodeo performance, the reason for that being he had needed to explain his absence from the office and, not wanting Blaney to know that he was coming to see you, he had said he was going to the rodeo, and wanted to be able to answer questions if he was asked about it. Then they drove up to Westchester. Conroy Blaney has a place up there, a shack in the hills where he lives and spends his evenings and week-ends thinking up novelties, and they had a date to see him there and discuss things.

"Mrs. Poor had persuaded Poor to go, thinking they might reach an agreement, but Poor hadn't wanted to, and on the way up he balked, so they stopped at a place near Scarsdale, Monty's Tavern, to debate. Poor won the debate. He wouldn't go. She left him at the tavern and went on to Blaney's place alone. The date was for six-fifteen and she got there right on the dot. . . . Are you awake?"

He grunted.

I went on: "Blaney wasn't there. He lives alone, and the doors were locked. She waited around and got cold. At ten minutes to seven she beat it back to the tavern. She and Poor ate dinner there, then drove back to town, put the car in the garage, and went home. Poor had had no cigar after dinner because they hadn't had his brand at the tavern and he wouldn't smoke anything else. He has been smoking Alta Vistas for years, ten to fifteen a day. So he hung up his hat and opened a fresh box. She didn't see him do it because she was in the bathroom. She heard the sound of the explosion—not very loud—and ran out, and there he was. She phoned downstairs, and the elevator man and hall man came and phoned for a doctor and the police. . . . Still awake?"

He grunted again.

"Okay. That's it. When I returned to the living-room everyone had left, including Poor's leftovers. Some friend had come to spend the night, and of course there was a cop out in the hall. When I got home you were in bed snoring."

He had long ago quit bothering to deny that he snored. Now he didn't bother about anything, but just sat there. I resumed with the plant records. Noon came and went, and still he was making no visible effort to earn five thousand dollars, or even five hundred. Finally he heaved a sigh, almost opened his eyes, and told me, "You say the face was unrecognizable."

"Yes, sir. As I described it."

"From something concealed in a cigar. Next to incredible. Phone Mr. Cramer. Tell him it is important that the identity of the corpse be established beyond question. Also, I want to see a photograph of Mr. Poor while still intact."

I goggled at him. "For God's sake, what do you think? That she doesn't know her own husband? She came home with him. Now, really. The old insurance gag? Your mind's in a rut. I will not phone Mr. Cramer merely to put myself on the receiving end of a horse laugh."

"Be quiet. Let me alone. Phone Mr. Cramer."

At lunch he discussed Yugoslav politics. That was all right, because he never talked business at the table, but when, back in the office, he went through the elaborate operations of getting himself settled with the atlas, I decided to apply spurs and sink them deep.

I arose and confronted him and announced, "I resign."

He muttered testily without looking up, "Nonsense. Do your work."

"No, sir. I'm going upstairs to pack. If you're too lazy to wiggle a finger, very well, that's not news. But you could at least send me to the Public Library to look up the genealogy—"

"Confound it!" He glared at me. "I engaged to give that information to the police, and have done so. Also to take any further action that might seem to me advisable. I have done that."

"Do you mean you're through with the case?"

"Certainly not. I haven't even started, because there's nothing to start on.

Mr. Cramer may do the job himself, or he may not. I hope he does. If you don't want to work, go to a movie."

I went upstairs to my room and tried to read a book, knowing it wouldn't work, because I can never settle down when a murder case is on. So I returned to the office and rattled papers, but even that didn't faze him. At four o'clock, when he went up to the plant-rooms, I went to the corner and got afternoon papers, but there was nothing in them but the usual stuff.

When he came down again at six it was more of the same, and I went out for a walk to keep from throwing a chair at him, and stayed until dinnertime. After dinner I went to a movie, and when I got home, a little after eleven, and found him sitting drinking beer and reading a magazine, I went upstairs to bed without saying good night.

Next morning, Thursday, there wasn't a peep out of him before nine o'clock, the time he went up to the damn' orchids.

I read the papers and had more coffee.

When Wolfe came down to the office at eleven I greeted him with a friendly suggestion.

"Look," I said; "you're an expert on murder. But this Poor murder bores you because you've already collected your fee. So how about this?"

I spread the morning *Gazette* on his desk and indicated. "Absolutely Grade A. Man's naked body found in an old orchard off a lonely lane four miles from White Plains, head crushed to a pancake, apparently by a car running square over him. It offers many advantages to a great detective like you. It might be Hitler, since his body has never been found. It is in a convenient neighborhood, easily reached by train, bus, or auto, electric lights and city gas. The man has been dead at least thirty-six hours, counting from now, so it has the antique quality you like, with the clues all—"

In another minute I would have had him sputtering with fury, but the doorbell rang. "Study it," I told him, and went to the hall and the front and, following routine, fingered the curtain edge aside for a look through the glass panel.

After one brief glance I went back to the office and told Wolfe casually, "It's only Cramer. To hell with him. Since he's working on the Poor case and you're not interested—"

"Archie. Confound you. Bring him in."

The bell was ringing again, and that irritates me, so I went and got him. He was wearing his raincoat and his determined look. I relieved him of the former in the hall and let him take the latter on into the office.

When I joined them, Cramer was lowering himself into the red leather chair and telling Wolfe, "I dropped in on my way uptown because I thought it was only fair, since you gave me that information. I think I'm going to arrest your client on a charge of murder."

I sat down and felt at home.

Wolfe grunted. He leaned back in his chair, got his finger tips touching in the locality of his midriff, and said offensively, "Nonsense. You can't arrest my client on any charge whatever. My client is dead. By the way, is he? Has the corpse been properly identified?"

Cramer nodded. "Certainly. With a face like that it's routine. Barber, dentist, and doctor—they're the experts. Why, what did you think it was, an insurance fake?"

"I didn't think. Then you can't arrest my client."

"Goodwin says Mrs. Poor is your client."

"Mr. Goodwin is impulsive. You read that receipt. So you're going to charge Mrs. Poor?"

"I think I am."

"Indeed."

Cramer scowled at him. "Don't 'indeed' me. Damn it, didn't I take the trouble to stop and tell you about it?"

"Go ahead and tell me."

"Very well." Cramer screwed up his lips, deciding where to start. "First, I'd appreciate an answer to a question. What is this identity angle, anyhow? There's not the slightest doubt it was Poor. Not only the corpse itself—other things, like the elevator man who took them up when they came home, and the people up at the tavern where they ate dinner. He was known there. And what did you want a photograph for?"

"Did you bring one?"

"No. Apparently there aren't any. I wasn't interested after the dentist and barber verified the corpse, but I understand the papers had to settle for sketches drawn from descriptions. One reason I came here, what's your idea doubting the identity of the corpse?"

Wolfe shook his head. "Evidently silly, since you're ready to take Mrs. Poor. You were telling me—"

"Yeah. Of course, Goodwin told you about the box of cigars."

"Something."

"Well, that was it, all right. Poor smoked about a box every two days, boxes of twenty-five. He bought them ten boxes at a time, from a place on Varick Street near his office and factory. There were four unopened boxes in his apartment and they're okay. The one he started on when he got home Tuesday night—the twenty-four left in it are all loaded. Any one of them would have killed him two seconds after he lit it."

Wolfe muttered, "That's hard to believe—inside a cigar—"

"Right. I thought so, too. The firm of Blaney & Poor has been making trick cigars for years, but they're harmless; all they do is *phut*, and make you jump. What's in these twenty-four is anything but harmless—a special kind of instantaneous fuse the size of an ordinary thread, and a very special explosive capsule that was invented during the war and is still on the secret list. Even this is confidential; it's made by the Becker Products Corporation, and their men and the FBI are raising hell trying to find out how this murderer got hold of them. That's not for publication."

"I'm not a publisher."

"Okay."

"Of course," Wolfe remarked, "the Alta Vista people deny all knowledge."

"Sure. We let them analyze five of the twenty-four, after removing the fuses and capsules, and they say the fillers are theirs but the wrappers are not. They say whoever sliced them open and inserted the things and rewrapped them was an expert, and anyhow anybody could see that.

"Now, then. There are six people connected with Blaney & Poor who are good at making trick cigars. Four of them are mixed up in this. Helen Vardis is one of their most highly skilled workers. Joe Groll is the foreman and can do anything. Blaney is the best of all; he shows them how. And Mrs. Poor worked there for four years when she was Martha Davis, up to two years ago, when she married Poor."

Wolfe shuddered. "Six people good at making trick cigars. Couldn't the murder have been a joint enterprise? Couldn't you convict all of them?"

"I don't appreciate jokes about murder," Cramer said morosely. "I wish I could. It's a defect of character. As for getting the loaded cigars into Poor's apartment, that also is wide open. He always had them delivered to his office, and the package would lie around there, sometimes as long as two or three days, until he took it home. So anybody might have substituted the loaded box. . . . But now, about Mrs. Poor. How do you like this? Naturally we gave the cigars and the box everything we had. It was a very neat job. But underneath the cigars we found two human hairs, one five inches long and one six and a half inches. We have compared them with hairs taken from various heads. Those two came from the head of Mrs. Poor. Unquestionably. So I think I'll charge her."

Wolfe's eyes half closed. "I wouldn't do it if I were you, Mr. Cramer."

"No, sir. Let me put it this way." Wolfe maneuvered himself into position for an uplift, and got to his feet. "You have her on trial. The hairs have been placed in evidence. I am the defense attorney. I am speaking to the jury."

Wolfe fixed his eyes on me. "Ladies and gentlemen, I respect your intelligence. The operation of turning those cigars into deadly bombs has been described to you as one requiring the highest degree of skill and the minutest attention. Deft fingers and perfect eyesight were essential. Since the slightest irregularity about the appearance of that box of cigars might have attracted the attention of a veteran smoker, you can imagine the anxious scrutiny with which each cigar was inspected as it was arranged in the box. And you can realize how incredible it is that such a person, so intently engaged on anything and everything the eye could see, could possibly have been guilty of such atrocious carelessness as to leave two of the hairs of her head in that box with those cigars. Ladies and gentlemen, I appeal to your intelligence! I put it to you that those hairs, far from being evidence that Martha Poor killed her husband, are, instead, evidence that Martha Poor did not kill her husband!"

Wolfe sat down and muttered, "Then they acquit her, and whom do you charge next?"

Cramer growled, "So she is your client, after all."

"No, sir, she is not. It was Mr. Poor who paid me. You said you came here because you wanted to be fair. *Pfui.* You came here because you had misgivings. You had them because you are not a ninny. A jury would want to know, anyone concerned would want to know, if those hairs did not get in the box through Mrs. Poor's carelessness, how did they get there? Who has had access to Mrs. Poor's head or hairbrush? Manifestly, that is a forlorn hope. The best chance, I would say, is the explosive capsules. Discover the tiniest link between anyone of the Becker Products Corporation and one of your suspects, and you have it—if not your case, at least your certainty. On that I couldn't help, since I am no longer connected with the War Department. You can't convict anybody at all, let alone Mrs. Poor, without an explanation of how he got the capsules. By the way, what about motive? Mrs. Poor was tired of smelling the smoke from her husband's cigars, perhaps?"

"No. Poor was a tightwad and she wanted money. She gets the whole works plus a hundred thousand insurance. Or, according to that girl, Helen Vardis, she wanted Joe Groll, and now they'll get married."

"Proof?"

"Oh, talk." Cramer looked frustrated. "It goes away back to when Mrs. Poor was working there."

Wolfe frowned. "Another thing, Mr. Cramer, about a jury. As you know, I am strongly disinclined to leave this house for any purpose whatever. I detest the idea of leaving it to go to a courtroom and sit for hours on those wooden abominations they think are seats, and the thing they provide for witnesses is even worse. I would strain a point to avoid that experience; but if it can't be avoided, Mr. Goodwin and I shall have to testify that Mr. Poor sat in that chair and told us of his conviction that Mr. Blaney was going to kill him. You know juries; you know how that would affect them. Suppose again that I am the defense attorney and—"

"Heaven help us," I thought, "he's going to address the jury again."

But I got a break in the form of an excuse to skip it when the doorbell rang. Winking at Cramer as I passed him on my way to the hall, I proceeded to the front door and took a peek. What I saw seemed to call for finesse, so I opened the door just enough to slip through out to the stoop, shut the door behind me, and said, "Hello, let's have a little conference."

Conroy Blaney squeaked at me, "What's the idea?"

I grinned at him amiably. "A policeman named Cramer is in Mr. Wolfe's office having a talk, and I thought maybe you had had enough of him for a while. Unless you're tailing him?"

"Inspector Cramer?"

"Yes," I said. "Are you tailing him?"

"Good heavens, no. I want to see Nero Wolfe."

"Okay; then follow me, and after we are inside don't talk. Get it?"

"I want to see Nero Wolfe immediately."

"Will you follow instructions or won't you? Do you also want to see Cramer?"

"Very well, open the door."

As I inserted my key I was telling myself, murder or not, I am going to be wishing this specimen was big enough to plug in the jaw before this is finished. He did, however, obey orders. I conducted him into the front room, the door connecting it with the office being closed, left him there on a chair, and went back by way of the hall.

"It can wait," I told Wolfe. "The man from Plehn's with the Dendrobiums."

But a minute later Cramer was standing up to go. Knowing how suspicious he was, as well as how many good reasons he had had for being suspicious on those premises, and also knowing how cops in general love to open doors that don't belong to them just to stick a head in, I escorted him to the front and let him out, then returned to the office and told Wolfe who the company was.

Wolfe frowned. "What does he want?"

"I think he wants to confess. I warn you, his squeak will get on your nerves."

"Bring him in. . . ."

I expected to enjoy it, and I did, only it didn't last long. Blaney started off by rejecting the red leather chair and choosing one of the spares, which irritated both of us, since we like our routine. Perched on it, he began, "I was thinking, on my way here, fate has thrown us together, Wolfe. You dominate your field and I dominate mine. We were bound to meet."

It caught Wolfe so completely off balance that he only muttered sarcastically, "Good heavens!"

Blaney nodded with satisfaction. "I knew we would have many things in common. That's my favorite expression, I use it all the time—Good heavens. But you probably want to know where I stand. I would if I were you. I did not come here because of any fear on my own account. There is not the remotest chance of my safety being endangered. But Tuesday evening up at Gene's apartment I heard a man saying to another man—I presume they were detectives—something about Mrs. Poor being Nero Wolfe's client, and in that case Mrs. Poor was as good as out of it, and Nero Wolfe had decided on Blaney, and, if so, Blaney might as well get his leg shaved for the electrode.

"I knew that might be just talk, but I really think it would be a shame for you to make yourself ridiculous, and I don't think you want to. I'm willing to take this trouble. You're not a man to reach a conclusion without reasons. That wouldn't be scientific, and you and I are both scientists. Tell me your reasons, one by one, and I'll prove they're no good. Go ahead."

"Archie." Wolfe looked at me. "Get him out of here."

There wasn't the slightest indication from Blaney that anyone had said anything except him, and I was too fascinated to move.

Blaney went on: "The truth is, you have no reasons. The fact that Gene was afraid I would kill him proves nothing. He was a born coward. I did describe to him some of the methods by which I could kill a man without detection, but that was merely to impress upon him the fact that he continued to own half of the business by my sufferance, and therefore my offer of twenty thousand dollars for his half was an act of generosity. *I* wouldn't condescend to kill a man. No man is worth that much to me, or that little."

He had performed a miracle. I saw it with my own eyes—Nero Wolfe fleeing in haste from his own office. He had chased many a fellow being from that room, but that was the first time he had ever, himself, been chased. It became evident that he wasn't even going to risk staying on that floor when the sound was heard of the door of his elevator banging open and shut.

I told Blaney, "Overlook it. He's eccentric."

Blaney said, "So am I."

I nodded. "Geniuses are."

Blaney was frowning. "Does he really think I killed Gene Poor?"

"Yeah. He does now."

"Why now?"

I waved it away. "Forget it. I'm eccentric, too."

The house phone buzzed, and I swung my chair around and took it. It was Wolfe, on his room extension:

"Archie. Is that man gone?"

"No, sir."

"Get him out of there at once. Phone Saul and tell him to come here as soon as possible."

"Yes, sir."

The line went dead. So he had actually been stirred up enough to blow some dough on the case. Saul Panzer, being merely the best all-round investigator west of Nantucket, not counting me, came to twenty bucks a day plus expenses.

To get Blaney out I nearly had to carry him. . . .

As luck would have it, Saul Panzer was not to be had at the moment. Since he was free-lancing, you never knew. I finally got it that he was out on Long Island on a job, and left word for him to call. He did so around three, and said he would be able to get to the office soon after six o'clock.

It became obvious that to Wolfe, who had been stirred up, money was no object, since he blew another $1.80 on a phone call to Washington. I got it through without any trouble to General Carpenter, head of G2, under whom I had been a major and for whom Wolfe had helped to solve certain problems connected with the war. The favor he asked of Carpenter, and of course got, was a telegram that would open doors at the premises of the Becker Products Corporation.

Not satisfied with that, he opened another valve. At ten minutes to four he said to me, "Archie, find out whether it seems advisable for me to talk with that man, Joe Groll."

"Yes, sir. Tea leaves? Or there's a palmist over on Seventh—"

"See him and find out."

So after he went up to the plant-rooms I phoned the office of Blaney & Poor and got Joe Groll. No persuasion was required. His tone implied that he would be glad to talk with anybody, anytime, anywhere, after business hours. He would be free at five-thirty. I told him to meet me at Pete's Bar & Grill on 19th Street.

In addition to good whisky, Pete's has booths partitioned to the ceiling, which furnishes privacy. Seated in one of them I was surprised to realize that you could make out a case for calling Joe Groll handsome. They had overdone it a little on the ears, but on the whole he was at least up to grade if not fancy.

After we got our drinks I remarked casually, "As I told you on the phone, I want to discuss this murder. You may have heard of Nero Wolfe. Poor and his wife came to see him Tuesday afternoon, to tell him Blaney was going to dissolve the partnership by killing Poor."

He nodded. "Yes, I know."

"Oh. The cops told you?"

"No, Martha told me yesterday. Mrs. Poor. She asked me to come up and help about things—the funeral." He made a gesture. "Gosh, one lousy civilian funeral makes more fuss than a thousand dead men over there did."

I nodded. "Sure; the retail business always has more headaches than the wholesale." I sipped my highball. "I don't go for this theory that it was Helen Vardis that killed Poor. Do you?"

"What?" He stared. "What are you talking about? What theory?" His fingers had tightened around his glass.

"Why, this idea that Helen Vardis would do anything for Blaney, God knows why, and she made the cigars for him, and she went there Tuesday night—"

"Well, for Pete's sake." He said that calmly, and then suddenly his voice went up high: "Who thought that one up? Was it that cop Rowcliff? That buzzard? Was it Nero Wolfe? Was it you?"

He sounded next door to hysterical. I sure had pushed the wrong button, or maybe the right one, but I didn't want him sore at me. "It wasn't me," I assured him. "Don't get excited."

He laughed. It sounded bitter but not hysterical. "That's right," he said, "I must remember that—not to get excited. Everybody is very thoughtful. They put you in uniform and teach you what every young man ought to know, and take you across the ocean in the middle of hell, bombs, bullets, shells, flame-throwers; your friends die right against you and bleed down your neck; and after two years of that they bring you home and turn you loose and tell you, now, remember, don't get excited."

He drank his highball, clear to the bottom, and put his glass down.

"I'm all right," he said calmly. "So I am loose again and come back to my job. Don't get excited. Here's what I find. A girl I had been sort of counting on, named Martha Davis, has married the boss, and no one told me. It wasn't her fault, she never promised me anything, not even to write to me; but I had been looking forward to seeing her. Oh, I saw her, because she was in trouble and asked me to help. She thought her husband was going to get killed, and knowing Blaney as I did, I saw no reason to doubt it. I met her places a few times because she wanted to talk it over with me, and she wanted me to watch Blaney. Why am I spilling all this to you? You weren't in the Army."

"I was in the Army," I said, "but I admit nobody bled down my neck. I did what I was told."

"So did I, brother. Didn't we all? Anyhow, I wasn't heartbroken, because she seemed a little older than I had remembered her, and, besides, there was another girl who had been nothing but a kid in the factory, but she had grown up. I'm not telling you anything the cops don't know. Gosh, the cops are something! That's Helen Vardis. You saw her the other night."

"Yeah, she seemed upset."

"Upset?" He laughed a one-second laugh. "Sure, she was upset. I fell for her like a Sherman tank roaring down a cliff. I certainly hit bottom. . . . All right, I guess I will. Thanks."

That was for the second drink, arriving. He picked it up and swallowed half.

"It is good whisky. . . . She seemed to reciprocate. I guess I was a little leery of all civilians, even her, but she seemed to reciprocate. I can't understand what that guy Poor had that attracted girls, and at his age, too. That I will never understand. First Martha, and then her. I saw her with him in a restaurant. Then I saw them together in his car. Then I followed her from the office and watched her meet him in Fourteenth Street, and they took a taxi and I lost them. Naturally, I sprung it on her, and she the same as told me to go to hell. She refused to explain."

He finished the drink. "So they say don't get excited. The cops told me yesterday and again today, don't get excited. Which one is it that thinks Helen Vardis was helping Blaney? Is it you?"

I shook my head. "I'm not a cop. It's just something I heard and I wondered what you thought of it. In a murder case you're apt to hear anything."

"Why do you listen?"

"Why not? I'm listening to you."

He laughed, somewhat better. "You're a hell of a guy to work on a murder. You don't try to hammer me and you don't try to uncle. Do you want to come along and help me do something?"

"I might if you'd describe it."

"Wait a minute. I want to make a phone call."

He slid along the seat and left the booth. I sipped my highball and lit a cigarette, wondering whether the feel of blood going down his neck had really loosed a screw in him or he was just temporarily rattled.

In less than five minutes he was back, sliding along the seat again, and announcing, "Blaney's up at his place in Westchester. I phoned to ask him about a job we're doing, but really to find out if he was up there."

"Good. Now we know. Is that where we're going?"

"No." He gazed at his glass. "I thought I drank that—Oh. You had it filled again. Thanks." He took some. "Anyway, that idea about Helen is silly, because it was obviously either Martha or Blaney, if the cops have any brains at all. Martha says she went to Blaney's place in Westchester at six-fifteen

Tuesday to keep a date she and Poor had with him, and there was no one there and she waited around until ten minutes to seven. Blaney says he was there all the time, from a quarter to six on, all evening, until he got the phone call from the police that Poor had been killed. So one of them is lying, and the one that's lying is obviously the one that killed Poor. So it's Blaney."

"Why—because Martha wouldn't lie?"

He frowned at me. "Now, don't smart up. What the hell would she kill him for? She only got him two years ago and he had everything he ever had. Anyway, it was Blaney, and I am fed up with all the gear-grinding, and he is now through with me and I'll be out of a job, so to hell with him. I'm going to see what I can find. On account of the trick cigars the cops wanted to go through the office and factory, and Blaney told them sure, go ahead, go as far as you like, but he didn't tell them about the abditories, and they didn't find them."

"How do you spell it?"

He spelled it: "Abditory. Place to hide things. Blaney says it's a scientific term. The office is full of them. I haven't had a chance before now since Tuesday night, but with him up in Westchester I'm going to take a look. With a nut like Blaney you never can tell. Want to come along?"

"Have you got keys?"

"Keys? I'm the foreman."

"Okay, finish your drink."

He did so, and I got the bill and paid it, and we got our hats and coats and emerged.

When we were on the sidewalk alongside my car I asked him to wait a minute, marched back to where a taxi was parked, jerked the door open, and stuck my head in, and said, "There's no sense in this, Helen. Come on and ride with us."

"Lookit, mister—" the taxi driver began, like a menace. "You'd better get out!"

"Everybody relax," I said pleasantly. "I can't get out because I'm not in; I'm only looking in." I told the temples, "This is absolutely childish. You don't know the first principles of tailing, and this driver you happened to get is, if anything, worse. If you insist on tailing Joe, okay; we'll put him in the cab and let them go ahead, and you ride with me and I'll show you how it's done."

"Yeah?" the menace croaked. "Show her how what's done?"

"See that," I told her. "See the kind of mind he's got."

"You're as smart as they come, aren't you?"

"That," I said, "you will learn more about as time goes on. I'm at least smarter than you are if you let that meter continue to tick. Pay him and come on."

She moved, so I stood aside and held the door while she got out. On the sidewalk she faced me and said, "You seem to be in charge of everything, so you pay him."

It was an unpleasant surprise, but I didn't hesitate—first, because I liked the way she was handling herself, and, second, because all expenses would come out of the five grand anyway. So I parted with two bucks, took her elbow and steered her to the sedan, opened the front door and told Joe Groll, "Move over a little. There's room for three."

She did so and I got in and slammed the door. By the time I had got the engine started and rolled to the corner and turned downtown, neither of them had said a word.

"If I were you folks," I told them, "I would incorporate and call it the Greater New York Mutual Tailing League. I don't see how you keep track of who is following whom on any given day. Of course, if one of you gets convicted of murder that will put a stop to it. You have now, however, the one good reason that I know of for getting married, the fact that a wife can't testify against a husband or vice versa."

I swerved around a pushcart. "The idea is, Helen, we are bound for the Blaney & Poor office to go through the abditories. We think he hid something in them."

"What?" she demanded.

"We don't know. Maybe a detailed estimate in triplicate of what it would cost to kill Poor. Maybe a blueprint of the cigar. Even a rough sketch would help."

"That's ridiculous. You sound to me like a clown."

"Good. It is a well-known fact that clowns have the biggest and warmest hearts on record except mothers and three characters in books by Dickens."

I pulled over to the curb in front of Blaney & Poor's on Varick Street. . . .

That office was no place for a stranger to poke around in. It was on the first floor of a dingy old building in the middle of the block, with part of the factory, so Joe said, in the rear, and the rest on the second floor. As soon as we were inside and had the lights turned on, Helen sat in a chair at a desk and looked disdainful, but as the search went on I noticed she kept her eyes open.

Joe tossed his hat and coat on a chair, got a screwdriver from a drawer, went to the typewriter on the desk Helen was sitting at, used the screwdriver, lifted out the typewriter roller, unscrewed an end of it and turned it vertical, and about four dozen dice rolled out. He held the open end of the roller so the light would hit it right, peered in, put the dice back in and screwed the end on, and put the roller back on the machine.

His fingers were as swift and accurate as any I had ever seen. Even if I had known about it, I would have needed at least ten minutes for the operation; he took about three.

"Trick dice?" I asked him.

"They're just a stock item," he said, and went over to a door in the rear wall, opened it, took it off its hinges, leaned it against a desk, knelt on the floor, removed a strip from the bottom edge of the door; and out came about ten dozen lead pencils.

"Trick pencils?"

"When you press, perfume comes out," he said, and stretched out flat to look into the abditory.

Joe continued his tour of the abditories, which were practically everywhere, in desk lamps, chair legs, water cooler, ash trays, even one in the metal base of a desk calendar that was on a big desk in the corner.

It was while he had that one open, jiggling things out of it, that I heard him mutter, "This is a new one on me." He walked over and put something on the desk in front of Helen and asked her, "What is that thing, do you know?"

She picked it up, inspected it, and shook her head. "Haven't the faintest idea."

"Let me see." I got up and went over, and Helen handed it to me. The second I saw it I stopped being casual inside, but I tried to keep the outside as before. It was a long, thin metal capsule, about three-quarters of an inch long and not over an eighth of an inch in diameter, smooth all over, with no seam or opening, except at one end, where a thread came through, a dark-brown, medium-sized thread as long as my index finger.

I grunted. "Where did you find it?"

"You saw me find it." Joe sounded either irritated or something else. "In that calendar on Blaney's desk."

"Oh, that's Blaney's desk? How many, just this one?"

"No, several." Joe went to Blaney's desk and then came back to us. "Three more. Four altogether."

I took them from him and compared. They were all the same. I regarded Helen's attractive face. She looked interested. I regarded Joe's handsome face if you didn't count the ears. He looked more interested.

"I think," I said, "that it was one of these things that was in the cigar that Poor never smoked. What do you think?"

Joe said, "I think we can damn soon find out. Give me one." He had a gleam in his eye.

I shook my head. "The idea doesn't appeal to me." I looked at my wrist. "Quarter to nine. Mr. Wolfe is in the middle of dinner. The proper thing is for you to take these objects to the police, but they're likely to feel hurt because you didn't tell them about the abditories when they were here. We can't interrupt Mr. Wolfe's dinner, even with a phone call, so I suggest that I buy you a meal somewhere, modest but nutritious, and then we all three go and deliver these gadgets, calendar included, to him."

"You take them to him," Joe said. "I think I'll go home."

"I think I'll go home, too," Helen said.

"No. Nothing doing. You'll just follow each other, and get all confused again. If I take these things to Wolfe without taking you he'll fly into a temper and phone the police to go get you. Not to flatter myself, wouldn't you prefer to come with me?"

Helen said in the nastiest possible tone, "I don't have to eat at the same table with him."

Joe said, trying to match her tone but failing because he wasn't a female, "If you did I wouldn't eat."

Which was all a lot of organic fertilizer. I took them to Gallagher's, where they not only ate at the same table, but devoured hunks of steak served from the same platter. It was a little after ten when we got to Nero Wolfe's place on 35th Street. . . .

Wolfe was seated behind his desk, with the evening beer—one empty bottle and two full ones—on a tray in front of him. Joe Groll, in the red leather chair, also had a bottle and glass, on the check-writing table beside him. Helen Vardis would have made a good cheesecake shot over by the big globe in the upholstered number that Wolfe, himself, sometimes used. I was at my desk, as usual, with my oral report all finished, watching Wolfe inspect the workmanship of the removable bottom of the desk calendar.

He put it down, picked up one of the metal capsules with its dangling thread, and gave it another look, put that down too, and turned his half-closed eyes on Joe:

"Mr. Groll."

"Yes, sir."

"I don't know how much sense you have. If you have slightly more than your share, you must realize that if I hand these things to the police with Mr. Goodwin's story, they will conclude that you are a liar. They will ask, why did you wait until witnesses were present to explore those hiding places? Why did you think they were worth exploring at all? Is it even remotely credible that Mr. Blaney, after preparing that murderous box of cigars, would leave these things there on his desk in a hiding place that a dozen people know about? They will have other questions, but that's enough to show that they will end by concluding that you put the capsules in the calendar yourself. Where did you get them?"

Joe said firmly, "I wouldn't know about how much sense I've got, but it happened exactly the way you've heard it. As for my waiting for witnesses, I didn't. I only waited until I was sure Blaney was out of range, up at his Westchester place, and then Goodwin was there, and I asked him to come along on the spur of the moment. As for its being remotely credible what you said, there's nothing Blaney wouldn't do. He's a maniac. You don't know him, so you don't know that."

Wolfe grunted. "The devil I don't. I do know that. How long have those hiding places been in existence?"

"Some of them for years. Some are more recent."

Wolfe tapped the desk calendar with a finger. "How long has this been there?"

"Oh—" Joe considered. "Four or five years. It was there before I got in the Army. . . . Look here, Mr. Wolfe, you seem to forget that when I saw those things tonight I had no idea what they were, and I still haven't. You seem to know they're the same as the loads in those cigars, and if you do, okay, but I don't."

"Neither do I."

"Then what the hell? Maybe they're full of Chanel Number Five or just fresh air."

Wolfe nodded. "I was coming to that. If I show them to Mr. Cramer he'll take them away from me, and also he'll arrest you as a material witness, and I may possibly need you. We'll have to find out for ourselves."

He pushed a button, and in a moment Fritz entered. Wolfe asked him, "Do you remember that metal percolator that someone sent us and we were fools enough to try?"

"Yes, sir."

"Did you throw it out?"

"No, sir, it's in the basement."

"Bring it here, please."

Fritz went. Wolfe picked up a capsule and frowned at it and then turned to me: "Archie. Get me a piece of newspaper, the can of household oil, and a piece of string."

Under the circumstances I would have preferred to go out for a walk, but there was a lady present who might need protection, so I did as I was told. When I got back, Fritz was there with the percolator, which was two-quart size, made of thick metal. We three men collected at Wolfe's desk to watch the preparations, but Helen stayed in her chair.

With my scissors Wolfe cut a strip of newspaper about two by eight inches, dropped oil on it and rubbed it in with his finger and rolled it tight into a long, thin, oiled wick. Then we held one end of it against the end of the capsule thread, overlapping a little, and Joe Groll, ready with the piece of string, tied them together. Wolfe opened the lid of the percolator.

"No," Joe objected. "That might stop it. Anyhow, we don't want this glass here."

He finished the job with his swift, sure fingers, while Wolfe and Fritz and I watched. Removing the glass cap and the inside contraption from the percolator, he lowered the capsule though the hole, hanging onto the free end of the oiled wick with one hand while with the other he stuffed a scrap of newspaper in the hole just tight enough to keep the wick from slipping on through. Wolfe nodded approvingly and leaned back in his chair. About two inches of the wick protruded.

"Put it on the floor." Wolfe pointed. "Over there."

Joe moved, taking a folder of matches from his pocket, but I intercepted him. "Wait a minute. Gimme." I took the percolator. "The rest of you go in the hall. I'll light it."

Fritz went, and so did Helen, but Joe merely backed to a corner and Wolfe didn't move from his chair.

I told Wolfe, "I saw Poor's face and you didn't. Go in the hall."

"Nonsense. That little thing?"

"Then I'll put a blanket over it."

"No. I want to see it."

"So do I," Joe said. "What the hell? I'll bet it's a dud."

I shrugged. "I hope Helen has had a course in first aid." I put the percolator on the floor over by the couch, about five paces from Wolfe's desk, lit a match and applied it to the end of the wick, and stood back and watched. An inch of the wick burned in three seconds. "See you at the hospital," I said cheerily, and beat it to the hall, leaving the door open a crack to see through.

It may have been ten seconds, but it seemed like three times that, before the bang came, and it was a man-size bang, followed immediately by another but different kind of bang. Helen grabbed my arm, but not waiting to enjoy that, I swung the door open and stepped through. Joe was still in the corner, looking surprised. Wolfe had twisted around in his chair to gaze at a bruise in the plaster of the wall behind him.

"The percolator lid," he muttered. "It missed me."

"Yeah." I moved across to observe angles and directions. "By about an inch." I stooped to pick up the percolator lid, bent out of shape. "This would have felt good on your skull."

Fritz and Helen were back in, and Joe came over with the percolator in his hand. "Feel it," he said. "Hot. Look how it's twisted. Some pill, that is. Dynamite or TNT would never do that, not that amount. I wonder what's in it?" He sniffed. "Do you smell anything? I don't."

"It's outrageous," Wolfe declared. I looked at him in surprise. Instead of being relaxed and thankful for his escape, he was sitting straight in his chair, which meant he was ready to pop with fury. "That thing nearly hit me in the head. This settles it. Against Mr. Poor there may have been a valid grievance. Against me, none."

"Well, for Pete's sake." I regarded him without approval. "That's illogical. Nobody aimed it at you. Didn't I tell you to go in the hall? However, if it made you mad enough to do a little work, fine. Here's Joe and Helen, you can start on them."

"No." He got to his feet. "I'm going to bed." He bowed to Helen. "Good night, Miss Vardis." He tilted his head a hundredth of an inch at Joe. "Good night, sir. . . . Archie, put these remaining capsules in the safe." He marched to the door and was gone.

"Quite a guy," Joe remarked. "He didn't bat an eye when that thing went off and the lid flew past his ear."

"Yeah," I growled. "He has fits. He's having one now. Instead of taking you two apart and turning you inside out, which is what he should have done, he didn't even tell you where to head in. Do you tell the police about tonight or not? I would say, for the present, *not*. . . . Come on. Taxis are hard to find around here, and I've got to put the car away anyhow. I'll drop you somewhere."

We went. When I got back, some time later, I made a little discovery. Opening the safe to follow my custom of checking the cash last thing at night, I found two hundred bucks gone and an entry in the book for that amount in Wolfe's handwriting, which said, "Saul Panzer, advance on expenses."

So, anyhow, Saul was working. . . .

Friday morning, having nothing else to do, I solved the case. I did it with cold logic. Everything fitted perfectly, and all I needed was enough evidence for a jury. Presumably that was what Saul Panzer was getting. I do not intend to put it all down here, the way I worked it out, because, first, it would take three full pages, and, second, I was wrong. Anyway, I had it solved when, a little before nine o'clock, I was summoned to Wolfe's room and given an errand to perform, with detailed instructions. It sent me to 20th Street.

I would have just as soon have dealt with one of the underlings, but Cramer himself was in his office and said to bring me in. As I sat down, he whirled his chair a quarter turn, folded his arms, and asked conversationally, "What have you two liars got cooked up now?"

I grinned at him. "Why don't you call Wolfe a liar to his face some day? Do it while I'm there." I took two of the capsules, with threads attached, from my vest pocket and put them on his desk, and inquired, "Do you need any more of these?"

He picked one of them up and gave it a good look, then the other one; put them in a drawer of his desk, folded his arms again, and looked me in the eye to shrivel me.

"All right," he said quietly. "Go on. They came in the mail, in a package addressed to Wolfe with letters cut out of a magazine."

"No, sir; not at all. Where I spent the night last night I was idly running my fingers through her lovely hair and felt something, and there they were." Cramer was strictly a family man and had stern ideas. Seeing I had him blushing, I went on, "Actually, it was like this."

I told him the whole story.

He had questions, both during the recital and at the end, and I answered what I could. The one I had expected him to put first he saved till the last.

"Well," he said, "for the present we'll assume that I believe you. You know what that amounts to, but we'll assume it. Even so, how are you on figures? How much are two and one?"

"I'm pretty good. Two plus one plus one equals four."

"Yes? Where do you get that second plus one?"

"So you *can* add," I conceded. "Mr. Wolfe thought maybe you couldn't. However, so can we. Four capsules were found. Two are there in your drawer. One, as I told you, was used in a scientific experiment in Wolfe's office and damn' near killed him. He's keeping the other one for the Fourth of July."

"Like hell he is. I want it."

"Try and get it." I stood up.

"Beat it. I'll get it."

I turned, with dignity, and went. . . .

When I got back to Wolfe's, Fritz met me in the hall to tell me there was a woman in the office, and when I entered I found it was Martha Poor.

I sat down at my desk and told her, "Mr. Wolfe will be engaged until eleven o'clock." I glanced at my wrist. "He'll be down in forty minutes."

She nodded. "I know. I'll wait."

She didn't look exactly bedraggled, nor would I say pathetic, but there was certainly nothing of the man-eater about her. She seemed older than she had on Tuesday. Anyone could have told at a glance that she was having trouble, but whether it was bereavement or bankruptcy was indicated neither by her clothes nor by her expression. She made you feel like going up to her, maybe putting your hand on her shoulder or patting her on the arm, and asking, "Anything I can do?"

I went to the kitchen and asked Fritz if he had told Wolfe who had come to see him, and Fritz said he hadn't, he had left that to me. So I returned to the office, buzzed the plant-rooms, got Wolfe, and told him, "Returned from mission. I gave them to Cramer himself, and he says he'll get the other one. Mrs. Poor is down here waiting to see you."

"Confound that woman. Send her away."

"But she–"

"No. I know what she wants. I studied her. She wants to know what I'm doing to earn that money. Tell her to go home and read that receipt."

The line died. I swung my chair around and told Martha, "Mr. Wolfe says for you to go home and read the receipt."

She stared. "What?"

"He thinks you came to complain because he isn't earning the money your husband paid him, and the idea of having to earn money offends him. It always has."

"But–that's ridiculous. Isn't it?"

"Certainly it is." I fought back the impulse to step over and pat her on the shoulder. "But my advice is to humor him, much as I enjoy having you here. Nobody alive can handle him but me. If he came down and found you here he would turn around and walk out. If you have anything special to say, tell me, and I'll tell him. He'll listen to me because he has to or fire me, and he can't fire me because then he would never do any work at all and would eventually starve to death."

"I shouldn't think–" She stopped and stood up. She took a step toward the door, then turned and said, "I shouldn't think a cold-blooded murder is something to joke about."

I had to fight back the impulse again. "I'm not joking," I declared. "Plain facts. What did you want to say to him?"

"I just wanted a talk with him. He hasn't come to see me. Neither have you." She tried to smile, but all she accomplished was to start her lip quivering. She stopped it. "You haven't even phoned me. I don't know what's happening. The police asked me about two of my hairs being in that box of cigars, and I suppose they have told Mr. Wolfe about it, and I don't even know what he thinks or what he told the police."

I grinned at her. "That's easy. He made a speech to the jury, demonstrating that those hairs in the box were evidence that you did not kill your husband." I went to her and put a hand on her arm, like a brother. "Listen, lady. Isn't the funeral this afternoon?"

"Yes."

"Okay. Go and have the funeral; that's enough for you for one day. Leave the rest to me. I mean, if anything occurs that it would help you to know about, I'll see that you know. Right?"

She didn't pull anything corny like grasping my hand, with hers firm and warm, or gazing at me with moist eyes filled with trust. She did meet my eyes, but only long enough to say, "Thank you, Mr. Goodwin," and turned to go. I went to the front door and let her out. . . .

After Wolfe came down, the relations between us were nothing to brag about. Apparently he had nothing to offer, and I was too sore to start in on him.

He passed the time until lunch going through catalogues, and at 2:30 P.M. with a veal cutlet and half a bushel of Fritz's best mixed salad stowed in the hold, he returned to the office and resumed the catalogues. That got interrupted before long, but not by me. The bell rang and I went to the front, and it was Saul Panzer.

I took him to the office, where Wolfe greeted him and then told me, "Archie. Go up and help Theodore with the pollen lists."

I did my best with Theodore and the pollen lists, not wanting to take it out on them. The conference with Saul seemed to be comprehensive, since a full hour passed before the house phone in the potting-room buzzed. Theodore answered it, and told me that I was wanted downstairs.

When I got there Saul was gone. I had a withering remark prepared, thinking to open up with it, but had to save it for some other time. Wolfe was seated behind his desk, leaning back with his eyes closed, and his lips were moving, pushing out and then in again, out and in.

So I sat down and kept my mouth shut. The brain had actually got on the job, and I knew better than to make remarks, withering or not, during the performance of miracles. The first result, which came in ten or twelve minutes after I entered, did not, however, seem to be very miraculous. He opened his eyes halfway, grunted, and muttered, "Archie. Yesterday you showed me an article in a paper about a man's body found in an orchard near White Plains, but I didn't look at it. Now I want it."

"Yes, sir. There was more this morning—"

"Have they identified the body?"

"No, sir. The head was smashed—"

"Get it."

I obeyed. Newspapers were kept in the office for three days. I opened it to the page and handed it to him. He would read a newspaper only one way, holding it out wide open, no folding, with his arms stretched. I had never tried to get him to do it more intelligently because it was the only strenuous exercise he ever got and was therefore good for him. He finished the Thursday piece and asked for Friday's, and finished that.

Then he told me, "Get the district attorney of Westchester County. What's his name? Fraser?"

"Right." I got busy with the phone. I had no trouble getting the office, but then they gave me the usual line about Mr. Fraser being in conference, and I had to put on pressure. Finally the elected person said hello.

Wolfe took it. "How do you do, Mr. Fraser? . . . Nero Wolfe. I have something to give you. That body found in an orchard Wednesday evening with the head crushed—has it been identified?"

Fraser was brusque: "No. What—?"

"Please. I'm giving you something. Put this down: Arthur Howell, 914 West 78th Street, New York. He worked for the Becker Products Corporation of Basston, New Jersey. They have an office at 622 East 42nd Street, New York. His dentist was Lewis Marley, 699 Park Avenue, New York. . . . That should help. Try that. In return for this, I would appreciate it very much if you will have me notified the moment the identification is made. Did you get it all down?"

"Yes. But what—?"

"No, sir. That's all. That's all you'll get from me until I get word of the identification."

There was some sputtering protest from the White Plains end, but it accomplished nothing. Wolfe hung up, with a self-satisfied smirk on his big face, cleared his throat importantly, and picked up a catalogue.

I growled at him, "So it's in the bag. A complete stranger named Arthur Howell. After snitching the capsules from Becker Products and making the cigars and getting them into Poor's home God knows how, he was overcome by remorse and went to an orchard and took his clothes off and lay down and ran a car over himself with radio control—"

"Archie. Shut up. We are ready to act, in any case, but it will make things a little simpler if that corpse proves to be Mr. Howell, so it is worth waiting for a report on it." He glanced at the clock, which said seven minutes to four, and put the catalogue down. "We might as well prepare it now. Get that capsule from the safe."

I thought to myself, "This time it may not miss him, but, as for me, I'm going outdoors."

However, it appeared that he was going to try some new gag instead of repeating with the percolator. By the time I got the capsule from the safe and convoyed it to him, he had taken two articles from a drawer and put them on his desk. One was a roll of Scotch tape. The other was a medium-sized photograph of a man, mounted on gray cardboard. I gave it a glance, then picked it up and did a thorough job of looking. It was unquestionably Eugene R. Poor.

"Goody," I said enthusiastically. "No wonder you're pleased. Even if Saul had to pay two hundred bucks for it—"

"Archie. Let me have that. . . . Here, hold this thing."

I helped. What I was to hold was the capsule, flat on the cardboard near a corner, while he tore off a piece of tape and fastened it there. When he lifted the photo and jiggled it to see if the fastening was firm, the thread dangled over Poor's right eye.

"Put it in an envelope and in the safe," he said, then glanced at the clock and made for the hall and the elevator.

At six o'clock he returned to the office, rang for Fritz to bring beer, and took up where he had left off with the catalogues. At eight o'clock Fritz summoned us to dinner. At nine-thirty we returned to the office. At a quarter to ten a phone call came from District Attorney Fraser. The body had been identified. It was Arthur Howell. An assistant district attorney and a pair of detectives were on their way to 35th Street to ask Wolfe how come and would he please supply all necessary details, including the present address of the murderer.

Wolfe hung up, leaned back and sighed, and muttered at me, "Archie. You'll have to pay a call on Mrs. Poor."

I objected, "She's probably in bed, tired out. The funeral was today."

"It can't be helped. Saul will go with you."

I stared. "Saul?"

"Yes. He's up in my room asleep. He didn't get to bed last night. You will take her that photograph of her husband. You should leave as soon as possible, before that confounded Westchester lawyer gets here. I don't want to see him. Tell Fritz to bolt the door after you go. Ring my room and tell Saul to come down at once. Then I'll give you your instructions." . . .

The appearance of the living-room in the Poor apartment on 84th Street was not the same as it had been when I had arrived there three evenings before. Not only was there no army of city employees present and no man of the house, with his face gone, huddled on the floor, but the furniture had been moved around. The chair Poor had sat in when he lit his last cigar was gone, probably to the cleaners on account of spots, the table Cramer had used for headquarters had been shifted to the other side of the room, and the radio had been moved to the other end of the couch. Martha Poor was sitting on the couch, and I was on a chair and I had pulled around to face her. She was wearing something that wasn't a bathrobe and wasn't exactly a dress, modest, with sleeves and only a proper amount of throat showing.

"I'm here under orders," I told her. "I said this morning that if anything happened that it would help you to know about I'd see that you knew, but this isn't it. This is different. Nero Wolfe sent me, with orders. I just want to make that clear. Item number one is to hand you this envelope and invite you to look at the contents."

She took it from me. With steady fingers, slow-moving rather than hurried, she opened the flap and pulled out the photograph.

I informed her, "That decoration may look like something by Dali, but it was Nero Wolfe's idea. I am not authorized to discuss it or the picture from any angle, just there it is, except to remark that it is a very good likeness of your husband. I only saw him that one time, the other afternoon at the office, but of course I had a long and thorough look at him. Wednesday we could have sold that photo to a newspaper for a nice amount, but of course we didn't have it Wednesday."

She had put the photo beside her on the couch and was pinching an edge of the cardboard between her index finger and thumbnail, with the nail sinking in. She was looking straight at me. The muscles of her throat had tightened, which no doubt accounted for the change in her voice when she spoke: "Where did you get it?"

I shook my head. "Out of bounds. As I said, I'm under orders. . . . Item number two is just a piece of information to the effect that a man named Saul Panzer is out in the back hall on this floor, standing by the door of the service elevator. Saul is not big, but he just had a nap and is alert. . . . Number three: That naked body found up in Westchester with the head smashed by running a car over it, in an orchard not more than ten minutes' drive from either Monty's Tavern or Blaney's place, has been identified as formerly belonging to a man named Arthur Howell, an employee of the Becker Products Corporation."

Her eyes hadn't moved. I hadn't even seen the lashes blink. She said, in a faraway voice, "I don't know why you tell me about that. Arthur Howell? Did you say Arthur Howell?"

"Yep, that's right. Howell, Arthur. Head flattened to a pancake, but enough left for the dentist. As for telling you about it, I'm only obeying orders." I glanced at my wrist. "Number four: It is now twenty past ten. At a quarter to eleven I am supposed either to arrive back at the office or phone. If I do neither, Nero Wolfe will phone Inspector Cramer, and then here they'll come. Not as many as Tuesday evening, I suppose, because they won't need all the scientists, but plenty."

I stopped, still meeting her eye, and then went on, "Let's see. Photo and capsule, Saul out back, Howell, cops at a quarter to eleven . . . that's all."

She got up and I thought she was going to take hold of me, but all she did was stand in front of me, about eight inches away, looking up at me. She came about up to my chin.

"Archie Goodwin," she said. "You think I'm terrible, don't you? You think I'm an awful woman, bad clear through. Don't you?"

"I'm not thinking, lady. I'm just an errand boy." The funny thing was that if at any moment up to then I had made a list of the ten most beautiful women she would not have been on.

"You've had lots of experience," she said, her head back to look up at me. "You know what women are like. I knew you did when you put your hand on my arm yesterday. You know I'm a man's woman, but it has to be the right man. Just one man's, forever."

She started to smile, and her lip began to quiver, and she stopped it. "But I didn't find the man until it was too late. I didn't find him until you put your hand on my arm yesterday. You could have had me then, forever yours, you could have me now if anything like that was possible. I mean—we could go away together—now—you wouldn't have to promise anything—only you could find out if you want me forever too—the way I want you—"

She lifted her hand and touched me, just a touch, the tips of her fingers barely brushing my sleeve.

I jerked back.

"Listen," I said, with my voice sounding peculiar, so I tried to correct it. "You are extremely good, no question about it, but, as you say, it's too late.

You are trying to go to bat when your side already has three out in the ninth, and that's against the rules. I'll hand it to you that you are extremely good. When you turn it on it flows. But in seven minutes, now, Nero Wolfe will be phoning the police, so you'd better fix your hair. You'll be having your picture taken."

She hauled off and smacked me in the face. I barely felt it and didn't even move my hands.

"I hate men," she said through her teeth. "God, how I hate men!"

She turned and walked to the bathroom, and entered and closed the door.

I didn't know whether she had gone to fix her hair or what, and I didn't care. Instead of crossing to the window and standing there without breathing, as I had done before, I sat down on the edge of the couch and did nothing but breathe. I suppose I did actually know what was going to happen. Anyhow, when it happened, when the noise came, not nearly as loud as it had been in Wolfe's office, because the capsule had been inside a metal percolator, I don't think I jumped or even jerked. I did not run, but walked, to the bathroom door and opened it, and entered.

Less than a minute later I went to the back door in the kitchen and opened that, and told Saul Panzer, "All over. She stuck it in her mouth and lit the fuse. You get out. Go and report to Wolfe. I'll phone the cops."

"But you must be—I'll stay—"

"No, go on. Step on it. I feel fine." . . .

At noon the next day, Saturday, I was getting fed up with all the jabber, because I had a question or two I wanted to ask myself. Cramer had come to Nero Wolfe's office prepared to attack from all sides at once, bringing not only Sergeant Purley Stebbins, but also a gang of civilians consisting of Helen Vardis, Joe Groll, and Conroy Blaney. Blaney had not been let in. On that Wolfe would not budge. Blaney was not to enter his house. The others had all been admitted and were now distributed around the office, with Cramer, of course, in the red leather chair. For over half an hour he and Wolfe had been closer to getting locked in a death grip than I had ever seen them before.

Wolfe was speaking. "Then arrest me," he said. "Shut up, get a warrant, and arrest me."

Cramer, having said about all an inspector could say, merely glared.

"Wording the charge would be difficult," Wolfe murmured. When he was maddest he murmured. "I have not withheld evidence, or obstructed justice, or shielded the guilty. I thought it possible that Mrs. Poor, confronted suddenly with that evidence, would collapse and confess."

"Nuts," Cramer said wearily. "How about confronting me with the evidence? Instead of evidence, what you confront me with is another corpse. And I know"—he tapped the chair arm with a stiff finger—"exactly why. The only evidence you had that was worth a damn was that photograph of Arthur Howell. If you had turned it over to me—"

"Nonsense. You already had a photograph of Arthur Howell. The Becker Products Corporation people gave you a picture of their missing employee on Thursday. So they told Saul Panzer when they gave him a duplicate for me. What good would one more picture of Howell do you?"

"Okay." Cramer was in a losing fight and knew it. "But I didn't know that Howell had come to see you on Tuesday with Mrs. Poor, passing himself off as her husband. Dressed in the same kind of suit and shirt and tie that Poor was wearing that day. Only you and Goodwin knew that."

"I knew it. Mr. Goodwin didn't. He thought it was a photograph of Mr. Poor."

I put in an entry: "Excuse me, but when you gentlemen finish the shadow-boxing I would like to ask a question." I was looking at Wolfe. "You say you knew Poor wasn't Poor. When and how?"

Of course, Wolfe faked. He sighed as if he was thinking, now, this is going to be an awful bore. Actually, he was always tickled stiff to show how bright he was.

His eyes came to me. "Wednesday evening you told me that Mr. Poor smoked ten to fifteen cigars a day. Thursday Mr. Cramer said the same thing. But the man who came here Tuesday, calling himself Poor, didn't even know how to hold a cigar, let alone smoke one."

"He was nervous."

"If he was he didn't show it, except with the cigar. You saw him. It was a ludicrous performance and he should never have tried it. When I learned that Mr. Poor was a veteran cigar smoker, the only question was who had impersonated him in this office? And the complicity of Mrs. Poor was obvious, especially with the added information, also furnished by Mr. Cramer, that no photograph of Mr. Poor was available. There are photographs of everybody nowadays. Mrs. Poor was an ass. She was supremely an ass when she selected me to bamboozle. She wanted to establish the assumption that Mr. Blaney was going to kill Mr. Poor. That was intelligent. She did not want to take her counterfeit Mr. Poor to the police, for fear someone there might be acquainted with the real Mr. Poor. That also was intelligent. But it was idiotic to choose me as the victim."

"She hated men," I remarked.

Wolfe nodded. "She must have had a low opinion of men. In order to get what she wanted, which presumably was something like half a million dollars—counting her husband's fortune, the insurance money, and a half-share in the business after Mr. Blaney had been executed for the murder of Mr. Poor—she was willing to kill three men, two by direct action and one indirectly. Incidentally, except for the colossal blunder of picking me, she was not a fool."

"The hell she wasn't," Cramer growled. "With all that trick setup? She was absolutely batty."

"No, sir." Wolfe shook his head. "She was not. Go back over it. She didn't manufacture the trick setup out of her head; she simply used what she had. On a certain day she found herself with these ingredients at hand: One, the hostility between the partners in the business, amply corroborated by such details as Mr. Poor having Miss Vardis spy on Mr. Blaney, and Mrs.

Poor, herself, having Mr. Groll do the same. . . . Two, her acquaintance with a man named Arthur Howell who had access to a supply of explosive capsules capable of concealment in a cigar, and who also sufficiently resembled her husband in build and general appearance, except for the face itself, and she intended to take care of the face.

"Ten of your men, Mr. Cramer, kept at it for a week or so, can probably trace her association with Mr. Howell. They're good at that. Unquestionably, it was those qualifications of Mr. Howell that suggested the details of her plan. She did not, of course, inform him that she hated men. Quite the contrary. She persuaded him to help her kill her husband, offering, presumably, a strong incentive."

"She was good at offering incentives," I declared. "She was good period. The way she pretended, here Tuesday afternoon, that she wanted Poor to skip it and go live in the country and grow roses, with her to cook and darn socks."

Wolfe nodded. "I admit she was ingenious. . . . By the way, Mr. Groll, did she have an opportunity to conceal those four capsules in that desk calendar?"

"Yes," Joe said. "Helen and I were discussing that. She came there Tuesday to go with Poor to the rodeo, and she could have done it then. Anyway, she had keys, she could have done it any time."

"That was well conceived," Wolfe said approvingly. "That and the hairs in the box of cigars. She was preparing for all contingencies. Neither of those touches was meant for you, Mr. Cramer, but for a jury, in case it ever got to that. She had sense enough to know what a good lawyer could do with complications of that sort. . . . Will you gentlemen have some beer?"

"No," Cramer said bluntly. "I'll have a question. Poor wasn't here Tuesday afternoon?"

"No, sir. Arthur Howell was."

"Then where was Poor?"

"At the rodeo." Wolfe pushed a button, two pushes for beer. "Again Mrs. Poor was ingenious. Look at her schedule for Tuesday. She went to the Blaney & Poor office—what time, Mr. Groll?"

Helen answered: "She came around noon. They went to lunch together and then were going to the rodeo."

"Thank you. So all she had to do was to make some excuse and see that he went to the rodeo alone. It was an ideal selection—Madison Square Garden, that enormous crowd. Then she met Arthur Howell somewhere near, having arranged for him to be dressed as her husband was dressed, and brought him here. She was driving her car—or her husband's car. They left here a little before five o'clock. Between here and Forty-second Street he got out and went to Grand Central to take a train to White Plains. A woman who could persuade a man to help her kill her husband could surely persuade him to take a train to White Plains."

Fritz brought beer, and Wolfe opened a bottle and poured.

"Then she continued to Fiftieth Street and met her husband as he left the rodeo, and they drove to Westchester, having an appointment to see Mr. Blaney at his place there. She talked her husband out of that, left him at a place called Monty's Tavern, drove somewhere, probably the White Plains railroad station, met Arthur Howell there as arranged, drove to an isolated spot probably previously selected, turned off the road into an orchard, killed Mr. Howell or knocked him unconscious with whatever she used for that purpose, removed his clothing and ran the car over him to obliterate his face."

A noise came from Helen Vardis. She had obliterated her own face by covering it with her hands. That gave Joe an excuse to touch her, which he did.

"Granted her basic premise," Wolfe went on, "she couldn't very well have been expected to let Arthur Howell continue to live. She would never have had a carefree moment. What if Mr. Goodwin or I had met him on the street? That thought should have occurred to him, but apparently something about Mrs. Poor had made him quit thinking. There are precedents. Since she was good at detail, I presume she spread his coat over his head so as to leave no telltale matter on her tires. What she then did with the clothing is no longer of interest—at least not to me."

He drank beer. "She proceeded. First to Mr. Blaney's place, to make sure, by looking through windows, that he was alone there, so that she could safely say that she had gone to see him and couldn't find him. Again she was providing for all contingencies. If Arthur Howell's body was, after all, identified, known as that of a man who was with the Becker Products Corporation and had access to those capsules, it would help to have it established that Mr. Blaney had not been at home during the time that Arthur Howell had been killed."

He emptied the glass. "The rest is anticlimax, though, of course, for her it was the grand consummation. She returned to Monty's Tavern, told her husband Mr. Blaney had not been at home, dined with him, drove back to New York and went to their apartment, and got him a nice fresh cigar from a new box. Everything worked perfectly. It sounds more complicated than it really was. Such details as making sure that no photographs of her husband would be available for the newspapers had no doubt been already attended to."

"That receipt you signed," Cramer growled.

"What? Oh. That gave her no difficulty. Arthur Howell gave the receipt to her, naturally, and she put it in her husband's pocket. That was important. It was probably the first thing she did after the cigar exploded."

"Meanwhile, you've got the five thousand dollars."

"Yes, sir. I have."

"But Poor didn't pay it to you. You never saw Poor. You weren't hired by him. If you want to say Mrs. Poor paid it, do you take money from murderers?"

It was one of Cramer's feeblest attempts to be nasty, certainly not up to his standard.

Wolfe merely poured beer and said, "*Pfui!* Whether Mr. Poor paid me or not, he got his money's worth."

Try analyzing the logic of that. I can't.

RIFT IN THE LOOT

by Stuart Palmer and Craig Rice

"I AM IN NO MOOD to face it now, whatever it is," said John J. Malone firmly as he came into his office shortly after 11 that morning. "Maggie, have we any aspirin in the place, and if not will you be a good girl and run down to the drug store?"

"No, *twice,*" said his long-suffering secretary. "You can sweat out your hangover the hard way. I've got to stay here by the phone, it's been buzzing all morning. First, Joe the Angel called and said that just after you left his bar last night a man came in asking for you. Joe said he could always smell a *wronggo* a block away and maybe you ought to watch yourself."

Malone watched himself in the little wall mirror, wincing slightly. He adjusted his lush Countess Mara tie, already well-dusted with cigar ashes. "So what? In the legal profession one meets all kinds of people."

"Joe the Angel seemed to think that this was one you wouldn't want to meet in a dark alley. And boss, it *may* be coincidence, but it says here in the *Tribune* that Eddie Vance busted his way out of Joliet yesterday."

The little lawyer's face brightened. "Eddie the Actor is loose? This may be good news—maybe he'll get to where he stashed that bank loot and finally pay me my fee!"

"Maybe he'll cut your throat, too," Maggie said darkly from behind her typewriter.

"But *why?* I saved him from the chair, didn't I? Never lost a client yet."

"Yes, you saved him. But he still got a hundred years at hard labor, remember? And before he went to the penitentiary he is reported to have squawked very loud that you double-crossed him and must have made some deal with the D.A.'s office."

Malone grinned. Harbin Hamilton, deputy district attorney for Cook County, had for years been trying to nail Malone's hide to the barn door, and the little lawyer wouldn't give him the correct time. But Malone's grin was feeble. "Yes," he admitted thoughtfully, "Vance may have got stir-happy. I suppose I could leave town until they pick him up."

"I have just seven dollars between me and a life of shame, which they say is nice work if you can get it. You couldn't get to Evanston on seven bucks." Maggie looked at her desk pad. "Also Miss Hildegarde Withers is in town, stopping off en route to New York on a holiday, and she wants to have lunch with you."

"Not that—not *today!*" Malone had three times been involved in murder cases with the irrepressible schoolma'am, always with considerable risk to life and limb and with no appreciable fee; but he still had an inexplicable fondness for her. "Okay, call her back and tell her I'll meet her at Henrici's at 1."

"Since *I* have to put up the money," said Maggie sensibly, "we'll make it Thompson's cafeteria." She reluctantly produced five dollars out of the remainder of her week-before-last's pay check. "And watch yourself, Malone. Eddie the Actor is a very nasty character, and I wouldn't be at all surprised if he's the man with the oily voice who's been calling all morning and trying to find out when you'll be in and refusing to give his name. *Why* we ever took that case—"

"I was appointed by the Court as a public defender," Malone reminded her. "Eddie was supposedly broke, though we all knew that he had some $50,000 of the bank's money hidden somewhere—only he never could get to it and wouldn't or couldn't tell me or anybody just where it was. If he'd talked and turned back the loot, I could maybe have got him off with only fifty years."

"Which still is a long time to hang by your thumbs or sit on a red-hot stove, anyway you look at it," Maggie said with a certain tone of veiled sarcasm.

"Not so long when you consider that a bank guard got killed during the caper. We were lucky."

"*We?*" Maggie echoed.

But she relented and went out for the aspirin.

"Exactly why," demanded Miss Hildegarde Withers over their luncheon coffee at Thompson's, "are you looking over your shoulder so often, Malone? Guilty conscience?"

"Maggie believes that I am a marked man," the little lawyer admitted hollowly.

"Another murder case?" cried the schoolteacher, brightening. She wore a hat which could have been put on top of a Dutch chimney for storks to nest in, but her gray-blue eyes were keener than ever. "I could stop over a day or so and help solve it."

He blinked. "This one was solved three years ago—no mystery about it at all."

"Then why are you as jittery as a Mexican jumping bean?"

"Well—I'll fill you in on the story. Eddie Vance, known in underworld circles as Eddie the Actor because he has a wardrobe of uniforms and always manages to look like somebody else when he pulls a bank job, knocked over the Irving Trust, dressed as a window cleaner, with the help of three masked confederates. During the fracas one of them, a cheap hood named Jack Shaw, lost his head and killed a guard. The other two accomplices were shot down by police outside the bank, but Eddie Vance and Shaw escaped in different directions. Eddie himself has never been known to carry a gun, but of course technically he was accessory in a murder. He got away with the loot, some $50,000 in small bills; he was free for just one day but during that time he managed to hide it somewhere. Shaw is still being sought by the police, but since he had no previous criminal record and they have no photographs or fingerprints to work on, it's a tough job. I was appointed to defend Eddie the Actor, and got him off with a hundred years, a minor victory."

"A hundred years is a rather long time," said Miss Withers.

"You took the words right out of Maggie's mouth. But there's still the matter of that cache of dough. Eddie promised me ten grand of it if I saved him from the chair—which I did, with a neat bit of legal sleight of hand, even if I say it myself—but I never saw a red cent of it. Now he's suddenly busted loose and Maggie thinks that maybe he has a grudge because I wasn't able to get him off with a lighter sentence. Maybe she's right, too. Eddie the Actor is a guy who could fight a rattlesnake and give it the first two bites."

"Dear me!" gasped the schoolteacher. "The company you criminal lawyers keep! Malone, it's obvious that you must get out of town for the next few weeks, until the police succeed in re-arresting this unlovely character. You can come along with me to New York; my convertible is having something done to its remission or whatever they call it, but they promised at the garage that it would be ready tomorrow."

Remembering her driving, Malone almost thought that he would rather face Eddie the Actor, but with his usual gallantry he refrained from saying so. "Maybe—"

"Maybe me no maybes. You're coming. I just got a nice bonus on that movie cartoon case I told you about, and I can afford to finance you if necessary, as I presume from past experience that it is. The first thing is to get you packed and out of your hotel before this Eddie character tracks you down. Come on, time is of the essence."

The little lawyer obediently followed her out of the restaurant and they took a taxicab to his hotel. "Maybe you should wait in the lobby?" Malone suggested.

She bridled. "Certainly! Do you think I'm in the habit of going to men's hotel rooms? Besides, the place is probably a shambles."

It was—not to the surprise of John J. Malone when he entered the room, since he had left it so. The only surprise was that a bellboy sat in the one easy chair, reading early editions of the *Herald-American*. On second look he was a rather mature bellboy with a very short haircut and the face of an intelligent weasel. The little lawyer did a double-take. "Eddie Vance!" he cried. He took a deep breath. "Now Eddie-boy, there's no need to get tough about this."

Vance smiled. "You got me entirely wrong, shyster." His hand hovered near his lapel, and it was fairly obvious that if Eddie the Actor had once had an allergy to firearms he had conquered it while in prison. "Siddown, shyster, and listen. I busted out of the pen, see? I came out in a can on the garbage truck—"

"Type casting," murmured Malone under his breath.

"—and I'm going to stay out, understand? I'm going away, to South America or Cuba maybe, but first I've got to get to that dough of mine. You help me get it and I'll see you're taken care of." He made an unpleasant gesture. "If you *don't*—"

Malone sat down very, very carefully on the unmade bed and tried to relight a cigar that was already glowing. "Er—an interesting idea, Eddie. Somewhat startling, and a little out of my line. Where is the stuff?"

"It's safe, in spite of that punk Shaw, the hophead who blew up and blasted the bank guard. He's been trying through the grapevine to get me to spill where I stashed the loot so he can dig it up and get his cut—or more likely, if I know him, to take it all and scram. I figure he's got nothing coming." Malone could see that point of view, and nodded. "Anyway," continued Eddie the Actor, "the place where I hid the stuff I can't go near it, see? On account of right now I'm hotter than a three-dollar pistol and there's always a chance that the law has a stake-out there. So you're going to pick it up for me."

"Have you ever considered that my face is as well-known to the police as yours, if for somewhat different reasons?"

Obviously Eddie hadn't. He thought. "Then you've got to get somebody else to go, somebody you can trust, if you want your fee—and you want to stay alive." The man, Malone thought, was obviously as tense as an E-string. "How about your secretary?" Vance suggested hopefully.

Malone shook his head. "Maggie is strictly on the up and up—she'd have none of it."

"Well then, somebody else—or *else!*" The man was desperate.

At that auspicious moment there came a sharp knock at the door. Malone started to rise, but a pistol popped into Eddie's hand, waving him back. The knock came again, and then a voice from the hallway. "Malone? I know you're there, so open up!"

"It's only—only a client I'm expecting," the little lawyer improvised hastily. "And I've just got the idea that she might be the answer to our problem." He rose and went to the door, to admit Miss Hildegarde Withers.

"Malone, I waited—" she began—and stopped, seeing the ersatz bellboy.

But Malone shook his head at her warningly. "Cut it, Tillie. You don't have to go into your act here. Toledo Tillie, this is Eddie the Actor, a former client of mine, and he wants something done that I think you can do better than anybody—for a reasonable cut, of course. Nothing rough, it just involves picking up some merchandise, and picking up maybe a grand for yourself."

Miss Withers sniffed, sighed resignedly, and sat down on a hard chair. "So what's the caper?" she inquired, in her best approximation of a voice likely to be Toledo Tillie's.

Eddie Vance was staring at her, almost incredulously. Malone said hastily, "I'm defending Tillie when her case comes up next month, charged with conning department stores. She's out on bail now."

"Hiya, Tillie," said Eddie, extending a hand. "You certainly got the front

–you look *too* respectable, almost." He turned to Malone. "Can we trust her?"

"I'd trust her as I would my sainted mother," swore the little lawyer shamelessly; his sainted mother had abandoned him on the steps of an orphanage when he was a few days old. "As you can see for yourself, Eddie, she could walk right past any police stake-out without the cops giving her a second look. She could go right into your girl friend's house, maybe peddling books or something–"

"Wait a minute!" cried Eddie the Actor. "How'd you know . . . ?"

"I didn't, until you just told me," Malone admitted. "Though it seemed only natural that you'd have stashed the loot at Ethel Megrim's house somewhere, just as it seems natural the cops would be looking for you to show up there now. Even if they searched the place at the time of your arrest and found nothing. They know how close it was with you and Ethel. Miss–I mean Tillie here can walk into the place and get Ethel to hand over the money. Well, what do you say?"

Eddie Vance scowled, looking at the schoolteacher rather as if she were a used car that he contemplated purchasing. "*Maybe*," he conceded. "Say something with uptown class in it."

"I *beg* your pardon!" Miss Withers sniffed again. " 'Beauty is truth, truth beauty; that is all ye know . . . and all ye need to know.' Keats."

"She's got the lingo," admitted Eddie the Actor grudgingly. "I'm not one to trust dames much. I didn't even trust Ethel when the thing happened; I sent her out for a jug that night and stashed the loot while she was gone. She has no idea of where it is, so she can't just hand it over to this old dame or anybody, see? And–" he continued as Miss Withers seethed inside, "–I don't want Ethel to know about it now, or she'd insist on tagging along with me to Cuba or somewhere and help spend the dough. I'll pick me a señorita down there."

"Very sensible," observed Malone coolly, avoiding Miss Withers's glare.

Eddie the Actor threw away his cigarette and nervously lighted another. "Only how do I know Tillie here doesn't just grab the loot and lam?"

"She wouldn't think of that–" began Malone.

But the schoolteacher interrupted. "Nobody can say that Toledo Tillie is a doublecrosser–there are ethics in my profession, Mr. Vance. I only steal from marks. Anyway, I don't need your dough, only I could use a small cut because of this con rap I'm in at the moment."

Vance nodded. "Okay. But remember, even if I'm hot I got connections, and if you did try to get out of town with my money you wouldn't get farther than Gary, Indiana, before you'd feel a shiv in your back. Understand?" He said it almost pleasantly. "Well, then–here's the dope." And he told them where the bank loot was hidden–under the rosebush in Ethel Megrim's backyard.

"How clever!" Miss Withers said admiringly. "It should be a cinch."

"Not unless we get Ethel out of the house while you do the job," Vance insisted. "She's sharp, and she'd catch on if you showed a sudden interest in the garden or anything. There's only one way to work the pickup." And he told them the address and the phone number and the plan—and a rather ingenious plan it was, too. "Take it from there," said Eddie the Actor. "I'll meet you—no, I'll phone Malone here sometime tonight or tomorrow. And no tricks. Understand?"

He went quickly out the door.

"It's much too tricky for me," said Miss Withers to Malone after she had got her breath. "I played along because you obviously wanted me to, but this isn't honest. We should call the police at once. Malone, I'm disappointed in you."

"We haven't much choice," pointed out the little lawyer wryly. "Go ahead, and don't ask too many questions." He picked up a bottle. "I don't suppose you'd care to join me in a highball?"

"There wouldn't be room enough," snapped the schoolteacher, and huffily departed. She had always known that the little lawyer cut corners now and then, but this—even under duress—was violating all sorts of laws about receiving stolen property and harboring a fugitive from justice and heaven knew what else. Well, she had given her word—or Toledo Tillie's word—and was morally or immorally bound to go through with it.

So she sought out a big bookstore on Michigan Boulevard and provided herself with the first volume of an expensive set of encyclopedias; thus armed she set forth for Rogers Park. Argyle Street was mostly lined with apartment houses and stores, but here and there were sandwiched brick bungalows of which Ethel Megrim's was one.

The block in question seemed to be deserted except for a woman with a baby carriage filled with groceries and baby, an empty taxicab, and two small boys who were manfully trying to wreck each other's tricycles. Yet she took no chances, working her way along the street from door to door, peddling her wares. Few people were home at this hour; most of the apartment houses had *No peddlers or agents* signs, or locked entry doors, but somewhat to her surprise she got orders for two sets of the encyclopedia before she finally came to the apartment building across the street from Ethel Megrim's home. It had been too good to last. There was a burly, pink-faced man in the lobby, leaning against the wall and reading a newspaper somewhat too elaborately; from where he stood he had an excellent view of Ethel's doorway. "Oh, my prophetic soul!" murmured Miss Withers. "The Law is already here." But, as she knew from experience, a frontal approach is often the best. So she came boldly up to him. "Excuse me, but do you have the time?"

He looked at her. "Three thirty," he said, unsmiling.

"Oh, dear, only that? And two more hours I've got to spend canvassing for this old encyclopedia before I can take my shoes off and relax." She sighed, and then smiled hopefully. "It's an excellent set—if you don't have one at home would you like to look at the sample volume?" She extended it. "Real buckram."

"No, lady," the man said, with considerable finality. The schoolteacher paid a token call at two apartments in the building, and then went across the street feeling that the man was watching her over his newspaper.

Prudently she first tried the house next door to Ethel Megrim's—and walked into an open-armed reception from a wrinkled old lady with incredible, henna-flaming hair, who was obviously dying for someone to talk to. The schoolteacher's pitch for the encyclopedia was almost drowned out by a spate of words; she had to accept a cup of tea and listen to the bright sayings of Mrs. Gardner's grandchildren, admire their snapshots, lend an ear to all the neighborhood gossip, and be regaled by a play-by-play account of a morning soap opera.

Finally in desperation Miss Withers rose to go. "And I'll think about the encyclopedia," Mrs. Gardner conceded. "You drop back tomorrow, and we'll have another chat and another nice cup of tea."

The schoolteacher nodded vaguely. "I must get back to work now, though. How about your neighbor, do you think she might be interested?"

"That Ethel Megrim? I shouldn't think she reads much—she's too busy hanging on that TV set of hers when she isn't carrying on with her boy friend. He's a taxi-driver and if you ask me—"

Finally Miss Withers tore herself away and rang the bell next door. Luckily Ethel Megrim was at home. She turned out to be a rather prettyish woman in her late thirties, carrying a bit of extra weight and somewhat long in the tooth. She was wearing a house-coat that had seen better days; the television set was blaring and she had evidently been enjoying a can or more of beer. She did not feel any desperate desire for a set of encyclopedias, which was no surprise to the schoolteacher; while polite, Ethel was evidently anxious to get back to her beer and her TV program. But as Miss Withers took her departure she managed to distract the younger woman's attention just long enough to press the button which disengaged the Yale-type lock of the front door. Hurdle one was over, anyway. She took the El back downtown and found John J. Malone in his hotel room, alone except for half a bottle of Canadian rye.

"I'm giving you a case of Antabuse for Christmas," she said tartly. But she condescended to report on the recent exploits of Toledo Tillie. Malone sobered up instantly.

"Then all we've got to do now," he announced, "is to figure out a way to lure Ethel out of the house."

"That shouldn't be difficult. Have your precious Eddie Vance call her up and ask her to meet him under the statue in Lincoln Park or somewhere.

"Fine. Only we don't have the faintest idea of where to reach him."

"Too true." Miss Withers tapped her somewhat prominent front teeth with a fingernail. "Wait—I have an inspiration! Ethel Megrim is *mad* for television. Suppose you phone her and pretend to be representing some TV program and if she'll be in the lobby of the Tribune Building at 8 tonight she'll be paged and taken up to the broadcasting studios to appear on a new secret giveaway program with a chance at a truck load of prizes if she can pick the right tune or something?"

Malone stared at her, then raised his glass. "To a brilliant suggestion!"

"And to a brilliant hangover tomorrow morning, if you keep trying to climb into that nasty bottle." But she smiled proudly. "Well, Malone, get on the phone."

It was no sooner said than done, or almost. Ethel Megrim was incredulous at first, but when Malone in his most histrionic manner assured her that her name had been chosen by lot out of the phone book she swallowed the thing hook, line, and sinker. Malone turned to Miss Withers. "We have time for dinner," he said. "Except that the only place I have credit is Joe the Angel's City Hall Bar. . . ." He ruefully surveyed the remains of Maggie's five-dollar bill.

"I insist on treating," the schoolteacher announced. "We'll go to the Empire Room at the Palmer House and fortify ourselves with succulent viands for the nefarious enterprise on which we are embarking."

"You have twisted my arm," Malone told her. "I always like to do my housebreaking on a full stomach."

A couple of hours later they came down Argyle Street in the misty rain, huddled under Miss Withers's umbrella and with Malone's Borsalino pulled well down over his eyes. But there was no sign of the man in the doorway. "Natch," said the little lawyer. "Ethel went out on our fake setup, and the cop tailed her hoping she'd lead him to Eddie the Actor." They went across the street to the narrow brick bungalow. The front door opened easily and they were inside the dark living room, which smelled of cheap perfume, beer, and dust.

"No lights," Malone warned Hildegarde quickly. He cupped his hand over the bulb of his flashlight and they walked through the deserted house which made up in depth for what it lacked in width; it had been built like a New York railroad flat. There was a bedroom and a bath, a dining room, and a long narrow old-fashioned kitchen which Miss Withers thought smelled faintly of mice. They went through a service porch and at last came out into the backyard."

"Holy St. Vitus!" gasped John J. Malone. There were at least *twenty* rosebushes in the narrow place, completely enclosed by a six-foot fence topped with barbed wire. And the only tools available seemed to be a rusty hoe and a trowel. "Where to begin?"

"'Begin at the beginning; go on until you come to the end and then stop,'" quoted Miss Withers. And so they set to work in the feeble glow of Chicago's moonlight, filtered through the scattering rain clouds, their labors only slightly lightened by the blare of radios from the open windows of the apartment house next door. One was playing a Crime Doesn't Pay program, which the schoolteacher thought especially appropriate under the circumstances. Gloves and fingers were torn on the savage thorns; stubborn roots clung tightly to the sticky clay. They dug and they dug and they still dug, and they still failed to come up with the money.

Suddenly Miss Withers dropped her trowel. "What was that, Malone? Wasn't it a scream?"

"Sure. On the radio programs they always scream. Or maybe a tomcat on one of the fences. Back to work, we've got seventeen more bushes to disinter."

She bent down, and then straightened up again. "Malone, we're wasting time."

"You mean Ethel found the dough? Believe me if she had she'd be halfway across the world by now."

"Not that. But remember, Vance said the money was buried under *the* rosebush, which he then replanted. Wouldn't that indicate—?"

"That when he stashed it she had only one, and later she planted others?"

"You know nothing of roses, except perhaps Four Roses, which I believe is a brand of whiskey. We have only to look for the *oldest* rose—the bush with the thickest stem."

Which they did, and it was there under a foot of muddy earth: a bundle of bills big enough to choke a horse, or at least a pony, wrapped tight and dry in one of the plastic bags ordinarily used to keep vegetables fresh in the refrigerator. Malone reached out his hand, but Miss Withers dusted off the package and placed it firmly in her capacious handbag. "Not so fast," she said firmly. "The disposition of this blood money has to be discussed, and I intend to make one last appeal to your conscience. It isn't rightfully yours, or Eddie Vance's, and—" She stopped short.

From where they were standing, in one corner of the garden, they could see part of the side of the long narrow house. A light had suddenly come on in the windows of the front room!

"She's come home ahead of time!" the little lawyer gulped. They were trapped, just at the moment of victory. He glanced at the fence. "Do you suppose—?"

"No, Malone. I couldn't climb that fence in my prime, which I am definitely not in. Nor could you. We've got to go out as we came in, if at all."

He nodded ruefully. "But *why* would she come back now?"

"I can guess. Suppose that on her way down to the studio Ethel just happened to remember that she had a *private* phone number, known to Eddie Vance but unlisted? So the TV people couldn't have picked her name out of the phone book for their program. She smelled a rat and came home. Now we're in for it."

"Maybe she'll get tired and go beddy-bye?" Malone suggested hopefully.

"You forget there's no second floor to the place. We have to go through her bedroom, and there's every chance that she'd wake up and grab a pistol and shoot us both for burglars—which in a sense we are." The schoolteacher shook her head. "I don't like any part of this, and besides I think I'm coming down with double pneumonia."

For an eternity of minutes the two conspirators huddled together in the chilly dark. Malone was shivering too, in spite of occasional nips at the trusty fifth in his topcoat pocket. "I'd rather dodge bullets," he whispered through chattering teeth, "than freeze to death. I'm going to reconnoiter. You wait here."

He tiptoed toward the back steps, but Miss Withers tiptoed right behind him.

"Where you go, I go," she told him firmly. "Up to a point, that is." They moved silently across the service porch, into the kitchen which was as dark as the bottom shaft of a coal mine, though somewhat warmer. Malone felt his way forward and into the dining room, with Miss Withers sticking closer than a sand-burr. His cupped flashlight cast a faint glow ahead.

Through the bedroom they crept, toward the faint crack of light under the door. Malone waved Hildegarde back, and cautiously squatted in front of the keyhole.

"What do you see?" the schoolteacher whispered.

"Nothing but a piece of wall," he muttered. "Hildegarde, it's *too* silent in there!"

"Maybe she's gone out again?" Miss Withers suggested hopefully.

He turned the knob, a fraction of an inch at a time, and then softly pulled the door toward him. As it swung open, the bright lights of the living room half blinded them—and then they saw it. Miss Withers bit her knuckles to keep from crying out.

Ethel Megrim lay sprawled in the center of the rug, her limbs every which way—like a puppet loosed of its string. There was red seeping through the bleached honey-color of her hair, and blood on her face. As the two intruders bent over her, she raised herself a little and moaned something through bruised and battered lips. Then they heard her say, "He—he hurt me—I didn't *know*, I *didn't*—" Her body gave a convulsive shiver, and she fell back again.

"Do something, Malone! Get an ambulance!"

He shook his head, and surreptitiously crossed himself. "There's nothing for us to do now but make tracks out of here—and quick!"

Malone was mistaken about that. They weren't going anywhere, according to a pink-faced, burly man who stood in the door of the front hallway, hands in the pockets of his gray topcoat. To Miss Withers he looked at least half again as tall and as broad as he had looked that afternoon, pretending to read his newspaper in the lobby across the street.

"Officer, we can explain *everything!*" she cried quickly. "We were out in the backyard, and we heard a scream. . . ."

He came slowly forward, tense and frightening. "I heard a scream too," he said. His hand went into his pocket, and they caught the flash of metal. "Kelleher, Fourth Precinct. Get back against the wall, both of you." He looked down at the dead woman, almost incuriously. "Pistol-whipped her, eh?"

"But we don't even have a gun!" Malone put in. "You can search us! The person who did this must have got out through the front door—"

"And if you were watching the house from across the street you must have seen him go out!" finished the schoolteacher triumphantly. "You did, didn't you?"

"I'll ask the questions," the big man said. "First, who are you and what in hell were you doing in the backyard at this time of night?" He looked at them. "Making mud pies?"

"See my lawyer," said Miss Withers, nodding at Malone.

Malone gulped. "Look, officer—I'm John J. Malone, the attorney. Call Captain Daniel von Flanagan at Twelfth Street, he'll vouch for me. I hope!" the little lawyer added under his breath.

"Shut up. So you're Malone, eh? The criminal attorney who defended Eddie Vance—and now you're caught red-handed over the corpse of his former girl friend! This is bigger than I thought. What did you come here for, Malone? And where is it?" The big man took a .45 automatic out of his pocket. "I said, *where is it?*"

He had backed Malone against the wall and was deftly frisking him. Then he stood back. "Okay, take off your clothes and throw 'em over here to me!"

"*Please!*" gasped Miss Hildegarde Withers in horror, stumbling swiftly into the bedroom and closing the door firmly behind her. There were sounds of fervent protestations from Malone, which suddenly ended. There was no arguing with a detective who packed a .45, Miss Withers conceded. Again she thought longingly of that back fence—if somehow she could hoist herself over it . . . And then a better idea came to her.

But ten minutes later, when the door was flung open, she was standing in the bedroom, looking as innocent as a newborn babe is supposed to look—by anyone who has never seen a newborn babe.

"*Your* turn, sister!" announced Kelleher.

"Over my dead body!" the schoolteacher snapped. "You have no right even to suggest such a thing! When you call Headquarters to report this you can ask them to send a matron, but until then—" She raised her omnipresent umbrella menacingly.

"That's the law," put in Malone, "as you know very well, officer."

The man hesitated uncertainly, and then compromised by patting her exterior somewhat gingerly. Next he reached for her handbag. "Give, sister."

"Has a lady no privacy?"

"Not when it's homicide, she hasn't." He snatched the bag from her fingers and unceremoniously dumped the contents on the floor. It was Malone's turn to gasp—there was everything in that magpie's nest *except* Eddie the Actor's loot! The little lawyer stared at her in wonder.

"Blast it!" their captor swore, with trimmings. He hesitated for a moment, then made up his mind. He snatched the tie which Malone was at the moment replacing around his neck and tossed it to Miss Withers. "Tie his hands behind him—behind the back of that chair!" The gun waved menacingly, and the schoolteacher obeyed. The belt was whipped from Malone's waist, and she had to strap it around his ankles. Then, horror of horrors, she was herself tied up in the same fashion with curtains ripped from the windows. "There, I guess *you'll* stay put," said the man with the gun. And he disappeared into the back of the house, whence echoed sounds of a frantic search.

Miss Withers looked from Malone to the stiffening corpse on the floor and back again. "For a policeman, he has very unorthodox methods," she said calmly.

"He's no cop," Malone agreed. "He didn't phone in, and cops in Chicago carry .38 pistols, not .45 automatics. He's obviously after that dough. Where'd you hide it?"

"Never you mind! We've got to get out of here, now!"

"Now, *how?*" the little lawyer asked reasonably.

"I tied you with a granny knot, naturally. It'll slip if you work at it."

"No!" But she had and it finally did, and they went into what was undoubtedly the fastest disappearing act in recent history. It was not until they were half a dozen blocks away that Malone slackened his pace and entered a drug store to telephone, emerging almost immediately. "That was quick," the schoolteacher remarked. "What did von Flanagan say?"

"I didn't talk to him. I just told the cop at the switchboard that I was a neighbor of Ethel Megrim's and that I'd heard a scream there . . ."

"But we ought to go back and be around when the police arrive!"

"You mean be around when that thug comes out shooting! And Hildegarde, he's a cinch to have found that money by now, wherever you hid it."

She shook her head, smiling a Mona Lisa smile. "No, Malone."

"Well, where is it?"

Another shake. "No, Malone."

"You don't trust me," the little lawyer said sadly.

"Of course I do—just the way I'd trust my poodle with a piece of T-bone. And now, if you don't mind, it's late and I'm wet and muddy and I've just had about all an old-maid schoolteacher can take for one day. Good night, Malone—phone me in the morning." And she popped into a waiting taxi and was off and away. Malone stared after her with some bitterness, and then noticed the lights of a Bar and Grill across the street, gleaming a welcome through the mist.

"With my luck it'll be a mirage," he muttered gloomily. But at this point even the mirage of a saloon would be better than nothing.

In the cold gray light of the early morning something awakened John J. Malone. He sat up in his own bed and gingerly shook his head to see if it would fall off, which it almost did but not quite. It was amazing that a man could get a hangover like this on one bottle and two bucks to spend in a bar; somebody must have liked the way he sang *By Killarney's Lakes and Dells* and set up the rest of the drinks.

Then the knock at the door came again, more insistently. He fumbled his way into a robe and shot the bolt. "Come in, Eddie," he said.

But it wasn't Eddie Vance, it was six feet of policeman in the shape of his ancient adversary, Captain Daniel von Flanagan, who almost trod on Malone's toes as he pushed his way into the room. He was smiling, but you could have refrigerated Death Valley in July with that smile. He folded his arms. "I should have known better," said that worthy if thumb-fingered policeman with some bitterness, "than to trust a lawyer any time, anywhere."

"Wha-a—huh?" muttered Malone brilliantly. "Look, Captain, I haven't even had breakfast—"

"Well, pour yourself three fingers of breakfast and then talk. See if you can talk yourself out of having your meals behind bars for the next dozen or so years. Let's start with Ethel Megrim, huh?" He plumped himself down in a chair.

"Oh, *her*." Malone drank, choked, and drank again.

"Yes, her. She up and got herself murdered last night, as if you didn't know."

The raw whiskey hit Malone's stomach with a comforting warm thud, and rose slowly to dispel some of the fog in his brain. "And just *why* should I know?"

Von Flanagan snorted. "Because you yourself called Twelfth Street before the poor woman was cold, and reported it without giving your name. Only the man at the switchboard happened to recognize your golden tenor voice." Malone said nothing, and the other pressed on. "There's them downtown that think you yourself killed her."

"Me? Why?"

"Maybe because she came home unexpectedly and found you burglarizing her place, looking for that loot of Eddie Vance's. Maybe it was you who was digging up her backyard?"

Malone's mind was dashing about like a bird-dog in a thicket. "How can you say such a thing, Captain?" Von Flanagan made no answer, but he was staring significantly at the heap of muddy clothing flung on the radiator last night. The little lawyer winced, and decided to retire to previously prepared positions. "All right," he said resignedly, "I'll tell you. It was the fake cop who did it. When Miss Withers and I—"

"Not *her* again?" cried von Flanagan. "This is too much!"

"I was saying that when Miss Withers and I came in out of the backyard we took him for a cop attracted by the scream—he was in the doorway, only he must have been just *leaving* instead of just coming *in*. Only he hadn't got what he came for, and went along with the gag when he saw us, thinking that maybe we had it . . ."

"The dough—Vance's loot! And you did have it? Where is it, Malone? Did he get it?" The questions came thick and fast.

Malone shrugged. "I'll swear by all the saints in heaven, I'll swear by the memory of my blessed mother, God rest her soul, that I have no idea of where on earth that loot is, unless it's still somewhere in Ethel's house."

"Phooey! My men tore up every inch of the backyard, they ripped up floors and knocked out walls, and I'll swear that there isn't even so much as a postage stamp that they missed! But go on talking."

Malone talked as he dressed. He told the whole story, with some cautious emendations—all about the talkative woman next door who had told Miss Withers's about Ethel's new boy friend who was a chauffeur or taxi-driver or something, about the fake summons from the TV studio that was supposed to keep Ethel safely out of the way, about the cop who wasn't a cop at all and who had tied them up while he went on searching the house . . . He told everything except about the money; at the moment that wasn't his secret anyway. "So there's your murder case, Captain," he concluded, "tied up in a bag. With Eddie Vance safe in prison, this guy started to cultivate the ex-girl friend, because he must have figured that she knew where the money was. Eddie's prison break forced his hand—he watched the house figuring Eddie might come there to pick up the cash. When Ethel left the house last night he tailed her, figuring maybe she was going to meet Eddie somewhere. She got wise, turned around, and came home, and he followed her in and tried to beat her into telling him where the loot was. But she couldn't tell him because she didn't know, and he lost his head and hit her too hard—just like he blew his top and killed that bank guard three years ago."

"*Shaw!*" cried von Flanagan triumphantly, as if it had been his own discovery.

"Who else? All you have to do is pick him up—"

"Phooey! If we couldn't pick up Shaw for that other killing after three years of trying, how do you expect us to pick him up for this one?" The policeman shook his head. "Get the rest of your clothes on, we're going down and see the D.A. This is one time you've overreached yourself, Malone."

The little lawyer thought fast. "And just what do you think Deputy District Attorney Harbin Hamilton will say when he finds out about a certain phone conversation we had yesterday?"

It didn't stop von Flanagan, but it slowed him down a little, and Malone worked fast on his temporary advantage. "I've got an idea," he said. "We're all in this pretty deep, but I see a way out. You want Eddie the Actor for prison break, you want the loot, and you want Shaw for two killings, right?" He went back to the selection of a tie, almost too casually. "What do you think of this one with the hand-painted flamingoes?"

"I wouldn't wear it to a dog fight. Yes, we want Vance and Shaw and the dough. But you've fixed it so all three slipped through our fingers . . ."

"Well, then," said Malone—and in a few well-chosen words he stuck his neck out farther than ever before in his checkered existence. It took some fast talking, but he was used to bedazzling twelve jurors and a judge, and von Flanagan was only one man and not too bright at that.

"It better work, before 7 o'clock tonight when I go off duty!" warned the detective from the doorway. "Or I know somebody who'll get disbarred but fast." He went out, slamming the door. Malone sighed, and knotted the tie with the pink flamingoes, but his heart wasn't in it. And what to tell Hildegarde when he called her? He decided to fortify himself first with another drop, but had barely lifted the bottle when there came a knock at the door.

"Western Union for Mr. Malone."

Wearily he opened the door, "Come in, Eddie." This time it *was* Eddie Vance, shaking the drops from his uniform cap. He kicked the door shut behind him.

"Well, shyster? What luck?"

"Plenty," Malone said quickly. "Sit down and have a drink. I have every reason to believe that Miss—I mean Toledo Tillie—was successful, but it's a ticklish situation and I haven't got in contact with her yet. You see, Ethel Megrim got killed last night—"

"I heard," Eddie said. "Poor Ethel. But what about my dough?"

"Tillie is under wraps because of the murder, but she'll find a way to get in touch with me. Only we've got to be careful—von Flanagan was just here."

"I saw him in the lobby," said Eddie the Actor. "And if you're thinking of making a deal with him—" He patted his pocket with an evil grin. "I want my dough and I want it today, see?"

"You name the place and we'll be there, or at least she will. How about Field's basement at closing time, or the IC station at Randolph when the commuters are all going home? Or the south lion in front of the Art Institute?"

Eddie hesitated. "I like to work in the open. I guess the Art Institute is best. Six o'clock, okay?"

"Okay. You can take the dough, hand over my fee and Tillie's cut, and lose yourself in the crowd."

"Check. But tell her to be there on the dot. And don't foul this up, Malone, or you'll both be using a marble slab for a mattress, see?" He went out, slamming the door. Malone took a deep breath and a deeper drink, then called up Miss Withers. The schoolteacher was in a somewhat better mood than last night, and agreed to buy him a cup of coffee in fifteen minutes. He went out of the hotel through the rear service entrance, just in case von Flanagan wasn't trusting him, and shortly thereafter he was seated in the Palmer House coffee shop opposite his partner in crime. Her guilty conscience was not preventing her from attacking a copious repast of oatmeal and bacon and eggs, all of which made Malone feel slightly green.

They were both slightly green when he told her what he had promised von Flanagan to get rid of him. Miss Withers dropped her spoon. "No!" she cried.

"Yes," he said. "Look, you know where the dough is, so that takes care of Point One. We can deliver Eddie Vance, who's so crazy-mad for his loot that he'll walk into the trap—I'll phone von Flanagan to have his men at the Art Institute at six. Then all we've got to do is to get ourselves off the murder rap by locating Jack Shaw—unless he found where you stashed the money and is far away by now."

She shook her head. "I'm positive he didn't, or the police either. Let me think, Malone. We know Shaw is a cab-driver. If we checked all the taxi companies—"

"It would take days, and undoubtedly he's using a phony name. It isn't as if we had a picture of him," the little lawyer objected. They sat for a while in glum silence. Then the schoolteacher's long and faintly equine face lighted up like a lamp.

"But I *have* a picture of him, indelibly imprinted on my mind! Don't you see? The man has gone scot-free so far because he had no police record, no photos or fingerprints on file, and he wore a mask on the bank job. But now it's different. Now two people know what he looks like! Malone, do you know any friendly newspaper reporters?"

"I know all of them," he said with some pride. "And they're all friendly."

"Well, one of them is going to have a story for the early afternoon editions. Because it will help if while we're looking for Mr. Shaw *he* is looking for *us!* We'll spill the news that there are two eye-witnesses to the Megrim murder who can positively identify him!"

"A trap—with you and me as the cheese? Look, Hildegarde, isn't it enough to have Vance and the police on our tail without bringing Shaw into the act too? I'm too young and too wicked to die just yet." But Miss Withers prevailed, as she had a way of doing, and Malone went ahead and phoned one Ned McKeon at the *Herald-American*. "He says he'll squeeze it on page one somehow," the little lawyer reported. " 'Two unidentified witnesses, names withheld, at scene of the Megrim murder . . .' Only Shaw can identify *us* all right."

"And so perhaps can your friend Captain von Flanagan?"

Malone said that he wasn't sure von Flanagan could read, and that if he could, and did see the story, he'd probably keep his promise to hold off long enough to give them rope to hang themselves. They could only wait, and hope. The waiting, they decided, should be in or around Malone's office; his name and address were in the book and if Shaw came sniffing after the bait he would presumably come there first.

It was Miss Withers who brought up the moot question of what, if anything, they could do with or to Mr. Shaw if he did come. Malone thought. "*Maggie!*" he said.

"I have the greatest admiration for your secretary, but—"

"Maggie has a brother, and the brother has friends," Malone explained.

So it was that some hours later—about the time the *Herald-American* hit the stands—Miss Withers found herself staked out in the vacant suite across the hall from Malone's office, in the company of the little lawyer and two very tough-looking characters indeed, who had mumbled, "Pleasetameecha," and then settled down to a fast game of pinochle.

"Gangsters?" she whispered.

"Worse," Malone came back. "From the circulation department of the *Gazette*—to them murder and mayhem are jolly pastimes."

"Are they armed?"

"Tire irons and a length of heavy chain, I gather," he said.

So they waited and waited—and still waited. The hands of the old-fashioned watch pinned to the schoolteacher's old-fashioned blouse crawled around and around. There was no sound anywhere but the snap of the cards and the occasional tinkle of small change. Nothing happened, and nothing kept on happening. " 'The watched pot—' " quoted Miss Withers.

And then the phone rang suddenly in Malone's office across the hall, whose door had been left invitingly open. Malone leaped eagerly to answer it, since Maggie for obvious reasons had been given the afternoon off and sent out of the combat area. "Hello?" he cried breathlessly, Miss Withers leaning over his shoulder. "Hello? John J. Malone's office—hello?" He put down the phone in disgust. "They hung up on me!"

"You mean *Shaw* hung up on you! Obviously he was making sure you were here. Malone, it's working!" She almost did a little dance.

"It had better work, before 7 o'clock!" he came back grimly. "Von Flanagan is a man of his word and if we don't make that deadline . . ." He shuddered, and they went back across the hall, eyes glued to the crack in the door, ears keyed to the sound of approaching footsteps . . .

Five o'clock—then 5:15. "I can almost hear the clang of that cell door right now," Malone murmured sadly.

"Well," the schoolteacher said sensibly, "why not get out of town? My car ought to be fixed by now—we could be halfway to New York by morning."

"And von Flanagan could have Wanted flyers out for us before that. We'd be hauled back in handcuffs." They waited some more. It became 5:30, then 5:45. "That's that," said Malone. "We've just got time to get to the Art Institute and keep the date with Eddie Vance. Let's go." He borrowed a ten from Miss Withers and slipped it to their troops, who departed in some disappointment.

"Von Flanagan should certainly settle for two-thirds of what you promised," the schoolteacher said. "Getting Eddie the Actor—and the money—"

"Maybe," said Malone, without much hope. "He is a reasonable man, but not very." They hurried out of the building. There was a taxi at the head of the line, the driver a shortish stocky man deep in a racing form, a battered uniform cap over his eyes.

They hustled inside. "The Art Institute, and hurry," Malone ordered. He leaned back in the seat, and refreshed himself from the remains of his bottle. It was the hour of densest traffic, and Miss Withers felt that they could have made better time by walking. Once or twice their driver cut through alleys with the dexterity of long practice, but always sooner or later they found themselves hemmed in with traffic again.

"Malone, isn't the Art Institute east of us, on the lake front?"

He barely opened his eyes. "Yes, Hildegarde."

"Well, our driver is going west."

"Probably making a circle to avoid the jam in the Loop."

She was silent for a block or so. "Malone!" she whispered. "Notice the door handles?"

He looked, then gaped—there weren't any! "Driver!" cried Malone, and tapped on the glass partition. The driver half turned, suddenly sitting up straight so that his bulk showed. He also showed an automatic pistol in his left hand, and his face was the face they had seen last in Ethel Megrim's living room over her dead body.

"*Shaw!*" gulped Malone.

Miss Withers was frantically pounding on the door window with her umbrella handle, and waving pleadingly at passers-by. One or two of them waved back at her, but that was all. She tried to scream . . .

Shaw rolled down the partition and waved the gun in their general direction. "Cut it out," he spat at them. "Or you'll get it here and now."

They cut it out. The man was driving like a madman, but evidently that was the way taxi-drivers were expected to drive. They beat red lights and raced past boulevard stops, heading west and south, with the driver keeping one eye on the rearview mirror. Miss Withers moved a little closer to Malone, as if for comfort, but he caught her lips moving almost soundlessly. "Next stop—the one, two, three." He nodded a quarter of an inch . . .

There was a moving van at the next light, waiting for a left turn, and the taxi had to screech to a stop. Miss Withers kicked Malone sharply on the shin, and then her trusty umbrella came up like a striking snake, the crook of its handle around Shaw's neck, and she jerked with all her strength. The gun went off through the top of the cab and John J. Malone lovingly brought down his whiskey bottle on the man's head to finish the job. "Bull's-eye," said Miss Withers placidly.

It took only seconds for the little lawyer to climb over into the front seat, shove the unconscious Mr. Shaw to one side, and take the wheel. It had all happened so fast that they had rounded the corner and were a block or so north again before he remembered to pick up the uniform cap and put it on his own head.

"It's only ten after 6!" announced the schoolteacher. "Perhaps we can still make the Art Institute in time!"

Malone's only answer was to put his foot on the accelerator and his hand on the horn. A traffic cop or two whistled shrilly after them, but as luck would have it they met no minions of the Law on wheels, and soon they were rocketing up the Boul Mich, now heading north. They roared up before the Art Institute at last, to find the area practically deserted. There was no sign of Eddie Vance, no sign of von Flanagan and his men. Two husky street cleaners were sweeping the gutters nearby and putting refuse into a Department of Sanitation truck—but both were too tall and brawny to be Eddie Vance. The only other figure in the vicinity was an art student with owlish glasses and a smock who was painting a portrait of one of the benign stone lions against a background of lighted skyscrapers. He was obviously not Vance either.

"You'd better get out and look around and let yourself be seen," advised Malone. "I'll stay here and sit on Shaw—maybe you'd better give me your scarf so I can tie him up."

Hildegarde left the cab, strolled up the sidewalk for half a block, and then back again. It was almost six thirty, and she had a deep presentiment that they had missed the boat. Back at the steps of the Institute again, she paused to pat the north lion, paused again to admire the painting of the solitary artist . . .

There were two sharp beeps from a cab which had just pulled up in front of Malone's. "Taxi, Tillie?" It was a voice she recognized, though it now wore a mustache.

She leaped a foot in the air, and then started down the steps, her knees trembling like jello. Her eyes flashed this way and that in a desperate appeal for help—but there seemed no help in sight. Malone was either bent over his bottle or his prisoner, or both. There was nothing to do but to get into that second taxi—and what Eddie the Actor would say and do when he found she had doublecrossed him . . .

Eddie leaned back to open the door for her and she stumbled inside. The taxi moved ahead.

And then suddenly the truck from the Department of Sanitation pulled out squarely in their way. One of the street cleaners produced a riot-gun, the other a pistol. Wonder of wonders, the artist on the Art Institute portico ripped off his glasses, kicked aside his easel, picture and all, and turned out to be Captain von Flanagan. Miss Hildegarde Withers flung herself to the floor of the cab, both hands over her ears—and then it was all over, without a shot being fired. Eddie the Actor came out into the street, both hands held as high as he possibly could. When frisked, his pockets produced only a water pistol.

"Take him away," said Captain von Flanagan to the two street cleaners, who turned out to be crack detectives from Fifty-fifth Street. "And him too," he ordered, when Malone opened the other cab door and Mr. Shaw rolled out into the gutter.

Miss Withers took Malone's arm, and they stood there, waiting for von Flanagan's applause. But the Captain squirmed out of his smock, hurled it to the ground, and faced them belligerently.

"I'll never hear the last of this down at Twelfth Street," he growled. "And say, you—where's that loot you were supposed to deliver?"

Malone shrugged, and looked at Miss Withers. "I could tell you," she said, "but I'd rather show you—if you don't mind a trip to Ethel Megrim's house."

"We searched that place with a fine-tooth comb!" von Flanagan roared. "I'll eat my hat—or your hat or *anybody's* hat—if there's so much as a dime there!"

"Did you ever read *The Purloined Letter* by the late Edgar Allan Poe?" she inquired sweetly. Von Flanagan snorted, but it was nothing to the snort he snorted when, after a fast ride uptown in a squad car, she led them to Ethel's refrigerator and took from the vegetable compartment a plastic bag containing lettuce. Inside the lettuce was a wad of currency large enough to choke a horse, or a small pony. "The loot, Captain," she beamed. "As Poe definitely would not have said, 'Look for the lettuce in the lettuce.' I put it there while Shaw was searching Malone's clothing for it, since at the time I trusted neither Shaw nor Malone."

There was a long silence. "Hildegarde, you wrong me," said the little lawyer sadly. "I was always going to turn it in, wasn't I, Captain? Didn't I phone you when all this started and promise to deliver it if you'd keep hands off for a day or so?"

The policeman nodded.

"Well, then," said Miss Withers. "I owe you an apology, Malone. I thought you were after the money, or a large slice of it. But virtue, this time, is its own reward."

Malone smiled. "There are *other* rewards. This is bank loot, remember—and banks have surety companies. We should not do too badly. Now let's get out of here before Captain von Flanagan keeps his promise and eats your hat!"

THE MAN WHO EXPLAINED MIRACLES

by Carter Dickson

WHEN TOM LOCKWOOD first saw her, she was running down the stairs in terror. Behind her stretched the great sweep of stairs up to the portico of St. Paul's; above, Paul's Dome almost shut out the gray spring sky. A pigeon fluttered its wings. But there were very few people to see what happened.

The girl glanced over her shoulder. She was still so badly frightened that Tom's first thought was instinctive: she might stumble and pitch headlong. So he ran towards her.

His next thought, born of his journalistic work, was the grotesqueness of this whole scene, as the bell boomed out the stroke of four: a very pretty girl, with dark hair and wide-spaced gray eyes, fleeing in blind panic from the House of God.

Then she did stumble.

Tom caught her before she fell, and lifted her up gently by the elbows.

"Steady does it, you know," he said, and smiled down at her. "There's nothing to be afraid of, really."

Instantly she recoiled; then she saw his expression, and hesitated. Tom Lockwood's own mother could not have called him handsome. But he had such an engaging and easy-going expression, especially in his smile, that almost any woman would have trusted him on sight—and would have been right.

"*Nothing* to be afraid of," he repeated.

"Isn't there?" the girl blurted out. "When last night, by some miracle no one can understand, they try to kill me? And now, just now, a voice speaks where no voice could have spoken? And tells me again I am going to die?"

Taxis hooted up Ludgate Hill. A rather sinister-looking policeman stood at the left-hand side of St. Paul's churchyard. Tom had a topsy-turvy sense that he did not really hear the words she was speaking.

She spoke with passion, in a beautiful voice with—was it?—some very faint tinge accent. Her hair really was black and shining, worn in a long bob; the gray eyes, their pupils dilated with fear, had long black lashes. Tom was so conscious of her physical presence that he hastily let go her elbows.

"You don't believe me!" she cried. "Very well! I must go."

"No! Wait!"

The girl hesitated, looking at the pavement.

And Tom Lockwood was inspired almost to eloquence.

"You're alone," he said. "Oh, there may have been people with you in the Cathedral! But you're alone in yourself; you feel lost; you don't trust anybody. Will you trust a perfect stranger, if I tell you I only want to help you?"

To his intense embarrassment, tears came into her eyes.

"What you need—" he began. It was on the tip of his tongue to say "a couple of whiskies," but, in his present exalted mood, he decided this was unromantic. "Across the road," he said, "there's a tea shop of sorts. What you need is to drink tea and tell me your troubles. After all, hang it, I'm a reasonably respectable bloke! You see that policeman over there?"

"Yes?"

"*He* knows me," said Tom. "No, no, not because I'm an old lag just out of jail! As a matter of fact, I'm a crime reporter for the *Daily Record.* Here's my press-card."

"You are journalist?"

Her eyes flashed up; she pronounced the word almost as *journaliste.*

"Not where you are concerned. Please believe that! And you—are you by any chance French?"

"I am English," she retorted proudly, and drew herself up to her full height of five feet one. "Ah, bah! I am named Jenny. Jenny Holden. That is English enough, surely?"

"Of course. And I'm Tom Lockwood."

"But, you see," Jenny continued, "I have lived most of my life in France. When they brought me here for a visit, things seemed all funny but very nice, until—"

Jenny glanced back over her shoulder. Fear struck again, as though some terrifying presence lurked inside the Cathedral.

"Mr. Lockwood," she said, "of course I will go with you. And we need not be introduced by a policeman." Then her passionate voice rose. "But let us hurry, hurry, hurry!"

They dodged across through the skittish traffic to the tea shop at the corner of Paternoster Row. They passed the policeman in question, who seemed to fascinate Jenny. He was one of the Old Brigade: bulky and almost seven feet tall, just what any foreign visitor would expect to see.

Tom waved at him by way of greeting. The law saluted gravely but, when Jenny's head turned away, gave her companion a wink of such outrageous knowingness that Tom's ears went red.

At the door of the tea shop, however, Tom hesitated and turned round.

"Stop a bit! Was there somebody with you at St. Paul's?"

"Yes, yes! My Aunt Hester and my Cousin Margot."

"*They* didn't frighten you?"

"No, of course not!" Jenny's lips became mutinous. "I do not like my Aunt

Hester. She behaves like a duchess, with a lorgnette, and you can hear her talking all over a restaurant. You know what I mean?"

"Bitterly well."

"My Cousin Margot, she is young and I like her. But I wish to get away from them. Please!"

"Right," said Tom, opening the door. "In you go."

He allowed the door to close very briefly behind her so that she should not hear him when his voice carried clearly across to the policeman.

"Dawson! You haven't seen us. Understand?"

The law did. His wink was more portentous than ever.

In the tea shop, more properly a tea bar, two girls chattered and banged tins behind the counter. But the place was deserted, including the two booths at the back. When the newcomers sat opposite each other in the farther booth, over thick mugs of a beverage which was at least hot, Jenny's terror was decreasing. She accepted a cigarette, had it lighted for her, and hesitated. Then she burst out: "You see, it is so difficult to say! I don't wish you to think I am silly, or have fancies, or am off my head. That is what *they* think."

" 'They'?"

"Aunt Hester. And others."

"Aunt Hester," said Tom, "shall be hung out on the clothes-line, preferably upside down, at the first opportunity. Meanwhile . . ."

He broke off, because Jenny bubbled with that laughter he came to know so well.

"You are nice!" she declared, like a magistrate imposing sentence. "Oh, how it is pleasant to meet people who make you laugh! Instead of—"

Jenny stopped, and disquiet settled on her again.

"It is silly," she insisted, "but I must say it. Can you explain miracles?"

"No. But I know a man who can. Did you ever hear of Sir Henry Merrivale?"

"Sir Henry *Merrivale?*"

"Yes."

"But he is awful!" cried Jenny. "He is fat and bald, and he swear and carry on and throw people out of windows."

"He is not, perhaps," Tom admitted, "quite the ladies' man he thinks he is. But he can explain miracles, Jenny. That's his purpose in life nowadays."

"You mean this?"

"Yes, I mean it."

"Then I had better explain from the beginning. My name—"

"I know your name," said Tom, looking at the table. "I am likely to remember it for a very long time."

There was a pause, while both of them hastily swallowed tea.

"Well!" said Jenny. "My father and mother went to live in France, at Cannes, before I was born. What with the war, and everything else, I had never been to England. My mother died during the war. My father died two years ago. My guardian is my father's old friend Général de Senneville. And I am now twenty-five: in France, I am what you would call in England an old maid."

"Are you, now?" breathed Tom, almost with awe. "Oh, crikey! Have you ever seen yourself in a mirror?"

Jenny looked at him, and then went on very quickly.

"It was always my father's wish I should come to England. I should see all the sights like any tourist: Westminster Abbey, the Tower of London, St. Paul's—"

"Steady, now!"

"Yes, I am steady. Général de Senneville, my guardian, said this plan was a good one, and did much honor to everyone. So he sent me, in charge of my Aunt Hester, just before I get married."

"Before you—!" Tom blurted out, and then stopped.

Jenny's face went pink. Tom, in the act of lighting a cigarette for himself, held the match for so long that it burned his fingers. He cursed, dropped both match and cigarette into the mug of tea; then, to hide his expression, he shoved the mug of tea down on the floor under the seat.

"But what else could I do?" Jenny asked defensively. "It was arranged many years ago, between my father and the général. At twenty-five, and an old maid, surely that was best?"

The damage had been done. They could not look at each other's eyes.

"And who's the bloke you're marrying?" he asked casually.

"Armand de Senneville. The général's son."

"Do you love him?"

All Jenny's English feelings warred with her strict French upbringing.

"But you are not practical!" she exclaimed, the more vehemently because her feelings won every time. "An arranged marriage always turns out best, as the général says. It is understood that I do not love Armand, and Armand does not love me. I marry him because—well! it must be done, at twenty-five. He marries me because he wishes to obtain my dowry, which is very large."

"*Does he, by God!*"

"How dare you!"

"These old French customs." Tom folded his arms moodily. "You hear about 'em, you know they exist, but they're still hard to believe. What about this Armand de Senneville? He has oily black hair, I suppose, and side-whiskers down his cheeks?"

"You must not speak so of my fiancé, and you know it!"

"All right, all right!"

"He has dark hair, yes, but none of the rest of it. He is charming. Also, he is one of the best businessmen in France. Armand is only thirty-five, but already he owns three newspapers, two in Paris and one in Bordeaux."

"Whereas I . . ."

"You said?"

"Nothing. He's with you, I suppose?"

"No, no! He was bitterly opposed to this holiday. He could not get away from business; he speaks no English and does not like the English. He has to consent, because his father wishes it. But he warns Aunt Hester to keep a sharp eye on me, in case I should be silly and fall in love with some dull, stupid Englishman—"

Abruptly Jenny paused. Her own cigarette, unnoticed, was burning her fingers; she threw it on the floor.

Tom looked straight at her.

"Which you might do, mightn't you?"

"No! Never! Besides, Aunt Hester and the de Sennevilles would never let me."

While Stella and Dolly clattered tins and banged cups behind the counter of a prosaic tea bar, Tom Lockwood took a great and secret and mighty resolve. But he did not show it in his brisk tone.

"Now, then! Let's get down to cases. What has frightened you so much?"

"Last night," answered Jenny, "someone tried to kill me. Someone turned on the tap of the gas heater in my bedroom. It was impossible for this to be done, because all the doors and windows were locked on the inside. But it *was* done. Already I had a note saying I was going to die."

Jenny's eyes seemed to turn inwards.

"By good luck, they save me. But I don't wish to speak of last night! This morning I am very—sick is not a nice word, is it?—no! I am ill. But Aunt Hester said this was nonsense, and it would revive me to go sightseeing again. That is why we went to St. Paul's. Do you know St. Paul's?"

"I'm afraid I haven't even been inside the place for a long time."

"It happened," said Jenny, "in the whispering gallery."

Whispering gallery.

The eerie sibilance tapped against the nerves even in this commonplace tea bar, with traffic rushing outside.

"You climb up stairs," said Jenny. "Spiral stairs. Stairs and stairs, until you are breathless and think you will never get to the top. Then there is a tiny little door, and you go out into the gallery."

Then Tom remembered—how vividly this whispering gallery had impressed him. It was dizzily high up, just under the curve of the dome: circular, some two hundred feet across, and with only an iron railing to keep you from pitching down interminably to the acres of folding chairs on the ground floor below.

Noises struck in with brittle sharpness. Gray light filtered in on the tall marble statues of saints round the vast circle. It was solemn, and it was lonely. Only one verger, black-clad, stood guard there.

More than ever Tom was conscious of Jenny's presence, of her parted lips and quick breathing.

"I am not a coward," she insisted. "But I did not like this place. If you sit on the stone bench round the wall, and someone—even two hundred feet away—whispers near the wall, that whisper comes round in a soft little gurgly voice out of nowhere.

"Please attend to me!" Jenny added, with deep sincerity. "I was not well—I admit it. But I was not unbalanced either. Ever since I have received that first note saying I would die, I have watch everyone. I trust nobody—you were right. But I trust you. And, on my oath, this happened as I tell it.

"There were only five persons in all that dusky gallery. You could see. My Aunt Hester and my Cousin Margot. A fat red-faced countryman who is come to see the sights with a packet of sandwiches and a thermos flask of tea. The verger, in a dark robe, who tells you about the gallery.

"That is all!

"First the verger showed us how the whispering gallery is worked. He leans against the wall to the left—you do not even have to be against the wall. He says something that we, on the right of the door, hardly hear at all. But it goes slipping and sliding and horrible round the dome. Something about 'This Cathedral, begun by Sir Christopher Wren—' and it jumps up in your ear from the other side.

"After that we separated, but only a little. I was nervous—yes, I admit that too! I sat down on the stone bench, all prim. Aunt Hester and Margot went to the railing round the open space, and looked over. Margot giggles and says, 'Mama, would it not be dreadful if I jumped over?'

"Meanwhile, the fat countryman has sat down fifty feet away from me. Calmly he opens the grease-proof paper and takes out a sandwich. He pours out tea from the thermos into the cup; he is taking a deep drink when the verger, who is outraged at sandwiches in St. Paul's, rushes towards him from ten feet away.

"Mr. Lockwood, I know what I saw! The countryman could not have spoken; he is really and truly gulping down tea. The verger could not have spoken—I could see his mouth—and anyway he is too far away from the wall. As for Aunt Hester or Margot, that is nonsense! And, anyway, they are much too far away from the wall, and leaning over the railing.

"But someone spoke in my ear just then.

"It was in English, and horrible. It said: 'I failed the first time, Jennifer. But I shall not fail the second time.' And it gloated. *And there was nobody there!*"

Jenny paused.

With all the nervousness of the past days, there were shadows under her eyes, and she was more than pale. But a passion of appeal met Tom across the table.

"No, I did not say anything!" she told him. "If I had, Aunt Hester would only say I was imagining things. Just as she said I was imagining things last night, and must have turned on the gas-tap myself, because the room was all locked up inside.

"No, no, no! I jumped up and ran out. I ran down those stairs so fast no one could have caught me. I did not know where I was going or what I should do. If I prayed anything, I think I prayed to meet . . ."

"To meet whom?" prompted Tom.

"Well! To meet someone like you."

After saying this, defiantly, Jenny drank stone-cold tea.

"But what am I to do?" she demanded, with tears on her eyelashes.

"I know Aunt Hester means me no harm—how could she? But I can't face her—I won't! Where am I to go?"

"I will tell you exactly," said Tom, reaching across and taking her hands. "You are going with me to see old H.M., otherwise Sir Henry Merrivale, at an office which nowadays is humorously called The Ministry of Miracles. Afterwards—"

Bang!

The door of the tea bar flew open with a crash which half shattered its glass panel. Tom, sitting with his back to the door, first craned round and then leaped to his feet.

Outside the door, but not yet looking into the tea bar, stood an imperious and stately lady who was addressing someone beyond her.

"I am well acquainted, constable," she was saying, "with Sir Richard Tringham, the Commissioner of Police. Your deliberate falsehoods will not help you when I report you to him personally. You have denied you saw any young lady run down the steps of the Cathedral. You have denied she met a young man in sports coat and gray flannels. Finally, you have denied they went into any of the shops or other disgusting places along here. Is this so, or is it not?"

" 'S right, marm," stolidly answered Police-Constable Dawson.

Whereupon Aunt Hester made her entrance like Lady Macbeth.

"I am Mrs. Hester Harpenden," she announced to the walls at large. "And I have *distinctly* different information from a newspaper seller. I have—"

Here she saw Tom, who was standing in the middle of the floor.

"That's the man," she said.

Up to this time Stella (rather bucktoothed) and Dolly (distinctly pretty) had remained stupefied and silent behind the counter. Now both of them gave tongue.

"Disgusting place, eh?" cried Dolly. "I like that!"

"Busted the door, officer," screamed Stella. "Busted the door, that's what she done!"

"Busted the door, did she?" repeated Police-Constable Dawson, in a sinister voice. "Oh, ah. I see." And he reached for his notebook.

Meanwhile, as Aunt Hester calmly advanced, Tom glanced back towards Jenny.

But Jenny was not there. She was gone; she was not anywhere in the place.

The sharp pang this gave him was not his only feeling. For an instant he believed he had strayed from St. Paul's churchyard into a world of monsters and twilight, where anything might happen; and, in a sense, he was not far wrong.

"Young man," Aunt Hester asked quietly, "where is my niece?"

"Do you see her here, madam?"

"No. But that does not mean . . . A back entrance! Ah, yes! Where is the back entrance here?"

"Just a moment," said Tom, stepping in front of her. "Have you a warrant to search these premises?"

"Do I need a warrant to find my own niece?"

"Yes, yer do and all!" screamed Stella. "Either yer orders tea and cakes, which is wot we're 'ere for, or out yer go straightaway. 'S right, officer?"

" 'S right, miss," agreed the law.

Aunt Hester was not fooled for a moment.

Seen close at hand, she was—or seemed—less formidable than bitter and bony, with a high-bridged nose and washed-out blue eyes, as though she had suffered some disappointment in youth and never forgotten it. Tom could tell her clothes were fashionable, as Jenny's were fashionable, without knowing why he knew.

"Then you are all against me, it seems," she smiled. "Well! This will indeed make a budget of news for my friend the Commissioner of Police!"

"By the way," Tom said casually, "*who* did you say is the Commissioner of Police?"

"But Sir Richard Tringham, of course!"

"Oh, put a sock in it," said Tom. "Sir Richard Tringham has been dead for seven years. The present Commissioner is Colonel Thomas Lockwood. And I ought to know—he's my father."

"Cor!" whispered Dolly.

" 'S right, marm," agreed Police-Constable Dawson.

Aunt Hester, not in the least impressed, merely raised her shoulders.

"Ah, well!" she smiled. "If police-officers are bribed to tell untruths, then I had better be off."

Majestically she strolled towards the front of the shop. With a gesture of contempt she opened her purse, took out a couple of pound-notes, and murmured something about paying for the glass door as she tossed the notes towards Stella.

Then, when she was within a step of the door, she whirled round and screamed at Tom like a harpy.

"*Where is my niece?*"

And Tom's temper crashed over too, like the glass platform of cakes which Dolly had been nervously handling.

"In a place where you'll never find her," he yelled back, only hoping he was telling the truth.

"If I prefer charges of abduction—"

"When she goes away of her own free will? Don't talk rot! And shall I tell you something else, Mrs. Harpenden?"

"By all means. If you can."

"That girl is of age," said Tom, advancing towards her. "Even under French law, her guardian no longer has any authority over her. But she doesn't seem to know that. She's being pushed and bullied and hounded into a marriage she doesn't want, by a lot of ghouls who are only interested in her money. And I tell you straight: I mean to stop it."

"Ah, I see. *You* want her money."

The steamy room was dead quiet, with fragments of shattered glass and colored cakes all over the counter and floor. Both Stella and Dolly had cowered back.

"Yes, that hurt," said Tom. "You knew it would hurt. All right: if you want open war, it's war from this time on. Agreed?"

"Oh, agreed," replied Aunt Hester, her head high. "And I have a feeling, dear Mr. Lockwood, that you are not going to win. *Good* day."

With all the honors she marched out, closed the door, and turned right toward Paternoster Row. They had time to see a brown-haired girl of seventeen or eighteen, with slanting eyes and a mischievous look, run after her. It could only have been Jenny's cousin Margot.

Tom, exasperated to see those two pound-notes lying on the counter, flung down another two to match them.

"That's for the smashed container and the cakes," he said.

"But, reolly, now!" protested Dolly, in an ultra-refined voice. "This is too much money. And is the Commissioner of Police reolly your father?"

"'S right, miss," said Police-Constable Dawson, and stolidly marched out.

"Ducks, ducks, ducks!" cried Stella, addressing Tom. Being not very pretty, she was more inclined to sympathize with his bedevilments. "You needn't worry about your young lady. 'Course there's another way out of 'ere!"

"There is?"

"'Course there is. At the back, and turn sideways. I saw your young lady run out as soon as we heard the old witch's voice outside. Either the young lady's still hiding in the passage past the washroom, or she's gorn out into Paternoster Row."

"My deepest thanks!" said Tom.

He turned and plunged towards the back—only to be stopped short by another figure materializing in this extraordinary tea shop.

This was a shortish, wiry man with his light-brown hair cropped close to the head after a prevailing American fashion. He was perhaps in his middle thirties; he wore loose-fitting clothes, and his tie could be seen at sixty paces in any crowd.

"Now hold it, brother!" he urged. "Don't go busting out of there or you'll louse up the whole deal."

Tom blinked at him.

"The old lady," continued the stranger, evidently referring to Aunt Hester, "left her car—it would be a limousine—parked in Paternoster Row. It's not there now. She'll be screaming for the cops again, and you'll run smack into her. Besides, the kid is safe now."

"The kid? You mean Jenny? Where is she?"

Something like a self-satisfied smile crept across the newcomer's face.

"I told the chauffeur," he said, "to drive her straight to a guy named Sir Henry Merrivale, at an address he seemed to know. Sit down for a minute, until the old dame stops yelling about her stolen car."

Tom Lockwood extended his hand.

"Maybe you won't want to shake hands," retorted the newcomer almost evilly, and put his hands behind his back, "when you hear what I am."

There was about him something distinctly foreign, in a way that no American is ever foreign. Though Tom could not analyze it, his companion enlightened him.

"Get it?" he asked. "I'm a Canadian. Lamoreux's the name—Steve Lamoreux. I was born in Montreal; I can speak French as well as I speak English. In Paris they say my accent is terrible; but they understand me. I'm a newsman for *L'Oeil*. Been in France for six months. Don't you get it *now?*"

"Well! I . . ."

Steve Lamoreux's shrewd brown eyes, in the hard yet sympathetic face, were almost glaring at him. And Lamoreux spoke bitterly.

"I'm the stooge," he said. "I'm the tail. In other words, I'm Armand de Senneville's hired spy to keep out of the way, never let the girl see me, but make sure she doesn't meet any boy friends. If she does . . ."

Tom, aware that both Stella and Dolly were listening with all their ears raised his voice.

"Could we have two more teas, please?" he called. Then, to Lamoreux: "Into the booth here. And keep your voice low."

They sat down opposite each other.

"What the hell?" said Lamoreux. "I'm only human. That girl's too innocent; I won't see her pushed around. What's more, I can't take this miracle stuff any longer—not for a hundred bucks a week or anything else. Do you realize that, but for a thousand-to-one chance, she'd be lying dead at the mortuary this very minute?"

It was a cold and ugly statement, just as the great bell of St. Paul's boomed out the hour of five.

"She didn't tell you how bad it was last night, did she?" asked Lamoreux.

"Not the details, no."

"No, you bet she didn't! The girl has guts—I'll say that for her."

"But how do you know she didn't tell me?"

"Because I overheard every word you two said in here! Look!" persisted Lamoreux, tapping a finger into his palm. "When they started out today, in their grand limousine, I followed in a taxi. Aunt Hester knows me, and knows all about me. Her husband, Uncle Fred, and young Margot—well, they've seen me once, here in England. I couldn't help that, but they'd never seen me before, and it doesn't matter. Jenny doesn't, and mustn't, even suspect.

"Those were my orders from young de Senneville. He didn't dare send a Frenchman as a tail—it might be too conspicuous. But Jenny's seen this map of mine more than once at the newspaper office; if she spotted me, it might shake her faith in good old Armand."

"Quiet!" Tom warned softly.

It was Dolly who appeared, demurely, setting down two mugs of tea already sugared. Though she seemed inclined to linger, Lamoreux's glance sent her away miffed.

"Armand de Senneville," Tom said between his teeth. "What I should like to do to that . . . !"

"Easy, now, brother! You're talking about my boss."

"He may not be your boss much longer. You may get a better one."

"How's that? Say it again."

"Never mind; get on with the story."

"Well! Aunt Hester and Margot and Jenny had the car parked in Paternoster Row. They told the chauffeur to wait there. I ditched my taxi, and sat in the car with the chauffeur. We could see the whole front of St. Paul's. We knew we could see 'em come out."

"And then?"

"You know what happened. About thirty-five minutes later, she comes tearing down the steps. You grab her. I think to myself, 'Steve, this is your job; this is where the balloon goes up.' Over you come to this place. I sneak in the back way, and I'm practically against a matchboard partition behind you. When I heard about a voice speaking in the whispering gallery, when no voice could have spoken, I damn near fainted. And there's another thing."

"Yes?"

Uneasily Lamoreux drew out a packet of Yellow French cigarettes. He struck an old-fashioned sulphur match; he brooded while holding the match until the sulphur burned away. Then, still lost in thought, he lit the cigarette and flicked away the match.

"When I first got a gander at you, see—" Lamoreux stopped.

"Well? What is it?"

"I thought it was an ordinary pick-up. Then, when I heard you two talking, I thought you were a right guy. And I still think so."

They glared at each other, because no man pays a compliment to another's face. Then, after an embarrassed pause:

"That's why I stuck my neck out. I could see Aunt Hester charging for this joint before either of you two did. I knew Jenny would duck for a way out. And *she* knew the car was parked just beside here. So I rushed out and told Pearson—that's the chauffeur—to drive her straight to this guy H.M. I'd heard of the old—the old gentleman; and I knew *he* was all right."

Lamoreux pointed his cigarette at Tom with grimacing emphasis.

"But get this!" he added. "I'm no guardian angel or *preux chevalier*. The hell with that stuff. Somebody in dead earnest tried to bump off that kid. Somebody'll try again, and I want no part of it. All I'd like to know, for the sweet suffering Moses's sake, is who's doing this and why?"

Lamoreux's voice rose up piercingly until he remembered they were in public.

Then it sank to a whisper. They sat and thought and worried.

"Armand de Senneville—" Tom began.

"Look," the other said wearily. "You've got that guy on the brain. De Senneville wants to marry her for her money. What good is it to him if she's knocked off here in England?"

"Yes. I suppose that's true."

"But take it the other way round!" argued Lamoreux. "Take that gang in their country house near Hampton Court. I don't doubt Aunt Hester, at least, will get a large slice of dough when this marriage comes off. She's been in

France dozens of times—she's cheering for matrimony like nobody's business. All right! Then what motive has she, or any of 'em, to kill Jenny and lose the money themselves?"

Steve Lamoreux at last took a sip of tea, which so disgusted him he did not speak for thirty seconds.

"It's nuts!" he said. "It makes no sense however you look at it."

"On the contrary," said Tom, "it's got to make sense! That's why you and I are going to see H.M. as fast as a taxi can take us."

"But I can't go there!"

"Why not?"

"Because Jenny's there, and she might spot me. All the same, if you want to reach me at any time before seven this evening, call me up at this number. If you want me any time after that, here's the number of my hotel near their house."

With a little gold pencil he scribbled two telephone numbers on a sheet torn from a notebook, and handed it to Tom.

"Locked rooms!" said Lamoreux. "Whispering voices! No motives! Brother, I'd give my last dime to go with you! What's the old—what's Sir Henry going to say about this one?"

In little more than twenty minutes, Tom Lockwood found out.

"Y'see," said Sir Henry Merrivale, with surprising meekness, "I'm sort of in trouble with the government."

"How do you mean?" asked Tom.

"Well, sort of," said H.M.

The old sinner, all sixteen stone of him, sat behind the desk in the familiar office, twiddling his thumbs over his corporation. His shell-rimmed spectacles were pulled down on his broad nose, and light from the windows behind him glistened on his bald head. On his face was the look of such martyrdom that it had won Jenny's complete sympathy and only enraged Tom.

"Well, y'see," H.M. pursued, "I've been abroad for maybe two or three years . . ."

"Ah, yes!" said Tom. "It was in New York, wasn't it, that you wrecked the subway at Grand Central Station and nabbed the right murderer on the wrong evidence?"

"Oh, son! I dunno what you're talkin' about," said H.M., giving him an austere look.

"And in Tangier, I think, you blew up a ship and let the real criminal escape just because you happened to like him?"

"Y'see how they treat me?" H.M. demanded, his powerful voice rising as he addressed Jenny. "They've got no respect for me, not a bit."

"Poor man!" Jenny said warmly.

"Oh, Lord," moaned Tom. Like most people, he could never resist the temptation to make fun of the great man; and then, to his astonishment, he found women sympathizing with H.M.'s most outrageous exploits.

"But why," he persisted, "are you in trouble with the government?"

"It seems I spent more money than I should have, or burn me, than I can account for. It also seems—would you believe it?—I shouldn't have had banking accounts in New York, Paris, Tangier, and Milan."

"You didn't know, of course, you weren't allowed to have those banking accounts?"

"*Me?*"

"Never mind," said Tom, smiting his forehead. "What happened to you?"

"Oh, Lord love a duck!" said H.M. "When I got back to England, you'd have thought I was Guy Fawkes and the Cato Street conspirators all rolled into one. They hoicked me up on the carpet before an old friend of mine. I won't say who this louse is, except to tell you he's the Attorney-General."

"No," said Tom. "By all means don't breathe a word."

"'Henry,' he says to me, 'I've got you over a barrel.'"

"Did the Attorney-General actually use those words?"

"Well . . . now!" said the great man, making a broad gesture and giving Tom a withering look. "I'm tellin' you the gist of it, that's all. 'Henry,' he says, 'on the evidence I have here I could have you fined a hundred thousand pounds or stuck in jail for practically a century.'" Here H.M. broke off and appealed to Jenny. "Was this just?" he demanded.

"Of course it wasn't!" cried Jenny.

"'However,' he says, 'you pay up in full, with a fine, and we'll forget it. *Provided*,' he says—"

"Provided what?"

"I'm to go back to my own office here, d'ye see? It used to be part of the War Office, before they messed everything about in the war. And I'm to be in charge of Central Office Eight of the Metropolitan Police."

"Please," said Jenny in her soft voice, "but what is Central Office Eight?"

"It's me," H.M. replied simply. "Anybody who calls it The Ministry of Miracles is going to get a thick ear. They had enough fun, curse 'em, with the late Ministry of Information. If anything rummy turns up at Scotland Yard—any loony case that doesn't make sense—they chuck it at my head."

Here H.M.'s expression changed.

"Y'know," he said, "strictly among ourselves, I don't mind so much. I'm gettin' old and mellow now—"

"I'll bet you are," Tom muttered sardonically under his breath.

"—and it's comfortable here, sort of. Well!" said H.M., sitting up briskly and rubbing his hands together. "The old man's in business again. You got any miracles you want explained?"

"Have we!" said Tom. "Jenny! Haven't you told him?"

He himself had just arrived, hurrying in to find H.M. pouring out his woes and tribulations. In the old dusty office, high above Whitehall, Tom and Jenny looked at each other.

That office, as H.M. had said, was comfortable. Above the fireplace still hung the Satanic portrait of Fouché, Minister of Police under Napoleon. There was a very impressive-looking safe, inscribed IMPORTANT STATE DOCU-

MENTS: *DO NOT TOUCH!*—but containing only a bottle of whiskey. The office had seen many strange things happen—it would see many more.

"I told him about what happened in the whispering gallery, yes!" said Jenny. "But I do not even know how I have come here at all! I hated to leave you in the tea shop, but Aunt Hester was so furious I could only run. Then, at the car, the chauffeur says that some Canadian gentleman—"

"That's all right. I can explain later."

"Some Canadian gentleman, who has been sitting with him in the car when we went into St. Paul's, told him to drive me straight to this H.M. of yours. You have said so too, so I go." Jenny's brow wrinkled. "And I was so, so wrong about your H.M.!"

"Oh?" enquired Tom.

"Yes, yes! He does not swear or carry on or throw people out of windows. He is what you call a poppet."

"Hem!" said the great man modestly.

"Frankly," said Tom, eyeing the stuffed owl across the desk, "I shouldn't call it a well-chosen word to apply to him. You'll find out. However! When I'd chucked out Aunt Hester, with the aid of two counter-girls and a friendly cop, I thought I'd never get here. I was afraid some infernal thing or other had happened to you, and I might never see you again."

"You may see me," said Jenny, and stretched out her hands, "whenever you wish."

"*Oi!*" interposed a thunderous voice.

The alleged poppet was now glaring at them with a malignancy which raised Jenny's hair.

"There's not goin' to be any canoodling in this office, is there?" he demanded. "All my life I've tripped over young people with no idea except to canoodle. —Now listen to me, my dolly."

His big voice altered and sharpened. The whole atmosphere of the office changed as his small eyes narrowed behind the spectacles. He might be irascible, unreasonable, and childish, but he was still the Old Maestro—and you trifled with him at your own risk.

So H.M. spoke gently.

"You understand, my dolly, what I've already told you? That neither Général de Senneville nor Armand de Senneville has any hold over you? And neither have Aunt Hester and Company? That you're a perfectly free woman?"

Jenny pressed her hands against her cheeks.

"Yes," she said. "I suppose I always knew that, really. But . . ."

"But what?"

"People are so *determined*. They don't yield a bit. And it's always gone on like that. So you say to yourself, 'Oh, what's the use?' "

"Yes, I know," nodded H.M. "But that's what causes so much unhappiness in this world, especially for gals. Well, what's your feeling now? Do you want to fight 'em and beat 'em hands down?"

"Yes!"

"Do you still want to go on staying at your Aunt Hester's house? What's-its-name? Near Hampton Court?"

"It's called Broadacres, on the river. Tomorrow, they tell me, they will save the best of the sights for last—they say they will take me to see Hampton Court Palace in the afternoon."

"They say that, hey?" H.M. muttered thoughtfully. Something flickered behind his glasses and was gone. "Never mind! Do you still want to stay at your Aunt Hester's?"

"No. But what else can I do, except return to Paris?"

"Well," glowered H.M. scratching the back of his neck, "I've got a house, and a wife, and two daughters, and two good-for-nothing sons-in-law I've had to support for eighteen years. So I expect you'd better move in too."

"You mean this?" cried Jenny, and sprang to her feet. "You would really want me?" she asked incredulously.

"Bah," said H.M.

"Sir H.M.! How to thank you I do not know . . . !"

"Shut up," said the great man austerely.

Jenny sat down again.

"Then there's your clothes," he mused. "That's a very fetchin' outfit you've got on now, and I expect you brought a whole trunkful?"

"Yes, my clothes! I forget!"

"Don't worry," said H.M. with a suggestion of ghoulish mirth. "I'll send a police-officer to fetch 'em. If that doesn't put the breeze up Aunt Hester to a howlin' gale, I don't know her kind. But understand this, my dolly!"

Again his tone sharpened and struck.

"Aunt Hester'll hit back. Don't think she won't. Also, you're likely to have the whole de Senneville tribe here and on your neck." H.M. blinked at Tom. "I say, son. Shall you and I handle 'em?"

"With pleasure!" said Tom. "And definitely without gloves."

"In the meantime," H.M. went on, looking very hard at Jenny, "I've heard about this rummy business in the whispering gallery, yes. But there's something else you've got to tell me, and very clearly, before I can help you at all."

"Just a minute!" interrupted Tom.

"Oh, for the love of Esau," howled H.M. "What's wrong *now?*"

"A voice spoke where no voice could possibly have spoken," said Tom. "Do you believe that?"

"Certainly."

"Then how was it done?"

"Oh, my son!" groaned H.M., with a pitying glance. "You don't mean to say that trick fooled you?"

"Do you know how it was done?"

"Sure I do."

"Then what's the explanation?"

"I'm not goin' to tell you."

Tom got up and did a little dance round his chair. H.M. sternly ordered him back into it.

"I'm not goin' to tell you," he went on with dignity, "because very shortly I'm goin' to *show* you. You can see with your own eyes. That's fair enough, hey?"

Whereupon his own eyes narrowed as he looked at Jenny.

"Stop a bit! We don't want Aunt Hester to pick up the trail too soon. You said you came here in a car, with a chauffeur. Is the car still waiting? Or did you send it back?"

"I have sent it back," retorted Jenny. "But I *know* I can trust Pearson—he is the chauffeur. I have told him to say I have gone off on my own, alone, to have tea at Lyons'."

"Which Lyons'?"

Jenny's gray eyes opened wide.

"I am English, I keep telling you!" she insisted. "But how can I know much of England if I am never here? Is there more than one Lyons'? The only London restaurants of which I have heard are Lyons and the Caprice and the Ivy."

"Those three grand old restaurants!" exclaimed Tom, and resisted an impulse to put his arms round her. "H.M., Aunt Hester will think Jenny is giving her the raspberry, which is exactly what you'd do yourself."

"Uh-huh. That'll do. Now then: about this first miracle—of a gas-tap being turned on in a locked room."

When H.M. produced his ancient black pipe, and began to load it with tobacco looking (and tasting) like the steel wool used on kitchen sinks, Tom knew he must brace himself for more trouble.

"My dolly," said H.M., "a lot of bits and pieces have come flyin' out of your story. I can *see* this aunt of yours. I can see her daughter, Margot, who's eighteen years old and up to mischief. I can see your Uncle Fred, who's tall and red-faced and looks like a retired major. I can see this white Georgian house, with long windows, set back from the river. But burn me if I can see the details!"

"How do you mean?"

"For instance. D'ye usually sleep with the windows closed, to say nothin' of being locked? Is that an old French custom?"

"No, no, of course not!"

"Well, then?"

"It is the details," said Jenny, biting her lip, "I have not wished to talk about. They are—bad. I feel the gas strangle me again. But never mind! First, Aunt Hester put me into a bedroom on the ground floor."

"Why?"

"And why not?" Jenny exclaimed reasonably. "It is a very nice room. But it has two windows stretching to the ground. Aunt Hester is frightened of burglars, and asks me please to keep the windows tight-locked. By the time I am ready for bed, I am so scared that I put both bolts on the door as well—on the inside. You see, it was at dinner I received the note."

"What note?"

"It was a little note, folded up in my napkin at the table. I thought—"

"Yes, my dolly?"

"At first," Jenny explained, peeping sideways at Tom, "I thought it was from a young man I met at a tea party they gave. He has made what you call the eyes at me. So—"

"*That's* an old French custom, if you like," Tom said politely. "You thought the note was from him, and you didn't want anybody else to know?"

Jenny turned on him flaming.

"I do not like this young man at the tea party! I do not wish to see him again! But if he has written a note to me, can I give the poor man away?"

"No. Sorry, Jenny. Shouldn't have said that."

"But it is not from him at all, or anything like that. I read it under the table. It was only one line, in a handwriting I never saw before. It said, '*You will die tonight, Jennifer.*' "

Jenny moistened her lips. H.M. had lighted the pipe, and an oily cloud of smoke crept over the desk.

"At first I thought it was a joke. What else can I think? Then I looked at the rest of them, all so normal, with the candles burning on the dinner table. And I know I am alone. I am a stranger, even if I am in my own country—and I am frightened!

"I did not even dare ask if the note was a joke. So I hid it, and afterwards I lost it. At eleven o'clock, when it was time to go to bed . . ."

"Yes, my dolly? Go on!"

"I sleep badly," said Jenny. "Always I have. No matter how late I go to bed, I always wake up at 5 or 5:30 in the morning. There was a custom I had in France, first when I lived with my parents and afterwards at the house of Général de Senneville. A maid brought me a cup of chocolate at six in the morning.

"When Aunt Hester asked if she could do anything more, I asked if I might have the chocolate, or else tea, at that time. I had been there several days, but it was the first time I venture to ask. Aunt Hester lifts her eyebrows and says, 'Do you think, Jennifer my dear, that is quite fair to the servants?'

"I said no, no, please to forget it. But Margot, who has green eyes and is nice, she is always up before six, she says, and will be glad to bring me a cup of tea then. Very well! I go to my room. I turn on the light. I fasten the bolts both at the top and bottom of the door. Then I turn round. And one of the windows, which I have left locked, is wide open."

Jenny paused.

H.M., wrapped in his cloud of nauseous smoke, was as expressionless as an idol.

"I rush across," continued Jenny, her voice rising. "I close and lock the window again. Then I think, 'Suppose someone is hiding in the room?' But I must not be stupid and rouse the whole house. And so—well! I search the room myself. Nobody is hiding there. I think perhaps some servant has opened the window to air the room, and I feel better.

"It is a warm night—very warm, they tell me, for an English spring. So I do not need to turn on the gas heater in the fireplace when I undress. I close the window curtains almost shut. But I smoke a cigarette or two, you can bet, before I have the nerve to turn out the light. But I do turn out the light, finally. And soon I am asleep. Then—"

"Hold on!" interposed H.M. softly, and took the pipe out of his mouth.

"Y-yes?"

"What time did you turn in? Do you remember?"

"Yes. I see my wrist watch. It is ten minutes past twelve."

"Did any of this family know beforehand about your habit of takin' chocolate at six in the morning?"

"N-no, I do not think so. How could they? I—"

Again Jenny was trembling; and, worst sign of all, she was again glancing over her shoulder. Tom got up and put his hands on her shoulders.

"Hadn't we better stop this, H.M.?" he demanded.

"We can't stop it, son, and you know we can't. That gal really *was* in a locked room. It's practically impossible to tamper with bolts when they're at the top and bottom of the door. Those Georgian window-locks are dead sure for safety. Unless I can get a hint about this, the old man's dished."

"I am very well, thank you," said Jenny. "I can go on, if you wish."

"Well?" said H.M., putting the pipe back in his mouth.

"First there was a dream. It was horrible, but I don't remember it now. Then I knew I was awake, and being strangled so I could not breathe. This part is hard to describe. But—when you are dying, or even losing consciousness, you can still hear sounds clearly even though you can barely see?"

"Yes, my dolly. That's right."

"I could tell it was just growing daylight, no more. But somebody was pounding on the outside of the door. And I hear Margot's voice crying my name. I tried to scream back, but there is no breath, and already—this is not pretty—I had been sick.

"Next, which is all confused, I heard a man's voice outside with Margot. It was an American voice I have never heard before. It said, 'What's wrong, kid? Isn't she okay?' Margot screams that the room is full of gas, and can't he smell it from under the door? He says, 'You won't break down that door. Where's the window?'

"Still I am just conscious. I can hear everything, though it must be like being hanged. I hear them run away, and someone else join them. Then I see—all blurry, because my eyes have nearly gone—I see someone's fist, wrapped in a coat, punch through the glass of the far window.

"This is my Uncle Fred, who has been roused too. He unlocks the window and pushes it all the way up. Someone runs to turn off the gas-tap at the heater. I think this is the American. I cannot see, but I hear him say a wicked word, and say, 'So-and-so, but it's turned full on!' He turns it off. Margot rushes towards me, spilling a tea tray on the carpet. That is all I remember, until the doctor is there."

Jenny lifted her hands, and let them fall on the handbag in her lap. As the oily smoke from H.M.'s pipe reached her at last, she began to cough.

H.M. put down the pipe and knocked it out.

"The doctor, hey?" he repeated. "And what did the doctor say?"

"It was not the doctor who spoke to me. It was Aunt Hester. She said, 'This is not very considerate of you, Jennifer. To try to kill yourself because you are not happy about your future husband.'"

Tom Lockwood's grip tightened on her shoulders. "Your Aunt Hester said that?"

"Yes! And it is not true! But they ask how anyone could have tried to kill me, when the room is all locked up inside?"

"Anything else, Jenny?"

"I say, 'Where is the American?' They say, 'What American?' and claim he is a delusion of mine. They stand round my bed, all big-eyed—Aunt Hester and Cousin Margot and even poor old Uncle Fred—and look down at me. They say it is a mercy the doctor is their family doctor, and will not report this to the police. Dear God, do you wonder I am afraid of them?"

"H.M.!" Tom said sharply, after a pause.

"Well?"

"You may have been wondering about this mysterious American . . ."

"Frankly, son, I have. I don't see where he fits in."

"He isn't an American," said Tom, "but he isn't a delusion either. That gang made a bad slip when they claimed he was. I'll tell you all about him at the proper time. Meanwhile, do you see any clue at all?"

H.M., who had been sitting with his eyes closed and a very mulish look on his face, now opened his eyes slowly and inspected Jenny.

"My dolly," he said, "I've got only one more question to ask now. But I want you to be awful careful how you answer it. You could hear all these voices clearly when you were nearly unconscious. You could hear the pounding on the door, the footsteps running away, and the rest of it. *Did you hear any other sound besides that?*"

"What—what kind of sound?"

"Any kind!"

"No, I don't think so."

"You're sure of that, now?"

"Yes, positive!"

"Oh, Lord love a duck," observed Sir Henry Merrivale, with his mouth falling open. "So *that's* how the locked room was worked!"

"How?" shouted Tom.

"I'm the old man," said H.M., tapping himself impressively on the chest. "You let me deal with this in my own way. I'm goin' into action at once."

H.M. reached for the telephone at his elbow. He dialed for an outside exchange, and then dialed the number. During a long pause, while they could hear the ringing tone go on interminably, Tom Lockwood listened to an air-vent which hummed and hummed in the ceiling, and at intervals he studied H.M.'s face, now as malignant as the Evil One's.

The ringing tone broke off. There ensued, from H.M.'s side, the following weird and wonderful conversation.

"Looky here, my wench. I want to speak to Sam. . . . Oh, yes, I can! This is the old man. You just tell him I squared it when he was givin' a beautiful party for sixteen beautiful gals without any clothes on, and the silly-ass coppers broke in. Yes, the old man! . . ."

A gratified note crept into H.M.'s big voice.

"That you, Sam? How are you . . . ? Never better, Sam! There's a question I want to ask you. . . . Thank'ee Sam. How many vents are working now? . . ."

Tom Lockwood looked up wildly at the air-ventilator humming and whacking above his head. He looked at an equally bewildered Jenny.

"Only three? You're sure of that? Right, Sam. Gimme their names and descriptions. Yes, I said descriptions! Uh-huh. . . . No, the first one's no good. Try the second. . . . Lord love a duck, that sounds like the one we want! But try the third, just for luck. . . . No, he's no good either. It's Charley Johnson. Gimme the address. It's nearly six o'clock—he's bound to be at home now. . . . Thanks a million, Sam. And try to keep to one woman next time, hey?—All right, all right!"

Ringing off with the handsome air of one who has made all things clear, Sir Henry Merrivale spun the dial once again.

"Sergeant? I want a squad car, to hold three people and a driver, as quick as kiss-your-hand. Two minutes? Outside the Horse Guards Avenue entrance? Right!"

Lumbering to his feet, H.M. took down from a rack an ancient Panama hat and thrust it on. This hat, which had a band of startling colors and whose brim was turned down all round like a bowl, gave an even more sinister look to the great man's unmentionable face.

"Sir!" protested Tom. "What in the name of sense is all this business of air-vents, and how can it help us?"

"You wanted a miracle explained, didn't you?" demanded the great man. "All right. Are you comin' with me, or not?"

Within the promised two minutes, and in the police car—Jenny and Tom sitting in the back seat, H.M. piled in front with the chauffeur—they whipped out of Horse Guards Avenue, turned left, and shot down Whitehall. H.M., who himself has never driven a car without landing through a shop window or against a lamp-post, made caustic comments about driving skill to a red-eared police driver.

Far beyond the towers of Westminster, behind its stately terraces and flats, lies a region of dingy, almost unknown, streets. The red-brick houses in these streets, by a show of brass knobs and letter-slots, try to keep up a brave pretense that they are private homes and not lodging houses.

But gritty winds make discarded newspapers dance along their gutters; children scream; there is an over-riding clatter of dustbins. Before one such dingy house, which did look like a private home and really was, the car stopped.

"Come on, you two," grunted H.M.

He impelled Jenny and Tom out of the car, and up a flight of stone steps to the front door. There he jabbed his finger at the bell.

"For the last time," said the desperate Tom, "will you tell what an air-vent–" H.M. pulled down the brim of his hat even harder.

"Who said anything about an air-vent?" he howled. "*I* didn't. I said 'vent.' That's the theatrical and professional term for a ventriloquist. –Didn't you ever hear a ventriloquist?"

Jenny's hands flew to her open mouth.

"According to your story," pursued H.M., "there were only four persons in the whispering gallery with you. This time we can acquit both your Aunt Hester and your Cousin Margot–they were leaning over the railing, much too far away from the wall.

"We can acquit the outraged verger in charge of the place. But who else was there? According to you, a fat and red-faced countryman–a little too thoroughly dressed up as a countryman, wasn't he?–who carried a packet of sandwiches and a thermos flask.

"When you heard the words, he was sitting against the walls and plainly drinking tea. All right, my fatheads! Who's the only man alive who can make his dummy speak clearly while he himself is walloping down a full glass of water? You know the answer.

"I rang up the king of all impresarios and found out the names and descriptions of the only three vents working in London. This Charley Johnson won't know much about the case. Somebody handed him a fiver to play what he thought, and probably still thinks, was a joke. But *he*, when we see him, can tell us who bribed him to–"

The front door was hurled open.

There is no other word for it–the door crashed against the wall and all but rebounded.

In the doorway there stood, swaying slightly, that same fat man Jenny recognized from the whispering gallery. His face was now less professionally red; he was bald, and wore no wig. Instead of his countryman's clothes, he was wrapped round in a somewhat grubby dressing gown of black and orange stripes. In one hand he held a whiskey-and-soda, in the other a half-eaten sandwich.

But what held them was the expression of his face. His eyes were so horribly wide open that a ring of white showed all the way round the iris.

"*Look out, you two!*" snapped H.M.

Tom dragged Jenny back just in time.

Charles Johnson, making a bubbling noise, took one step forward. Then he pitched headlong down the stone steps, turning over twice before he lay face down on the pavement.

The smashed glass, the half-eaten sandwich, had flown wide and fallen. Because of the man's tiger-striped dressing gown, it was a moment or two before any of them saw the black handle of the knife driven into his back just under the left shoulder blade.

Nobody moved until the police driver sprang out of the car. It did not need the driver's nod, looking up, to tell them Johnson was dead.

Children's roller skates crashed past on the opposite side of the street, amid shouting. A few windows banged up; a few women's heads were thrust out. That was all.

H.M.'s face was white.

"Easy, my dolly," he said, putting his hand on Jenny's arm and speaking with surprising gentleness. "Is that the man you saw at the whispering gallery?"

The shock was too great. Jenny could only nod.

"Then that means," said H.M., "this is no straight business of frightening a gal out of her wits. It means there's somebody who's dead-determined, crazy-mad, to get what he or she wants. Somebody got here before us and shut Johnson's mouth. Murder with a knife is all in the day's work. And that means . . ."

He brooded so long, ruffling his fingers at his temples, that Tom could not remain quiet.

"H.M.!" he said. "What is it?"

"It means there's been a slight change of plans," he answered.

"How?"

"You, my dolly," said H.M., "aren't going to spend the night at my house after all. If you've got the nerve, you're goin' straight back to spend the night at Aunt Hester's."

A golden sky was becoming tinged with purple over the thin Tudor chimneys of Hampton Court Palace.

Sir Henry Merrivale, in his most maddening mood, sat on an upended wheelbarrow, in one of the few remaining Tudor quadrangles: of dark red brick, with its white stone lions uprearing from the walls beside sly little windows. H.M. was again smoking his black pipe, and looked up at Tom without favor.

"Well," he asked querulously, "where's the whole party *now?*"

"As far as I know, they're still tramping through miles and miles of picture galleries."

"But looky here, son!" protested the great man. "According to my watch, and the notices posted up, this place should have been closed for a long time. Shouldn't they all have been flung out of here hours ago?"

"Yes. But it seems Uncle Fred has a lot of influence with the director or the curator or whatever they call him. They're being taken over the whole show at their leisure, particularly since Jenny's keen to see the maze; and that's a long way from here."

"Maze, hey?" H.M. repeated thoughtfully.

"Now listen to me!" roared Tom, assuming an oratorical posture. "Since a few minutes past six yesterday afternoon, when you got rid of us all, until half an hour ago, when I set eyes on your ugly dial again, you've asked questions by the bucket. But you won't answer a single question yourself. Why?"

"'Cause I'm the old man."

"And you think that's a good enough reason?"

"Sure it is. I say, son. How is . . . I mean, how is . . . ?"

Tom regarded him bitterly.

"How is Jenny taking this?" he asked. "What the devil do you expect, after that asinine order she was to go back to Aunt Hester's last night? She's taking it badly, of course! But she won't let any of 'em see for a minute she's afraid."

Here the old sinner had at least the grace to look discomfited.

"Well . . . now!" he growled. "I had my reasons, hadn't I? Burn me," and H.M.'s voice rose up passionately, "people are always sayin', 'What an old cloth-head he is; stick him upside down in the dustbin.' Then they see what I mean. And they yell, 'Why, Henry; pull him out and dust him off; we should never have guessed it.' And of course they wouldn't have guessed it, the star-gazin' goops! Only—"

H.M.'s eloquence was interrupted only by a back-wash taste from his own black pipe. Then he simply sat and looked evil.

"All right, all right!" he said. "What did you do last night?"

"Steve Lamoreux and I stood guard outside Jenny's windows all night—"

"Stop a bit, son. Does the gal know who Lamoreux is?"

"She doesn't know he's Armand de Senneville's spy, naturally! And she can't meet him. But, for all practical purposes, he *isn't* a spy. He won't stand for violence—"

"Uh-huh. I know. I talked to him in my office today. You were sayin'?"

"Well, while the rest of 'em were at dinner, Steve and I sneaked into her bedroom and dismantled the gas heater . . ."

Tom paused in even more exasperation. H.M., with a silent and ghoulish mirth, was rocking in ecstasy.

"Oh, son! You didn't think the murderer would try *that* simple little trick again?"

"*Simple* little trick?"

"Easy as shellin' peas."

"Will you acknowledge to me," demanded Tom, after a hard-breathing pause, "that the door of the room really was tightly bolted on the inside and couldn't have been tampered with?"

"Sure."

"Will you acknowledge that both windows were securely locked on the inside and that they weren't tampered with in any way?"

"Agreed without a struggle."

"Will you finally acknowledge that, with no funny business about outside gas meters or the like, somebody—*somebody actually in that room*—turned on the gas-tap?"

"That's right, son."

"*Then how in hell did the murderer get in and out of that room?*"

"I'm not goin' to tell you. Now wait!" said H.M., and pointed with the stem of his pipe. "Yesterday you raved and danced about the 'miracle' of the ventriloquist, didn't you? But that was easy. And this is just as easy, maybe easier, if you think about it. I want you to think about it. Meanwhile, you'd better think of something and somebody you've rather neglected."

"Oh? Who's that?"

"Armand de Senneville himself. You hated him from instinct and from jealousy. But maybe your instincts were right. *I* had him investigated today."

"Well?"

"He's tough, son," H.M. said somberly. "He's tougher than you think. He's an outstanding businessman, a first-class journalist, a mechanical expert, and he was liaison officer with the Yanks for four years during the war. Finally, he's as conceited as the devil; he swears, in private, there's *nothing* he ever wanted that he hasn't got."

"But Armand de Senneville's in Paris!"

"He doesn't have to be here, don't you see?" H.M. asked patiently. "Now listen. You, and the gal Jenny, and even Steve Lamoreux, have all thought there was a whole conspiracy of the Harpenden family—Uncle Fred, young Margot, and Aunt Hester—against Jenny Holden."

"And isn't there?"

"No! Coincidence has mixed you up. There's only *one*, one of those three, who has any knowledge of it. One of them, bribed by Armand de Senneville, would pay any price to have Jenny Holden frightened out of her wits. I give you three: which one?"

It was growing darker in the ancient quadrangle. Tom paced up and down the paving stones, his footfalls stirring back ghostly echoes from the walls.

H.M. knocked out his pipe and replaced it.

"Burn me," he said in a worried voice, "where's that whole family now? You were supposed to be keepin' track of 'em, weren't you?"

"I couldn't! Aunt Hester knows me too well, from that bang-up row in the tea shop! But Steve is trailing 'em, and giving me signals from windows whenever he can."

"But they can't stay in there forever! It'll be pitch dark! I'd give my ears to know where they've gone!"

It was unnecessary to sacrifice H.M.'s ears.

From under the archway to a second quadrangle the sound of "*S-s-t!*" hissed at them in a way which made H.M. leap up from the overturned wheelbarrow.

Steve Lamoreux approached as warily as a red Indian. Tom, not without difficulty, had persuaded him to put on a dark suit and an inconspicuous necktie. But his short brown hair stood up as wirily as ever, and he infuriated H.M. by addressing the great man as Pop.

"They're outside," he said, "at the back of the joint. They're going along that broad path, at the back of the palace, that runs a long way to the left between the palace and the gardens. They've got the oldest guide here, who's deaf and practically blind.—And for the love of Pete, Pop, get a wiggle on or they'll close the inner gates and *we'll* be locked in!"

H.M., not without much ruffling of his dignity, was hauled and impelled through the archway, across another quadrangle, and then through a very long archway at whose end they could see the last gleam of daylight.

They stopped at the outer edge of the arch. Just ahead lay the immense gardens, their straight-ruled lines of flower beds draining of color in twilight.

Peering round the edge of the arch to the left, Tom saw the very broad, sanded path beside ancient walls.

Five persons, their backs to the conspirators in the archway, strolled along this path about a hundred yards ahead. Though it was too dark to discern faces at that distance, Tom knew who they were as they walked abreast.

First, on the extreme left, doddered an old guide in uniform. Next, marching briskly, strode Aunt Hester. Jenny walked nervously between the giggling Margot, who danced with short steps, and the firm military stride of Uncle Fred on the extreme right.

"All right," whispered Tom. "What do we do now?"

"I know what we *could* do," said Lamoreux.

"You do, hey?" sneered H.M.

"Yes! They can't recognize us in this light. If we just strolled after 'em, three abreast but keeping back, they'd take us for another privileged tourist party like themselves. That is, if somebody could do a little spiel like a guide."

The role of guide caught Sir Henry Merrivale's fancy at once.

"Hem!" he said, tapping himself on the chest. "Me."

Lamoreux looked doubtful.

"Okay, Pop, you're the boss. But are you sure you know enough about the history of this joint?"

"*Me?*" said the outraged H.M. "The palace of Hampton Court," he bellowed, "begun by Cardinal Wolsey in the year 1515, was in 1526 pinched from this worthy prelate by that howlin' old ram King Henry the Eighth, whose wives I shall now proceed to—"

"Pop! Quiet!"

"Am I a guide," H.M. asked loftily, "or ain't I?"

"You are," snapped Tom. "And if the balloon goes up, it goes up. Anyway, I can *see* Jenny. They can't hurt her now. Let's go."

Out they marched, trying to tread softly, with Lamoreux on the inner side, Tom in the middle, and H.M. on the outer side.

It was quiet, so intense that they could hear the footsteps of those far ahead of them as well as their own. Peace lay in the hollow of a warm spring night, with the fragrance of grass and trees. You would never have guessed that death was walking with them along the broad white path—and moving closer at every pace.

Tom Lockwood did not know this, of course. But he sensed danger-fangs everywhere. He kept his eyes fixed on Jenny as though she might disappear, and his nerves were twitching like a landed fish.

So he quite literally jumped as a mighty voice smote through his thoughts.

"On our right," it thundered, "we got the famous Hampton Court gardens, forty-four acres of elegant spinach, first laid out by King William the Third and completed in 1734."

"For God's sake be careful," whispered Tom. "William the Third died in 1702."

H.M. swung round, fists on hips.

"And d'ye think I don't know that?" he bellowed. "I didn't say the old sour-puss finished 'em, did I? I just said he laid 'em out—which is what I'm goin' to do to you, young man, if you don't shut up and stop interruptin' my lecture."

"Pop! The soft pedal! Give it the old soft pedal! Holy cats, they'll hear you as far as Thames Ditton!"

But, whatever devilment H.M. had meditated—and Tom knew he had planned it in advance—the damage was done. Five persons, mere shapes in the twilight, turned round and looked back.

Out from the group, head high, marched Aunt Hester. She strode along the full distance that separated them, and looked straight at H.M.

"You, I fancy," she said coolly, "must be the man Merrivale?"

"On our left," bellowed H.M., "we see the celebrated tennis court. The game of tennis, originally played with a wooden ball, was designed with the laudable purpose of knockin' somebody's eye out—which it generally did. One famous match—"

"Answer me, please!" said Aunt Hester. "On whose authority, may I ask, are you in these grounds after official visiting hours."

H.M. gave her a wicked look.

"On Sir Hugh Rossiter's," he said. "The same as yours. Want to ring him and find out?"

Since H.M. knew everybody, this might possibly be true. Aunt Hester did not dare risk the challenge. Besides, she was more interested in someone else.

"One of you, I believe," she stated crisply, "I have already met. Indeed, Mr. Lockwood, I wish to have a word with you."

"Fire away," said Tom.

"Ever since you abducted my niece yesterday, and afterwards returned her in—I *hope*—a condition suitable to a bride, poor Jennifer has been talking nonsense which I propose to stamp out here and now."

"Oh?"

"Yes. Absurdly enough, the girl believes she is in love with you . . ."

"Is she, by God!" exclaimed Tom.

Whereupon he completely lost his head. Raising his voice, he shouted clearly and loudly through the twilight.

"*Jenny!*" he called. "*Jenny! Do you love me?*"

Jenny spun round in the broad white path.

"*Yes!*" she shouted back.

"*Will you marry me?*"

"*Yes!*"

Dead silence.

"Well . . . now!" observed Sir Henry Merrivale, with much complacence. "Since that's all settled and finished—"

"Oh, cripes!" breathed Steve Lamoreux, in a voice Tom had never heard him use. "If that's how people propose to each other in England, maybe it's true you're kind of casual. Do you just get married on the telephone, or what?"

But Aunt Hester was not amused. The paint stood out against her pale face; she was alert, smiling—and dangerous.

"How interesting!" she laughed. "It surely will interest her dear guardian and," Aunt Hester's eyes slid sideways, "the *fiancé* to whom she is pledged. Tell me, Mr. Lockwood, what is your yearly income?"

Tom stared at the ground.

"Well! I didn't want to . . ."

"Come, Mr. Lockwood!" said Aunt Hester, with honeyed sweetness. "You are a reporter on the *Record*, we know. Just what *is* your yearly income?"

"Tell her, son," growled H.M.

"All right!" said Tom, raising his head. "When death duties are subtracted, it'll be about twelve thousand pounds a year."

"*Twelve—thou—*"

"I didn't earn it," snapped Tom. "My mother left it to me. I've published just one unsuccessful novel. When I walked up Ludgate Hill yesterday, I was thinking about chucking my job and trying full-time writing. That's what I'll do, when Jenny marries me. It's why I told you, Steve, you might get a better boss; you can have my job, and they'll hand it to you on a plate. But I've never given two hoots about Jenny's money, and I'd rather prefer it if she didn't have a penny to her name."

"This is the most fantastic—" Aunt Hester was beginning, when she stopped dead.

H.M. slowly extended his neck, and gave her such a look as could not have been matched by Satan himself.

"Madam," he said, "you've got no business with us. Sling your hook."

"I absolutely refuse—"

H.M. extended his finger until it almost touched Aunt Hester's nose.

"Madam," he said, "are you goin' to hop it? Or do you prefer to find yourself, sittin' down, in the middle of King William's spinach?"

Aunt Hester hopped it. Before that glare, which would have caused the Angels of Light themselves to retire to prepared positions, she could have done nothing else.

She ran hard towards the group ahead, and appeared to be talking rapidly. The whole group faced round and began hurrying, at a faster pace, in their original direction. Jenny seemed violently to object, but Margot gripped her arm and hastened her on.

Tom Lockwood, a powerfully built young man, was all for charging forward and starting a fight at once. His companions held him back.

"Easy, son!" said H.M. "Not just yet, I tell you! We've got 'em in sight. They can't get away."

"Pop," declared Lamoreux, whose face was pale and pinched, "you're a so-and-so. You're a so-and-so and a this-and-that. You deliberately yelled all that guff about spinach and tennis balls, just so the old dame would come tearing back here. Why did you do it?"

"Well . . . now!" said H.M. with a modest look. "I rather wanted to know, d'ye see, if some person would meet some other person. Am I making myself clear?"

"No. You're not."

"Never mind, son," soothed H.M. "I haven't been so much worried about that gal as about another person. Besides, I repeat, they can't get away. We've got 'em in sight."

Lamoreux stopped in his tracks.

"Oh, no, we haven't!" he said in a high voice. "Where are they now? They've disappeared!"

It was true.

Once past the gardens and the long line of the palace, the road was closed in by tall trees, dusky and spectral against a windless night, with an occasional bench on either side. Five persons had vanished from the road.

"H.M.," said Tom, seizing his companion's arm, "you seem to be the expert on Hampton Court. Where does this road lead?"

"Steady, son! It leads to one of the main entrances—the Lion Gate. But, if you turn to the left before you reach the gate, you'll soon get to the open space where they've got the maze—"

"The maze!" said Tom, and every nameless fear boiled up inside him. "Run, you blighters! *Run!*"

That H.M. himself did run, despite his large corporation and his dislike of any pedestrian exercise, can only be stated as a fact. Lifting his chin so as to cleave the air, he belted along that road as fast as his younger companions.

Some hundred and twenty yeards farther on, they saw the dim gleam of a light past an avenue of trees branching to the left. Into this they flew abreast, found themselves in a large open space, and stopped.

For the first time they heard the wheezing, rusty voice of the old guide.

"Now, miss," he was pleading, "you don't really want to go into the maze, do you? 'Tisn't very difficult, not what we like to pretend it is. But that's in the daytime. You don't want to go in at night, miss."

"But I do!" Jenny insisted firmly. "All my life I've been reading about the Hampton Court maze, and I'll die if I don't explore it. Won't you lend me your electric torch?"

In the clearing, a hut or small pavilion had been set well back, evidently used as somebody's living quarters; on a pole against the side of the hut burned a sickly electric bulb.

The famous maze was set well out from the hut. It was roughly oval in shape, a little higher than a man's head, of green hedge raggedly trimmed. Illumined in bright green and dead shadow by the sickly light, it loomed up less as a place of comedy than as a secret, malicious trap.

The entrance must be at the far side, because the entire party was assembled there. Slant-eyed Margot was jumping up and down with joy.

"May I go in too, Mama?" she shrilled. "*May* I go?"

"No, you may not," said Aunt Hester sharply. "Afterwards, perhaps, if dear Jennifer—"

"Lot of nonsense, *I* call it," grumbled Uncle Fred from under his gray military mustache.

"*Please* may I have the electric torch?" said Jenny in a voice no man could resist.

"Ah, well," mumbled the guide. "'Ere's the torch. I s'pose I can always climb up on top of the stepladder by the entrance, and give you directions if you get lost. Be nippy, now."

"I will! I will!"

"Jenny!" called Tom. "Jenny, wait! I'm going with you!"

His words did not carry to her. Faintly he heard the creak of a small gate, and the brushing of Jenny's body against the narrow sides of the maze.

Tom sprang forward. Instantly Sir Henry Merrivale locked both his arms from behind, and held him back.

"No, son," said H.M., in so soft and deadly a voice that Tom was startled. "You're not goin' into that maze."

"Why not?"

"Whose life," asked H.M., glancing round him, "d'ye think I've been worried about, as much or more than the little gal's herself? *Yours*."

"Are you crazy?"

"No. But you're not goin' inside that maze."

Tom, with one sudden heave and jerk, tore loose even from H.M.'s powerful grip.

"I'm sorry, sir. But that's where I'm going, and neither you nor anybody else is going to stop me."

He ran across the sanded space, and round the side to the entrance. He saw the startled face of Uncle Fred, who was swinging a heavy yellow cane. He saw Aunt Hester, with rigid mouth. He saw the pretty, mischievous face of Margot, who was slipping away in another direction.

The guide had already shakily mounted to the top of the stepladder beside the entrance. Tom swung open the little gate, twisted sideways as he plunged into the maze, and attempted to run.

It was impossible.

The hedge-walls were so narrow that tendrils stung his face. Though it was not pitch-dark, just enough light filtered down from the dim bulb outside to distort the eyesight and turn dark shapes into illusions. He might run slap into a hedge-wall at any second, and just saved himself from doing so.

Gently, now!

Stopping at a turn, Tom felt down on his left and found the thin wall, of hard and curved wire, built a little below waist height. In this maze, he remembered it had been said, you must always turn to the left. He did so, and presently turned left again.

That was when he saw, deeper inside these thinnish walls, the firefly glimmer of Jenny's torch. It vanished again—but it was there.

"Jenny!" he called. "Wait for me! It's Tom!"

"Tom! Darling!" Her voice slipped through the walls rather than above them. "Where are you?"

"I don't know. Where are *you?*"

"Very near the center of the maze, I think."

"Then stop where you are! Wait until I catch up with you!"

"Oh, no!" Jenny retorted demurely. "I'll get to the center and turn off the torch. Then you can find me and tell me how much you love me."

"Jenny, wait!"

But the firefly glimmer danced away. He could hear her brushing and hurrying on. In a moment or two there was a cry of pleasure, as evidently she found the center of the maze. The light of her torch went out.

Tom moved forward, more slowly and carefully. The electric bulb at the hut was now so distant and so dim that it gave scarcely any light. Tom didn't know where he was. Walls loomed up and closed round him. It wasn't pleasant, being shut into a twisting maze where . . .

Then he stopped, listening.

Somebody was following him stealthily through the maze.

Somebody, not much lighter than his own weight, was stalking him—with what intent? Tom ran forward and stopped. The footsteps behind him ran forward and stopped. Tom ran again. But he was not left in doubt long.

A closer footfall, a looming of a shape in near-darkness, made him glance over his shoulder. He saw the upsurge of someone's silhouette. A distant gleam flashed on the blade of the knife as if lifted high—and struck.

All that saved Tom from being stabbed in the back, as Johnson the ventriloquist had been stabbed, was the dim light and the attacker's misjudgment. The blade of the knife ripped through the cloth of the coat over Tom's shoulder. The attacker, plunging forward so hard that he collided with Tom, sent his victim sprawling one way and drove his own head and shoulders, grotesquely, straight into the hedge on the other side.

Somebody screamed one word, nothing more.

With a crackling of branches, the attacker wrenched out his left arm and then withdrew his head. Before he could disengage his knife-hand, Tom landed a vicious right-hander that opened his assailant's cheekbone and drew first blood.

Then they faced each other, two dim shapes, between the narrow walls. There were no Queensbury Rules here. Neither man was a boxer. But both were enraged and both meant murder.

The attacker held his knife blade out, to leap forward and rip up. Just as he lunged, Tom kicked him in the groin. The attacker, in intense agony, began to double up; his knife fell and tinkled. Tom hit him again.

The attacker, straightening up, flew in with both fists. Tom hit him twice, left and right, in the belly. Then he put all his strength into a right cross to the man's jaw—which, if it had landed, would have broken Tom's hand.

But it did not land on the jaw. Instead it landed, with just as murderous effect, in the soft flesh under the man's left ear. The attacker, brain paralyzed and legs suddenly gone to water, reeled backwards and fell.

"Now where the devil," Tom was thinking, "did we get so much space?"

Then he realized they had been fighting very near the entrance to the center of the maze. For the first time he heard voices, and bodies thrashing about in the maze.

Behind him loomed up the blaze of an electric torch. Above it showed the malignant countenance of Sir Henry Merrivale. Next, cowering away in one side of the maze's center, Jenny switched on her own torch.

Both beams converged on the man who lay on his back in the center of the maze. His eyes were closed; he breathed stertorously; sluggish blood flowed from a cut in his cheek.

Jenny's face grew so white, and she turned her head away so abruptly, that Tom thought she was going to be sick.

But his own feelings were swallowed up in incredulity.

"This is impossible!" he said, pointing to the man on the ground. "That's Steve Lamoreux, the reporter!"

"Oh, no, it's not," said Sir Henry Merrivale. *"That's Armand de Senneville himself."*

"Explanations?" demanded H.M., in a tone of dismal surprise. "You don't mean to tell me you *need* explanations?"

Jenny and Tom, both seated beside the desk in H.M.'s office at the end of the following day, instantly and vehemently said they did need explanations.

H.M. sighed.

"Y'know, my dolly," he said, "you ought to have seen through your *fiancé*, Armand de Senneville, sooner than you did. He tried to prevent your trip to England. He couldn't prevent it—his father's word was law. But he knew how much you'd been repressed and kept under the thumb in France. He knew, as he casually warned Aunt Hester, you'd probably fall bang for the first presentable, easy-going Englishman who made you laugh and didn't think correct behavior was everything in life. Which is what you did."

"I did not!" Jenny cried indignantly. "I have fall bang for Tom, yes. But that is a different thing!"

Tom hastily intervened in order to evade the devastating question, "How is it different?"

"Then de Senneville," he said, "had only to crop his hair, have it dyed brown, wear very loud clothes, and pose as a French Canadian reporter from one of his own papers?"

"But Armand," insisted Jenny, "speaks no English!"

"No?" said H.M. "That's what he told you, my dolly. But as I explained to Tom here, the bloke was attached for four years to the American Army as a liaison officer. So surely he could speak English. In fact, his ear was perfect; his American was perfect. But he had to play the part of a French Canadian to explain how he spoke both languages."

"And yet," exclaimed Jenny, her eyes clouding, "I still do not understand this Armand! If he wished to keep men away from me, why did he not say he spoke English and go with the whole party of us?"

"You don't understand that, my dolly? Though it's the key to his whole character?"

"No! Why is it the key?"

"Because he was too proud," said H.M., "and he was far too conceited. He wouldn't demean himself in public by showin' he was concerned. He wouldn't admit that any man alive could take you away from the great Armand.

"Listen, my dolly, he never wanted to kill *you!* Neither did Aunt Hester. All they wanted to do was scare you so much that you'd run straight back to France. Don't you remember what you said yourself, in this office? I asked, 'Do you still want to stay at your Aunt Hester's?' And you cried out, 'No, but what else can I do except return to Paris?'—Got it now?"

"Then," Jenny blurted out, "just to get my dowry, this Armand has . . ."

"Oh, he wanted your money," said H.M. somberly. "But, towards the end, I don't think that was all. That murderous fight in the maze wasn't done altogether for money. I expect, in his own queer way, he was a little bit in love with you."

Again, since Jenny's eyes were clouding worse than ever, Tom intervened.

"But the locked room!" he said. "Where the gas-tap was turned on even while windows and door were both locked on the inside!"

"Well . . . now," H.M. sighed wearily. "I'd better tell you about it, because that locked room told me the whole ruddy truth before I even knew who was behind it.

"On the famous Night of Terrors," he added, pointing at Jenny, "you found, in your napkin at dinner, a note readin', 'You will die tonight, Jennifer.' Eh?"

"But who wrote the note?" interrupted Tom.

"Aunt Hester wrote it," snapped H.M. "There's never been much mystery about her. Her words and actions were too plain. She was the dominatin' character of her family, the only one, as I more than hinted, whom de Senneville bribed and prompted.

"After dinner," H.M. continued, still pointing at Jenny, "you went to your room at a little past eleven o'clock. One of the long windows, which you'd left closed, was now wide open. Correct?"

"Yes," said Jenny, and shuddered.

"You closed and locked the window again. You didn't need to touch or go near the gas fire. At shortly past twelve you went to bed, and soon fell asleep. The next thing you knew, Margot was bangin' on the door at six o'clock. A mysterious 'American' voice is asking what's wrong. They ran round to the window, pickin' up Uncle Fred on the way. Uncle Fred smashes the window. The mysterious 'American,' whom you can't see because you're too far gone, rushes over to the gas fire. He says, 'So-and-so, but it's turned full on!' And, apparently, he turns it off. Correct again?"

"Yes, yes."

"Not to me it isn't," said H.M., shaking his head. "Whoever this mysterious American was, he was the joker behind the trick. He told a flat lie. That gas *couldn't* have been turned full on."

"Why not?"

"Because you'd have been dead," H.M. said simply. "Let's suppose somebody, in the middle of the night, sneaks in and turns on the gas full-strength. Never mind what time it was. Let's even say it was as late, as impossibly late, as five o'clock in the morning. But there's no person in the world, breathing full-strength gas in an unventilated room, who can breathe it for an hour and still live. So I asked you a question to prove it."

"What question?"

"Oh, my dolly! You could describe every small noise you heard even when you were only half conscious. But you *didn't* hear any noise of a gas fire turned on full, which would have roared like a tornado. That's all."

"Oh!" exclaimed Jenny, caught up with a jolt. "Then . . . ?"

"Yes! Just before you retired to your room, Armand de Senneville—alias Steve Lamoreux—sneaked in and turned on the gas heater a tiny thread—only a tiny thread, not noticeable at all. He went out, leavin' the window wide open for good ventilation.

"You came in and closed the window. Well! What does happen, in very big rooms like that one, with such a tiny leak of gas? You can't hear it, you can't even smell it, for well over an hour. The bed is too far away. And it's caused tragedy before this. Meanwhile, for nearly six hours, the room is very slowly fillin' up with gas. When they found you, you were in just the condition I'd have expected.

"That's pretty much everything, my dolly. Armand de Senneville was lurkin' close outside, of course. You bet he was! He'd calculated his times, as he always does, but he was damned near too late to bust in himself, as he intended.

"He *had* to meet Margot—he couldn't help it. But that gal's a silly kind of wench, so excited she never wondered what he was doin' there. Uncle Fred barely noticed him. Later, it was easy for Aunt Hester to look 'em straight in the eye and tell 'em both they'd been dreaming. She was the only one who knew our Armand by sight. But, as for the 'miracle' of the locked room . . ."

"And that is all?" cried Jenny.

"Sure. What else did you expect?"

"I am disappoint!" suddenly exclaimed Jenny, hammering her fists on her knees. "I think this is a miracle. I think it cannot be solved. And then you show it is easy as eating sweets. Sir H.M., I hate you!"

The subsequent behavior of Sir Henry Merrivale, his martyrdom and his passionate addresses to the ceiling, is best left undescribed.

"So that's all the thanks I get, hey? They come to me and say, 'It's a miracle.' I say, 'It ain't,' and show 'em how it's done. Then they say, 'Oh, is that all? Silly old dummy! Stick him in the dustbin again.'"

It was fully half an hour before they smoothed him down.

"Very well!" he said, with a dark look at Jenny. "I'll not state what I think of some people. I'll just tell you what happened next and upset the whole apple cart. Aunt Hester had to drag a very sick and scared gal all the way to St. Paul's, so that Armand's hired ventriloquist could perform on time.

"But the apple cart was upset with an awful smash. 'Steve Lamoreux,' sittin' in the car just as he said he did, saw you run down the steps of St. Paul's and literally fall into this young feller's arms. When you went into the tea shop—well, Bob's your uncle. You bet he sneaked in and listened behind the partition. What he heard was just what he'd feared. You two were practically fallin' into each others' arms over the tea."

"I feel like this," Jenny confessed.

"I still feel like it," said Tom.

"Shut up," said the great man. "There were several courses open to 'Steve Lamoreux.' He chose the best, which was winnin' Tom Lockwood's confidence and stayin' close to him. So he deliberately sent this gal to me, supremely and conceitedly thinkin' the old goop would never see through *his* scheme.

"After Aunt Hester's row in the tea shop," here H.M. looked at Tom, "he went in and told his story. He more than won your confidence, son. He won your friendship."

"Yes," admitted Tom, and looked down at a closed fist. "He did."

"Of course, he couldn't go with you when you came to my office. He admitted the gal mustn't meet him. What he did is easy to guess. He followed you, and hung about in Horse Guards Avenue. D'ye know, I think I can see his face when we three piled downstairs and out to a police car, and I gave the address of his own hired ventriloquist.

"He got to the house about fifty seconds before we did, probably by waving a fiver in under a taxi-driver's nose. He nipped in by the back door, struck faster than a snake, and nipped out the same way while Johnson's body rolled down the front steps.

"And that tore it. As I said, the whole aspect of the business had changed.

"According to what I could deduce about the gas fire and the whispering gallery, *nobody* was actually trying to kill this gal. Somebody was trying to frighten her so much that she'd take the first plane back to Paris.

"Now who would be interested in doin' that, in conjunction with Aunt Hester? Who? You guess. And what about this odd 'American' or 'Canadian' who kept turning up all over the place without any explanation? Everybody promised to explain him; but nobody did."

H.M. pulled down his spectacles and glowered at Jenny over them.

"You see, my dolly, why I wanted you to go back to your aunt's house that night? You weren't in any real danger. And it wasn't likely somebody would try any games that night. If anything happened at all, it would happen during the expedition to Hampton Court next day—for one thing, Aunt Hester was far too insistent about takin' you there.

"And I could be there to stop it. And yet, burn me, I nearly missed it!"

The somber spectacles were now turned towards Tom.

"Son," observed H.M., "did you see the look on 'Steve Lamoreux's' face when you shouted along the path and asked this gal to marry you? And she said yes?"

"No, but I heard his voice. It was a voice I'd never heard him use before."

"Well! When it turned out you had tons of money and they couldn't accuse you of being a fortune hunter, did you notice him at any time after *that?*"

"Yes! His face was all pinched up and as pale as dough. But I thought—"

"Maybe you did. He had a knife with him, just in case. And that was the time he finally decided you were goin' to die."

Jenny pressed her face in her hands, and turned away.

"Oh, I was the villain!" said H.M. "In my role of guide, I wanted to see how Aunt Hester would act when she met Steve Lamoreux face to face. She behaved pretty well, but she couldn't keep her eyes from slidin' away when she mentioned the gal's *fiancé*.

"It was a silly-ass thing to do. I admit it. 'Cause I'd already made up my mind. That same day, since Armand de Senneville had been attached to the Yanks, I got his record and saw his photograph. To put the tin hat on it, 'Steve Lamoreux' had the star-gazin' cheek to walk into my office and spin his yarn.

"Even if I hadn't known already, the idiot gave himself away. He *would* smoke Yellow French cigarettes, and use sulphur matches. Even when he was very excited, he automatically held the match away from him until the sulphur had burned off—"

"Yes," interrupted Tom. "I saw him do that. But what about it?"

"Oh, son! He claimed he'd been in France only six months—"

"Yes, that's what he told me too!"

"And no foreigner on earth, after only six months in France, can get used to those sulphur matches. You always forget and swallow a lungful of sulphur. Only a Frenchman native-born automatically holds the match away for a few seconds. There, in my own office, was a Frenchman speakin' the most exquisite Yank.

"But *you* were the one in real danger, son. If I'd known beforehand you'd spent the night before prowlin' round this gal's windows with Armand de Senneville, I'd have had a fit. I repeat: he struck like a snake and killed poor old Johnson. Why? Just because he didn't want this gal to find out that it was *he* who was scaring her, or he'd lose her.

"Finally, last night at Hampton Court, I still don't know what funny business de Senneville, or Aunt Hester, or both of 'em, had planned. There wasn't time—the fireworks went up with a bang. I tried to keep you from goin' into that maze. Didn't you see me look round? Didn't you notice Lamoreux had slipped away? You dashed into the maze. He must have crawled up on top of it—we didn't see him enter—and followed you. But sometimes, for chivalrous young fools like you, there is mercy. You met the tough egg with his knife, and you knocked him flat. And that was the end."

There was a long silence, until Tom cleared his throat.

"H.M. What will they do to him?"

"Oh, they can't prove yet he killed Johnson. Not yet. In the meantime, he'll do a long stretch on two counts of attempted murder: with gas and with a knife. Then the coppers will snaffle him for killing Johnson. And he'll get what he deserves, son—he'll hang."

Jenny stood up suddenly, trembling. Tom put his arms around her, and held her tightly.

"It's all right!" he insisted. "Jenny, dear, it's all right!"

"Yes," said Jenny, holding him just as tightly, "but that is why you must not leave me, ever. It is all right—*now!*"

For once in his life, Sir Henry Merrivale did not roar out about canoodling in his office. Slowly, somberly, he got up from his chair and wandered over to one of the windows. There, his hands folded behind his back, he stood looking out over the river and the mighty curve of London.

REBECCA

by Daphne du Maurier

CHAPTER ONE

LAST NIGHT I dreamt I went to Manderley again. It seemed to me I stood by the iron gate leading to the drive, and for a while I could not enter for the way was barred to me. There was a padlock and a chain upon the gate. I called in my dream to the lodge-keeper, and had no answer, and peering closer through the rusted spokes of the gate I saw that the lodge was uninhabited.

No smoke came from the chimney, and the little lattice windows gaped forlorn. Then, like all dreamers, I was possessed of a sudden with supernatural powers and passed like a spirit through the barrier before me. The drive wound away in front of me, twisting and turning as it had always done, but as I advanced I was aware that a change had come upon it; it was narrow and unkept, not the drive that we had known. At first I was puzzled and did not understand, and it was only when I bent my head to avoid the low swinging branch of a tree that I realised what had happened. Nature had come into her own again and, little by little, in her stealthy, insidious way had encroached upon the drive with long, tenacious fingers. The woods, always a menace even in the past, had triumphed in the end. They crowded, dark and uncontrolled, to the borders of the drive. The beeches with white, naked limbs leant close to one another, their branches intermingled in a strange embrace, making a vault above my head like the archway of a church. And there were other trees as well, trees that I did not recognise, squat oaks and tortured elms that straggled cheek by jowl with the beeches, and had thrust themselves out of the quiet earth, along with monster shrubs and plants, none of which I remembered.

The drive was a ribbon now, a thread of its former self, with gravel surface gone, and choked with grass and moss. The trees had thrown out low branches, making an impediment to progress; the gnarled roots looked like skeleton claws. Scattered here and again amongst this jungle growth I would recognise shrubs that had been land-marks in our time, things of culture and of grace, hydrangeas whose blue heads had been famous. No hand had checked their progress, and they had gone native now, rearing to monster height without a bloom, black and ugly as the nameless parasites that grew beside them.

On and on, now east now west, wound the poor thread that once had been our drive. Sometimes I thought it lost, but it appeared again, beneath a fallen tree perhaps, or struggling on the other side of a muddied ditch created by the winter rains. I had not thought the way so long. Surely the miles had multiplied, even as the trees had done, and this path led but to a labyrinth, some choked wilderness, and not to the house at all. I came upon it suddenly; the approach masked by the unnatural growth of a vast shrub that spread in all directions, and I stood, my heart thumping in my breast, the strange prick of tears behind my eyes.

There was Manderley, our Manderley, secretive and silent as it had always been, the grey stone shining in the moonlight of my dream, the mullioned windows reflecting the green lawns and the terrace. Time could not wreck the perfect symmetry of those walls, nor the site itself, a jewel in the hollow of a hand.

The terrace sloped to the lawns, and the lawns stretched to the sea, and turning I could see the sheet of silver, placid under the moon, like a lake undisturbed by wind or storm. No waves would come to ruffle this dream water, and no bulk of cloud, wind-driven from the west, obscure the clarity of this pale sky. I turned again to the house, and though it stood inviolate, untouched, as though we ourselves had left but yesterday, I saw that the garden had obeyed the jungle law, even as the woods had done. The rhododendrons stood fifty feet high, twisted and entwined with bracken, and they had entered into alien marriage with a host of nameless shrubs, poor, bastard things that clung about their roots as though conscious of their spurious origin. A lilac had mated with a copper beech, and to bind them yet more closely to one another the malevolent ivy, always an enemy to grace, had thrown her tendrils about the pair and made them prisoners. Ivy held prior place in this lost garden, the long strands crept across the lawns, and soon would encroach upon the house itself. There was another plant too, some half-breed from the woods, whose seed had been scattered long ago beneath the trees and then forgotten, and now, marching in unison with the ivy, thrust its ugly form like a giant rhubarb towards the soft grass where the daffodils had blown.

Nettles were everywhere, the van-guard of the army. They choked the terrace, they sprawled about the paths, they leant, vulgar and lanky, against the very windows of the house. They made indifferent sentinels, for in many places their ranks had been broken by the rhubarb plant, and they lay with crumpled heads and listless stems, making a path-way for the rabbits. I left the drive and went on to the terrace, for the nettles were no barrier to me, a dreamer, I walked enchanted, and nothing held me back.

Moonlight can play odd tricks upon the fancy, even upon a dreamer's fancy. As I stood there, hushed and still, I could swear that the house was not an empty shell but lived and breathed as it had lived before.

Light came from the windows, the curtains blew softly in the night air, and there, in the library, the door would stand half open as we had left it, with my handkerchief on the table beside the bowl of autumn roses.

The room would bear witness to our presence. The little heap of library books marked ready to return, and the discarded copy of *The Times*. Ash-trays, with the stub of a cigarette; cushions, with the imprint of our heads upon them, lolling in the chairs; the charred embers of our log fire still smouldering against the morning. And Jasper, dear Jasper, with his soulful eyes and great, sagging jowl, would be stretched upon the floor, his tail a-thump when he heard his master's footsteps.

A cloud, hitherto unseen, came upon the moon, and hovered an instant like a dark hand before a face. The illusion went with it, and the lights in the windows were extinguished. I looked upon a desolate shell, soulless at last, unhaunted, with no whisper of the past about its staring walls.

The house was a sepulchre, our fear and suffering lay buried in the ruins. There would be no resurrection. When I thought of Manderley in my waking hours I would not be bitter. I should think of it as it might have been, could I have lived there without fear. I should remember the rose-garden in summer, and the birds that sang at dawn. Tea under the chestnut tree, and the murmur of the sea coming up to us from the lawns below.

I would think of the blown lilac, and the Happy Valley. These things were permanent, they could not be dissolved. They were memories that cannot hurt. All this I resolved in my dream, while the clouds lay across the face of the moon, for like most sleepers I knew that I dreamed. In reality I lay many hundred miles away in an alien land, and would wake, before many seconds had passed, in the bare little hotel bedroom, comforting in its very lack of atmosphere. I would sigh a moment, stretch myself and turn, and opening my eyes, be bewildered at that glittering sun, that hard, clean sky, so different from the soft moonlight of my dream. The day would lie before us both, long no doubt, and uneventful, but fraught with a certain stillness, a dear tranquillity we had not known before. We would not talk of Manderley, I would not tell my dream. For Manderley was ours no longer. Manderley was no more.

CHAPTER TWO

WE CAN NEVER go back again, that much is certain. The past is still too close to us. The things we have tried to forget and put behind us would stir again, and that sense of fear, of furtive unrest, struggling at length to blind unreasoning panic—now mercifully stilled, thank God—might in some manner unforeseen become a living companion, as it had been before.

He is wonderfully patient and never complains, not even when he remembers . . . which happens, I think, rather more often than he would have me know.

I can tell by the way he will look lost and puzzled suddenly, all expression dying away from his dear face as though swept clean by an unseen hand, and in its place a mask will form, a sculptured thing, formal and cold, beautiful still but lifeless. He will fall to smoking cigarette after cigarette, not bothering to extinguish them, and the glowing stubs will lie around on the ground like petals. He will talk quickly and eagerly about nothing at all, snatching at any subject as a panacea to pain. I believe there is a theory that men and women emerge finer and stronger after suffering, and that to advance in this or any world we must endure ordeal by fire. This we have done in full measure, ironic though it seems. We have both known fear, and loneliness, and very great distress. I suppose sooner or later in the life of everyone comes a moment of trial. We all of us have our particular devil who rides us and torments us, and we must give battle in the end. We have conquered ours, or so we believe.

The devil does not ride us any more. We have come through our crisis, not unscathed of course. His premonition of disaster was correct from the beginning; and like a ranting actress in an indifferent play, I might say that we have paid for freedom. But I have had enough melodrama in this life, and would willingly give my five senses if they could ensure us our present peace and security. Happiness is not a possession to be prized, it is a quality of thought, a state of mind. Of course we have our moments of depression; but there are other moments too, when time, unmeasured by the clock, runs on into eternity and, catching his smile, I know we are together, we march in unison, no clash of thought or of opinion makes a barrier between us.

We have no secrets now from one another. All things are shared. Granted that our little hotel is dull, and the food indifferent, and that day after day dawns very much the same, yet we would not have it otherwise. We should meet too many of the people he knows in any of the big hotels. We both appreciate simplicity, and if we are sometimes bored—well, boredom is a pleasing antidote to fear. We live very much by routine, and I—I have developed a genius for reading aloud. The only time I have known him show impatience is when the postman lags, for it means we must wait another day before the arrival of our English mail. We have tried wireless, but the noise is such an irritant, and we prefer to store up our excitement; the result of a cricket match played many days ago means much to us.

Oh, the Test matches that have saved us from ennui, the boxing bouts, even the billiard scores. Finals of schoolboy sports, dog racing, strange little competitions in the remoter counties, all these are grist to our hungry mill. Sometimes old copies of the *Field* come my way, and I am transported from this indifferent island to the realities of an English spring. I read of chalk streams, of the mayfly, of sorrel growing in green meadows, of rooks circling above the woods as they used to do at Manderley. The smell of wet earth comes to me from those thumbed and tattered pages, the sour tang of moorland peat, the feel of soggy moss spattered white in places by a heron's droppings.

Once there was an article on wood pigeons, and as I read it aloud it seemed to me that once again I was in the deep woods at Manderley, with pigeons fluttering above my head. I heard their soft, complacent call, so comfortable and cool on a hot summer's afternoon, and there would be no disturbing of their peace until Jasper came loping through the undergrowth to find me, his damp muzzle questing the ground. Like old ladies caught at their ablutions, the pigeons would flutter from their hiding-place, shocked into silly agitation, and, making a monstrous to-do with their wings, streak away from us above the tree-tops, and so out of sight and sound. When they were gone a new silence would come upon the place, and I—uneasy for no known reason—would realise that the sun no longer wove a pattern on the rustling leaves, that the branches had grown darker, the shadows longer; and back at the house there would be fresh raspberries for tea. I would rise from my bed of bracken then, shaking the feathery dust of last year's leaves from my skirt and whistling to Jasper, set off towards the house, despising myself even as I walked for my hurrying feet, my one swift glance behind.

How strange that an article on wood pigeons could so recall the past and make me falter as I read aloud. It was the grey look on his face that made me stop abruptly, and turn the pages until I found a paragraph on cricket, very practical and dull—Middlesex batting on a dry wicket at the Oval and piling up interminable dreary runs. How I blessed those stolid, flannelled figures, for in a few minutes his face had settled back into repose, the colour had returned, and he was deriding the Surrey bowling in healthy irritation.

We were saved a retreat into the past, and I had learnt my lesson. Read English news, yes, and English sport, politics and pomposity, but in future keep the things that hurt to myself alone. They can be my secret indulgence. Colour and scent and sound, rain and the lapping of water, even the mists of autumn and the smell of the flood tide, these are memories of Manderley that will not be denied. Some people have a vice of reading Bradshaws. They plan innumerable journeys across country for the fun of linking up impossible connections. My hobby is less tedious, if as strange. I am a mine of information on the English countryside. I know the name of every owner of every British moor, yes—and their tenants too. I know how many grouse are killed, how many partridge, how many head of deer. I know where trout are rising, and where the salmon leap. I attend all meets, I follow every run. Even the names of those who walk hound puppies are familiar to me. The state of the crops, the price of fat cattle, the mysterious ailments of swine, I relish them all. A poor pastime, perhaps, and not a very intellectual one, but I breathe the air of England as I read, and can face this glittering sky with greater courage.

The scrubby vineyards and the crumbling stones become things of no account, for if I wish I can give rein to my imagination, and pick foxgloves and pale campions from a wet, streaking hedge.

Poor whims of fancy, tender and un-harsh. They are the enemy to bitterness and regret, and sweeten this exile we have brought upon ourselves.

Because of them I can enjoy my afternoon, and return, smiling and refreshed, to face the little ritual of our tea. The order never varies. Two slices of bread-and-butter each, and China tea. What a hide-bound couple we must seem, clinging to custom because we did so in England. Here, on this clean balcony, white and impersonal with centuries of sun, I think of half-past four at Manderley, and the table drawn before the library fire. The door flung open, punctual to the minute, and the performance, never-varying, of the laying of the tea, the silver tray, the kettle, the snowy cloth. While Jasper, his spaniel ears a-droop, feigns indifference to the arrival of the cakes. That feast was laid before us always, and yet we ate so little.

Those dripping crumpets, I can see them now. Tiny crisp wedges of toast, and piping-hot, flaky scones. Sandwiches of unknown nature, mysteriously flavoured and quite delectable, and that very special gingerbread. Angel cake, that melted in the mouth, and his rather stodgier companion, bursting with peel and raisins. There was enough food there to keep a starving family for a week. I never knew what happened to it all, and the waste used to worry me sometimes.

But I never dared ask Mrs. Danvers what she did about it. She would have looked at me in scorn, smiling that freezing, superior smile of hers, and I can imagine her saying: "There were never any complaints when Mrs. de Winter was alive." Mrs. Danvers. I wonder what she is doing now. She and Favell. I think it was the expression on her face that gave me my first feeling of unrest. Instinctively I thought, "She is comparing me to Rebecca"; and sharp as a sword the shadow came between us. . . .

Well, it is over now, finished and done with. I ride no more tormented, and both of us are free. Even my faithful Jasper has gone to the happy hunting grounds, and Manderley is no more. It lies like an empty shell amidst the tangle of the deep woods, even as I saw it in my dream. A multitude of weeds, a colony of birds. Sometimes perhaps a tramp will wander there, seeking shelter from a sudden shower of rain and, if he is stout-hearted, he may walk there with impunity. But your timid fellow, your nervous poacher —the woods of Manderley are not for him. He might stumble upon the little cottage in the cove and he would not be happy beneath its tumbled roof, the thin rain beating a tattoo. There might linger there still a certain atmosphere of stress. . . . That corner in the drive, too, where the trees encroach upon the gravel is not a place in which to pause, not after the sun has set. When the leaves rustle, they sound very much like the stealthy movement of a woman in evening dress, and when they shiver suddenly, and fall, and scatter away along the ground, they might be the patter, patter, of a woman's hurrying footstep, and the mark in the gravel the imprint of a high-heeled satin shoe.

It is when I remember these things that I turn with relief to the prospect from our balcony. No shadows steal upon this hard glare, the stony vineyards shimmer in the sun and the bougainvillaea is white with dust. I may one day look upon it with affection. At the moment it inspires me, if not with love, at least with confidence. And confidence is a quality I prize, although it has come to me a little late in the day. I suppose it is his dependence upon me that has made me bold at last. At any rate I have lost my diffidence, my timidity, my shyness with strangers. I am very different from that self who drove to Manderley for the first time, hopeful and eager, handicapped by a rather desperate gaucherie and filled with an intense desire to please. It was my lack of poise of course that made such a bad impression on people like Mrs. Danvers. What must I have seemed like after Rebecca? I can see myself now, memory spanning the years like a bridge, with straight, bobbed hair and youthful, unpowdered face, dressed in an ill-fitting coat and skirt and a jumper of my own creation, trailing in the wake of Mrs. Van Hopper like a shy, uneasy colt. She would precede me in to lunch, her short body ill-balanced upon tottering, high heels, her fussy, frilly blouse a compliment to her large bosom and swinging hips, her new hat pierced with a monster quill aslant upon her head, exposing a wide expanse of forehead bare as a schoolboy's knee. One hand carried a gigantic bag, the kind that holds passports, engagement diaries, and bridge scores, while the other hand toyed with that inevitable lorgnette, the enemy to other people's privacy.

She would make for her usual table in the corner of the restaurant, close to the window, and lifting her lorgnette to her small pig's eyes survey the scene to right and left of her, then she would let the lorgnette fall at length upon its black ribbon and utter a little exclamation of disgust: "Not a single well-known personality, I shall tell the management they must make a reduction on my bill. What do they think I come here for? To look at the page-boys?" And she would summon the waiter to her side, her voice sharp and staccato, cutting the air like a saw.

How different the little restaurant where we eat to-day to that vast dining-room, ornate and ostentatious, the hotel Côte d'Azur at Monte Carlo; and how different my present companion, his steady, well-shaped hands peeling a mandarin in quiet, methodical fashion, looking up now and again from his task to smile at me, compared to Mrs. Van Hopper, her fat, bejewelled fingers questing a plate heaped high with ravioli, her eyes darting suspiciously from her plate to mine for fear I should have made the better choice. She need not have disturbed herself, for the waiter, with the uncanny swiftness of his kind, had long sensed my position as inferior and subservient to hers, and had placed before me a plate of ham and tongue that somebody had sent back to the cold buffet half-an-hour before as badly carved. Odd, that resentment of servants, and their obvious impatience. I remember staying once with Mrs. Van Hopper in a country house, and the maid never answered my timid bell, or brought up my shoes, and early morning tea, stone cold, was dumped outside my bedroom door. It was the same at the Côte d'Azur, though to a lesser degree, and sometimes the studied indifference turned to familiarity, smirking and offensive, which made buying stamps from the reception clerk an ordeal I would avoid. How young and inexperienced I must have seemed, and how I felt it, too. One was too sensitive, too raw, there were thorns and pin-pricks in so many words that in reality fell lightly on the air.

I remember well that plate of ham and tongue. It was dry, unappetising, cut in a wedge from the outside, but I had not the courage to refuse it. We ate in silence, for Mrs. Van Hopper liked to concentrate on food, and I could tell by the way the sauce ran down her chin that her dish of ravioli pleased her.

It was not a sight that engendered into me great appetite for my own cold choice, and looking away from her I saw that the table next to ours, left vacant for three days, was to be occupied once more. The maître d'hôtel, with the particular bow reserved for his more special patrons, was ushering the new arrival to his place.

Mrs. Van Hopper put down her fork, and reached for her lorgnette. I blushed for her while she stared, and the new-comer, unconscious of her interest, cast a wondering eye over the menu. Then Mrs. Van Hopper folded her lorgnette with a snap, and leant across the table to me, her small eyes bright with excitement, her voice a shade too loud.

"It's Max de Winter," she said, "the man who owns Manderley. You've heard of it, of course. He looks ill, doesn't he? They say he can't get over his wife's death. . . ."

CHAPTER THREE

I WONDER what my life would be to-day, if Mrs. Van Hopper had not been a snob.

Funny to think that the course of my existence hung like a thread upon that quality of hers. Her curiosity was a disease, almost a mania. At first I had been shocked, wretchedly embarrassed; I would feel like a whipping boy who must bear his master's pains when I watched people laugh behind her back, leave a room hurriedly upon her entrance, or even vanish behind a Service door on the corridor upstairs. For many years now she had come to the hotel Côte d'Azur, and, apart from bridge, her one pastime, which was notorious by now in Monte Carlo, was to claim visitors of distinction as her friends had she but seen them once at the other end of the post-office. Somehow she would manage to introduce herself, and before her victim had scented danger she had proffered an invitation to her suite. Her method of attack was so downright and sudden that there was seldom opportunity to escape. At the Côte d'Azur she staked a claim upon a certain sofa in the lounge, midway between the reception hall and the passage to the restaurant, and she would have her coffee there after luncheon and dinner, and all who came and went must pass her by. Sometimes she would employ me as a bait to draw her prey, and, hating my errand, I would be sent across the lounge with a verbal message, the loan of a book or paper, the address of some shop or other, the sudden discovery of a mutual friend. It seemed as though notables must be fed to her, much as invalids are spooned their jelly; and though titles were preferred by her, any face once seen in a social paper served as well. Names scattered in a gossip column, authors, artists, actors and their kind, even the mediocre ones, as long as she had learnt of them in print.

I can see her as though it were but yesterday, on that unforgettable afternoon—never mind how many years ago—when she sat at her favourite sofa in the lounge, debating her method of attack. I could tell by her abrupt manner, and the way she tapped her lorgnette against her teeth, that she was questing possibilities. I knew, too, when she had missed the sweet and rushed through dessert, that she had wished to finish luncheon before the new arrival and so install herself where he must pass. Suddenly she turned to me, her small eyes alight.

"Go upstairs quickly and find that letter from my nephew. You remember, the one written on his honeymoon, with the snapshot. Bring it down to me right away."

I saw then that her plans were formed, and the nephew was to be the means of introduction. Not for the first time I resented the part that I must play in her schemes. Like a juggler's assistant I produced the props, then silent and attentive I waited on my cue. This newcomer would not welcome intrusion, I felt certain of that. In the little I had learnt of him at luncheon, a smattering of hearsay garnered by her ten months ago from the daily papers and stored in her memory for future use, I could imagine, in spite of my youth and inexperience of the world, that he would resent this sudden bursting in upon his solitude. Why he should have chosen to come to the Côte d'Azur at Monte Carlo was not our concern, his problems were his own, and anyone but Mrs. Van Hopper would have understood. Tact was a quality unknown to her, discretion too, and because gossip was the breath of life to her this stranger must be served for her dissection. I found the letter in a pigeon-hole in her desk, and hesitated a moment before going down again to the lounge. It seemed to me, rather senselessly, that I was allowing him a few more moments of seclusion.

I wished I had the courage to go by the Service staircase and so by roundabout way to the restaurant, and there warn him of the ambush. Convention was too strong for me though, nor did I know how I should frame my sentence. There was nothing for it but to sit in my usual place beside Mrs. Van Hopper while she, like a large, complacent spider, spun her wide net of tedium about the stranger's person.

I had been longer than I thought, for when I returned to the lounge I saw he had already left the dining-room, and she, fearful of losing him, had not waited for the letter, but had risked a barefaced introduction on her own. He was even now sitting beside her on the sofa. I walked across to them, and gave her the letter without a word. He rose to his feet at once, while Mrs. Van Hopper, flushed with her success, waved a vague hand in my direction and mumbled my name.

"Mr. de Winter is having coffee with us, go and ask the waiter for another cup," she said, her tone just casual enough to warn him of my footing. It meant I was a youthful thing and unimportant, and that there was no need to include me in the conversation. She always spoke in that tone when she wished to be impressive, and her method of introduction was a form of self-protection, for once I had been taken for her daughter, an acute embarrassment for us both. This abruptness showed that I could safely be ignored, and women would give me a brief nod which served as a greeting and a dismissal in one, while men, with large relief, would realise they could sink back into a comfortable chair without offending courtesy.

It was a surprise, therefore, to find that this new-comer remained standing on his feet, and it was he who made a signal to the waiter.

"I'm afraid I must contradict you," he said to her, "you are both having coffee with me"; and before I knew what had happened he was sitting in my usual hard chair, and I was on the sofa beside Mrs. Van Hopper.

For a moment she looked annoyed, this was not what she had intended, but she soon composed her face, and thrusting her large self between me and the table she leant forward to his chair, talking eagerly and loudly, fluttering the letter in her hand.

"You know I recognised you just as soon as you walked into the restaurant," she said, "and I thought, 'Why, there's Mr. de Winter, Billy's friend, I simply must show him those snaps of Billy and his bride taken on their honeymoon,' and here they are. There's Dora. Isn't she just adorable? That little, slim waist, those great big eyes. Here they are sun-bathing at Palm Beach. Billy is crazy about her, you can imagine. He had not met her of course when he gave that party at Claridge's, and where I saw you first. But I dare say you don't remember an old woman like me?"

This with a provocative glance, and a gleam of teeth.

"On the contrary I remember you very well," he said, and before she could trap him into a resurrection of their first meeting he had handed her his cigarette case, and the business of lighting-up stalled her for the moment. "I don't think I should care for Palm Beach," he said, blowing the match, and glancing at him I thought how unreal he would look against a Florida background. He belonged to a walled city of the fifteenth century, a city of narrow, cobbled streets, and thin spires, where the inhabitants wore pointed shoes and worsted hose. His face was arresting, sensitive, medieval in some strange inexplicable way, and I was reminded of a portrait seen in a gallery I had forgotten where, of a certain Gentleman Unknown. Could one but rob him of his English tweeds, and put him in black, with lace at his throat and wrists, he would stare down at us in our new world from a long distant past—a past where men walked cloaked at night, and stood in the shadow of old doorways, a past of narrow stairways and dim dungeons, a past of whispers in the dark, of shimmering rapier blades, of silent, exquisite courtesy.

I wished I could remember the Old Master who had painted that portrait. It stood in a corner of the gallery, and the eyes followed one from the dusky frame. . . .

They were talking though, and I had lost the thread of conversation. "No, not even twenty years ago," he was saying. "That sort of thing has never amused me."

I heard Mrs. Van Hopper give her fat, complacent laugh. "If Billy had a home like Manderley he would not want to play around in Palm Beach," she said. "I'm told it's like fairy-land, there's no other word for it."

She paused, expecting him to smile, but he went on smoking his cigarette, and I noticed, faint as gossamer, the line between his brows.

"I've seen pictures of it, of course," she persisted, "and it looks perfectly enchanting. I remember Billy telling me it had all those big places beat for beauty. I wonder you can ever bear to leave it."

His silence now was painful, and would have been patent to anyone else, but she ran on like a clumsy goat, trampling and trespassing on land that was preserved, and I felt the colour flood my face, dragged with her as I was into humiliation.

"Of course you Englishmen are all the same about your homes," she said, her voice becoming louder and louder, "you depreciate them so as not to seem proud. Isn't there a minstrels' gallery at Manderley, and some very valuable portraits?" She turned to me by way of explanation. "Mr. de Winter is so modest he won't admit to it, but I believe that lovely home of his has been in his family's possession since the Conquest. They say that minstrels' gallery is a gem. I suppose your ancestors often entertained royalty at Manderley, Mr. de Winter?"

This was more than I had hitherto endured, even from her, but the swift lash of his reply was unexpected. "Not since Ethelred," he said, "the one who was called Unready. In fact, it was while staying with my family that the name was given him. He was invariably late for dinner."

She deserved it, of course, and I waited for her change of face, but incredible as it may seem his words were lost on her, and I was left to writhe in her stead, feeling like a child that had been smacked.

"Is that really so?" she blundered. "I'd no idea. My history is very shaky, and the kings of England always muddled me. How interesting though. I must write and tell my daughter, she's a great scholar."

There was a pause, and I felt the colour flood into my face. I was too young, that was the trouble. Had I been older I would have caught his eye and smiled, her unbelievable behaviour making a bond between us; but as it was I was stricken into shame, and endured one of the frequent agonies of youth.

I think he realised my distress, for he leant forward in his chair and spoke to me, his voice gentle, asking if I would have more coffee, and when I refused and shook my head I felt that his eyes were still upon me, puzzled, reflective. He was pondering my exact relationship to her, and wondering whether he must bracket us together in futility.

"What do you think of Monte Carlo, or don't you think of it at all?" he said. This including of me in the conversation found me at my worst, the raw ex-schoolgirl, red-elbowed and lanky-haired, and I said something obvious and idiotic about the place being artificial, but before I could finish my halting sentence Mrs. Van Hopper interrupted.

"She's spoilt, Mr. de Winter, that's her trouble. Most girls would give their eyes for the chance of seeing Monte."

"Wouldn't that rather defeat the purpose?" he said smiling.

She shrugged her shoulders, blowing a great cloud of smoke into the air. I don't think she understood him for a moment. "I'm faithful to Monte," she told him; "the English winter gets me down, and my constitution just won't stand it. What brings you here? You're not one of the regulars. Are you going to play 'Chemy,' or have you brought your golf-clubs?"

"I have not made up my mind," he said, "I came away in rather a hurry."

His own words must have jolted a memory, for his face clouded again and he frowned very slightly. She babbled on, impervious. "Of course you miss the fogs at Manderley, it's quite another matter; the west country must be delightful in the spring." He reached for the ash-tray, squashing his cigarette, and I noticed the subtle change in his eyes, the indefinable something that lingered there, momentarily, and I felt I had looked upon something personal to himself with which I had no concern.

"Yes," he said shortly, "Manderley was looking its best."

A silence fell upon us, during a moment or two, a silence that brought something of discomfort in its train, and stealing a glance at him I was reminded more than ever of my Gentleman Unknown who, cloaked and secret, walked a corridor by night. Mrs. Van Hopper's voice pierced my dream like an electric bell.

"I suppose you know a crowd of people here, though I must say Monte is very dull this winter. One sees so few well-known faces. The Duke of Middlesex is here in his yacht, but I haven't been aboard yet." She never had, to my knowledge. "You know Nell Middlesex of course," she went on. "What a charmer she is. They always say that second child isn't his, but I don't believe it. People will say anything, won't they, when a woman is attractive? And she is so very lovely. Tell me, is it true the Caxton-Hyslop marriage is not a success?" She ran on, through a tangled fringe of gossip, never seeing that these names were alien to him, they meant nothing, and that as she prattled unaware he grew colder and more silent. Never for a moment did he interrupt or glance at his watch, it was as though he had set himself a standard of behaviour, since the original lapse when he had made a fool of her in front of me, and clung to it grimly rather than offend again. It was a page-boy in the end who released him, with the news that a dressmaker awaited Mrs. Van Hopper in the suite.

He got up at once, pushing back his chair. "Don't let me keep you," he said. "Fashions change so quickly nowadays they may even have altered by the time you get upstairs."

The sting did not touch her, she accepted it as a pleasantry. "It's so delightful to have run into you like this, Mr. de Winter," she said, as we went towards the lift; "now I've been brave enough to break the ice I hope I shall see something of you. You must come and have a drink some time in the suite. I may have one or two people coming in to-morrow evening. Why not join us?" I turned away so that I should not watch him search for an excuse.

"I'm so sorry," he said, "to-morrow I am probably driving to Sospel, I'm not sure when I shall get back."

Reluctantly she left it, but we still hovered at the entrance to the lift.

"I hope they've given you a good room, the place is half empty, so if you are uncomfortable mind you make a fuss. Your valet has unpacked for you

I suppose?" This familiarity was excessive, even for her, and I caught a glimpse of his expression.

"I don't possess one," he said quietly, "perhaps you would like to do it for me?"

This time his shaft had found its mark, for she reddened, and laughed a little awkwardly.

"Why, I hardly think . . ." she began, and then suddenly, and unbelievably she turned upon me. "Perhaps you could make yourself useful to Mr. de Winter, if he wants anything done. You're a capable child in many ways."

There was a momentary pause, while I stood stricken, waiting for his answer. He looked down at us, mocking, faintly sardonic, a ghost of a smile on his lips.

"A charming suggestion," he said, "but I cling to the family motto. He travels the fastest who travels alone. Perhaps you have not heard of it."

And without waiting for her answer he turned and left us.

"What a funny thing," said Mrs. Van Hopper, as we went upstairs in the lift, "do you suppose that sudden departure was a form of humour? Men do such extraordinary things. I remember a well-known writer once who used to dart down the Service staircase whenever he saw me coming. I suppose he had a penchant for me and wasn't sure of himself. However, I was younger then."

The lift stopped with a jerk. We arrived at our floor. The page-boy flung open the gates. "By-the-way, dear," she said, as we walked along the corridor, "don't think I mean to be unkind, but you put yourself just a teeny bit forward this afternoon. Your efforts to monopolise the conversation quite embarrassed me, and I'm sure it did him. Men loathe that sort of thing."

I said nothing. There seemed no possible reply. "Oh, come, don't sulk," she laughed, and shrugged her shoulders; "after all, I am responsible for your behaviour here, and surely you can accept advice from a woman old enough to be your mother. Eh bien, Blaize, je viens . . ." and humming a tune she went into the bedroom where the dressmaker was waiting for her.

I knelt on the window seat and looked out upon the afternoon. The sun shone very brightly still, and there was a gay high wind. In half-an-hour we should be sitting to our bridge, the windows tightly closed, the central heating turned to the full. I thought of the ash-trays I would have to clear, and how the squashed stubs, stained with lipstick, would sprawl in company with discarded chocolate creams. Bridge does not come easily to a mind brought up on Snap and Happy Families; besides, it bored her friends to play with me.

I felt my youthful presence put a curb upon their conversation, much as a parlour-maid does until the arrival of dessert, and they could not fling themselves so easily into the melting-pot of scandal and insinuation. Her men-friends would assume a sort of forced heartiness, and ask me jocular questions about history or painting, guessing I had not long left school and that this would be my only form of conversation.

I sighed, and turned away from the window. The sun was so full of promise, and the sea was whipped white with a merry wind. I thought of that corner in Monaco which I had passed a day or two ago, and where a crooked house leant to a cobbled square. High up in the tumbled roof there was a window, narrow as a slit. It might have held a presence medieval; and, reaching to the desk for pencil and paper, I sketched in fancy with an absent mind a profile, pale and aquiline. A sombre eye, a high-bridged nose, a scornful upper lip. And I added a pointed beard and lace at the throat, as the painter had done, long ago in a different time.

Someone knocked at the door, and the lift-boy came in with a note in his hand. "Madame is in the bedroom," I told him, but he shook his head and said it was for me. I opened it, and found a single sheet of note-paper inside, with a few words written in an unfamiliar hand.

"Forgive me. I was very rude this afternoon." That was all. No signature, and no beginning. But my name was on the envelope, and spelt correctly, an unusual thing.

"Is there any answer?" asked the boy.

I looked up from the scrawled words. "No," I said. "No, there isn't any answer."

When he had gone I put the note away in my pocket, and turned once more to my pencil drawing, but for no known reason it did not please me any more, the face was stiff and lifeless, and the lace collar and the beard were like props in a charade.

CHAPTER FOUR

THE MORNING AFTER the bridge party Mrs. Van Hopper woke with a sore throat and a temperature of a hundred and two. I rang up her doctor, who came round at once and diagnosed the usual influenza. "You are to stay in bed until I allow you to get up," he told her; "I don't like the sound of that heart of yours, and it won't get better unless you keep perfectly quiet and still. I should prefer," he went on, turning to me, "that Mrs. Van Hopper had a trained nurse. You can't possibly lift her. It will only be for a fortnight or so."

I thought this rather absurd, and protested, but to my surprise she agreed with him. I think she enjoyed the fuss it would create, the sympathy of the people, the visits and messages from friends, and the arrival of flowers. Monte Carlo had begun to bore her, and this little illness would make a distraction.

The nurse would give her injections, and a light massage, and she would have a diet. I left her quite happy after the arrival of the nurse, propped up on pillows with a falling temperature, her best bed-jacket round her shoulders and be-ribboned boudoir cap upon her head. Rather ashamed of my light heart, I telephoned her friends, putting off the small party she had arranged for the evening, and went down to the restaurant for lunch, a good half hour before our usual time. I expected the room to be empty, nobody lunched generally before one o'clock. It was empty, except for the table next to ours. This was a contingency for which I was unprepared. I thought he had gone to Sospel. No doubt he was lunching early because he hoped to avoid us at one o'clock. I was already half-way across the room and could not go back. I had not seen him since we disappeared in the lift the day before, for wisely he had avoided dinner in the restaurant, possibly for the same reason that he lunched early now.

It was a situation for which I was ill-trained. I wished I was older, different. I went to our table, looking straight before me, and immediately paid the penalty of gaucherie by knocking over the vase of stiff anemones as I unfolded my napkin. The water soaked the cloth, and ran down on to my lap. The waiter was at the other end of the room, nor had he seen. In a second though my neighbour was by my side, dry napkin in hand.

"You can't sit at a wet tablecloth," he said brusquely, "it will put you off your food. Get out of the way."

He began to mop the cloth, while the waiter, seeing the disturbance, came swiftly to the rescue.

"I don't mind," I said, "it doesn't matter a bit. I'm all alone."

He said nothing, and then the waiter arrived and whipped away the vase and the sprawling flowers.

"Leave that," he said suddenly, "and lay another place at my table. Mademoiselle will have luncheon with me."

I looked up in confusion. "Oh, no," I said, "I couldn't possibly."

"Why not?" he said.

I tried to think of an excuse. I knew he did not want to lunch with me. It was his form of courtesy. I should ruin his meal. I determined to be bold and speak the truth.

"Please," I begged, "don't be polite. It's very kind of you but I shall be quite all right if the waiter just wipes the cloth."

"But I'm not being polite," he insisted, "I would like you to have luncheon with me. Even if you had not knocked over that vase so clumsily I should have asked you." I suppose my face told him my doubt, for he smiled. "You don't believe me," he said, "never mind, come and sit down. We needn't talk to each other unless we feel like it."

We sat down, and he gave me the menu, leaving me to choose, and went on with his *hors d'œuvre* as though nothing had happened.

His quality of detachment was peculiar to himself, and I knew that we might continue thus, without speaking, throughout the meal and it would not matter. There would be no sense of strain. He would not ask me questions on history.

"What's happened to your friend?" he said. I told him about the influenza. "I'm so sorry," he said, and then, after pausing a moment, "you got my note I suppose. I felt very much ashamed of myself. My manners were atrocious. The only excuse I can make is that I've become boorish through living alone. That's why it's so kind of you to lunch with me to-day."

"You weren't rude," I said, "at least, not the sort of rudeness she would understand. That curiosity of hers—she does not mean to be offensive, but she does it to everyone. That is, everyone of importance."

"I ought to be flattered then," he said, "why should she consider me of any importance?" I hesitated a moment before replying.

"I think because of Manderley," I said.

He did not answer, and I was aware again of that feeling of discomfort, as though I had trespassed on forbidden ground. I wondered why it was that this home of his, known to so many people by hearsay, even to me, should so inevitably silence him, making as it were a barrier between him and others.

We ate for a while without talking, and I thought of a picture post-card I had bought once at a village shop, when on holiday as a child in the west country. It was the painting of a house, crudely done of course and highly coloured, but even those faults could not destroy the symmetry of the building, the wide stone steps before the terrace, the green lawns stretching to the sea. I paid twopence for the painting—half my weekly pocket money—and then asked the wrinkled shop woman what it was meant to be. She looked astonished at my ignorance.

"That's Manderley," she said, and I remember coming out of the shop feeling rebuffed, yet hardly wiser than before.

Perhaps it was the memory of this post-card, lost long ago in some forgotten book, that made me sympathise with his defensive attitude. He resented Mrs. Van Hopper and her like with their intruding questions. Maybe there was something inviolate about Manderley that made it a place apart, it would not bear discussion. I could imagine her tramping through the rooms, perhaps paying sixpence for admission, ripping the quietude with her sharp, staccato laugh. Our minds must have run in the same channel for he began to talk about her.

"Your friend," he began, "she is very much older than you. Is she a relation? Have you known her long?" I saw he was still puzzled by us.

"She's not really a friend," I told him, "she's an employer. She's training me to be a thing called a companion, and she pays me ninety pounds a year."

"I did not know one could buy companionship," he said; "it sounds a primitive idea. Rather like the eastern slave market."

"I looked up the word companion once in the dictionary," I admitted, "and it said 'a companion is a friend of the bosom.'"

"You haven't much in common with her," he said.

He laughed, looking quite different, younger somehow and less detached. "What do you do it for?" he asked me.

"Ninety pounds is a lot of money to me," I said.

"Haven't you any family?"

"No—they're dead."

"You have a very lovely and unusual name."

"My father was a lovely and unusual person."

"Tell me about him," he said.

I looked at him over my glass of citronade. It was not easy to explain my father, and usually I never talked about him. He was my secret property.

Preserved for me alone, much as Manderley was preserved for my neighbour. I had no wish to introduce him casually over a table in a Monte Carlo restaurant.

There was a strange air of unreality about that luncheon, and looking back upon it now it is invested for me with a curious glamour. There was I, so much of a schoolgirl still, who only the day before had sat with Mrs. Van Hopper, prim, silent and subdued, and twenty-four hours afterwards my family history was mine no longer, I shared it with a man I did not know. For some reason I felt impelled to speak, because his eyes followed me in sympathy like the Gentleman Unknown.

My shyness fell away from me, loosening as it did so my reluctant tongue, and out they all came, the little secrets of childhood, the pleasures and the pains. It seemed to me as though he understood, from my poor description, something of the vibrant personality that had been my father's, and something too of the love my mother had for him, making it a vital, living force, with a spark of divinity about it, so much that when he died that desperate winter, struck down by pneumonia, she lingered behind him for five short weeks and stayed no more. I remember pausing, a little breathless, a little dazed. The restaurant was filled now with people who chatted and laughed to an orchestral background and a clatter of plates, and glancing at the clock above the door I saw that it was two o'clock. We had been sitting there an hour and a half, and the conversation had been mine alone.

I tumbled down into reality, hot-handed and self-conscious, with my face aflame, and began to stammer my apologies. He would not listen to me.

"I told you at the beginning of lunch you had a lovely and unusual name," he said. "I shall go further, if you will forgive me, and say that it becomes you as well as it became your father. I've enjoyed this hour with you more than I have enjoyed anything for a very long time. You've taken me out of myself, out of despondency and introspection, both of which have been my devils for a year."

I looked at him, and believed he spoke the truth, he seemed less fettered than he had been before, more modern, more human, he was not hemmed in by shadows.

"You know," he said, "we've got a bond in common, you and I. We are both alone in the world. Oh, I've got a sister, though we don't see much of each other, and an ancient grandmother whom I pay duty visits to three times a year, but neither of them make for companionship. I shall have to congratulate Mrs. Van Hopper. You're cheap at ninety pounds a year."

"You forget," I said, "you have a home and I have none."

The moment I spoke I regretted my words, for the secret, inscrutable look came back in his eyes again, and once again I suffered the intolerable discomfort that floods one after lack of tact. He bent his head to light a cigarette, and did not reply immediately.

"An empty house can be as lonely as a full hotel," he said at length. "The trouble is that it is less impersonal." He hesitated, and for a moment I thought he was going to talk of Manderley at last, but something held him back, some phobia that struggled to the surface of his mind and won supremacy, for he blew out his match and his flash of confidence at the same time.

"So the friend of the bosom has a holiday?" he said, on a level plane again, an easy camaraderie between us. "What does she propose to do with it?"

I thought of the cobbled square in Monaco, and the house with the narrow window. I could be off there by three o'clock with my sketch-book and pencil, and I told him as much, a little shyly perhaps, like all untalented persons with a pet hobby.

"I'll drive you there in the car," he said, and would not listen to protests.

I remembered Mrs. Van Hopper's warning of the night before about putting myself forward, and was embarrassed that he might think my talk of Monaco was a subterfuge to win a lift. It was so blatantly the type of thing that she would do herself, and I did not want him to bracket us together. I had already risen in importance from my lunch with him, for as we got up from the table the little maître d'hôtel rushed forward to pull away my chair. He bowed and smiled—a total change from his usual attitude of indifference—picked up my handkerchief that had fallen on the floor, and hoped "Mademoiselle had enjoyed her lunch." Even the page-boy by the swing doors glanced at me with respect.My companion accepted it as natural, of course, he knew nothing of the ill-carved ham of yesterday. I found the change depressing, it made me despise myself. I remembered my father and his scorn of superficial snobbery.

"What are you thinking about?" We were walking along the corridor to the lounge, and looking up I saw his eyes fixed on me in curiosity.

"Has something annoyed you?" he said.

The attentions of the maître d'hôtel had opened up a train of thought, and as we drank our coffee I told him about Blaize, the dressmaker. She had been so pleased when Mrs. Van Hopper had bought three frocks, and I, taking her to the lift afterwards, had pictured her working upon them in her own small salon, behind the stuffy little shop, with a consumptive son wasting upon her sofa. I could see her, with tired eyes, threading needles, and the floor covered with snippets of material.

"Well?" he said smiling, "wasn't your picture true?"

"I don't know," I said, "I never found out." And I told him how I had rung the bell for the lift, and as I had done so she had fumbled in her bag and gave me a note for a hundred francs. "Here," she had whispered, her tone intimate and unpleasant, "I want you to accept this small commission in return for bringing your patron to my shop." When I had refused, scarlet with embarrassment, she had shrugged her shoulders disagreeably. "Just as you like," she had said, "but I assure you it's quite usual. Perhaps you would rather have a frock. Come along to the shop sometime without Madame and I will fix you up without charging you a sou." Somehow, I don't know why, I had been aware of that sick, unhealthy feeling I had experienced as a child when turning the pages of a forbidden book. The vision of the consumptive son faded, and in its stead arose the picture of myself had I been different, pocketing that greasy note with an understanding smile, and perhaps slipping round to Blaize's shop on this my free afternoon and coming away with a frock I had not paid for.

I expected him to laugh, it was a stupid story, I don't know why I told him, but he looked at me thoughtfully as he stirred his coffee.

"I think you've made a big mistake," he said, after a moment.

"In refusing that hundred francs?" I asked, revolted.

"No—good heavens, what do you take me for? I think you've made a mistake in coming here, in joining forces with Mrs. Van Hopper. You are not made for that sort of job. You're too young, for one thing, and too soft. Blaize and her commission, that's nothing. The first of many similar incidents from other Blaizes. You will either have to give in, and become a sort of Blaize yourself, or stay as you are and be broken. Who suggested you take on this thing in the first place?" It seemed natural for him to question me, nor did I mind. It was as though we had known one another for a long time, and had met again after a lapse of years.

"Have you ever thought about the future?" he asked me, "and what this sort of thing will lead to? Supposing Mrs. Van Hopper gets tired of her 'friend of the bosom,' what then?"

I smiled, and told him that I did not mind very much. There would be other Mrs. Van Hoppers, and I was young, and confident, and strong. But even as he spoke I remembered those advertisements seen often in good class magazines where a friendly society demands succour for young women in reduced circumstances; I thought of the type of boarding-house that answers the advertisement and gives temporary shelter, and then I saw myself, useless sketch-book in hand, without qualifications of any kind, stammering replies to stern employment agents. Perhaps I should have accepted Blaize's ten per cent.

"How old are you?" he said, and when I told him he laughed, and got up from his chair. "I know that age, it's a particularly obstinate one, and a thousand bogies won't make you fear the future. A pity we can't change over. Go upstairs and put your hat on, and I'll have the car brought round."

As he watched me into the lift I thought of yesterday, Mrs. Van Hopper's chattering tongue, and his cold courtesy. I had ill-judged him, he was neither hard nor sardonic, he was already my friend of many years, the brother I had never possessed. Mine was a happy mood that afternoon, and I remember it well. I can see the rippled sky, fluffy with cloud, and the white-whipped sea. I can feel again the wind on my face, and hear my laugh, and his that echoed it. It was not the Monte Carlo I had known, or perhaps the truth was that it pleased me better. There was a glamour about it that had not been there before. I must have looked upon it before with dull eyes. The harbour was a dancing thing, with fluttering paper boats, and the sailors on the quay were jovial, smiling fellows, merry as the wind. We passed the yacht, beloved of Mrs. Van Hopper because of its ducal owner, and snapped our fingers at the glistening brass, and looked at one another and laughed again. I can remember as though I wore it still my comfortable, ill-fitting flannel suit, and how the skirt was lighter than the coat through harder wear. My shabby hat, too broad about the brim, and my low-heeled shoes, fastened with a single strap. A pair of gauntlet gloves clutched in a grubby hand. I had never looked more youthful, I had never felt so old. Mrs. Van Hopper and her influenza did not exist for me. The bridge and the cocktail parties were forgotten, and with them my own humble status.

I was a person of importance, I was grown up at last. That girl, who, tortured by shyness, would stand outside the sitting-room door twisting a handkerchief in her hands, while from within came that babble of confused chatter so unnerving to the intruder—she had gone with the wind that afternoon. She was a poor creature, and I thought of her with scorn if I considered her at all.

The wind was too high for sketching, it tore in cheerful gusts around the corner of my cobbled square, and back to the car we went and drove I know not where. The long road climbed the hills, and the car climbed with it, and we circled in the heights like a bird in the air. How different his car to Mrs. Van Hopper's hireling for the season, a square old-fashioned Daimler that took us to Mentone on placid afternoons, when I, sitting on the little seat with my back to the driver, must crane my neck to see the view. This car had the wings of Mercury I thought, for higher yet we climbed, and dangerously fast, and the danger pleased me because it was new to me, because I was young.

I remember laughing aloud, and the laugh being carried by the wind away from me; and, looking at him, I realised he laughed no longer, he was once more silent and detached, the man of yesterday wrapped in his secret self.

I realised, too, that the car could climb no more, we had reached the summit, and below us stretched the way that we had come, precipitous and hollow. He stopped the car, and I could see that the edge of the road bordered a vertical slope that crumbled into vacancy, a fall of perhaps two thousand feet. We got out of the car and looked beneath us. This sobered me at last, I knew that but half the car's length had lain between us and the fall. The sea, like a crinkled chart, spread to the horizon, and lapped the sharp outline of the coast, while the houses were white shells in a rounded grotto, pricked here and there by a great orange sun. We knew another sunlight on our hill, and the silence made it harder, more austere. A change had come upon our afternoon, it was not the thing of gossamer it had been. The wind dropped, and it suddenly grew cold.

When I spoke my voice was far too casual, the silly, nervous voice of someone ill at ease. "Do you know this place?" I said. "Have you been here before?" He looked down at me without recognition, and I realised with a little stab of anxiety that he must have forgotten all about me, perhaps for some considerable time, and that he himself was so lost in the labyrinth of his own unquiet thoughts that I did not exist. He had the face of one who walks in his sleep, and for a wild moment the idea came to me that perhaps he was not normal, not altogether sane. There were people who had trances, I had surely heard of them, and they followed strange laws of which we could know nothing, they obeyed the tangled orders of their own sub-conscious minds. Perhaps he was one of them, and here we were within six foot of death.

"It's getting late, shall we go home?" I said, and my careless tone, my little ineffectual smile would scarcely have deceived a child.

I had misjudged him, of course, there was nothing wrong after all, for as soon as I spoke this second time he came clear of his dream and began to apologise. I had gone white, I suppose, and he had noticed it.

"That was an unforgivable thing for me to do," he said, and taking my arm he pushed me back towards the car, and we climbed in again, and he slammed the door. "Don't be frightened, the turn is far easier than it looks," he said, and while I, sick and giddy, clung to the seat with both hands, he manœuvred the car gently, very gently, until it faced the sloping road once more.

"Then you have been here before?" I said to him, my sense of strain departing, as the car crept away down the twisting narrow road.

"Yes," he said, and then, after pausing a moment, "but not for many years. I wanted to see if it had changed."

"And has it?" I asked him.

"No," he said. "No, it has not changed."

I wondered what had driven him to this retreat into the past, with me an unconscious witness of his mood. What gulf of years stretched between him and that other time, what deed of thought and action, what difference in temperament? I did not want to know. I wished I had not come.

Down the twisting road we went without a check, without a word, a great ridge of clouds stretched above the setting sun, and the air was cold and clean. Suddenly he began to talk about Manderley. He said nothing of his life there, no word about himself, but he told me how the sun set there, on a spring afternoon, leaving a glow upon the headland. The sea would look like slate, cold still from the long winter, and from the terrace you could hear the ripple of the coming tide washing in the little bay. The daffodils were in bloom, stirring in the evening breeze, golden heads cupped upon lean stalks, and however many you might pick there would be no thinning of the ranks, they were massed like an army, shoulder to shoulder. On a bank below the lawns, crocuses were planted, golden, pink, and mauve, but by this time they would be past their best, dropping and fading, like the pallid snowdrops. The primrose was more vulgar, a homely pleasant creature who appeared in every cranny like a weed. Too early yet for bluebells, their heads were still hidden beneath last year's leaves, but when they came, dwarfing the more humble violet, they choked the very bracken in the woods, and with their colour made a challenge to the sky.

He never would have them in the house, he said. Thrust into vases they became dank and listless, and to see them at their best you must walk in the woods in the morning, about twelve o'clock, when the sun was overhead. They had a smoky, rather bitter smell, as though a wild sap ran in their stalks, pungent and juicy. People who plucked bluebells from the woods were vandals, he had forbidden it at Manderley. Sometimes, driving in the country, he had seen bicyclists with huge bunches strapped before them on the handles, the bloom already fading from the dying heads, the ravaged stalks straggling naked and unclean.

The primrose did not mind it quite so much, although a creature of the wilds it had a leaning towards civilisation, and preened and smiled in a jam-jar in some cottage window without resentment, living quite a week if given water. No wild flowers came in the house at Manderley. He had special cultivated flowers, grown for the house alone, in the walled garden. A rose was one of the few flowers, he said, that looked better picked than growing. A bowl of roses in a drawing-room had a depth of colour and scent they had not possessed in the open. There was something rather blowsy about roses in full bloom, something shallow and raucous, like women with untidy hair. In the house they became mysterious and subtle. He had roses in the house at Manderley for eight months in the year. Did I like syringa, he asked me? There was a tree on the edge of the lawn he could smell from his bed-room window. His sister, who was a hard, rather practical person, used to complain that there were too many scents at Manderley, they made her drunk. Perhaps she was right. He did not care. It was the only form of in-toxication that appealed to him. His earliest recollection was of great branches of lilac, standing in white jars, and they filled the house with a wistful, poignant smell.

The little pathway down the valley to the bay had clumps of azalea and rhododendron planted to the left of it, and if you wandered down it on a May evening after dinner it was just as though the shrubs had sweated in the air. You could stoop down and pick a fallen petal, crush it between your fingers, and you had there, in the hollow of your hand, the essence of a thousand scents, unbearable and sweet. All from a curled and crumpled petal. And you came out of the valley, heady and rather dazed, to the hard white shingle of the beach and the still water. A curious, perhaps too sudden contrast. . . .

As he spoke the car became one of many once again, dusk had fallen without my noticing it, and we were in the midst of light and sound in the streets of Monte Carlo. The clatter jagged on my nerves, and the lights were far too brilliant, far too yellow. It was a swift, unwelcome anti-climax.

Soon we would come to the hotel, and I felt for my gloves in the pocket of the car. I found them, and my fingers closed upon a book as well, whose slim covers told of poetry. I peered to read the title as the car slowed down before the door of the hotel. "You can take it and read it if you like," he said, his voice casual and indifferent now that the drive was over, and we were back again, and Manderley was many hundreds of miles distant.

I was glad, and held it tightly with my gloves. I felt I wanted some possession of his, now that the day was finished.

"Hop out," he said, "I must go and put the car away. I shan't see you in the restaurant this evening as I'm dining out. But thank you for to-day."

I went up the hotel steps alone, with all the despondency of a child whose treat is over. My afternoon had spoilt me for the hours that still remained, and I thought how long they would seem until my bed-time, how empty too my supper all alone. Somehow I could not face the bright enquiries of the nurse upstairs, or the possibilities of Mrs. Van Hopper's husky interrogation, so I sat down in the corner of the lounge behind a pillar and ordered tea.

The waiter appeared bored, seeing me alone there was no need for him to press, and anyway it was that dragging time of day, a few minutes after half-past five, when the normal tea is finished and the hour for drinks remote.

Rather forlorn, more than a little dissatisfied, I leant back in my chair and took up the book of poems. The volume was well-worn, well-thumbed, falling open automatically at what must be a much-frequented page.

> "I fled Him, down the nights and down the days;
> I fled Him, down the arches of the years;
> I fled Him, down the labyrinthine ways
> Of my own mind; and in the mist of tears
> I hid from Him, and under running laughter.
> Up vistaed slopes I sped
> And shot, precipitated
> Adown Titanic glooms of chasmed fears,
> From those strong feet that followed, followed after."

I felt rather like someone peering through the keyhole of a locked door, and a little furtively I laid the book aside. What hound of heaven had driven him to the high hills this afternoon? I thought of his car, with half a length between it and that drop of two thousand feet, and the blank expression on his face. What footsteps echoed in his mind, what whispers, and what memories, and why, of all poems, must he keep this one in the pocket of his car? I wished he were less remote; and I anything but the creature that I was in my shabby coat and skirt, my broad-brimmed schoolgirl hat.

The sulky waiter brought my tea, and while I ate bread-and-butter dull as sawdust I thought of the pathway through the valley he had described to me this afternoon, the smell of the azaleas, and the white shingle of the bay. If he loved it all so much why did he seek the superficial froth of Monte Carlo? He had told Mrs. Van Hopper he had made no plans, he came away in rather a hurry. And I pictured him running down that pathway in the valley with his own hound of heaven at his heels.

I picked up the book again, and this time it opened at the title-page, and I read the dedication. "Max–from Rebecca. May 17th," written in a curious, slanting hand. A little blob of ink marred the white page opposite, as though the writer, in impatience, had shaken her pen to make the ink flow freely. And then as it bubbled through the nib, it came a little thick, so that the name Rebecca stood out black and strong, the tall and sloping R dwarfing the other letters.

I shut the book with a snap, and put it away under my gloves; and stretching to a near-by chair, I took up an old copy of *L'Illustration* and turned the pages. There were some fine photographs of the châteaux of the Loire, and an article as well. I read it carefully, referring to the photographs, but when I finished I knew I had not understood a word. It was not Blois with its thin turrets and its spires that stared up at me from the printed page. It was the face of Mrs. Van Hopper in the restaurant the day before, her small pig's eyes darting to the neighbouring table, her fork, heaped high with ravioli, pausing in mid-air.

"An appalling tragedy," she was saying, "the papers were full of it of course. They say he never talks about it, never mentions her name. She was drowned you know, in a bay near Manderley. . . ."

CHAPTER FIVE

I AM GLAD it cannot happen twice, the fever of first love. For it is a fever, and a burden, too, whatever the poets may say. They are not brave, the days when we are twenty-one. They are full of little cowardices, little fears without foundation, and one is so easily bruised, so swiftly wounded, one falls to the first barbed word. To-day, wrapped in the complacent armour of approaching middle age, the infinitesimal pricks of day by day brush one but lightly and are soon forgotten, but then—how a careless word would linger, becoming a fiery stigma, and how a look, a glance over a shoulder, branded themselves as things eternal. A denial heralded the thrice crowing of a cock, and an insincerity was like the kiss of Judas. The adult mind can lie with untroubled conscience and a gay composure, but in those days even a small deception scoured the tongue, lashing one against the stake itself.

"What have you been doing this morning?" I can hear her now, propped against her pillows, with all the small irritability of the patient who is not really ill, who has lain in bed too long, and I, reaching to the bed-side drawer for the pack of cards, would feel the guilty flush form patches on my neck.

"I've been playing tennis with the professional," I told her, the false words bringing me to panic, even as I spoke, for what if the professional himself should come up to the suite, then, that very afternoon, and bursting in upon her complain that I had missed my lesson now for many days?

"The trouble is with me laid up like this you haven't got enough to do," she said, mashing her cigarette in a jar of cleansing cream, and taking the cards in her hand she mixed them in the deft, irritating shuffle of the inveterate player, shaking them in threes, snapping the backs.

"I don't know what you find to do with yourself all day," she went on, "you never have any sketches to show me, and when I do ask you to do some shopping for me you forget to buy my Taxol. All I can say is that I hope your tennis will improve, it will be useful to you later on. A poor player is a great bore. Do you still serve underhand?" She flipped the Queen of Spades into the pool, and the dark face stared up at me like Jezebel.

"Yes," I said, stung by her question, thinking how just and appropriate her word. It described me well. I was underhand. I had not played tennis with the professional at all, I had not once played since she had lain in bed, and that was little over a fortnight now. I wondered why it was I clung to this reserve, and why it was I did not tell her that every morning I drove with de Winter in his car, and lunched with him too, at his table in the restaurant.

"You must come up to the net more, you will never play a good game until you do," she continued, and I agreed, flinching at my own hypocrisy, covering her Queen with the weak-chinned Knave of Hearts.

I have forgotten much of Monte Carlo, of those morning drives, of where we went, even our conversation; but I have not forgotten how my fingers trembled, cramming on my hat, and how I ran along the corridor and down the stairs, too impatient to wait for the slow whining of the lift, and so outside brushing the swing doors before the commissionaire could help me.

He would be there, in the driver's seat, reading a paper while he waited, and when he saw me he would smile, and toss it behind him in the back seat, and open the door, saying, "Well, how is the friend of the bosom this morning, and where does she want to go?" If he had driven round in circles it would not have mattered to me, for I was in that first flushed stage when to climb into the seat beside him, and lean forward to the wind-screen hugging my knees, was almost too much to bear. I was like a little scrubby schoolboy with a passion for a sixth-form prefect, and he kinder, and far more inaccessible.

"There's a cold wind this morning, you had better put on my coat."

I remember that, for I was young enough to win happiness in the wearing of his clothes, playing the schoolboy again who carries his hero's sweater and ties it about his throat choking with pride, and this borrowing of his coat, wearing it around my shoulders for even a few minutes at a time, was a triumph in itself, and made a glow about my morning.

Not for me the languor and the subtlety I had read about in books. The challenge and the chase. The sword-play, the swift glance, the stimulating smile. The art of provocation was unknown to me, and I would sit with his map upon my lap, the wind blowing my dull, lanky hair, happy in his silence yet eager for his words. Whether he talked or not made little difference to my mood. My only enemy was the clock on the dash-board, whose hands would move relentlessly to one o'clock. We drove east, we drove west, amidst the myriad villages that cling like limpets to the Mediterranean shore, and to-day I remember none of them.

All I remember is the feel of the leather seats, the texture of the map upon my knee, its frayed edges, its worn seams, and how one day, looking at the clock, I thought to myself, "This moment now, at twenty past eleven, this must never be lost," and I shut my eyes to make the experience more lasting. When I opened my eyes we were by a bend in the road, and a peasant girl in a black shawl waved to us; I can see her now, her dusty skirt, her gleaming, friendly smile, and in a second we had passed the bend and could see her no more. Already she belonged to the past, she was only a memory.

I wanted to go back again, to recapture the moment that had gone, and then it came to me that if we did it would not be the same, even the sun would be changed in the sky, casting another shadow, and the peasant girl would trudge past us along the road in a different way, not waving this time, perhaps not even seeing us. There was something chilling in the thought, something a little melancholy, and looking at the clock I saw that five more minutes had gone by. Soon we would have reached our time limit, and must return to the hotel.

"If only there could be an invention," I said impulsively, "that bottled up a memory, like scent. And it never faded, and it never got stale. And then, when one wanted it, the bottle could be uncorked, and it would be like living the moment all over again." I looked up at him, to see what he would say. He did not turn to me, he went on watching the road ahead.

"What particular moments in your young life do you wish uncorked?" he said. I could not tell from his voice whether he was teasing me or not. "I'm not sure," I began, and then blundered on, rather foolishly, not thinking of my words, "I'd like to keep this moment and never forget it."

"Is that meant to be a compliment to the day, or to my driving?" he said, and as he laughed, like a mocking brother, I became silent, overwhelmed suddenly by the great gulf between us, and how his very kindness to me widened it.

I knew then that I would never tell Mrs. Van Hopper about these morning expeditions, for her smile would hurt me as his laugh had done. She would not be angry, nor would she be shocked, she would raise her eyebrows very faintly, as though she did not altogether believe my story, and then with a tolerant shrug of the shoulder she would say, "My dear child, it's extremely sweet and kind of him to take you driving, the only thing is—are you sure it does not bore him dreadfully?" And then she would send me out to buy Taxol, patting me on the shoulder. What degradation lay in being young, I thought, and fell to tearing at my nails.

"I wish," I said savagely, still mindful of his laugh and throwing discretion to the wind, "I wish I was a woman of about thirty-six dressed in black satin with a string of pearls."

"You would not be in this car with me if you were," he said, "and stop biting those nails, they are ugly enough already."

"You'll think me impertinent and rude I dare say," I went on, "but I would like to know why you ask me to come out in the car, day after day. You are being kind, that's obvious, but why do you choose me for your charity?"

I sat up stiff and straight in my seat with all the poor pomposity of youth.

"I ask you," he said gravely, "because you are not dressed in black satin, with a string of pearls, nor are you thirty-six." His face was without expression, I could not tell whether he laughed inwardly or not.

"It's all very well," I said, "you know everything there is to know about me. There's not much, I admit, because I have not been alive for very long and nothing much has happened to me, except people dying, but you—I know nothing more about you than I did the first day we met."

"And what did you know then?" he asked.

"Why, that you lived at Manderley and—and that you had lost your wife." There, I had said it at last, the word that had hovered on my tongue for days. Your wife. It came out with ease, without reluctance, as though the mere mention of her must be the most casual thing in all the world. Your wife. The word lingered in the air once I had uttered it, dancing before me, and because he received it silently, making no comment, the word magnified itself into something heinous and appalling, a forbidden word, unnatural to the tongue. And I could not call it back, it could never be unsaid. Once again I saw the inscription on the fly-leaf of that book of poems, and the curious slanting R. I felt sick at heart and cold. He would never forgive me, and this would be the end of our friendship.

I remember staring straight in front of me at the wind-screen, seeing nothing of the flying road, my ears still tingling with that spoken word. The silence became minutes, and the minutes became miles, and everything is over now, I thought, I shall never drive with him again. To-morrow he will go away. And Mrs. Van Hopper will be up again. She and I will walk along the terrace as we did before. The porter will bring down his trunks, I shall catch a glimpse of them in the luggage lift, with new-plastered labels. The bustle and finality of departure. The sound of the car changing gear as it turned the corner, and then even that sound merging into the common traffic, and being lost, and so absorbed forever.

I was so deep in my picture, I even saw the porter pocketing his tip and going back through the swing-door of the hotel, saying something over his shoulder to the commissionaire, that I did not notice the slowing-down of the car, and it was only when we stopped, drawing up by the side of the road, that I brought myself back to the present once again. He sat motionless, looking without his hat and with his white scarf round his neck, more than ever like someone medieval who lived within a frame. He did not belong to the bright landscape, he should be standing on the steps of a gaunt cathedral, his cloak flung back, while a beggar at his feet scrambled for gold coins.

The friend had gone, with his kindliness and his easy camaraderie, and the brother too, who had mocked me for nibbling at my nails. This man was a stranger. I wondered why I was sitting beside him in the car.

Then he turned to me and spoke. "A little while ago you talked about an invention," he said, "some scheme for capturing a memory. You would like, you told me, at a chosen moment to live the past again. I'm afraid I think rather differently from you. All memories are bitter, and I prefer to ignore them. Something happened a year ago that altered my whole life, and I want to forget every phase in my existence up to that time. Those days are finished. They are blotted out. I must begin living all over again. The first day we met, your Mrs. Van Hopper asked me why I came to Monte Carlo. It put a stopper on those memories you would like to resurrect. It does not always work, of course, sometimes the scent is too strong for the bottle, and too strong for me. And then the devil in one, like a furtive peeping Tom, tries to draw the cork. I did that in the first drive we took together. When we climbed the hills and looked down over the precipice. I was there some years ago, with my wife. You asked me if it was still the same, if it had changed at all. It was just the same, but—I was thankful to realise—oddly impersonal. There was no suggestion of the other time. She and I had left no record. It may have been because you were with me. You have blotted out the past for me, you know, far more effectively than all the bright lights of Monte Carlo. But for you I should have left long ago, gone on to Italy, and Greece, and further still perhaps. You have spared me all those wanderings. Damn your puritanical little tight-lipped speech to me. Damn your idea of my kindness and my charity. I ask you to come with me because I want you and your company, and if you don't believe me you can leave the car now and find your own way home. Go on, open the door, and get out."

I sat still, my hands in my lap, not knowing whether he meant it or not.

"Well," he said, "what are you going to do about it?"

Had I been a year or two younger I think I should have cried. Children's tears are very near the surface, and come at the first crisis. As it was I felt them prick behind my eyes, felt the ready colour flood my face, and catching a sudden glimpse of myself in the glass above the wind-screen saw in full the sorry spectacle that I made, with troubled eyes and scarlet cheeks, lank hair flopping under broad felt hat.

"I want to go home," I said, my voice perilously near to trembling, and without a word he started up the engine, let in the clutch, and turned the car round the way that we had come.

Swiftly we covered the ground, far too swiftly, I thought, far too easily, and the callous countryside watched us with indifference. We came to the bend in the road that I had wished to imprison as a memory, and the peasant girl was gone, and the colour was flat, and it was no more after all than any bend in any road passed by a hundred motorists. The glamour of it had gone with my happy mood, and at the thought of it my frozen face quivered into feeling, my adult pride was lost, and those despicable tears rejoicing at their conquest welled into my eyes and strayed upon my cheeks.

I could not check them, for they came unbidden, and had I reached in my pocket for a handkerchief he would have seen. I must let them fall untouched, and suffer the bitter salt upon my lips, plumbing the depths of humiliation. Whether he had turned his head to look at me I do not know, for I watched the road ahead with blurred and steady stare, but suddenly he put out his hand and took hold of mine, and kissed it, still saying nothing, and then he threw his handkerchief on my lap, which I was too ashamed to touch.

I thought of all those heroines of fiction who looked pretty when they cried, and what a contrast I must make with blotched and swollen face, and red rims to my eyes. It was a dismal finish to my morning, and the day that stretched ahead of me was long. I had to lunch with Mrs. Van Hopper in her room, because the nurse was going out, and afterwards she would make me play bezique with all the tireless energy of the convalescent. I knew I should stifle in that room. There was something sordid about the tumbled sheets, the sprawling blankets and the thumped pillows, and that bed-side table dusty with powder, spilt scent, and melting liquid rouge. Her bed would be littered with the separated sheets of the daily papers folded anyhow, while French novels with curling edges and the covers torn kept company with American magazines. The mashed stubs of cigarettes lay everywhere, in cleansing cream, in a dish of grapes, and on the floor beneath the bed. Visitors were lavish with their flowers, and the vases stood cheek-by-jowl in any fashion, hothouse exotics crammed beside mimosa, while a great be-ribboned casket crowned them all, with tier upon tier of crystallised fruit. Later her friends would come in for a drink, which I must mix for them, hating my task, shy and ill-at-ease in my corner hemmed in by their parrot chatter, and I would be a whipping boy again, blushing for her when, excited by her little crowd, she must sit up in bed and talk too loudly, laugh too long, reach to the portable gramophone and start a record, shrugging her large shoulders to the tune. I preferred her irritable and snappy, her hair done up in pins, scolding me for forgetting her Taxol. All this awaited me in the suite, while he, once he had left me at the hotel, would go away somewhere alone, towards the sea perhaps, feel the wind on his cheek, follow the sun; and it might happen that he would lose himself in those memories that I knew nothing of, that I could not share, he would wander down the years that were gone.

The gulf that lay between us was wider now than it had ever been, and he stood away from me, with his back turned, on the further shore. I felt young and small and very much alone, and now, in spite of my pride, I found his handkerchief and blew my nose, throwing my drab appearance to the winds. It could never matter.

"To hell with this," he said suddenly, as though angry, as though bored, and he pulled me beside him, and put his arm round my shoulder, still looking straight ahead of him, his right hand on the wheel. He drove, I remember, even faster than before. "I suppose you are young enough to be my daughter, and I don't know how to deal with you," he said. The road narrowed then to a corner, and he had to swerve to avoid a dog. I thought he would release me, but he went on holding me beside him, and when the corner was passed, and the road came straight again he did not let me go. "You can forget all I said to you this morning," he said, "that's all finished and done with. Don't let's ever think of it again. My family always call me Maxim, I'd like you to do the same. You've been formal with me long enough." He felt for the brim of my hat, and took hold of it, throwing it over his shoulder to the back seat, and then bent down and kissed the top of my head. "Promise me you will never wear black satin," he said. I smiled then, and he laughed back at me, and the morning was gay again, the morning was a shining thing. Mrs. Van Hopper and the afternoon did not matter a flip of the finger. It would pass so quickly, and there would be to-night, and another day to-morrow. I was cocksure, jubilant, at that moment I almost had the courage to claim equality. I saw myself strolling into Mrs. Van Hopper's bedroom rather late for my bezique, and when questioned by her yawning carelessly, saying, "I forgot the time. I've been lunching with Maxim."

I was still child enough to consider a Christian name like a plume in the hat, though from the very first he had called me by mine. The morning, for all its shadowed moments, had promoted me to a new level of friendship, I did not lag so far behind as I had thought. He had kissed me too, a natural business, comforting and quiet. Not dramatic as in books. Not embarrassing. It seemed to bring about an ease in our relationship, it made everything more simple. The gulf between us had been bridged after all. I was to call him Maxim. And that afternoon playing bezique with Mrs. Van Hopper was not so tedious as it might have been, though my courage failed me and I said nothing of my morning. For when, gathering her cards together at the end, and reaching for the box, she said casually, "Tell me, is Max de Winter still in the hotel?" I hesitated a moment, like a diver on the brink, then lost my nerve and my tutored self-possession, saying, "Yes, I believe so—he comes into the restaurant for his meals."

Someone has told her, I thought, someone has seen us together, the tennis professional has complained, the manager has sent a note, and I waited for her attack. But she went on putting the cards back into the box, yawning a little, while I straightened the tumbled bed. I gave her the bowl of powder, the rouge compact, and the lip-stick, and she put away the cards and took up the hand glass from the table by her side. "Attractive creature," she said, "but queer-tempered I should think, difficult to know. I thought he might have made some gesture of asking one to Manderley that day in the lounge, but he was very close."

I said nothing. I watched her pick up the lip-stick and outline a bow upon her hard mouth. "I never saw her," she said, holding the glass away to see the effect, "but I believe she was very lovely. Exquisitely turned out, and brilliant in every way. They used to give tremendous parties at Manderley. It was all very sudden and tragic, and I believe he adored her. I need the darker shade of powder with this brilliant red, my dear, fetch it, will you, and put this box back in the drawer?"

And we were busy then with powder, scent, and rouge, until the bell rang and her visitors came in. I handed them their drinks, dully, saying little; I changed the records on the gramophone, I threw away the stubs of cigarettes.

"Been doing any sketching lately, little lady?" The forced heartiness of an old banker, his monocle dangling on a string, and my bright smile of insincerity: "No, not very lately; will you have another cigarette?"

It was not I that answered, I was not there at all. I was following a phantom in my mind, whose shadowy form had taken shape at last. Her features were blurred, her colouring indistinct, the setting of her eyes and the texture of her hair was still uncertain, still to be revealed.

She had beauty that endured, and a smile that was not forgotten. Somewhere her voice still lingered, and the memory of her words. There were places she had visited, and things that she had touched. Perhaps in cupboards there were clothes that she had worn, with the scent about them still. In my bedroom, under my pillow, I had a book that she had taken in her hands, and I could see her turning to that first white page, smiling as she wrote, and shaking the bent nib. Max from Rebecca. It must have been his birthday, and she had put it amongst her other presents on the breakfast table. And they had laughed together as he tore off the paper and the string. She leant, perhaps, over his shoulder, while he read. Max. She called him Max. It was familiar, gay, and easy on the tongue. The family could call him Maxim if they liked. Grandmothers and aunts. And people like myself, quiet and dull and youthful, who did not matter. Max was her choice, the word was her possession, she had written it with so great a confidence on the fly-leaf of that book. That bold, slanting hand, stabbing the white paper, the symbol of herself, so certain, so assured.

How many times she must have written to him thus, in how many varied moods.

Little notes, scrawled on half-sheets of paper, and letters, when he was away, page after page, intimate, *their* news. Her voice, echoing through the house, and down the garden, careless and familiar like the writing in the book.

And I had to call him Maxim.

CHAPTER SIX

PACKING UP. The nagging worry of departure. Lost keys, unwritten labels, tissue paper lying on the floor. I hate it all. Even now, when I have done so much of it, when I live, as the saying goes, in my boxes. Even to-day, when shutting drawers and flinging wide a hotel wardrobe, or the impersonal shelves of a furnished villa, is a methodical matter of routine, I am aware of sadness, of a sense of loss. Here, I say, we have lived, we have been happy. This has been ours, however brief the time. Though two nights only have been spent beneath a roof, yet we leave something of ourselves behind. Nothing material, not a hair-pin on a dressing-table, not an empty bottle of Aspirin tablets, not a handkerchief beneath a pillow, but something indefinable, a moment of our lives, a thought, a mood.

This house sheltered us, we spoke, we loved within those walls. That was yesterday. To-day we pass on, we see it no more, and we are different, changed in some infinitesimal way. We can never be quite the same again. Even stopping for luncheon at a way-side inn, and going to a dark, unfamiliar room to wash my hands, the handle of the door unknown to me, the wall-paper peeling in strips, a funny little cracked mirror above the basin, for this moment, it is mine, it belongs to me. We know one another. This is the present. There is no past and no future. Here I am washing my hands and the cracked mirror shows me to myself, suspended as it were, in time; this is me, this moment will not pass.

And then I open the door and go to the dining-room, where he is sitting waiting for me at a table, and I think how in that moment I have aged, and passed on, how I have advanced one step towards an unknown destiny.

We smile, we choose our lunch, we speak of this and that, but—I say to myself—I am not she who left him five minutes ago. She has stayed behind. I am another woman, older, more mature. . . .

I saw in a paper the other day that the hotel Côte d'Azur at Monte Carlo had gone to new management, and had a different name. The rooms had been re-decorated, and the whole interior changed. Perhaps Mrs. Van Hopper's suite on the first floor exists no more. Perhaps there is no trace of the small bedroom that was mine. I knew I should never go back, that day I knelt on the floor and fumbled with the awkward catch of her trunk.

The episode was finished, with the snapping of the lock. I glanced out of the window, and it was like turning the page of a photograph album. Those roof tops and that sea were mine no more. They belonged to yesterday, to the past. The rooms already wore an empty air, stripped of our possessions, and there was something hungry about the suite, as though it wished us gone, and the new arrivals, who would come to-morrow, in our place. The heavy luggage stood ready strapped and locked in the corridor outside. The smaller stuff would be finished later. Waste-paper baskets groaned under litter. All her half-empty medicine bottles and discarded face-cream jars, with torn-up bills and letters. Drawers in tables gaped, the bureau was stripped bare.

She had flung a letter at me the morning before, as I poured out her coffee at breakfast. "Helen is sailing for New York on Saturday. Little Nancy has a threatened appendix, and they've cabled her to go home. That's decided me. We're going too. I'm tired to death of Europe, and we can come back in the early fall. How d'you like the idea of seeing New York?"

The thought was worse than prison. Something of my misery must have shown in my face, for at first she looked astonished, then annoyed.

"What an odd, unsatisfactory child you are. I can't make you out. Don't you realise that at home girls in your position without any money can have the grandest fun? Plenty of boys and excitement. All in your own class. You can have your own little set of friends, and needn't be at my beck and call as much as you are here. I thought you didn't care for Monte?"

"I've got used to it," I said lamely, wretchedly, my mind a conflict.

"Well, you'll just have to get used to New York, that's all. We're going to catch that boat of Helen's, and it means seeing about our passage at once. Go down to the reception office right away, and make that young clerk show some sign of efficiency. Your day will be so full that you won't have time to have any pangs about leaving Monte!" She laughed disagreeably, squashing her cigarette in the butter, and went to the telephone to ring up all her friends.

I could not face the office right away. I went into the bathroom and locked the door, and sat down on the cork mat, my head in my hands. It had happened at last, the business of going away. It was all over. To-morrow evening I should be in the train, holding her jewel case and her rug, like a maid, and she in that monstrous new hat with the single quill, dwarfed in her fur-coat, sitting opposite me in the wagon-lit. We would wash and clean our teeth in that stuffy little compartment with the rattling doors, the splashed basin, the damp towel, the soap with a single hair on it, the carafe half-filled with water, the inevitable notice on the wall *"Sous le lavabo se trouve une vase,"* while every rattle, every throb and jerk of the screaming train would tell me that the miles carried me away from him, sitting alone in the restaurant of the hotel, at the table I had known, reading a book, not minding, not thinking.

I should say good-bye to him in the lounge, perhaps, before we left. A furtive, scrambled farewell, because of her, and there would be a pause, and a smile, and words like "Yes, of course, do write," and "I've never thanked you properly for being so kind," and "You must forward those snapshots," "What about your address?" "Well, I'll have to let you know." And he would light a cigarette casually, asking a passing waiter for a light, while I thought, "Four and a half more minutes to go. I shall never see him again."

Because I was going, because it was over, there would suddenly be nothing more to say, we would be strangers, meeting for the last and only time, while my mind clamoured painfully, crying, "I love you so much. I'm terribly unhappy. This has never come to me before, and never will again." My face would be set in a prim, conventional smile, my voice would be saying, "Look at that funny old man over there, I wonder who he is, he must be new here." And we would waste the last moments laughing at a stranger, because we were already strangers to one another. "I hope the snapshots come out well," repeating oneself in desperation, and he "Yes, that one of the square ought to be good, the light was just right." Having both of us gone into all that at the time, having agreed upon it, and anyway I would not care if the result was fogged and black, because this was the last moment, the final good-bye had been attained.

"Well," my dreadful smile stretching across my face, "thanks most awfully once again, it's been so ripping . . ." using words I had never used before. Ripping: what did it mean?—God knows, I did not care; it was the sort of word that schoolgirls had for hockey, wildly inappropriate to those past weeks of misery and exultation. Then the doors of the lift would open upon Mrs. Van Hopper and I would cross the lounge to meet her, and he would stroll back again to his corner and pick up a paper.

Sitting there, ridiculously, on the cork mat of the bathroom floor I lived it all, and our journey too, and our arrival in New York. The shrill voice of Helen, a narrower edition of her mother, and Nancy, her horrid little child. The college boys that Mrs. Van Hopper would have me know, and the young bank clerks, suitable to my station. "Let's make Wednesday night a date." "D'you like hot music?" Snub-nosed boys, with shiny faces. Having to be polite. And wanting to be alone with my own thoughts as I was now, locked behind the bathroom door. . . .

She came and rattled on the door. "What are you doing?"

"All right—I'm sorry, I'm coming now," and I made a pretence of turning on the tap, of bustling about and folding a towel on a rail.

She glanced at me curiously as I opened the door. "What a time you've been. You can't afford to dream this morning, you know, there's too much to be done."

He would go back to Manderley, of course, in a few weeks, I felt certain of that. There would be a great pile of letters waiting for him in the hall, and mine amongst them, scribbled on the boat. A forced letter, trying to amuse, describing my fellow passengers. It would lie about inside his blotter, and he would answer it weeks later, one Sunday morning in a hurry, before lunch, having come across it when he paid some bills. And then no more. Nothing until the final degradation of the Christmas card. Manderley itself perhaps, against a frosted background. The message printed, saying "A happy Christmas and a prosperous New Year from Maximilian de Winter." Gold lettering. But to be kind he would have run his pen through the printed name and written in ink underneath "from Maxim," as a sort of sop, and if there was space, a message, "I hope you are enjoying New York." A lick of the envelope, a stamp, and tossed in a pile of a hundred others.

"It's too bad you are leaving to-morrow," said the reception clerk, telephone in hand, "the Ballet starts next week you know. Does Mrs. Van Hopper know?" I dragged myself back from Christmas at Manderley to the realities of the wagon-lit.

Mrs. Van Hopper lunched in the restaurant for the first time since her influenza, and I had a pain in the pit of my stomach as I followed her into the room. He had gone to Cannes for the day, that much I knew, for he had warned me the day before, but I kept thinking the waiter might commit an indiscretion and say: "Will Mademoiselle be dining with Monsieur to-night as usual?" I felt a little sick whenever he came near the table, but he said nothing.

The day was spent in packing, and in the evening people came to say good-bye. We dined in the sitting-room, and she went to bed directly afterwards. Still I had not seen him. I went down to the lounge about half-past nine on the pretext of getting luggage labels and he was not there. The odious reception clerk smiled when he saw me. "If you are looking for Mr. de Winter we had a message from Cannes to say he would not be back before midnight."

"I want a packet of luggage labels," I said, but I saw by his eye that he was not deceived. So there would be no last evening after all. The hour I had looked forward to all day must be spent by myself alone, in my own bedroom, gazing at my Revelation suitcase and the stout hold-all. Perhaps it was just as well, for I should have made a poor companion, and he must have read my face.

I know I cried that night, bitter youthful tears that could not come from me to-day. That kind of crying, deep into a pillow, does not happen after we are twenty-one. The throbbing head, the swollen eyes, the tight, contracted throat. And the wild anxiety in the morning to hide all traces from the world, sponging with cold water, dabbing eau-de-Cologne, the furtive dash of powder that is significant in itself. The panic, too, that one might cry again, the tears swelling without control, and a fatal trembling of the mouth lead one to disaster. I remember opening wide my window and leaning out, hoping the fresh morning air would blow away the tell-tale pink under the powder, and the sun had never seemed so bright, nor the day so full of promise. Monte Carlo was suddenly full of kindliness and charm, the one place in the world that held sincerity. I loved it. Affection overwhelmed me. I wanted to live there all my life. And I was leaving it to-day. This is the last time I brush my hair before the looking-glass, the last time I shall clean my teeth into the basin. Never again sleep in that bed. Never more turn off the switch of that electric light. There I was, padding about in a dressing-gown, making a slough of sentiment out of a common-place hotel bedroom.

"You haven't started a cold, have you?" she said at breakfast.

"No," I told her, "I don't think so," clutching at a straw, for this might serve as an excuse later, if I was over-pink about the eyes.

"I hate hanging about once everything is packed," she grumbled; "we ought to have decided on the earlier train. We could get it if we made the effort, and then have longer in Paris. Wire Helen not to meet us, but arrange another *rendezvous*. I wonder"—she glanced at her watch—"I suppose they could change the reservations. Anyway it's worth trying. Go down to the office and see."

"Yes," I said, a dummy to her moods, going into my bedroom and flinging off my dressing-gown, fastening my inevitable flannel skirt and stretching my home-made jumper over my head. My indifference to her turned to hatred. This was the end then, even my morning must be taken from me. No last half-hour on the terrace, not even ten minutes perhaps to say good-bye. Because she had finished breakfast earlier than she expected, because she was bored. Well then, I would fling away restraint and modesty, I would not be proud any more. I slammed the door of the sitting-room and ran along the passage. I did not wait for the lift, I climbed the stairs, three at a time, up to the third floor. I knew the number of his room, 148, and I hammered at the door, very flushed in the face and breathless.

"Come in," he shouted, and I opened the door, repenting already, my nerve failing me, for perhaps he had only just woken up, having been late last night, and would be still in bed, tousled in the head and irritable.

He was shaving by the open window, a camel-hair jacket over his pyjamas, and I in my flannel suit and heavy shoes felt clumsy and overdressed. I was merely foolish, when I had felt myself dramatic.

"What do you want," he said, "is something the matter?"

"I've come to say good-bye," I said, "we're going this morning."

He stared at me, then put his razor down on the wash-stand. "Shut the door," he said.

I closed it behind me, and stood there, rather self-conscious, my hands hanging by my side. "What on earth are you talking about?" he asked.

"It's true, we're leaving to-day. We were going by the later train, and now she wants to catch the earlier one, and I was afraid I shouldn't see you again. I felt I must see you before I left, to thank you."

They tumbled out, the idiotic words, just as I had imagined them. I was stiff and awkward, in a moment I should say he had been ripping.

"Why didn't you tell me about this before?" he said.

"She only decided yesterday. It was all done in a hurry. Her daughter sails for New York on Saturday, and we are going with her. We're joining her in Paris, and going through to Cherbourg."

"She's taking you with her to New York?"

"Yes, and I don't want to go. I shall hate it; I shall be miserable."

"Why in heaven's name go with her then?"

"I have to, you know that. I work for a salary. I can't afford to leave her." He picked up his razor again, and took the soap off his face. "Sit down," he said. "I shan't be long. I'll dress in the bathroom, and be ready in five minutes."

He took his clothes off the chair and threw them on the bathroom floor, and went inside, slamming the door. I sat down on the bed and began biting my nails. The situation was unreal, and I felt like a lay-figure. I wondered what he was thinking, what he was going to do. I glanced round the room, and it was the room of any man, untidy and impersonal. Lots of shoes, more than were ever needed, and strings of ties. The dressing-table was bare, except for a large bottle of hair-wash and a pair of ivory hair-brushes. No photographs. No snapshots. Nothing like that. Instinctively I had looked for them, thinking there would be one photograph at least beside his bed, or in the middle of the mantelpiece. One large one, in a leather frame. There were only books though, and a box of cigarettes.

He was ready, as he had promised, in five minutes. "Come down to the terrace while I eat my breakfast," he said.

I looked at my watch. "I haven't time," I told him. "I ought to be in the office now, changing the reservations."

"Never mind about that, I've got to talk to you," he said.

We walked down the corridor and he rang for the lift. He can't realise, I thought, that the early train leaves in about an hour and a half. Mrs. Van Hopper will ring up the office, in a moment, and ask if I am there. We went down in the lift, not talking, and so out to the terrace, where the tables were laid for breakfast.

"What are you going to have?" he said.

"I've had mine already," I told him, "and I can only stay four minutes anyway."

"Bring me coffee, a boiled egg, toast, marmalade, and a tangerine," he said to the waiter. And he took an emery board out of his pocket and began filing his nails.

"So Mrs. Van Hopper has had enough of Monte Carlo," he said, "and now she wants to go home. So do I. She to New York and I to Manderley. Which would you prefer? You can take your choice."

"Don't make a joke about it, it's unfair," I said, "and I think I had better see about those tickets, and say good-bye now."

"If you think I'm one of the people who try to be funny at breakfast you're wrong," he said. "I'm invariably ill-tempered in the early morning. I repeat to you, the choice is open to you. Either you go to America with Mrs. Van Hopper or you come home to Manderley with me."

"Do you mean you want a secretary or something?"

"No, I'm asking you to marry me, you little fool."

The waiter came with the breakfast, and I sat with my hands in my lap, watching while he put down the pot of coffee and the jug of milk.

"You don't understand," I said, when the waiter had gone, "I'm not the sort of person men marry."

"What the devil do you mean?" he said, staring at me, laying down his spoon.

I watched a fly settle on the marmalade, and he brushed it away impatiently.

"I'm not sure," I said slowly. "I don't think I know how to explain. I don't belong to your sort of world for one thing."

"What is my world?"

"Well—Manderley. You know what I mean."

He picked up his spoon again and helped himself to marmalade.

"You are almost as ignorant as Mrs. Van Hopper, and just as unintelligent. What do you know of Manderley? I'm the person to judge that, whether you would belong there or not. You think I ask you this on the spur of the moment, don't you? Because you say you don't want to go to New York. You think I ask you to marry me for the same reason you believed I drove you about in the car, yes, and gave you dinner that first evening. To be kind. Don't you?"

"Yes," I said.

"One day," he went on, spreading his toast thick, "you may realise that philanthropy is not my strongest quality. At the moment I don't think you realise anything at all. You haven't answered my question. Are you going to marry me?"

I don't believe, even in my fiercest moments, I had considered this possibility. I had once, when driving with him and we had been silent for many miles, started a rambling story in my head about him being very ill, delirious I think, and sending for me and I having to nurse him. I had reached the point in my story where I was putting eau-de-Cologne on his head when we arrived at the hotel, and so it finished there. And another time I had imagined living in a lodge in the grounds of Manderley, and how he would visit me sometimes, and sit in front of the fire. This sudden talk of marriage bewildered me, even shocked me I think. It was as though the King asked one. It did not ring true. And he went on eating his marmalade as though everything were natural. In books men knelt to women, and it would be moonlight. Not at breakfast, not like this.

"My suggestion doesn't seem to have gone too well," he said. "I'm sorry. I rather thought you loved me. A fine blow to my conceit."

"I do love you," I said. "I love you dreadfully. You've made me very unhappy and I've been crying all night because I thought I should never see you again."

When I said this I remember he laughed, and stretched his hand to me across the breakfast table. "Bless you for that," he said; "one day, when you reach that exalted age of thirty-five which you told me was your ambition, I'll remind you of this moment. And you won't believe me. It's a pity you have to grow up."

I was ashamed already, and angry with him for laughing. So women did not make those confessions to men. I had a lot to learn.

"So that's settled, isn't it?" he said, going on with his toast and marmalade; "instead of being companion to Mrs. Van Hopper you become mine, and your duties will be almost exactly the same. I also like new library books, and flowers in the drawing-room, and bezique after dinner. And someone to pour out my tea. The only difference is that I don't take Taxol, I prefer Eno's, and you must never let me run out of my particular brand of toothpaste."

I drummed with my fingers on the table, uncertain of myself and of him. Was he still laughing at me, was it all a joke? He looked up, and saw the anxiety on my face. "I'm being rather a brute to you, aren't I?" he said; "this isn't your idea of a proposal. We ought to be in a conservatory, you in a white frock with a rose in your hand, and a violin playing a waltz in the distance. And I should make violent love to you behind a palm tree. You would feel then you were getting your money's worth. Poor darling, what a shame. Never mind, I'll take you to Venice for our honeymoon and we'll hold hands in the gondola. But we won't stay too long, because I want to show you Manderley."

He wanted to show me Manderley. . . . And suddenly I realised that it would all happen, I would be his wife, we would walk in the garden together, we would stroll down that path in the valley to the shingle beach. I knew how I would stand on the steps after breakfast, looking at the day, throwing crumbs to the birds, and later wander out in a shady hat with long scissors in my hand, and cut flowers for the house. I knew now why I had bought that picture post-card as a child, it was a premonition, a blank step into the future.

He wanted to show me Manderley. . . . My mind ran riot then, figures came before me and picture after picture—and all the while he ate his tangerine, giving me a piece now and then, and watching me. We would be in a crowd of people, and he would say, "I don't think you have met my wife." Mrs. de Winter. I would be Mrs. de Winter. I considered my name, and the signature on cheques, to tradesmen, and in letters asking people to dinner. I heard myself talking on the telephone "Why not come down to Manderley next week-end?" People, always a throng of people. "Oh, but she's simply charming, you must meet her——" This about me, a whisper on the fringe of a crowd, and I would turn away, pretending I had not heard.

Going down to the lodge with a basket on my arm, grapes and peaches for the old lady who was sick. Her hands stretched out to me, "The Lord bless you, Madam, for being so good," and my saying "Just send up to the house for anything you want." Mrs. de Winter. I would be Mrs. de Winter. I saw the polished table in the dining-room, and the long candles. Maxim sitting at the end. A party of twenty-four. I had a flower in my hair. Everyone looked towards me, holding up his glass. "We must drink the health of the bride," and Maxim saying afterwards, "I have never seen you look so lovely." Great cool rooms, filled with flowers. My bedroom, with a fire in the winter, someone knocking at the door. And a woman comes in, smiling, she is Maxim's sister, and she is saying, "It's really wonderful how happy you have made him, everyone is so pleased, you are such a success." Mrs. de Winter. I would be Mrs. de Winter.

"The rest of the tangerine is sour, I shouldn't eat it," he said, and I stared at him, the words going slowly to my head, then looked down at the fruit on my plate. The quarter was hard and pale. He was right. The tangerine was very sour. I had a sharp, bitter taste in my mouth, and I had only just noticed it.

"Am I going to break the news to Mrs. Van Hopper or are you?" he said. He was folding up his napkin, pushing back his plate, and I wondered how it was he spoke so casually, as though the matter was of little consequence, a mere adjustment of plans. Whereas to me it was a bombshell, exploding in a thousand fragments.

"You tell her," I said, "she'll be so angry."

We got up from the table, I excited and flushed, trembling already in anticipation. I wondered if he would tell the waiter, take my arm smilingly and say, "You must congratulate us, Mademoiselle and I are going to be married." And all the other waiters would hear, would bow to us, would smile, and we would pass into the lounge, a wave of excitement following us, a flutter of expectation. But he said nothing. He left the terrace without a word, and I followed him to the lift. We passed the reception desk and no one even looked at us. The clerk was busy with a sheaf of papers, he was talking over his shoulder to his junior. He does not know, I thought, that I am going to be Mrs. de Winter. I am going to live at Manderley. Manderley will belong to me. We went up in the lift to the first floor, and so along the passage. He took my hand and swung it as we went along. "Does forty-two seem very old to you?" he said.

"Oh, no," I told him, quickly, too eagerly perhaps. "I don't like young men."

"You've never known any," he said.

We came to the door of the suite. "I think I had better deal with this alone," he said; "tell me something—do you mind how soon you marry me? You don't want a trousseau, do you, or any of that nonsense? Because the whole thing can be so easily arranged in a few days. Over a desk, with a licence, and then off in the car to Venice or anywhere you fancy."

"Not in a church?" I asked. "Not in white, with bridesmaids, and bells, and choir boys? What about your relations, and all your friends?"

"You forget," he said, "I had that sort of wedding before."

We went on standing in front of the door of the suite, and I noticed that the daily paper was still thrust through the letter-box. We had been too busy to read it at breakfast.

"Well?" he said, "what about it?"

"Of course," I answered, "I was thinking for the moment we would be married at home. Naturally I don't expect a church, or people, or anything like that."

And I smiled at him. I made a cheerful face. "Won't it be fun?" I said.

He had turned to the door though, and opened it, and we were inside the suite in the little entrance passage.

"Is that you?" called Mrs. Van Hopper from the sitting-room, "what in the name of Mike have you been doing? I've rang the office three times and they said they hadn't seen you."

I was seized with a sudden desire to laugh, to cry, to do both, and I had a pain, too, at the pit of my stomach. I wished, for one wild moment, that none of this had happened, that I was alone somewhere, going for a walk, and whistling.

"I'm afraid it's all my fault," he said, going into the sitting-room, shutting the door behind him, and I heard her exclamation of surprise.

Then I went into my bedroom and sat down by the open window. It was like waiting in the ante-room at a doctor's. I ought to turn over the pages of a magazine, look at photographs that did not matter and read articles I should never remember, until the nurse came, bright and efficient, all humanity washed away by years of disinfectant: "It's all right, the operation was quite successful. There is no need to worry at all. I should go home and have some sleep."

The walls of the suite were thick, I could hear no hum of voices. I wondered what he was saying to her, how he phrased his words. Perhaps he said, "I fell in love with her, you know, the very first time we met. We've been seeing one another every day." And she in answer, "Why, Mr. de Winter, it's quite the most romantic thing I've ever heard." Romantic, that was the word I had tried to remember coming up in the lift. Yes, of course. Romantic. That was what people would say. It was all very sudden and romantic. They suddenly decided to get married and there it was. Such an adventure. I smiled to myself as I hugged my knees on the window seat, thinking how wonderful it was, how happy I was going to be. I was to marry the man I loved. I was to be Mrs. de Winter. It was foolish to go on having that pain in the pit of my stomach when I was so happy. Nerves of course. Waiting like this; the doctor's ante-room. It would have been better, after all, more natural surely to have gone into the sitting-room hand in hand, laughing, smiling at one another and for him to say "We're going to be married, we're very much in love."

In love. He had not said anything yet about being in love. No time perhaps. It was all so hurried at the breakfast table. Marmalade, and coffee, and that tangerine. No time. The tangerine was very bitter. No, he had not said anything about being in love. Just that we would be married. Short and definite, very original. Original proposals were much better. More genuine. Not like other people. Not like younger men who talked nonsense probably, not meaning half they said. Not like younger men being very incoherent, very passionate, swearing impossibilities. Not like him the first time, asking Rebecca. . . . I must not think of that. Put it away. A thought forbidden, prompted by demons. Get thee behind me, Satan. I must never think about that, never, never, never. He loves me, he wants to show me Manderley. Would they ever have done with their talking, would they ever call me into the room?

There was the book of poems lying beside my bed. He had forgotten he had ever lent them to me. They could not mean much to him then. "Go on," whispered the demon, "open the title-page, that's what you want to do, isn't it? Open the title-page." Nonsense, I said, I'm only going to put the book with the rest of the things. I yawned, I wandered to the table beside the bed. I picked up the book. I caught my foot in the flex of the bedside lamp, and stumbled, the book falling from my hands on to the floor. It fell open, at the title-page. "Max from Rebecca." She was dead, and one must not have thoughts about the dead. They slept in peace, the grass blew over their graves. How alive was her writing though, how full of force. Those curious, sloping letters. The blob of ink. Done yesterday. It was just as if it had been written yesterday. I took my nail scissors from the dressing-case and cut the page, looking over my shoulder like a criminal.

I cut the page right out of the book. I left no jagged edges, and the book looked white and clean when the page was gone. A new book, that had not been touched. I tore the page up in many little fragments and threw them into the waste-paper basket. Then I went and sat on the window seat again. But I kept thinking of the torn scraps in the basket, and after a moment I had to get up and look in the basket once more. Even now the ink stood up on the fragments thick and black, the writing was not destroyed. I took a box of matches and set fire to the fragments. The flame had a lovely light, staining the paper, curling the edges, making the slanting writing impossible to distinguish. The fragments fluttered to grey ashes. The letter R was the last to go, it twisted in the flame, it curled outwards for a moment, becoming larger than ever. Then it crumpled too; the flame destroyed it. It was not ashes even, it was feathery dust. . . . I went and washed my hands in the basin. I felt better, much better. I had the clean, new feeling that one has when the calendar is hung on the wall at the beginning of the year. January the 1st. I was aware of the same freshness, the same gay confidence. The door opened and he came into the room.

"All's well," he said; "shock made her speechless at first, but she's beginning to recover, so I'm going downstairs to the office, to make certain she will catch the first train. For a moment she wavered, I think she had hopes of acting witness at the wedding, but I was very firm. Go and talk to her."

He said nothing about being glad, about being happy. He did not take my arm and go into the sitting-room with me. He smiled, and waved his hand, and went off down the corridor alone. I went to Mrs. Van Hopper, uncertain, rather self-conscious, like a maid who has handed in her notice through a friend.

She was standing by the window, smoking a cigarette, an odd, dumpy little figure I should not see again, her coat stretched tight over her large breasts, her ridiculous hat perched sideways on her head.

"Well," she said, her voice dry and hard, not the voice she would have used to him, "I suppose I've got to hand it to you for a doubletime worker. Still waters certainly run deep in your case. How did you manage it?"

I did not know what to answer. I did not like her smile.

"It was a lucky thing for you I had the influenza," she said. "I realise now how you spent your days, and why you were so forgetful. Tennis lessons my eye. You might have told me, you know."

"I'm sorry," I said.

She looked at me curiously, she ran her eyes over my figure. "And he tells me he wants to marry you in a few days. Lucky again for you that you haven't a family to ask questions. Well, it's nothing to do with me any more, I wash my hands of the whole affair. I rather wonder what his friends will think, but I suppose that's up to him. You realise he's years older than you?"

"He's only forty-two," I said, "and I'm old for my age."

She laughed, she dropped cigarette ash on the floor. "You certainly are," she said. She went on looking at me in a way she had never done before. Appraising me, running her eyes over my points like a judge at a cattle show. There was something inquisitive about her eyes, something unpleasant.

"Tell me," she said, intimate, a friend to a friend, "have you been doing anything you shouldn't?"

She was like Blaize, the dressmaker, who had offered me that ten per cent.

"I don't know what you mean," I said.

She laughed, she shrugged her shoulders. "Oh, well . . . never mind. But I always said English girls were dark horses, for all their hockey-playing attitude. So I'm supposed to travel to Paris alone, and leave you here while your beau gets a marriage licence? I notice he doesn't ask me to the wedding."

"I don't think he wants anyone, and anyway you would have sailed," I said.

"H'm, h'm," she said. She took out her vanity case and began powdering her nose. "I suppose you really do know your own mind," she went on; "after all, the whole thing has been very hurried, hasn't it? A matter of a few weeks. I don't suppose he's too easy, and you'll have to adapt yourself to his ways. You've led an extremely sheltered life up to now, you know, and you can't say that I've run you off your feet. You will have your work cut out as mistress of Manderley. To be perfectly frank, my dear, I simply can't see you doing it."

Her words sounded like the echo of my own an hour before.

"You haven't the experience," she continued, "you don't know that milieu. You can scarcely string two sentences together at my bridge teas, what are you going to say to all his friends? The Manderley parties were famous when she was alive. Of course he's told you all about them?"

I hesitated, but she went on, thank heaven, not waiting for my answer. "Naturally one wants you to be happy, and I grant you he's a very attractive creature but—well, I'm sorry; and personally I think you are making a big mistake—one you will bitterly regret."

She put down the box of powder, and looked at me over her shoulder. Perhaps she was being sincere at last, but I did not want that sort of honesty. I did not say anything. I looked sullen, perhaps, for she shrugged her shoulders and wandered to the looking-glass, straightening her little mushroom hat. I was glad she was going, glad I should not see her again. I grudged the months I had spent with her, employed by her, taking her money, trotting in her wake like a shadow, drab and dumb. Of course I was inexperienced, of course I was idiotic, shy and young. I knew all that. She did not have to tell me. I supposed her attitude was deliberate, and for some odd feminine reason she resented this marriage, her scale of values had received a shock.

Well, I would not care, I would forget her and her barbed words. A new confidence had been born in me when I burnt that page and scattered the fragments. The past would not exist for either of us, we were starting afresh, he and I. The past had blown away like the ashes in the waste-paper basket. I was going to be Mrs. de Winter. I was going to live at Manderley.

Soon she would be gone, rattling alone in the wagon-lit without me, and he and I would be together in the dining-room of the hotel, lunching at the same table, planning the future. The brink of a big adventure. Perhaps, once she had gone, he would talk to me at last, about loving me, about being happy. Up to now there had been no time, and anyway those things are not easily said, they must wait their moment. I looked up, and caught her reflection in the looking-glass. She was watching me, a little tolerant smile on her lips. I thought she was going to be generous after all, hold out her hand and wish me luck, give me encouragement and tell me that everything was going to be all right. But she went on smiling, twisting a stray hair into place beneath her hat.

"Of course," she said, "you know why he is marrying you, don't you? You haven't flattered yourself he's in love with you? The fact is that empty house got on his nerves to such an extent he nearly went off his head. He admitted as much before you came into the room. He just can't go on living there alone. . . ."

CHAPTER SEVEN

WE CAME TO Manderley in early May, arriving, so Maxim said, with the first swallows and the bluebells. It would be the best moment, before the full flush of summer, and in the valley the azaleas would be prodigal of scent, and the blood-red rhododendrons in bloom. We motored, I remember, leaving London in the morning in a heavy shower of rain, coming to Manderley about five o'clock, in time for tea. I can see myself now, unsuitably dressed as usual, although a bride of seven weeks, in a tan-coloured stockinette frock, a small fur known as a stone marten round my neck, and over all a shapeless mackintosh, far too big for me and dragging to my ankles. It was, I thought, a gesture to the weather, and the length added inches to my height. I clutched a pair of gauntlet gloves in my hands, and carried a large leather handbag.

"This is London rain," said Maxim when we left, "you wait, the sun will be shining for you when we come to Manderley"; and he was right, for the clouds left us at Exeter, they rolled away behind us, leaving a great blue sky above our heads and a white road in front of us.

I was glad to see the sun, for in superstitious fashion I looked upon rain as an omen of ill-will, and the leaden skies of London had made me silent.

"Feeling better?" said Maxim, and I smiled at him, taking his hand, thinking how easy it was for him, going to his own home, wandering into the hall, picking up letters, ringing a bell for tea, and I wondered how much he guessed of my nervousness, and whether his question "Feeling better?" meant that he understood. "Never mind, we'll soon be there. I expect you want your tea," he said, and he let go my hand because we had reached a bend in the road, and must slow down.

I knew then that he had mistaken my silence for fatigue, and it had not occurred to him I dreaded this arrival at Manderley as much as I had longed for it in theory. Now the moment was upon me I wished it delayed, I wanted to draw up at some way-side inn and stay there, in a coffee-room, by an impersonal fire. I wanted to be a traveller on the road, a bride in love with her husband. Not myself coming to Manderley for the first time, the wife of Maxim de Winter. We passed many friendly villages where the cottage windows had a kindly air. A woman, holding a baby in her arms, smiled at me from a doorway, while a man clanked across a road to a well, carrying a pail.

I wished we could have been one with them, perhaps their neighbours, and that Maxim could lean over a cottage gate in the evenings, smoking a pipe, proud of a very tall hollyhock he had grown himself, while I bustled in my kitchen, clean as a pin, laying the table for supper. There would be an alarm clock on the dresser ticking loudly, and a row of shining plates, while after supper Maxim would read his paper, boots on the fender, and I reach for a great pile of mending in the dresser drawer. Surely it would be peaceful and steady, that way of living, and easier, too, demanding no set standard?

"Only two miles further," said Maxim; "you see that great belt of trees on the brow of the hill there, sloping to the valley, with a scrap of sea beyond? That's Manderley, in there. Those are the woods."

I forced a smile, and did not answer him, aware now of a stab of panic, an uneasy sickness that could not be controlled. Gone was my glad excitement, vanished my happy pride. I was like a child brought to her first school, or a little untrained maid who has never left home before, seeking a situation. Any measure of self-possession I had gained hitherto, during the brief seven weeks of marriage, was like a rag now, fluttering before the wind; it seemed to me that even the most elementary knowledge of behaviour was unknown to me now, I should not know my right hand from my left, whether to stand or sit, what spoons and forks to use at dinner.

"I should shed that mackintosh," he said, glancing down at me, "it has not rained down here at all, and put your funny little fur straight. Poor lamb, I've bustled you down here like this, and you probably ought to have bought a lot of clothes in London."

"It doesn't matter to me, as long as you don't mind," I said.

"Most women think of nothing but clothes," he said absently, and turning a corner we came to a cross-road, and the beginning of a high wall.

"Here we are," he said, a new note of excitement in his voice, and I gripped the leather seat of the car with my two hands.

The road curved, and before us, on the left, were two high iron gates beside a lodge, open wide to the long drive beyond. As we drove through I saw faces peering through the dark window of the lodge, and a child ran round from the back, staring curiously. I shrank back against the seat, my heart beating quickly, knowing why the faces were at the window, and why the child stared.

They wanted to see what I was like. I could imagine them now, talking excitedly, laughing in the little kitchen. "Only caught sight of the top of her hat," they would say, "she wouldn't show her face. Oh, well, we'll know by to-morrow. Word will come from the house." Perhaps he guessed something of my shyness at last for he took my hand, and kissed it, and laughed a little, even as he spoke.

"You mustn't mind if there's a certain amount of curiosity," he said, "everyone will want to know what you are like. They have probably talked of nothing else for weeks. You've only got to be yourself and they will all adore you. And you don't have to worry about the house, Mrs. Danvers does everything. Just leave it all to her. She'll be stiff with you at first, I dare say, she's an extraordinary character, but you mustn't let it worry you. It's just her manner. See those shrubs? It's like a blue wall along here when the hydrangeas are in bloom."

I did not answer him, for I was thinking of that self who long ago bought a picture post-card in a village shop, and came out into the bright sunlight twisting it in her hands, pleased with her purchase, thinking "This will do for my album. 'Manderley,' what a lovely name." And now I belonged here, this was my home, I would write letters to people saying, "We shall be down at Manderley all the summer, you must come and see us," and I would walk along this drive, strange and unfamiliar to me now, with perfect knowledge, conscious of every twist and turn, marking and approving where the gardeners had worked, here a cutting back of the shrubs, there a lopping of a branch, calling at the lodge by the iron gates on some friendly errand, saying, "Well, how's the leg to-day?" while the old woman, curious no longer, bade me welcome to her kitchen. I envied Maxim, careless and at ease, and the little smile on his lips which meant he was happy to be coming home.

It seemed remote to me, and far too distant, the time when I too should smile and be at ease, and I wished it could come quickly, that I could be old even, with grey hair, and slow of step, having lived here many years, anything but the timid, foolish creature I felt myself to be.

The gates had shut to with a crash behind us, the dusty high-road was out of sight, and I became aware that this was not the drive I had imagined would be Manderley's, this was not a broad and spacious thing of gravel, flanked with neat turf at either side, kept smooth with rake and brush.

This drive twisted and turned as a serpent, scarce wider in places than a path, and above our heads was a great colonnade of trees, whose branches nodded and intermingled with one another, making an archway for us, like the roof of a church. Even the midday sun would not penetrate the interlacing of those green leaves, they were too thickly entwined, one with another, and only little flickering patches of warm light would come in intermittent waves to dapple the drive with gold. It was very silent, very still. On the high-road there had been a gay west wind blowing in my face, making the grass on the hedges dance in unison, but here there was no wind. Even the engine of the car had taken a new note, throbbing low, quieter than before. As the drive descended to the valley so the trees came in upon us, great beeches with lovely smooth white stems, lifting their myriad branches to one another, and other trees, trees I could not name, coming close, so close that I could touch them with my hands. On we went, over a little bridge that spanned a narrow stream, and still this drive that was no drive twisted and turned like an enchanted ribbon through the dark and silent woods, penetrating even deeper to the very heart surely of the forest itself, and still there was no clearing, no space to hold a house.

The length of it began to nag at my nerves, it must be this turn, I thought, or round that further bend, but as I leant forward in my seat I was forever disappointed, there was no house, no field, no broad and friendly garden, nothing but the silence and deep woods. The lodge gates were a memory, and the high-road something belonging to another time, another world.

Suddenly I saw a clearing in the dark drive ahead, and a patch of sky, and in a moment the dark trees had thinned, the nameless shrubs had disappeared, and on either side of us was a wall of colour, blood-red, reaching far above our heads. We were amongst the rhododendrons. There was something bewildering, even shocking, about the suddenness of their discovery. The woods had not prepared me for them. They startled me with their crimson faces, massed one upon the other in incredible profusion, showing no leaf, no twig, nothing but the slaughterous red, luscious and fantastic, unlike any rhododendron plant I had seen before.

I glanced at Maxim. He was smiling. "Like them?" he said.

I told him "Yes," a little breathlessly, uncertain whether I was speaking the truth or not, for to me a rhododendron was a homely, domestic thing, strictly conventional, mauve or pink in colour, standing one beside the other in a neat round bed. And these were monsters, rearing to the sky, massed like a battalion, too beautiful I thought, too powerful, they were not plants at all.

We were not far from the house now, I saw the drive broaden to the sweep I had expected, and with the blood-red wall still flanking us on either side, we turned the last corner, and so came to Manderley. Yes, there it was, the Manderley I had expected, the Manderley of my picture post-card long ago. A thing of grace and beauty, exquisite and faultless, lovelier even than I had ever dreamed, built in its hollow of smooth grass-land and mossy lawns, the terraces sloping to the gardens, and the gardens to the sea. As we drove up to the wide stone steps and stopped before the open door, I saw through one of the mullioned windows that the hall was full of people, and I heard Maxim swear under his breath. "Damn that woman," he said, "she knows perfectly well I did not want this sort of thing," and he put on the brakes with a jerk.

"What's the matter?" I said, "who are all those people?"

"I'm afraid you will have to face it now," he said, in irritation. "Mrs. Danvers has collected the whole damned staff in the house and on the estate to welcome us. It's all right, you won't have to say anything, I'll do it all."

I fumbled for the handle of the door, feeling slightly sick, and cold now too from the long drive, and as I fumbled with the catch the butler came down the steps, followed by a footman, and he opened the door for me.

He was old, he had a kind face, and I smiled up at him, holding out my hand, but I don't think he could have seen, for he took the rug instead, and my small dressing-case, and turned to Maxim, helping me from the car at the same time.

"Well, here we are, Frith," said Maxim, taking off his gloves, "it was raining when we left London. You don't seem to have had it here. Everyone well?"

"Yes, sir, thank you, sir. No, we have had a dry month on the whole. Glad to see you home, and hope you have been keeping well. And Madam too."

"Yes, we are both well, thank you, Frith. Rather tired from the drive, and wanting our tea. I didn't expect this business." Her jerked his head to the hall.

"Mrs. Danvers' orders, sir," said the man, his face expressionless.

"I might have guessed it," said Maxim abruptly, "come on," he turned to me, "it won't take long, and then you shall have your tea."

We went together up the flight of steps, Frith and the footman following with the rug and my mackintosh, and I was aware of a little pain at the pit of my stomach, and a nervous contraction in my throat.

I can close my eyes now, and look back on it, and see myself as I must have been, standing on the threshold of the house, a slim, awkward figure in my stockinette dress, clutching in my sticky hands a pair of gauntlet gloves. I can see the great stone hall, the wide doors open to the library, the Peter Lelys and the Vandykes on the walls, the exquisite staircase leading to the minstrels' gallery, and there, ranged one behind the other in the hall, overflowing to the stone passages beyond, and to the dining-room, a sea of faces, open-mouthed and curious, gazing at me as though they were the watching crowd about the block, and I the victim with my hands behind my back. Someone advanced from the sea of faces, someone tall and gaunt, dressed in deep black, whose prominent cheek-bones and great, hollow eyes gave her a skull's face, parchment-white, set on a skeleton's frame.

She came towards me, and I held out my hand, envying her for her dignity and her composure; but when she took my hand hers was limp and heavy, deathly cold, and it lay in mine like a lifeless thing.

"This is Mrs. Danvers," said Maxim, and she began to speak, still leaving that dead hand in mine, her hollow eyes never leaving my eyes, so that my own wavered and would not meet hers, and as they did so her hand moved in mine, the life returned to it, and I was aware of a sensation of discomfort and of shame.

I cannot remember her words now, but I know that she bade me welcome to Manderley, in the name of herself and the staff, a stiff, conventional speech rehearsed for the occasion, spoken in a voice as cold and lifeless as her hands had been. When she had finished she waited, as though for a reply, and I remember blushing scarlet, stammering some sort of thanks in return, and dropping both my gloves in my confusion. She stooped to pick them up, and as she handed them to me I saw a little smile of scorn upon her lips, and I guessed at once she considered me ill-bred. Something, in the expression of her face, gave me a feeling of unrest, and even when she had stepped back, and taken her place amongst the rest, I could see that black figure standing out alone, individual and apart, and for all her silence I knew her eye to be upon me. Maxim took my arm and made a little speech of thanks, perfectly easy and free from embarrassment, as though the making of it was no effort to him at all, and then he bore me off to the library to tea, closing the doors behind us, and we were alone again.

Two cocker spaniels came from the fireside to greet us. They pawed at Maxim, their long, silken ears strained back with affection, their noses questing his hands, and then they left him and came to me, sniffing at my heels, rather uncertain, rather suspicious. One was the mother, blind in one eye, and soon she had enough of me, and took herself with a grunt to the fire again, but Jasper, the younger, put his nose into my hand, and laid a chin upon my knee, his eyes deep with meaning, his tail a-thump when I stroked his silken ears.

I felt better when I had taken my hat off, and my wretched little fur, and thrown them both beside my gloves and my bag on to the window seat. It was a deep, comfortable room, with books lining the walls to the ceiling, the sort of room a man would move from never, did he live alone; solid chairs beside a great open fire-place, baskets for the two dogs in which I felt they never sat, for the hollows in the chairs had tell-tale marks. The long windows looked out upon the lawns, and beyond the lawns to the distant shimmer of the sea.

There was an old quiet smell about the room, as though the air in it was little changed, for all the sweet lilac scent and the roses brought to it throughout the early summer. Whatever air came to this room, whether from the garden or from the sea, would lose its first freshness, becoming part of the unchanging room itself, one with the books, musty and never read, one with the scrolled ceiling, the dark panelling, the heavy curtains.

It was an ancient mossy smell, the smell of a silent church where services are seldom held, where rusty lichen grows upon the stones and ivy tendrils creep to the very windows. A room for peace, a room for meditation.

Soon tea was brought to us, a stately little performance enacted by Frith and the young footman, in which I played no part until they had gone, and while Maxim glanced through his great pile of letters I played with two dripping crumpets, crumbled cake with my hands, and swallowed my scalding tea.

Now and again he looked up at me and smiled, and then returned to his letters, the accumulation of the last months I supposed, and I thought how little I knew of his life here at Manderley, of how it went, day by day, of the people he knew, of his friends, men and women, of what bills he paid, what orders he gave about his household. The last weeks had gone so swiftly, and I—driving by his side through France and Italy—thought only of how I loved him, seeing Venice with his eyes, echoing his words, asking no questions of the past and future, content with the little glory of the living present.

For he was gayer than I had thought, more tender than I had dreamed, youthful and ardent in a hundred happy ways, not the Maxim I had first met, not the stranger who sat alone at the table in the restaurant, staring before him, wrapped in his secret self. My Maxim laughed and sang, threw stones into the water, took my hand, wore no frown between his eyes, carried no burden on his shoulder. I knew him as a lover, as a friend, and during those weeks I had forgotten that he had a life, orderly, methodical, a life which must be taken up again, continued as before, making vanished weeks a brief discarded holiday.

I watched him read his letters, saw him frown at one, smile at another, dismiss the next with no expression, and but for the grace of God I thought, my letter would be lying there, written from New York, and he would read it in the same indifferent fashion, puzzled at first perhaps by the signature, and then tossing it with a yawn to the pile of others in the basket, reaching for his cup of tea. The knowledge of this chilled me, how narrow a chance had stood between me and what might-have-been, for he would have sat there to his tea, as he sat now, continuing his home life as he would in any case, and perhaps he would not have thought of me much, not with regret anyway, while I, in New York, playing bridge with Mrs. Van Hopper would wait day after day for a letter that never came.

I leant back in my chair, glancing about the room, trying to instil into myself some measure of confidence, some genuine realisation that I was here, at Manderley, the house of the picture post-card, the Manderley that was famous; I had to teach myself that all this was mine now, mine as much as his, the deep chair I was sitting in, that mass of books stretching to the ceiling, the pictures on the walls, the gardens, the woods, the Manderley I had read about, all of this was mine now because I was married to Maxim.

We should grow old here together, we should sit like this to our tea as old people, Maxim and I, with other dogs, the successors of these, and the library would wear the same ancient musty smell that it did now. It would know a period of glorious shabbiness and wear when the boys were young—our boys—for I saw them sprawling on the sofa with muddy boots, bringing with them always a litter of rods, and cricket bats, great clasp-knives, bows-and-arrows.

On the table there, polished now and plain, an ugly case would stand containing butterflies and moths, and another one with birds' eggs, wrapped in cotton wool. "Not all this junk in here," I would say, "take them to the schoolroom, darlings," and they would run off, shouting, calling to one another, but the little one staying behind, pottering on his own, quieter than the others.

My vision was disturbed by the opening of the door, and Frith came in with the footman to clear the tea. "Mrs. Danvers wondered, Madam, whether you would like to see your room," he said to me, when the tea had been taken away.

Maxim glanced up from his letters. "What sort of job have they made of the east wing?" he said.

"Very nice indeed, sir, it seems to me; the men made a mess when they were working, of course, and for a time Mrs. Danvers was rather afraid it would not be finished by your return. But they cleared out last Monday. I should imagine you would be very comfortable there, sir, it's a lot lighter of course on that side of the house."

"Have you been making alterations?" I asked.

"Oh, nothing much," said Maxim briefly, "only redecorating and painting the suite in the east wing, which I thought we would use for ours. As Frith says, it's much more cheerful on that side of the house, and it has a lovely view of the rose-garden. It was the visitors' wing when my mother was alive. I'll just finish these letters and then I'll come up and join you. Run along and make friends with Mrs. Danvers, it's a good opportunity."

I got up slowly, my old nervousness returning, and went out into the hall. I wished I could have waited for him, and then, taking his arm, seen the rooms together. I did not want to go alone, with Mrs. Danvers. How vast the great hall looked now that it was empty. My feet rang on the flagged stones, echoing to the ceiling, and I felt guilty at the sound, as one does in church, self-conscious, aware of the same constraint. My feet made a stupid pitter-patter as I walked, and I thought that Frith, with his felt soles, must have thought me foolish.

"It's very big, isn't it?" I said, too brightly, too forced, a schoolgirl still, but he answered me in all solemnity. "Yes, Madam, Manderley is a big place. Not so big as some, of course, but big enough. This was the old banqueting hall, in old days. It is used still on great occasions, such as a big dinner, or a ball. And the public are admitted here, you know, once a week."

"Yes," I said, still aware of my loud footsteps, feeling, as I followed him, that he considered me as he would one of the public visitors, and I behaved like a visitor too, glancing politely to right and left, taking in the weapons on the wall, and the pictures, touching the carved staircase with my hands.

A black figure stood waiting for me at the head of the stairs, the hollow eyes watching me intently from the white skull's face. I looked round for the stolid Frith, but he had passed along the hall and into the further corridor.

I was alone now with Mrs. Danvers. I went up the great stairs towards her, and she waited motionless, her hands folded before her, her eyes never leaving my face. I summoned a smile, which was not returned, nor did I blame her, for there was no purpose to the smile, it was a silly thing, bright and artificial. "I hope I haven't kept you waiting," I said.

"It's for you to make your own time, Madam," she answered, "I'm here to carry out your orders," and then she turned, through the archway of the gallery, to the corridor beyond. We went along a broad, carpeted passage, and then turned left, through an oak door, and down a narrow flight of stairs and up a corresponding flight, and so to another door. This she flung open, standing aside to let me pass, and I came to a little ante-room, or boudoir, furnished with a sofa, chairs, and writing desk, which opened out to a large double bedroom with wide windows, and a bathroom beyond. I went at once to the window, and looked out. The rose-garden lay below, and the eastern part of the terrace, while beyond the rose-garden rose a smooth grass bank, stretching to the near woods.

"You can't see the sea from here then," I said, turning to Mrs. Danvers.

"No, not from this wing," she answered, "you can't even hear it, either. You would not know the sea was anywhere near, not from this wing."

She spoke in a peculiar way, as though something lay behind her words, and she laid an emphasis on the words, "this wing," as if suggesting that the suite where we stood now held some inferiority.

"I'm sorry about that, I like the sea," I said.

She did not answer, she just went on staring at me, her hands folded before her.

"However, it's a very charming room," I said, "and I'm sure I shall be comfortable. I understand that it's been done up for our return."

"Yes," she said.

"What was it like before?" I asked.

"It had a mauve paper, and different hangings; Mr. de Winter did not think it very cheerful. It was never much used, except for occasional visitors. But Mr. de Winter gave special orders in his letter that you would have this room."

"Then this was not his bedroom originally?" I said.

"No, Madam, he's never used the rooms in this wing before."

"Oh," I said, "he didn't tell me that," and I wandered to the dressing-table and began combing my hair. My things were already unpacked, my brushes and comb upon the tray. I was glad Maxim had given me a set of brushes, and that they were laid out there, upon the dressing-table, for Mrs. Danvers to see. They were new, they had cost money, I need not be ashamed of them.

"Alice has unpacked for you and will look after you until your maid arrives," said Mrs. Danvers. I smiled at her again, I put down the brush upon the dressing-table.

"I don't have a maid," I said awkwardly, "I'm sure Alice, if she is the housemaid, will look after me all right."

She wore the same expression that she had done on our first meeting, when I dropped my gloves so gauchely on the floor.

"I'm afraid that would not do for very long," she said, "it's usual, you know, for ladies in your position, to have a personal maid."

I flushed, and reached for my brush again. There was a sting in her words I understood too well. "If you think it necessary perhaps you would see about it for me," I said, avoiding her eyes, "some young girl perhaps, wanting to train."

"If you wish," she said. "It's for you to say."

There was silence between us, I wished she would go away. I wondered why she must go on standing there, watching me, her hands folded on her black dress.

"I suppose you have been at Manderley for many years," I said, making a fresh effort, "longer than anyone else?"

"Not so long as Frith," she said, and I thought how lifeless her voice was, and cold, like her hand when it had lain in mine; "Frith was here when the old gentleman was living, when Mr. de Winter was a boy."

"I see," I said, "so you did not come till after that?"

"No," she said, "not till after that."

Once more I glanced up at her, and once more I met her eyes, dark and sombre, in that white face of hers, instilling into me, I knew not why, a strange feeling of disquiet, of foreboding. I tried to smile, and could not, I found myself held by those eyes, that had no light, no flicker of sympathy towards me.

"I came here when the first Mrs. de Winter was a bride," she said, and her voice, which had hitherto, as I said, been dull and toneless, was harsh now with unexpected animation, with life and meaning, and there was a spot of colour on the gaunt cheek-bones.

The change was so sudden that I was shocked, and a little scared. I did not know what to do, or what to say. It was as though she had spoken words that were forbidden, words that she had hidden within herself for a long time and now would be repressed no longer. Still her eyes never left my face, they looked upon me with a curious mixture of pity and of scorn, until I felt myself to be even younger and more untutored to the ways of life than I had believed.

I could see she despised me, marking with all the snobbery of her class that I was no great lady, that I was humble, shy, and diffident. Yet there was something beside scorn in those eyes of hers, something surely of positive dislike, or actual malice?

I had to say something, I could not go on sitting there, playing with my hair-brush, letting her see how much I feared and mistrusted her.

"Mrs. Danvers," I heard myself saying, "I hope we shall be friends and come to understand one another. You must have patience with me, you know, because this sort of life is new to me, I've lived rather differently. And I do want to make a success of it, and above all to make Mr. de Winter happy. I know I can leave all household arrangements to you, Mr. de Winter said so, and you must just run things as they have always been run, I shan't want to make any changes."

I stopped, a little breathless, still uncertain of myself and whether I was saying the right thing, and when I looked up again I saw that she had moved, and was standing with her hand on the handle of the door.

"Very good," she said; "I hope I shall do everything to your satisfaction. The house has been in my charge now for more than a year, and Mr. de Winter has never complained. It was very different of course when the late Mrs. de Winter was alive, there was a lot of entertaining then, a lot of parties, and though I managed for her she liked to supervise things herself."

Once again I had the impression that she chose her words with care, that she was feeling her way, as it were, into my mind, and watching for the effect upon my face.

"I would rather leave it to you," I repeated, "much rather," and into her face came the same expression I had noticed before, when first I had shaken hands with her in the hall, a look surely of derision, of definite contempt. She knew that I would never withstand her, and that I feared her too.

"Can I do anything more for you?" she said, and I pretended to glance round the room. "No," I said. "No, I think I have everything. I shall be very comfortable here. You have made the room so charming,"—this last a final crawling sop to win her approval. She shrugged her shoulders, and still she did not smile. "I only followed out Mr. de Winter's instructions," she said.

She hesitated by the doorway, her hand on the handle of the open door. It was as though she still had something to say to me, and could not decide upon the words, yet waited there, for me to give her opportunity.

I wished she would go, she was like a shadow standing there, watching me, appraising me with her hollow eyes, set in that dead skull's face.

"If you find anything not to your liking you will tell me at once?" she asked.

"Yes," I said. "Yes, of course, Mrs. Danvers," but I knew this was not what she had meant to say, and silence fell between us once again.

"If Mr. de Winter asks for his big wardrobe," she said suddenly, "you must tell him it was impossible to move. We tried, but we could not get it through these narrow doorways. These are smaller rooms than those in the west wing. If he doesn't like the arrangement of this suite he must tell me. It was difficult to know how to furnish these rooms."

"Please don't worry, Mrs. Danvers," I said, "I'm sure he will be pleased with everything. But I'm sorry it's given you so much trouble. I had no idea he was having rooms redecorated and furnished, he shouldn't have bothered. I'm sure I should have been just as happy and comfortable in the west wing."

She looked at me curiously, and began twisting the handle of the door.

"Mr. de Winter said you would prefer to be on this side," she said, "the rooms in the west wing are very old. The bedroom in the big suite is twice as large as this, a very beautiful room too, with a scrolled ceiling. The tapestry chairs are very valuable, and so is the carved mantelpiece. It's the most beautiful room in the house. And the windows look down across the lawns to the sea."

I felt uncomfortable, a little shy. I did not know why she must speak with such an undercurrent of resentment, implying as she did at the same time that this room, where I found myself to be installed, was something inferior, not up to Manderley standard, a second-rate room, as it were, for a second-rate person.

"I suppose Mr. de Winter keeps the most beautiful room to show to the public," I said. She went on twisting the handle of the door, and then looked up at me again, watching my eyes, hesitating before replying, and when she spoke her voice was quieter even, and more toneless, than it had been before.

"The bedrooms are never shown to the public," she said, "only the hall and the gallery, and the rooms below." She paused an instant, feeling me with her eyes. "They used to live in the west wing and use those rooms when Mrs. de Winter was alive. That big room, I was telling you about, that looked down to the sea, was Mrs. de Winter's bedroom."

Then I saw a shadow flit across her face, and she drew back against the wall, effacing herself, as a step sounded outside and Maxim came into the room.

"How is it?" he said to me, "all right? Do you think you'll like it?"

He looked round with enthusiasm, pleased as a schoolboy. "I always thought this a most attractive room," he said. "It was wasted all those years as a guest-room, but I always thought it had possibilities. You've made a great success of it, Mrs. Danvers, I give you full marks."

"Thank you, sir," she said, her face expressionless, and then she turned, and went out of the room, closing the door softly behind her.

Maxim went and leant out of the window. "I love the rose-garden," he said; "one of the first things I remember is walking after my mother, on very small, unsteady legs, while she picked off the dead heads of the roses. There's something peaceful and happy about this room, and it's quiet too. You could never tell you were within five minutes of the sea, from this room."

"That's what Mrs. Danvers said," I told him.

He came away from the window, he prowled about the room, touching things, looking at the pictures, opening wardrobes, fingering my clothes, already unpacked.

"How did you get on with old Danvers?" he said abruptly.

I turned away, and began combing my hair again before the looking-glass. "She seems just a little bit stiff," I said, after a moment or two, "perhaps she thought I was going to interfere with the running of the house."

"I don't think she would mind your doing that," he said. I looked up and saw him watching my reflection in the looking-glass, and then he turned away and went over to the window again, whistling quietly, under his breath, rocking backwards and forwards on his heels.

"Don't mind her," he said, "she's an extraordinary character in many ways, and possibly not very easy for another woman to get on with. You mustn't worry about it. If she really makes herself a nuisance we'll get rid of her. But she's efficient, you know, and will take all housekeeping worries off your hands. I dare say she's a bit of a bully to the staff. She doesn't dare bully me though. I'd have given her the sack long ago if she had tried."

"I expect we shall get on very well when she knows me better," I said quickly, "after all, it's natural enough that she should resent me a bit at first."

"Resent you, why resent you? What the devil do you mean?" he said. He turned from the window, frowning, an odd, half-angry expression on his face. I wondered why he should mind, and wished I had said something else.

"I mean, it must be much easier for a housekeeper to look after a man alone," I said. "I dare say she had got into the way of doing it, and perhaps she was afraid I should be very overbearing."

"Overbearing, my God . . ." he began, "if you think . . ." and then he stopped, and came across to me, and kissed me on the top of my head. "Let's forget about Mrs. Danvers," he said; "she doesn't interest me very much I'm afraid. Come along, and let me show you something of Manderley."

I did not see Mrs. Danvers again that evening, and we did not talk about her any more. I felt happier, when I had dismissed her from my thoughts, less of an interloper, and as we wandered about the rooms downstairs, and looked at the pictures, and Maxim put his arm round my shoulder, I began to feel more like the self I wanted to become, the self I had pictured in my dreams, who made Manderley her home.

My footsteps no longer sounded foolish on the stone flags of the hall, for Maxim's nailed shoes made far more noise than mine, and the pattering feet of the two dogs was a comfortable, pleasing note.

I was glad, too, because it was the first evening, and we had only been back a little while, and the showing of the pictures had taken time, when Maxim, looking at the clock, said it was too late to change for dinner, so that I was spared the embarrassment of Alice, the maid, asking what I should wear, and of her helping me to dress, and myself walking down that long flight of stairs to the hall, cold, with bare shoulders, in a dress that Mrs. Van Hopper had given me because it did not suit her daughter. I had dreaded the formality of dinner in that austere dining-room, and now, because of the little fact that we had not changed, it was quite all right, quite easy, just the same as when we had dined together in restaurants. I was comfortable in my stockinette dress, I laughed and talked about things we had seen in Italy and France, we even had the snapshots on the table, and Frith and the footman were impersonal people, as the waiters had been, they did not stare at me as Mrs. Danvers had done.

We sat in the library after dinner, and presently the curtains were drawn, and more logs thrown on to the fire. It was cool for May; I was thankful for the warmth that came from the steady burning logs.

It was new for us to sit together like this, after dinner, for in Italy we had wandered about, walked or driven, gone into little cafés, leant over bridges. Maxim made instinctively now for the chair on the left of the open fireplace, and stretched out his hand for the papers. He settled one of the broad cushions behind his head, and lit a cigarette. "This is his routine," I thought, "this is what he always does, this has been his custom now for years."

He did not look at me, he went on reading his paper, contented, comfortable, having assumed his way of living, the master of his house. And as I sat there, brooding, my chin in my hands, fondling the soft ears of one of the spaniels, it came to me that I was not the first one to lounge there in possession of the chair, someone had been before me, had surely left an imprint of her person on the cushions, and on the arm where her hand had rested. Another one had poured the coffee from that same silver coffee pot, had placed the cup to her lips, had bent down to the dog, even as I was doing.

Unconsciously I shivered, as though someone had opened the door behind me, and let a draught into the room. I was sitting in Rebecca's chair, I was leaning against Rebecca's cushion, and the dog had come to me and laid his head upon my knee because that had been his custom, and he remembered, in the past, she had given sugar to him there.

CHAPTER EIGHT

I HAD NEVER REALISED, of course, that life at Manderley would be so orderly and planned. I remember now, looking back, how on that first morning Maxim was up and dressed and writing letters, even before breakfast, and when I got downstairs, rather after nine o'clock, a little flurried by the booming summons of the gong, I found he had nearly finished, he was already peeling his fruit.

He looked up at me and smiled. "You mustn't mind," he said, "this is something you will have to get used to. I've no time to hang about at this hour of the day. Running a place like Manderley, you know, is a full-time job. The coffee and the hot dishes are on the side-board. We always help ourselves at breakfast." I said something about my clock being slow, about having been too long in the bath, but he did not listen, he was looking down at a letter, frowning at something.

How impressed I was, I remember well; impressed and a little over-awed by the magnificence of the breakfast offered to us. There was tea, in a great silver urn, and coffee too, and on the heater, piping hot, dishes of scrambled eggs, of bacon, and another of fish. There was a little clutch of boiled eggs as well, in their own special heater, and porridge, in a silver porringer. On another side-board was a ham, and a great piece of cold bacon. There were scones too, on the table, and toast, and various pots of jam, marmalade, and honey, while dessert dishes, piled high with fruit, stood at either end. It seemed strange to me that Maxim, who in Italy and France had eaten a *croissant* and fruit only, and drunk a cup of coffee, should sit down to this breakfast at home, enough for a dozen people, day after day probably, year after year, seeing nothing ridiculous about it, nothing wasteful.

I noticed he had eaten a small piece of fish. I took a boiled egg. And I wondered what happened to the rest, all those scrambled eggs, that crisp bacon, the porridge, the remains of the fish. Were there menials, I wondered, whom I should never know, never see, waiting behind kitchen doors for the gift of our breakfast? Or was it all thrown away, shovelled into dustpans? I would never know, of course, I would never dare to ask.

"Thank the Lord I haven't a great crowd of relations to inflict upon you," said Maxim, "a sister I very rarely see, and a grandmother who is nearly blind. Beatrice, by-the-way, asks herself over to lunch. I half expected she would. I suppose she wants to have a look at you."

"To-day?" I said, my spirits sinking to zero.

"Yes, according to the letter I got this morning. She won't stay long. You'll like her, I think. She's very direct, believes in speaking her mind. No humbug at all. If she doesn't like you she'll tell you so, to your face."

I found this hardly comforting, and wondered if there was not some virtue in the quality of insincerity. Maxim got up from his chair, and lit a cigarette. "I've a mass of things to see to this morning, do you think you can amuse yourself?" he said. "I'd like to have taken you round the garden, but I must see Crawley, my agent. I've been away from things too long. He'll be in to lunch, too, by-the-way. You don't mind, do you, you will be all right?"

"Of course," I said, "I shall be quite happy."

Then he picked up his letters, and went out of the room, and I remember thinking this was not how I had imagined my first morning; I had seen us walking together, arms linked, to the sea, coming back rather late and tired and happy to a cold lunch, alone, and sitting afterwards under that chestnut tree I could see from the library window.

I lingered long over my first breakfast, spinning out the time, and it was not until I saw Frith come in and look at me, from behind the Service screen, that I realised it was after ten o'clock. I sprang to my feet at once, feeling guilty, and apologised for sitting there so late, and he bowed, saying nothing, very polite, very correct, but I caught a flicker of surprise in his eyes. I wondered if I had said the wrong thing. Perhaps it did not do to apologise. Perhaps it lowered me in his estimation. I wished I knew what to say, what to do. I wondered if he suspected, as Mrs. Danvers had done, that poise, and grace, and assurance were not qualities inbred in me, but were things to be acquired, painfully perhaps, and slowly, costing me many bitter moments.

As it was, leaving the room, I stumbled, not looking where I was going, catching my foot on the step by the door, and Frith came forward to help me, picking up my handkerchief, while Robert, the young footman, who was standing behind the screen, turned away to hide his smile.

I heard the murmur of their voices as I crossed the hall, and one of them laughed, Robert, I supposed. Perhaps they were laughing about me. I went upstairs again, to the privacy of my bedroom, but when I opened the door I found the housemaids in there doing the room, one was sweeping the floor, the other dusting the dressing-table. They looked at me in surprise. I quickly went out again. It could not be right then, for me to go to my room at that hour in the morning. It was not expected of me. It broke the household routine. I crept downstairs once more, silently, thankful of my slippers that made no sound on the stone flags, and so into the library which was chilly, the windows flung wide open, the fire laid but not lit.

I shut the windows, and looked round for a box of matches. I could not find one. I wondered what I should do. I did not like to ring. But the library, so snug and warm last night with the burning logs, was like an ice-house now, in the early morning. There were matches upstairs in the bedroom, but I did not like to go for them because it would mean disturbing the housemaids at their work. I could not bear their moon faces staring at me again. I decided that when Frith and Robert had left the dining-room I would fetch the matches from the side-board. I tiptoed out into the hall and listened. They were still clearing, I could hear the sound of voices, and the movement of trays. Presently all was silent, they must have gone through the Service doors into the kitchen quarters, so I went across the hall and into the dining-room once more. Yes, there was a box of matches on the side-board, as I expected. I crossed the room quickly, and picked them up, and as I did so Frith came back into the room. I tried to cram the box furtively into my pocket, but I saw him glance at my hand in surprise.

"Did you require anything, Madam?" he said.

"Oh, Frith," I said awkwardly, "I could not find any matches." He at once proffered me another box, handing me the cigarettes too, at the same time. This was another embarrassment, for I did not smoke.

"No, the fact is," I said, "I felt rather cool in the library, I suppose the weather seems chilly to me, after being abroad, and I thought perhaps I would just put a match to the fire."

"The fire in the library is not usually lit until the afternoon, Madam," he said. "Mrs. de Winter always used the morning-room. There is a good fire in there. Of course if you should wish to have the fire in the library as well I will give orders for it to be lit."

"Oh, no," I said, "I would not dream of it. I will go into the morning-room. Thank you, Frith."

"You will find writing-paper, and pens, and ink, in there, Madam," he said. "Mrs. de Winter always did all her correspondence and telephoning in the morning-room, after breakfast. The house telephone is also there, should you wish to speak to Mrs. Danvers."

"Thank you, Frith," I said.

I turned away into the hall again, humming a little tune to give me an air of confidence. I could not tell him that I had never seen the morning-room, that Maxim had not shown it to me the night before. I knew he was standing in the entrance to the dining-room, watching me, as I went across the hall, and that I must make some show of knowing my way. There was a door to the left of the great staircase, and I went recklessly towards it, praying in my heart that it would take me to my goal, but when I came to it and opened it I saw that it was a garden-room, a place for odds and ends, there was a table where flowers were done, there were basket chairs stacked against the wall, and a couple of mackintoshes too, hanging on a peg. I came out, a little defiantly, glancing across the hall, and saw Frith still standing there. I had not deceived him though, not for a moment.

"You go through the drawing-room to the morning-room, Madam," he said, "through the door there, on your right, this side of the staircase. You go straight through the double drawing-room, and turn to your left."

"Thank you, Frith," I said humbly, pretending no longer.

I went through the long drawing-room, as he had directed, a lovely room this, beautifully proportioned, looking out upon the lawns down to the sea. The public would see this room, I supposed, and Frith, if he showed them round, would know the history of the pictures on the wall, and the period of the furniture. It was beautiful of course, I knew that, and those chairs and tables probably without price, but for all that I had no wish to linger there, I could not see myself sitting ever in those chairs, standing before that carved mantelpiece, throwing books down on to the tables. It had all the formality of a room in a museum, where alcoves were roped off, and a guardian, in cloak and hat like the guides in the French châteaux, sat in a chair beside the door. I went through then, and turned to the left, and so on to the little morning-room I had not seen before.

I was glad to see the dogs there, sitting before the fire, and Jasper, the younger, came over to me at once, his tail wagging, and thrust his nose into my hand. The old one lifted her muzzle at my approach, and gazed in my direction with her blind eyes, but when she had sniffed the air a moment, and found I was not the one she sought, she turned her head away with a grunt, and looked steadily into the fire again. Then Jasper left me, too, and settled himself by the side of his companion, licking his side. This was their routine. They knew, even as Frith had known, that the library fire was not lit until the afternoon. They came to the morning-room from long custom. Somehow I guessed, before going to the window, that the room looked out upon the rhododendrons. Yes, there they were, blood-red and luscious, as I had seen them the evening before, great bushes of them, massed beneath the open window, encroaching on to the sweep of the drive itself. There was a little clearing too, between the bushes, like a miniature lawn, the grass a smooth carpet of moss, and in the centre of this, the tiny statue of a naked faun, his pipes to his lips.

The crimson rhododendrons made his background, and the clearing itself was like a little stage, where he would dance, and play his part. There was no musty smell about this room, as there had been in the library. There were no old well-worn chairs, no tables littered with magazines and papers, seldom if ever read, but left there from long custom, because Maxim's father, or even his grandfather perhaps, had wished it so.

This was a woman's room, graceful, fragile, the room of someone who had chosen every particle of furniture with great care, so that each chair, each vase, each small, infinitesimal thing should be in harmony with one another, and with her own personality. It was as though she who had arranged this room had said: "This I will have, and this, and this," taking piece by piece from the treasures in Manderley each object that pleased her best, ignoring the second-rate, the mediocre, laying her hand with sure and certain instinct only upon the best. There was no intermingling of style, no confusing of period, and the result was perfection in a strange and startling way, not coldly formal like the drawing-room shown to the public, but vividly alive, having something of the same glow and brilliance that the rhododendrons had, massed there, beneath the window. And I noticed then that the rhododendrons, not content with forming their theatre on the little lawn outside the window, had been permitted to the room itself. Their great warm faces looked down upon me from the mantelpiece, they floated in a bowl upon the table by the sofa, they stood, lean and graceful, on the writing-desk beside the golden candlesticks.

The room was filled with them, even the walls took colour from them, becoming rich and glowing in the morning sun. They were the only flowers in the room, and I wondered if there was some purpose in it, whether the room had been arranged originally with this one end in view, for nowhere else in the house did the rhododendrons obtrude. There were flowers in the dining-room, flowers in the library, but orderly and trim, rather in the background, not like this, not in profusion. I went and sat down at the writing-desk, and I thought how strange it was that this room, so lovely and so rich in colour, should be, at the same time, so business-like and purposeful. Somehow I should have expected that a room furnished as this was in such exquisite taste, for all the exaggeration of the flowers, would be a place of decoration only, languorous and intimate.

But this writing-table, beautiful as it was, was no pretty toy where a woman would scribble little notes, nibbling the end of a pen, leaving it, day after day, in carelessness, the blotter a little askew. The pigeon-holes were docketed, "letters-unanswered," "letters-to-keep," "household," "estate," "menus," "miscellaneous," "addresses"; each ticket written in that same scrawling pointed hand that I knew already. And it shocked me, even startled me, to recognise it again, for I had not seen it since I had destroyed the page from the book of poems, and I had not thought to see it again.

I opened a drawer at hazard, and there was the writing once more, this time in an open leather book, whose heading "Guests at Manderley" showed at once, divided into weeks and months, what visitors had come and gone, the rooms they had used, the food they had eaten. I turned over the pages, and saw that the book was a complete record of a year, so that the hostess, glancing back, would know to the day, almost to the hour, what guest had passed what night under her roof, and where he had slept, and what she had given him to eat. There was note-paper also in the drawer, thick white sheets, for rough writing, and the note-paper of the house, with the crest, and the address, and visiting cards, ivory-white, in little boxes.

I took one out and looked at it, unwrapped it from its thin tissue of paper. "Mrs. M. de Winter" it said, and in the corner "Manderley." I put it back in the box again, and shut the drawer, feeling guilty suddenly, and deceitful, as though I were staying in somebody else's house and my hostess had said to me, "Yes, of course, write letters at my desk," and I had unforgivably, in a stealthy manner, peeped at her correspondence. At any moment she might come back into the room, and she would see me there, sitting before her open drawer, which I had no right to touch.

And when the telephone rang, suddenly, alarmingly, on the desk in front of me, my heart leapt and I started up in terror, thinking I had been discovered. I took the receiver off with trembling hands, and "Who is it?" I said, "who do you want?" There was a strange buzzing at the end of the line, and then a voice came, low and rather harsh, whether that of a woman or a man I could not tell, and "Mrs. de Winter?" it said, "Mrs. de Winter?"

"I'm afraid you have made a mistake," I said, "Mrs. de Winter has been dead for over a year." I sat there, waiting, staring stupidly into the mouthpiece, and it was not until the name was repeated again, the voice incredulous, slightly raised, that I became aware, with a rush of colour to my face, that I had blundered irretrievably, and could not take back my words. "It's Mrs. Danvers, Madam," said the voice, "I'm speaking to you on the house telephone." My faux-pas was so palpably obvious, so idiotic and unpardonable, that to ignore it would show me to be an even greater fool if possible, than I was already.

"I'm sorry, Mrs. Danvers," I said stammering, my words tumbling over one another, "the telephone startled me, I didn't know what I was saying, I didn't realise the call was for me, and I never noticed I was speaking on the house telephone."

"I'm sorry to have disturbed you, Madam," she said, and she knows, I thought, she guesses I have been looking through the desk, "I only wondered whether you wished to see me, and whether you approved of the menus for to-day."

"Oh," I said. "Oh, I'm sure I do, that is, I'm sure I approve of the menus, just order what you like, Mrs. Danvers, you needn't bother to ask me."

"It would be better I think if you read the list," continued the voice, "you will find the menu of the day on the blotter, beside you."

I searched feverishly about me on the desk, and found at last a sheet of paper I had not noticed before. I glanced hurriedly through it, curried prawns, roast veal, asparagus, cold chocolate mousse—was this lunch or dinner, I could not see, lunch I suppose.

"Yes, Mrs. Danvers," I said, "very suitable, very nice indeed."

"If you wish anything changed please say so," she answered, "and I will give orders at once. You will notice I have left a blank space beside the sauce, for you to mark your preference. I was not sure what sauce you are used to having served with the roast veal. Mrs. de Winter was most particular about her sauces, and I always had to refer to her."

"Oh," I said. "Oh, well . . . let me see, Mrs. Danvers, I hardly know; I think we had better have what you usually have, whatever you think Mrs. de Winter would have ordered."

"You have no preference, Madam?"

"No," I said. "No, really, Mrs. Danvers."

"I rather think Mrs. de Winter would have ordered a wine sauce, Madam."

"We will have the same then, of course," I said.

"I'm very sorry I disturbed you while you were writing, Madam."

"You didn't disturb me at all," I said, "please don't apologise."

"The post leaves at midday, and Robert will come for your letters, and stamp them himself," she said; "all you have to do is to ring through to him, on the telephone, if you have anything urgent to be sent, and he will give orders for them to be taken in to the post-office immediately."

"Thank you, Mrs. Danvers," I said. I listened for a moment, but she said no more, and then I heard a little click at the end of the telephone, which meant she had replaced the receiver. I did the same. Then I looked down again at the desk, and the note-paper, ready for use, upon the blotter. In front of me stared the ticketed pigeon-holes, and the words upon them "letters-unanswered," "estate," "miscellaneous," were like a reproach to me for my idleness. She who sat here before me had not wasted her time, as I was doing. She had reached out for the house telephone and given her orders for the day, swiftly, efficiently, and run her pencil through an item in the menu that had not pleased her. She had not said "Yes, Mrs. Danvers," and "Of course, Mrs. Danvers," as I had done. And then, when she had finished, she began her letters, five, six, seven perhaps to be answered, all written in that same curious, slanting hand I knew so well. She would tear off sheet after sheet of that smooth white paper, using it extravagantly, because of the long strokes she made when she wrote, and at the end of her personal letters she put her signature, "Rebecca," that tall sloping R dwarfing its fellows.

I drummed with my fingers on the desk. The pigeon-holes were empty now. There were no "letters-unanswered" waiting to be dealt with, no bills to pay that I knew anything about. If I had anything urgent, Mrs. Danvers said, I must telephone through to Robert and he would give orders for it to be taken to the post. I wondered how many urgent letters Rebecca used to write, and who they were written to. Dressmakers perhaps—"I must have the white satin on Tuesday, without fail," or to her hair-dresser—"I shall be coming up next Friday, and want an appointment at three o'clock with Monsieur Antoine himself. Shampoo, massage, set, and manicure." No, letters of that type would be a waste of time. She would have a call put through to London, Frith would do it. Frith would say "I am speaking for Mrs. de Winter." I went on drumming with my fingers on the desk. I could think of nobody to write to. Only Mrs. Van Hopper. And there was something foolish, rather ironical, in the realisation that here I was sitting at my own desk in my own home with nothing better to do than to write a letter to Mrs. Van Hopper, a woman I disliked, whom I should never see again. I pulled a sheet of note-paper towards me. I took up the narrow, slender pen, with the bright pointed nib. "Dear Mrs. Van Hopper," I began. And as I wrote, in halting, laboured fashion, saying I hoped the voyage had been good, that she had found her daughter better, that the weather in New York was fine and warm, I noticed for the first time how cramped and unformed was my own hand-writing, without individuality, without style, uneducated even, the writing of an indifferent pupil taught in a second-rate school.

CHAPTER NINE

WHEN I HEARD the sound of the car in the drive I got up in sudden panic, glancing at the clock, for I knew that it meant Beatrice and her husband had arrived. It was only just gone twelve, they were much earlier than I expected. And Maxim was not yet back. I wondered if it would be possible to hide, to get out of the window into the garden, so that Frith, bringing them to the morning-room, would say "Madam must have gone out," and it would seem quite natural, they would take it as a matter of course. The dogs looked up enquiringly as I ran to the window, and Jasper followed me, wagging his tail.

The window opened out on to the terrace and the little grass clearing beyond, but as I prepared to brush past the rhododendrons the sound of voices came close, and I backed again into the room. They were coming to the house by way of the garden, Frith having told them doubtless that I was in the morning-room. I went quickly into the big drawing-room, and made for a door near me on the left. It led into a long stone passage, and I ran along it, fully aware of my stupidity, despising myself for this sudden attack of nerves, but I knew I could not face these people, not for a moment anyway. The passage seemed to be taking me to the back regions, and as I turned a corner, coming upon another staircase, I met a servant I had not seen before, a scullery-maid perhaps, she carried a mop and a pail in her hands. She stared at me in wonder, as though I were a vision, unexpected in this part of the house, and "Good-morning," I said, in great confusion, making for the stairway, and "Good-morning, Madam," she returned, her mouth open, her round eyes inquisitive as I climbed the stairs.

They would lead me, I supposed, to the bedrooms, and I could find my suite in the east wing, and sit up there a little while, until I judged it nearly time for lunch, when good manners would compel me to come down again.

I must have lost my bearings, for passing through a door at the head of the stairs I came to a long corridor that I had not seen before, similar in some ways to the one in the east wing, but broader and darker–dark owing to the panelling of the walls.

I hesitated, then turned left, coming upon a broad landing and another staircase. It was very quiet and dark. No one was about. If there had been housemaids here, during the morning, they had finished their work by now and gone downstairs. There was no trace of their presence, no lingering dust smell of carpets lately swept, and I thought, as I stood there, wondering which way to turn, that the silence was unusual, holding something of the same oppression as an empty house does, when the owners have gone away.

I opened a door at hazard, and found a room in total darkness, no chink of light coming through the closed shutters, while I could see dimly, in the centre of the room, the outline of furniture swathed in white dust-sheets. The room smelt close and stale, the smell of a room seldom if ever used, whose ornaments are herded together in the centre of a bed and left there, covered with a sheet. It might be too that the curtains had not been drawn from the window since some preceding summer, and if one crossed there now and pulled them aside, opening the creaking shutters, a dead moth who had been imprisoned behind them for many months would fall to the carpet and lie there, beside a forgotten pin, and a dried leaf blown there before the windows were closed for the last time. I shut the door softly, and went uncertainly along the corridor, flanked on either side by doors, all of them closed, until I came to a little alcove, set in an outside wall, where a broad window gave me light at last. I looked out, and I saw below me the smooth grass lawns stretching to the sea, and the sea itself, bright green with white-topped crests, whipped by a westerly wind and scudding from the shore.

It was closer than I had thought, much closer; it ran surely, beneath that little knot of trees below the lawns, barely five minutes away, and if I listened now, my ear to the window, I could hear the surf breaking on the shores of some little bay I could not see. I knew then I had made the circuit of the house, and was standing in the corridor of the west wing. Yes, Mrs. Danvers was right. You could hear the sea from here. You might imagine, in the winter, it would creep up on to those green lawns and threaten the house itself, for even now, because of the high wind, there was a mist upon the window-glass, as though someone had breathed upon it. A mist salt-laden, borne upwards from the sea. A hurrying cloud hid the sun for a moment as I watched, and the sea changed colour instantly, becoming black, and the white crests with them very pitiless suddenly, and cruel, not the gay sparkling sea I had looked on first.

Somehow I was glad my rooms were in the east wing. I preferred the rose-garden, after all, to the sound of the sea. I went back to the landing then, at the head of the stairs, and as I prepared to go down, one hand upon the banister, I heard the door behind me open, and it was Mrs. Danvers. We stared at one another for a moment without speaking, and I could not be certain whether it was anger I read in her eyes or curiosity, for her face became a mask directly she saw me. Although she said nothing I felt guilty and ashamed, as though I had been caught trespassing, and I felt the tell-tale colour come up into my face.

"I lost my way," I said, "I was trying to find my room."

"You have come to the opposite side of the house," she said, "this is the west wing."

"Yes, I know," I said.

"Did you go into any of the rooms?" she asked me.

"No," I said. "No, I just opened a door, I did not go in. Everything was dark, covered up in dust-sheets. I'm sorry. I did not mean to disturb anything. I expect you like to keep all this shut up."

"If you wish to open up the rooms I will have it done," she said, "you have only to tell me. The rooms are all furnished, and can be used."

"Oh, no," I said. "No, I did not mean you to think that."

"Perhaps you would like me to show you all over the west wing?" she said.

I shook my head. "No, rather not," I said. "No, I must go downstairs." I began to walk down the stairs, and she came with me, by my side, as though she were a warder, and I in custody.

"Any time, when you have nothing to do, you have only to ask me, and I will show you the rooms in the west wing," she persisted, making me vaguely uncomfortable, I knew not why. Her insistence struck a chord in my memory, reminding me of a visit to a friend's house, as a child, when the daughter of the house, older than I, took my arm and whispered in my ear, "I know where there is a book, locked in a cupboard, in my mother's bedroom. Shall we go and look at it?" I remembered her white, excited face, and her small, beady eyes, and the way she kept pinching my arm.

"I will have the dust-sheets removed, and then you can see the rooms as they looked when they were used," said Mrs. Danvers. "I would have shown you this morning, but I believed you to be writing letters in the morning-room. You have only to telephone through to my room, you know, when you want me. It would only take a short while to have the rooms in readiness."

We had come down the short flight of stairs, and she opened another door, standing aside for me to pass through, her dark eyes questing my face.

"It's very kind of you, Mrs. Danvers," I said. "I will let you know some time."

We passed out together on to the landing beyond, and I saw we were at the head of the main staircase now, behind the minstrels' gallery.

"I wonder how you came to miss your way?" she said, "the door through to the west wing is very different to this."

"I did not come this way," I said.

"Then you must have come up the back way, from the stone passage?" she said.

"Yes," I said, not meeting her eyes. "Yes, I came through a stone passage."

She went on looking at me, as though she expected me to tell her why I left the morning-room in sudden panic, going through the back regions, and I felt suddenly that she knew, that she must have watched me, that she had seen me wandering perhaps in that west wing from the first, her eye to a crack in the door. "Mrs. Lacy, and Major Lacy, have been here some time," she said. "I heard their car drive up shortly after twelve."

"Oh!" I said. "I had not realised that."

"Frith will have taken them to the morning-room," she said, "it must be getting on for half-past twelve. You know your way now, don't you?"

"Yes, Mrs. Danvers," I said. And I went down the big stairway into the hall, knowing she was standing there above me, her eyes watching me.

I knew I must go back now, to the morning-room, and meet Maxim's sister and her husband. I could not hide in my bedroom now. As I went into the drawing-room I glanced back, over my shoulder, and I saw Mrs. Danvers still standing there at the head of the stairs, like a black sentinel.

I stood for a moment outside the morning-room, with my hand on the door, listening to the hum of voices. Maxim had returned then, while I had been upstairs, bringing his agent with him I supposed, for it sounded to me as if the room was full of people. I was aware of the same feeling of sick uncertainty I had experienced so often as a child, when summoned to shake hands with visitors, and turning the handle of the door I blundered in, to be met at once, it seemed, with a sea of faces and a general silence.

"Here she is at last," said Maxim. "Where have you been hiding? We were thinking of sending out a search party. Here is Beatrice, and this is Giles, and this is Frank Crawley. Look out, you nearly trod on the dog."

Beatrice was tall, broad-shouldered, very handsome, very much like Maxim about the eyes and jaw, but not as smart as I had expected, much tweedier; the sort of person who would nurse dogs through distemper, know about horses, shoot well. She did not kiss me. She shook hands very firmly, looking me straight in the eyes, and then she turned to Maxim, "Quite different from what I expected. Doesn't answer to your description at all."

Everyone laughed, and I joined in, not quite certain if the laugh was against me or not, wondering secretly what it was she had expected, and what had been Maxim's description.

And "This is Giles," said Maxim, prodding my arm, and Giles stretched out an enormous paw and wrung my hand, squeezing the fingers limp, genial eyes smiling from behind horn-rimmed glasses.

"Frank Crawley," said Maxim, and I turned to the agent, a colourless, rather thin man with a prominent Adam's apple, in whose eyes I read relief as he looked upon me. I wondered why, but I had no time to think of that, because Frith had come in, and was offering me sherry, and Beatrice was talking to me again. "Maxim tells me you only got back last night. I had not realised that, or of course we would never have thrust ourselves upon you so soon. Well, what do you think of Manderley?"

"I've scarcely seen anything of it yet," I answered, "it's beautiful, of course."

She was looking me up and down, as I had expected, but in a direct, straightforward fashion, not maliciously like Mrs. Danvers, not with unfriendliness. She had a right to judge me, she was Maxim's sister, and Maxim himself came to my side now, putting his arm through mine, giving me confidence.

"You're looking better, old man," she said to him, her head on one side, considering him, "you've lost that fine-drawn look, thank goodness. I suppose we've got you to thank for that?" nodding at me.

"I'm always very fit," said Maxim shortly, "never had anything wrong with me in my life. You imagine everyone ill who doesn't look as fat as Giles."

"Bosh," said Beatrice, "you know perfectly well you were a perfect wreck six months ago. Gave me the fright of my life when I came and saw you. I thought you were in for a breakdown. Giles, bear me out. Didn't Maxim look perfectly ghastly last time we came over, and didn't I say he was heading for a breakdown?"

"Well, I must say, old chap, you're looking a different person," said Giles. "Very good thing you went away. Doesn't he look well, Crawley?"

I could tell by the tightening of Maxim's muscles under my arm that he was trying to keep his temper. For some reason this talk about his health was not welcome to him, angered him even, and I thought it tactless of Beatrice to harp upon it in this way, making so big a point of it.

"Maxim's very sunburnt," I said shyly, "it hides a multitude of sins. You should have seen him in Venice, having breakfast on the balcony, trying to get brown on purpose. He thinks it makes him better-looking."

Everyone laughed, and Mr. Crawley said, "It must have been wonderful in Venice, Mrs. de Winter, this time of the year," and "Yes," I said, "we had really wonderful weather. Only one bad day, wasn't it, Maxim?" the conversation drawing away happily from his health, and so to Italy, safest of subjects, and the blessed topic of fine weather. Conversation was easy now, no longer an effort, Maxim and Giles and Beatrice were discussing the running of Maxim's car, and Mr. Crawley was asking if it was true there were no more gondolas in the canals now, only motor-boats. I don't think he would have cared at all had there been steamers at anchor in the Grand Canal, he was saying this to help me, it was his contribution to the little effort of steering the talk away from Maxim's health, and I was grateful to him, feeling him an ally, for all his dull appearance.

"Jasper wants exercise," said Beatrice, stirring the dog with her foot; "he's getting much too fat, and he's barely two years old. What do you feed him on, Maxim?"

"My dear Beatrice, he has exactly the same routine as your dogs," said Maxim. "Don't show off and make out you know more about animals than I do."

"Dear old boy, how can you pretend to know what Jasper has been fed on when you've been away for a couple of months? Don't tell me Frith walks to the lodge gates with him twice a day. This dog hasn't had a run for weeks, I can tell by the condition of his coat."

"I'd rather he looked colossal than half-starved like that half-wit dog of yours," said Maxim.

"Not a very intelligent remark when Lion won two firsts at Crufts' last February," said Beatrice.

The atmosphere was becoming rather strained again, I could tell by the narrow line of Maxim's mouth, and I wondered if brothers and sisters always sparred like this, making it uncomfortable for those who listened. I wished that Frith would come in and announce lunch. Or would we be summoned by a booming gong? I did not know what happened at Manderley.

"How far away from us are you?" I asked, sitting down by Beatrice, "did you have to make a very early start?"

"We're fifty miles away, my dear, in the next county, the other side of Trowchester. The hunting is so much better with us. You must come over and stay, when Maxim can spare you. Giles will mount you."

"I'm afraid I don't hunt," I confessed, "I learnt to ride, as a child, but very feebly, I don't remember much about it."

"You must take it up again," she said, "you can't possibly live in the country and not ride. You wouldn't know what to do with yourself. Maxim says you paint. That's very nice, of course, but there's no exercise in it, is there? All very well on a wet day when there's nothing better to do."

"My dear Beatrice, we are not all such fresh-air fiends as you," said Maxim.

"I wasn't talking to you, old boy. We all know you are perfectly happy slopping about the Manderley gardens and never breaking out of a slow walk."

"I'm very fond of walking too," I said swiftly, "I'm sure I shall never get tired of rambling about Manderley. And I can bathe too, when it's warmer."

"My dear, you are an optimist," said Beatrice, "I can hardly ever remember bathing here. The water is far too cold, and the beach is shingle."

"I don't mind that," I said. "I love bathing. As long as the currents are not too strong. Is the bathing safe in the bay?"

Nobody answered, and I realised suddenly what I had said. My heart thumped, and I felt my cheeks go flaming red. I bent down to stroke Jasper's ear, in an agony of confusion. "Jasper could do with a swim, and get some of that fat off," said Beatrice, breaking the pause, "but he'd find it a bit too much for him in the bay, wouldn't you, Jasper? Good old Jasper. Nice old man." We patted the dog together, not looking at one another.

"I say, I'm getting infernally hungry, what on earth is happening to lunch?" said Maxim.

"It's only just on one now," said Mr. Crawley, "according to the clock on the mantelpiece."

"That clock was always fast," said Beatrice.

"It's kept perfect time now for months," said Maxim.

At that moment the door opened and Frith announced that luncheon was served.

"I say, I must have a wash," said Giles, looking at his hands.

We all got up and wandered through the drawing-room to the hall in great relief, Beatrice and I a little ahead of the men, she taking my arm.

"Dear old Frith," she said, "he always looks exactly the same, and makes me feel like a girl again. You know, don't mind me saying so, but you are even younger than I expected. Maxim told me your age, but you're an absolute child. Tell me, are you very much in love with him?"

I was not prepared for this question, and she must have seen the surprise in my face for she laughed lightly, and squeezed my arm.

"Don't answer," she said, "I can see what you feel. I'm an interfering bore, aren't I? You mustn't mind me. I'm devoted to Maxim, you know, though we always bicker like cat and dog when we meet. I congratulate you again on his looks. We were all very worried about him this time last year, but of course you know the whole story." We had come to the dining-room by now, and she said no more, for the servants were there and the others had joined us, but as I sat down, and unfolded my napkin, I wondered what Beatrice would say did she realise that I knew nothing of that preceding year, no details of the tragedy that had happened down there, in the bay, that Maxim kept these things to himself, that I questioned him never.

Lunch passed off better than I had dared to hope. There were few arguments, or perhaps Beatrice was exercising tact at last, at any rate she and Maxim chatted about matters concerning Manderley, her horses, the garden, mutual friends, and Frank Crawley, on my left, kept up an easy patter with me for which I was grateful, as it required no effort. Giles was more concerned with food than with the conversation, though now and again he remembered my existence and flung me a remark at hazard.

"Same cook I suppose, Maxim?" he said, when Robert had offered him the cold soufflé for the second time. "I always tell Bee, Manderley's the only place left in England where one can get decent cooking. I remember this soufflé of old."

"I think we change cooks periodically," said Maxim, "but the standard of cooking remains the same. Mrs. Danvers has all the recipes, she tells them what to do."

"Amazing woman, that Mrs. Danvers," said Giles, turning to me, "don't you think so?"

"Oh, yes," I said, "Mrs. Danvers seems to be a wonderful person."

"She's no oil painting though, is she?" said Giles, and he roared with laughter. Frank Crawley said nothing, and looking up I saw Beatrice was watching me. She turned away then, and began talking to Maxim.

"Do you play golf at all, Mrs. de Winter?" said Mr. Crawley.

"No, I'm afraid I don't," I answered, glad that the subject had been changed again, that Mrs. Danvers was forgotten, and even though I was no player, knew nothing of the game, I was prepared to listen to him as long as he pleased; there was something solid and safe and dull about golf, it could not bring us into any difficulties. We had cheese, and coffee, and I wondered whether I was supposed to make a move. I kept looking at Maxim, but he gave no sign, and then Giles embarked upon a story, rather difficult to follow, about digging a car out of a snow-drift—what had started the train of thought I could not tell—and I listened to him politely, nodding my head now and again and smiling, aware of Maxim becoming restive at his end of the table. At last he paused, and I caught Maxim's eye. He frowned very slightly, and jerked his head towards the door.

I got up at once, shaking the table clumsily as I moved my chair, and upsetting Giles's glass of port. "Oh, dear," I said, hovering, wondering what to do, reaching ineffectively for my napkin, but "All right, Frith will deal with it," said Maxim, "don't add to the confusion. Beatrice, take her out in the garden, she's scarcely seen the place yet."

He looked tired, rather jaded. I began to wish none of them had come. They had spoilt our day anyway. It was too much of an effort, just as we returned. I felt tired too, tired and depressed. Maxim had seemed almost irritable when he suggested we should go into the garden. What a fool I had been, upsetting that glass of port.

We went out on to the terrace and walked down on to the smooth green lawns.

"I think it's a pity you came back to Manderley so soon," said Beatrice, "it would have been far better to potter about in Italy for three or four months, and then come back in the middle of the summer. Done Maxim a power of good too, besides being easier from your point of view. I can't help feeling it's all going to be rather a strain here for you at first."

"Oh, I don't think so," I said. "I know I shall come to love Manderley."

She did not answer, and we strolled backwards and forwards on the lawns.

"Tell me a bit about yourself," she said at last, "what was it you were doing in the south of France? Living with some appalling American woman, Maxim said."

I explained about Mrs. Van Hopper, and what had led to it, and she seemed sympathetic but a little vague, as though she was thinking of something else.

"Yes," she said, when I paused, "it all happened very suddenly, as you say. But of course we were all delighted, my dear, and I do hope you will be happy."

"Thank you, Beatrice," I said, "thank you very much."

I wondered why she said she hoped we would be happy, instead of saying she knew we would be so. She was kind, she was sincere, I liked her very much, but there was a tiny doubt in her voice that made me afraid.

"When Maxim wrote and told me," she went on, taking my arm, "and said he had discovered you in the south of France, and you were very young, very pretty, I must admit it gave me a bit of a shock. Of course we all expected a social butterfly, very modern and plastered with paint, the sort of girl you expect to meet in those sort of places. When you came into the morning-room before lunch you could have knocked me down with a feather."

She laughed, and I laughed with her. But she did not say whether or not she was disappointed in my appearance or relieved.

"Poor Maxim," she said, "he went through a ghastly time, and let's hope you have made him forget about it. Of course he adores Manderley."

Part of me wanted her to continue her train of thought, to tell me more of the past, naturally, and easily like this, and something else, way back in my mind, did not want to know, did not want to hear.

"We are not a bit alike, you know," she said, "our characters are poles apart. I show everything on my face, whether I like people or not, whether I am angry or pleased. There's no reserve about me. Maxim is entirely different. Very quiet, very reserved. You never know what's going on in that funny mind of his. I lose my temper on the slightest provocation, flare up, and then it's all over. Maxim loses his temper once or twice in a year, and when he does—my God—he *does* lose it. I don't suppose he ever will with you. I should think you are a placid little thing."

She smiled, and pinched my arm, and I thought about being placid, how quiet and comfortable it sounded, someone with knitting on her lap, with calm unruffled brow. Someone who was never anxious, never tortured by doubt and indecision, someone who never stood as I did, hopeful, eager, frightened, tearing at bitten nails, uncertain which way to go, what star to follow.

"You won't mind me saying so, will you?" she went on, "but I think you ought to do something to your hair. Why don't you have it waved? It's so very lanky, isn't it, like that? Must look awful under a hat. Why don't you sweep it back behind your ears?"

I did so obediently, and waited for her approval. She looked at me critically, her head on one side. "No," she said. "No, I think that's worse. It's too severe, and doesn't suit you. No, all you need is a wave, just to pinch it up. I never have cared for that Joan of Arc business or whatever they call it. What does Maxim say? Does he think it suits you?"

"I don't know," I said, "he's never mentioned it."

"Oh, well," she said, "perhaps he likes it. Don't go by me. Tell me, did you get any clothes in London or Paris?"

"No," I said, "we had no time. Maxim was anxious to get home. And I can always send for catalogues."

"I can tell by the way you dress that you don't care a hoot what you wear," she said. I glanced at my flannel skirt apologetically.

"I do," I said. "I'm very fond of nice things. I've never had much money to spend on clothes up to now."

"I wonder Maxim did not stay a week or so in London and get you something decent to wear," she said. "I must say, I think it's rather selfish of him. So unlike him too. He's generally so particular."

"Is he?" I said; "he's never seemed particular to me. I don't think he notices what I wear at all. I don't think he minds."

"Oh," she said. "Oh, well, he must have changed then."

She looked away from me, and whistled to Jasper, her hands in her pockets, and then stared up at the house above us.

"You're not using the west wing then," she said.

"No," I said. "No, we have the suite in the east wing. It's all been done up."

"Has it?" she said, "I didn't know that. I wonder why."

"It was Maxim's idea," I said, "he seems to prefer it."

She said nothing, she went on looking at the windows, and whistling. "How do you get on with Mrs. Danvers?" she said suddenly.

I bent down, and began patting Jasper's head, and stroking his ears. "I have not seen very much of her," I said, "she scares me a little. I've never seen anyone quite like her before."

"I don't suppose you have," said Beatrice.

Jasper looked up at me with great eyes, humble, rather self-conscious. I kissed the top of his silken head, and put my hand over his black nose.

"There's no need to be frightened of her," said Beatrice, "and don't let her see it, whatever you do. Of course I've never had anything to do with her, and I don't think I ever want to either. However, she's always been very civil to me." I went on patting Jasper's head.

"Did she seem friendly?" said Beatrice.

"No," I said. "No, not very."

Beatrice began whistling again, and she rubbed Jasper's head with her foot. "I shouldn't have more to do with her than you can help," she said.

"No," I said. "She runs the house very efficiently, there's no need for me to interfere."

"Oh, I don't suppose she'd mind that," said Beatrice. That was what Maxim had said, the evening before, and I thought it odd that they should both have the same opinion. I should have imagined that interference was the one thing Mrs. Danvers did not want.

"I dare say she will get over it in time," said Beatrice, "but it may make things rather unpleasant for you at first. Of course she's insanely jealous. I was afraid she would be."

"Why?" I asked, looking up at her, "why should she be jealous? Maxim does not seem to be particularly fond of her."

"My dear child, it's not Maxim she's thinking of," said Beatrice, "I think she respects him and all that, but nothing more very much. No, you see"—she paused, frowning a little, looking at me uncertainly—"she resents your being here at all, that's the trouble."

"Why?" I said, "why should she resent me?"

"I thought you knew," said Beatrice; "I thought Maxim would have told you. She simply adored Rebecca."

"Oh," I said. "Oh, I see."

We both went on patting and stroking Jasper, who, unaccustomed to such attention, rolled over on his back in ecstasy.

"Here are the men," said Beatrice, "let's have some chairs out and sit under the chestnut. How fat Giles is getting, he looks quite repulsive beside Maxim. I suppose Frank will go back to the office. What a dull creature he is, never has anything interesting to say. Well, all of you. What have you been discussing? Pulling the world to bits I suppose." She laughed, and the others strolled towards us, and we all stood about. Giles threw a twig for Jasper to retrieve. We all looked at Jasper. Mr. Crawley looked at his watch. "I must be off," he said, "thank you very much for lunch, Mrs. de Winter."

"You must come often," I said, shaking hands.

I wondered if the others would go too. I was not sure whether they had just come over for lunch, or to spend the day. I hoped they would go. I wanted to be alone with Maxim again, and that it would be like when we were in Italy. We all went and sat down under the chestnut tree. Robert brought out chairs and rugs. Giles lay down on his back and tipped his hat over his eyes. After a while he began to snore, his mouth open.

"Shut up, Giles," said Beatrice. "I'm not asleep," he muttered, opening his eyes, and shutting them again. I thought him unattractive. I wondered why Beatrice had married him. She could never have been in love with him. Perhaps that was what she was thinking about me. I caught her eye upon me now and again, puzzled, reflective, as though she was saying to herself "What on earth does Maxim see in her?" but kind at the same time, not unfriendly. They were talking about their grandmother.

"We must go over and see the old lady," Maxim was saying, and "She's getting gaga," said Beatrice, "drops food all down her chin, poor darling."

I listened to them both, leaning against Maxim's arm, rubbing my chin on his sleeve. He stroked my hand absently, not thinking, talking to Beatrice.

"That's what I do to Jasper," I thought. "I'm being like Jasper now, leaning against him. He pats me now and again, when he remembers, and I'm pleased, I get closer to him for a moment. He likes me in the way I like Jasper."

The wind had dropped. The afternoon was drowsy, peaceful. The grass had been new-mown, it smelt sweet and rich, like summer. A bee droned above Giles's head, and he flicked at it with his hat. Jasper sloped in to join us, too warm in the sun, his tongue lolling from his mouth. He flopped beside me, and began licking his side, his large eyes apologetic. The sun shone on the mullioned windows of the house, and I could see the green lawns and the terrace reflected in them. Smoke curled thinly from one of the near chimneys, and I wondered if the library fire had been lit, according to routine.

A thrush flew across the lawn to the magnolia tree outside the dining-room window. I could smell the faint, soft magnolia scent as I sat here, on the lawn. Everything was quiet and still. Very distant now came the washing of the sea in the bay below. The tide must have gone out. The bee droned over us again, pausing to taste the chestnut blossom above our heads. "This is what I always imagined," I thought, "this is how I hoped it would be, living at Manderley."

I wanted to go on sitting there, not talking, not listening to the others, keeping the moment precious for all time, because we were peaceful all of us, we were content and drowsy even as the bee who droned above our heads. In a little while it would be different, there would come to-morrow, and the next day, and another year. And we would be changed perhaps, never sitting quite like this again. Some of us would go away, or suffer, or die, the future stretched away in front of us, unknown, unseen, not perhaps what we wanted, not what we planned. This moment was safe though, this could not be touched. Here we sat together, Maxim and I, hand-in-hand, and the past and the future mattered not at all. This was secure, this funny fragment of time he would never remember, never think about again. He would not hold it sacred, he was talking about cutting away some of the undergrowth in the drive, and Beatrice agreed, interrupting with some suggestion of her own, and throwing a piece of grass at Giles at the same time. For them it was just after lunch, quarter-past-three on a haphazard afternoon, like any hour, like any day. They did not want to hold it close, imprisoned and secure, as I did. They were not afraid.

"Well, I suppose we ought to be off," said Beatrice, brushing the grass from her skirt, "I don't want to be late, we've got the Cartrights dining."

"How is old Vera?" asked Maxim.

"Oh, same as ever, always talking about her health. He's getting very old. They're sure to ask all about you both."

"Give them my love," said Maxim.

We got up. Giles shook the dust off his hat. Maxim yawned and stretched. The sun went in. I looked up at the sky. It had changed already, a mackerel sky. Little clouds scurrying in formation, line upon line.

"Wind's backing," said Maxim.

"I hope we don't run into rain," said Giles.

"I'm afraid we've had the best of the day," said Beatrice.

We wandered slowly towards the drive and the waiting car.

"You haven't seen what's been done to the east wing," said Maxim.

"Come upstairs," I suggested, "it won't take a minute." We went into the hall, and up the big staircase, the men following behind.

It seemed strange that Beatrice had lived here for so many years. She had run down these same stairs as a little girl, with her nurse. She had been born here, bred here, she knew it all, she belonged here more than I should ever do. She must have many memories locked inside her heart. I wondered if she ever thought about the days that were gone, ever remembered the lanky pigtailed child that she had been once, so different from the woman she had become, forty-five now, vigorous and settled in her ways, another person. . . .

We came to the rooms, and Giles, stooping under the low doorway, said, "How very jolly, this is a great improvement, isn't it, Bee?" and "I say, old boy, you have spread yourself," said Beatrice, "new curtains, new beds, new everything. You remember, Giles, we had this room that time you were laid up with your leg? It was very dingy then. Of course Mother never had much idea of comfort. And then, you never put people here, did you, Maxim? Except when there was an overflow. The bachelors were always dumped here. Well, it's charming, I must say. Looks over the rose-garden too, which was always an advantage. May I powder my nose?"

The men went downstairs, and Beatrice peered in the mirror.

"Did old Danvers do all this for you?" she said.

"Yes," I said. "I think she's done it very well."

"So she should, with her training," said Beatrice. "I wonder what on earth it cost. A pretty packet, I bet. Did you ask?"

"No, I'm afraid I did not," I said.

"I don't suppose it worried Mrs. Danvers," said Beatrice; "do you mind if I use your comb? These are nice brushes. Wedding present?"

"Maxim gave them to me."

"H'm. I like them. We must give you something of course. What do you want?"

"Oh, I don't really know. You mustn't bother," I said.

"My dear, don't be absurd. I'm not one to grudge you a present, even though we weren't asked to your wedding!"

"I hope you did not mind about that. Maxim wanted it to be abroad."

"Of course not. Very sensible of you both. After all, it wasn't as though . . ." she stopped in the middle of her sentence, and dropped her bag. "Damn, have I broken the catch? No, all is well. What was I saying? I can't remember. Oh, yes, wedding presents. We must think of something. You probably don't care for jewellery."

I did not answer. "It's so different from the ordinary young couple," she said. "The daughter of a friend of mine got married the other day, and of course they were started off in the usual way, with linen, and coffee sets, and dining-room chairs, and all that. I gave rather a nice standard lamp. Cost me a fiver at Harrod's. If you do go up to London to buy clothes mind you go to my woman, Madame Carroux. She has damn good taste, and she doesn't rook you."

She got up from the dressing-table, and pulled at her skirt.

"Do you suppose you will have a lot of people down?" she said.

"I don't know. Maxim hasn't said."

"Funny old boy, one never quite knows with him. At one time one could not get a bed in the house, the place would be chock-a-block. I can't somehow see you . . ." she stopped abruptly, and patted my arm. "Oh, well," she said, "we'll see. It's a pity you don't ride or shoot, you must miss such a lot. You don't sail by any chance, do you?"

"No," I said.

"Thank God for that," she said.

She went to the door, and I followed her down the corridor.

"Come and see us if you feel like it," she said. "I always expect people to ask themselves. Life is too short to send out invitations."

"Thank you very much," I said.

We came to the head of the stairs looking down upon the hall. The men were standing on the steps outside. "Come on, Bee," shouted Giles, "I felt a spot of rain, so we've put on the cover. Maxim says the glass is falling."

Beatrice took my hand, and bending down gave me a swift peck on my cheek. "Good-bye," she said, "forgive me if I've asked you a lot of rude questions, my dear, and said all sort of things I shouldn't. Tact never was my strong point, as Maxim will tell you. And, as I told you before, you're not a bit what I expected." She looked at me direct, her lips pursed in a whistle, and then took a cigarette from her bag, and flashed her lighter.

"You see," she said, snapping the top, and walking down the stairs, "you are so very different from Rebecca."

And we came out on to the steps and found the sun had gone behind a bank of cloud, a little thin rain was falling, and Robert was hurrying across the lawn to bring in the chairs.

CHAPTER TEN

WE WATCHED the car disappear round the sweep of the drive, and then Maxim took my arm and said, "Thank God that's that. Get a coat quickly, and come out. Damn the rain, I want a walk. I can't stand this sitting about." He looked white and strained, and I wondered why the entertaining of Beatrice and Giles, his own sister and brother-in-law, should have tired him so.

"Wait while I run upstairs for my coat," I said.

"There's a heap of mackintoshes in the flower-room, get one of them," he said impatiently, "women are always half-an-hour when they go to their bedrooms. Robert, fetch a coat from the flower-room, will you, for Mrs. de Winter? There must be half-a-dozen raincoats hanging there, left by people at one time or another." He was already standing in the drive, and calling to Jasper. "Come on, you lazy little beggar, and take some of that fat off." Jasper ran round in circles, barking hysterically at the prospect of his walk. "Shut up, you idiot," said Maxim, "what on earth is Robert doing?"

Robert came running out of the hall carrying a raincoat, and I struggled into it hurriedly, fumbling with the collar. It was too big, of course, and too long, but there was no time to change it, and we set off together across the lawn to the woods, Jasper running in front. "I find a little of my family goes a very long way," said Maxim. "Beatrice is one of the best people in the world, but she invariably puts her foot in it."

I was not sure where Beatrice had blundered, and thought it better not to ask. Perhaps he still resented the chat about his health before lunch.

"What did you think of her?" he went on.

"I liked her very much," I said, "she was very nice to me."

"What did she talk to you about out here, after lunch?"

"Oh, I don't know. I think I did most of the talking. I was telling her about Mrs. Van Hopper, and how you and I met, and all that. She said I was quite different to what she expected."

"What the devil did she expect?"

"Someone much smarter, more sophisticated, I imagine. A social butterfly, she said."

Maxim did not answer for a moment, he bent down, and threw a stick for Jasper. "Beatrice can sometimes be infernally unintelligent," he said.

We climbed the grass bank above the lawns, and plunged into the woods. The trees grew very close together, and it was dark. We trod upon broken twigs, and last year's leaves, and here and there the fresh green stubble of the young bracken, and the shoots of the bluebells soon to blossom. Jasper was silent now, his nose to the ground. I took Maxim's arm.

"Do you like my hair?" I said.

He stared down at me in astonishment. "Your hair?" he said, "why on earth do you ask? Of course I like it. What's the matter with it?"

"Oh, nothing," I said, "I just wondered."

"How funny you are," he said.

We came to a clearing in the woods, and there were two paths, going in opposite directions. Jasper took the right-hand path without hesitation.

"Not that way," called Maxim, "come on, old chap."

The dog looked back at us and stood there, wagging his tail, but did not return. "Why does he want to go that way?" I asked.

"I suppose he's used to it," said Maxim briefly, "it leads to a small cove, where we used to keep a boat. Come on, Jasper, old man."

We turned into the left-hand path, not saying anything, and presently I looked over my shoulder and saw that Jasper was following us.

"This brings us to the valley I told you about," said Maxim, "and you shall smell the azaleas. Never mind the rain, it will bring out the scent."

He seemed all right again now, happy and cheerful, the Maxim I knew and loved, and he began talking about Frank Crawley and what a good fellow he was, so thorough and reliable, and devoted to Manderley.

"This is better," I thought, "this is like it was in Italy," and I smiled up at him, squeezing his arm, relieved that the odd strained look on his face had passed away, and while I said "Yes," and "Really?" and "Fancy, darling," my thoughts wandered back to Beatrice, wondering why her presence should have disturbed him, what she had done; and I thought too of all she had said about his temper, how he lost it, she told me, about once or twice a year.

She must know him, of course; she was his sister. But it was not what I had thought; it was not my idea of Maxim. I could see him moody, difficult, irritable perhaps, but not angry as she had inferred, not passionate. Perhaps she had exaggerated; people very often were wrong about their relatives.

"There," said Maxim suddenly, "take a look at that."

We stood on a slope of a wooded hill, and the path wound away before us to a valley, by the side of a running stream. There were no dark trees here, no tangled undergrowth, but on either side of the narrow path stood azaleas and rhododendrons, not blood-coloured like the giants in the drive, but salmon, white, and gold, things of beauty and of grace, drooping their lovely, delicate heads in the soft summer rain.

The air was full of their scent, sweet and heady, and it seemed to me as though their very essence had mingled with the running waters of the stream, and become one with the falling rain and the dank rich moss beneath our feet. There was no sound here but the tumbling of the little stream, and the quiet rain. When Maxim spoke, his voice was hushed too, gentle and low, as if he had no wish to break upon the silence.

"We call it the Happy Valley," he said.

We stood quite still, not speaking, looking down upon the clear white faces of the flowers closest to us, and Maxim stooped, and picked up a fallen petal and gave it to me. It was crushed and bruised, and turning brown at the curled edge, but as I rubbed it across my hand the scent rose to me, sweet and strong, vivid as the living tree from which it came.

Then the birds began. First a blackbird, his note clear and cool above the running stream, and after a moment he had answer, from his fellow hidden in the woods behind us, and soon the still air about us was made turbulent with song, pursuing us as we wandered down into the valley, and the fragrance of the white petals followed us too. It was disturbing, like an enchanted place. I had not thought it could be as beautiful as this.

The sky, now overcast and sullen, so changed from the early afternoon, and the steady, insistent rain could not disturb the soft quietude of the valley; the rain and the rivulet mingled with one another, and the liquid note of the blackbird fell upon the damp air in harmony with them both. I brushed the dripping heads of the azaleas as I passed, so close they grew together, bordering the path. Little drops of water fell on to my hands from the soaked petals. There were petals at my feet too, brown and sodden, bearing their scent upon them still, and a richer, older scent as well, the smell of deep moss and bitter earth, the stems of bracken, and the twisted buried roots of trees. I held Maxim's hand and I had not spoken. The spell of the Happy Valley was upon me. This at last was the core of Manderley, the Manderley I would know and learn to love. The first drive was forgotten, the black, herded woods, the glaring rhododendrons, luscious and over-proud. And the vast house too, the silence of that echoing hall, the uneasy stillness of the west wing, wrapped in dust-sheets. There I was an interloper, wandering in rooms that did not know me, sitting at a desk and in a chair that was not mine. Here it was different. The Happy Valley knew no trespassers. We came to the end of the path, and the flowers formed an archway above our heads. We bent down, passing underneath, and when I stood straight again, brushing the raindrops from my hair, I saw that the valley was behind us, and the azaleas, and the trees, and, as Maxim had described to me that afternoon many weeks ago in Monte Carlo, we were standing in a little narrow cove, the shingle hard and white under our feet, and the sea was breaking on the shore beyond us.

Maxim smiled down at me, watching the bewilderment on my face.

"It's a shock, isn't it?" he said, "no one ever expects it. The contrast is too sudden, it almost hurts." He picked up a stone and flung it across the beach for Jasper. "Fetch it, good man," and Jasper streaked away in search of the stone, his long black ears flapping in the wind.

The enchantment was no more, the spell was broken. We were mortal again, two people playing on a beach. We threw more stones, went to the water's edge, flung ducks and drakes, and fished for driftwood. The tide had turned, and came lapping in the bay. The small rocks were covered, the seaweed washed on the stones. We rescued a big floating plank and carried it up the beach above high-water mark. Maxim turned to me, laughing, wiping the hair out of his eyes, and I unrolled the sleeves of my mackintosh caught by the sea spray. And then we looked round, and saw that Jasper had disappeared. We called and whistled, and he did not come. I looked anxiously towards the mouth of the cove where the waves were breaking upon the rocks.

"No," said Maxim, "we should have seen him, he can't have fallen. Jasper, you idiot, where are you? Jasper, Jasper?"

"Perhaps he's gone back to the Happy Valley?" I said.

"He was by that rock a minute ago, sniffing a dead sea-gull," said Maxim.

We walked up the beach towards the valley once again. "Jasper, Jasper?" called Maxim.

In the distance, beyond the rocks to the right of the beach, I heard a short, sharp bark. "Hear that?" I said. "He's climbed over this way." I began to scramble up the slippery rocks in the direction of the bark.

"Come back," said Maxim sharply, "we don't want to go that way. The fool of a dog must look after himself."

I hesitated, looking down from my rock. "Perhaps he's fallen," I said, "poor little chap. Let me fetch him." Jasper barked again, further away this time. "Oh, listen," I said, "I must get him. It's quite safe, isn't it? The tide won't have cut him off?"

"He's all right," said Maxim irritably, "why not leave him? He knows his own way back."

I pretended not to hear, and began scrambling over the rocks towards Jasper. Great jagged boulders screened the view, and I slipped and stumbled on the wet rocks, making my way as best I could in Jasper's direction. It was heartless of Maxim to leave Jasper, I thought, and I could not understand it. Besides, the tide was coming in. I came up beside the big boulder that had hidden the view, and looked beyond it. And I saw, to my surprise, that I was looking down into another cove, similar to the one I had left, but wider and more rounded. A small stone breakwater had been thrown out across the cove for shelter, and behind it the bay formed a tiny natural harbour. There was a buoy anchored there, but no boat. The beach in the cove was white shingle, like the one behind me, but steeper, shelving suddenly to the sea. The woods came right down to the tangle of seaweed marking high water, encroaching almost to the rocks themselves, and at the fringe of the woods was a long low building, half cottage, half boat-house, built of the same stone as the breakwater.

There was a man on the beach, a fisherman perhaps, in long boots and a sou'wester, and Jasper was barking at him, running round him in circles, darting at his boots. The man took no notice, he was bending down, and scraping in the shingle. "Jasper," I shouted, "Jasper, come here."

The dog looked up, wagging his tail, but he did not obey me. He went on baiting the solitary figure on the beach.

I looked over my shoulder. There was still no sign of Maxim. I climbed down over the rocks to the beach below. My feet made a crunching noise across the shingle, and the man looked up at the sound. I saw then that he had the small slit eyes of an idiot, and the red, wet mouth. He smiled at me, showing toothless gums.

"G'day," he said. "Dirty, ain't it?"

"Good afternoon," I said. "No, I'm afraid it's not very nice weather."

He watched me with interest, smiling all the while. "Diggin' for shell," he said. "No shell here. Been diggin' since forenoon."

"Oh," I said, "I'm sorry you can't find any."

"That's right," he said, "no shell here."

"Come on, Jasper," I said, "it's getting late. Come on, old boy."

But Jasper was in an infuriating mood. Perhaps the wind and sea had gone to his head, for he backed away from me, barking stupidly, and began racing round the beach after nothing at all. I saw he would never follow me, and I had no lead. I turned to the man, who had bent down again to his futile digging.

"Have you got any string?" I said.

"Eh?" he said.

"Have you got any string?" I repeated.

"No shell here," he said, shaking his head. "Been diggin' since forenoon." He nodded his head at me, and wiped his pale blue watery eyes.

"I want something to tie the dog," I said. "He won't follow me."

"Eh?" he said. And he smiled his poor idiot's smile.

"All right," I said, "it doesn't matter." He looked at me uncertainly, and then leant forward, and poked me in the chest.

"I know that dog," he said, "he comes fro' the house."

"Yes," I said. "I want him to come back with me now."

"He's not yourn," he said.

"He's Mr. de Winter's dog," I said gently. "I want to take him back to the house."

"Eh?" he said.

I called Jasper once more, but he was chasing a feather blown by the wind. I wondered if there was any string in the boat-house, and I walked up the beach towards it. There must have been a garden once, but now the grass was long and overgrown, crowded with nettles. The windows were boarded up. No doubt the door was locked, and I lifted the latch without much hope. To my surprise it opened after the first stiffness, and I went inside, bending my head because of the low door. I expected to find the usual boat store, dirty and dusty with disuse, ropes and blocks and oars upon the floor. The dust was there, and the dirt too in places, but there were no ropes or blocks. The room was furnished, and ran the whole length of the cottage. There was a desk in the corner, a table and chairs, and a sofa-bed pushed against the wall. There was a dresser too, with cups and plates. Bookshelves, the books inside them, and models of ships standing on the top of the shelves. For a moment I thought it must be inhabited—perhaps the poor man on the beach lived here—but I looked around me again, and saw no sign of recent occupation. That rusted grate knew no fire, this dusty floor no footsteps, and the china there on the dresser was blue-spotted with the damp. There was a queer musty smell about the place. Cobwebs spun threads upon the ship's models, making their own ghostly rigging. No one lived here. No one came here. The door had creaked on its hinges when I opened it. The rain pattered on the roof with a hollow sound, and tapped upon the boarded windows. The fabric of the sofa-bed had been nibbled by mice or rats. I could see the jagged holes, and the frayed edges. It was damp in the cottage, damp and chill. Dark, and oppressive. I did not like it. I had no wish to stay there. I hated the hollow sound of the rain pattering on the roof. It seemed to echo in the room itself, and I heard the water dripping too into the rusted grate.

I looked about me for some string. There was nothing that would serve my purpose, nothing at all. There was another door at the end of the room, and I went to it, and opened it, a little fearful now, a little afraid, for I had the odd, uneasy feeling that I might come upon something unawares, that I had no wish to see. Something that might harm me, that might be horrible.

It was nonsense of course, and I opened the door. It was only a boat store after all. Here were the ropes and blocks I had expected, two or three sails, fenders, a small punt, pots of paints, all the litter and junk that goes with the using of boats. A ball of twine lay on a shelf, a rusted clasp-knife beside it. This would be all I needed for Jasper. I opened the knife, and cut a length of twine, and came back into the room again. The rain still fell upon the roof, and into the grate. I came out of the cottage hurriedly, not looking behind me, trying not to see the torn sofa and the mildewed china, the spun cobwebs on the model ships, and so through the creaking gate and on to the white beach.

The man was not digging any more, he was watching me, Jasper at his side.

"Come along, Jasper," I said, "come on, good dog." I bent down, and this time he allowed me to touch him and pull hold of his collar. "I found some string in the cottage," I said to the man.

He did not answer, and I tied the string loosely round Jasper's collar.

"Good afternoon," I said, tugging at Jasper. The man nodded, staring at me with his narrow idiot's eyes. "I saw 'ee go in yonder," he said.

"Yes," I said, "it's all right. Mr. de Winter won't mind."

"She don't go in there now," he said.

"No," I said, "not now."

"She's gone in the sea, ain't she?" he said, "she won't come back no more?"

"No," I said, "she'll not come back."

"I never said nothing, did I?" he said.

"No, of course not, don't worry," I said.

He bent down again to his digging, muttering to himself. I went across the shingle and I saw Maxim waiting for me by the rocks, his hands in his pockets.

"I'm sorry," I said. "Jasper would not come. I had to get some string."

He turned abruptly on his heel, and made towards the woods.

"Aren't we going back over the rocks?" I said.

"What's the point, we're here now," he said briefly.

We went up past the cottage and struck into a path through the woods. "I'm sorry I was such a time, it was Jasper's fault," I said, "he kept barking at the man. Who was he?"

"Only Ben," said Maxim; "he's quite harmless, poor devil. His old father used to be one of the keepers, they live near the home farm. Where did you get that piece of twine?"

"I found it in the cottage on the beach," I said.

"Was the door open?" he asked.

"Yes, I pushed it open. I found the string in the other room, where the sails were, and a small boat."

"Oh," he said shortly. "Oh, I see," and then he added, after a moment or two: "That cottage is supposed to be locked, the door has no business to be open."

I said nothing, it was not my affair.

"Did Ben tell you the door was open?"

"No," I said, "he did not seem to understand anything I asked him."

"He makes out he's worse than he is," said Maxim. "He can talk quite intelligibly if he wants to. He's probably been in and out of the cottage dozens of times, and did not want you to know."

"I don't think so," I answered; "the place looked deserted, quite untouched. There was dust everywhere, and no footmarks. It was terribly damp. I'm afraid those books will be quite spoilt, and the chairs, and that sofa. There are rats there too, they have eaten away some of the covers."

Maxim did not reply. He walked at a tremendous pace, and the climb up from the beach was steep. It was very different from the Happy Valley. The trees were dark here and close together, there were no azaleas brushing the path. The rain dripped heavily from the thick branches. It splashed on my collar and trickled down my neck. I shivered, it was unpleasant, like a cold finger. My legs ached, after the unaccustomed scramble over the rocks. And Jasper lagged behind, weary from his wild scamper, his tongue hanging from his mouth.

"Come on, Jasper, for God's sake," said Maxim. "Make him walk up, pull at the twine or something, can't you? Beatrice was right. The dog is much too fat."

"It's your fault," I said, "you walk so fast. We can't keep up with you."

"If you had listened to me instead of rushing wildly over those rocks we would have been home by now," said Maxim, "Jasper knew his way back perfectly. I can't think what you wanted to go after him for."

"I thought he might have fallen, and I was afraid of the tide," I said.

"Is it likely I should have left the dog had there been any question of the tide?" said Maxim. "I told you not to go on those rocks, and now you are grumbling because you are tired."

"I'm not grumbling," I said. "Anyone, even if they had legs of iron, would be tired walking at this pace. I thought you would come with me when I went after Jasper anyway, instead of staying behind."

"Why should I exhaust myself careering after the damn dog?" he said.

"It was no more exhausting careering after Jasper on the rocks than it was careering after driftwood on the beach," I answered. "You just say that because you have not any other excuse."

"My good child, what am I supposed to excuse myself about?"

"Oh, I don't know," I said wearily, "let's stop this."

"Not at all, you began it. What do you mean by saying I was trying to find an excuse? Excuse for what?"

"Excuse for not having come with me over the rocks, I suppose," I said.

"Well, and why do you think I did not want to cross to the other beach?"

"Oh, Maxim, how should I know? I'm not a thought-reader. I know you did not want to, that's all. I could see it in your face."

"See what in my face?"

"I've already told you. I could see you did not want to go. Oh, do let's have an end to it. I'm sick to death of the subject."

"All women say that when they've lost an argument. All right, I did not want to go to the other beach. Will that please you? I never go near the bloody place, or that God-damned cottage. And if you had my memories you would not want to go there either, or talk about it, or even think about it. There. You can digest that if you like, and I hope it satisfies you."

His face was white, and his eyes strained and wretched with that dark lost look they had had when I first met him. I put out my hand to him, I took hold of his, holding it tight.

"Please, Maxim, please," I said.

"What's the matter?" he said roughly.

"I don't want you to look like that," I said. "It hurts too much. Please, Maxim. Let's forget all we said. A futile silly argument. I'm sorry, darling, I'm sorry. Please let everything be all right."

"We ought to have stayed in Italy," he said. "We ought never to have come back to Manderley. Oh, God, what a fool I was to come back."

He brushed through the trees impatiently, striding even faster than before, and I had to run to keep pace with him, catching at my breath, tears very near the surface, dragging poor Jasper after me on the end of his string.

At last we came to the top of the path, and I saw its fellow branching left to the Happy Valley. We had climbed the path then that Jasper had wished to take at the beginning of the afternoon. I knew now why Jasper had turned to it. It led to the beach he knew best, and the cottage. It was his old routine.

We came out on to the lawns, and went across them to the house without a word. Maxim's face was hard, with no expression. He went straight into the hall and on to the library without looking at me. Frith was in the hall.

"We want tea at once," said Maxim, and he shut the library door.

I fought to keep back my tears. Frith must not see them. He would think we had been quarrelling, and he would go to the servants' hall and say to them all, "Mrs. de Winter was crying in the hall just now. It looks as though things are not going very well." I turned away, so that Frith should not see my face. He came towards me though, he began to help me off with my mackintosh.

"I'll put your raincoat away for you in the flower-room, Madam," he said.

"Thank you, Frith," I replied, my face still away from him.

"Not a very pleasant afternoon for a walk I fear, Madam."

"No," I said. "No, it was not very nice."

"Your handkerchief, Madam?" he said, picking up something that had fallen on the floor. "Thank you," I said, putting it in my pocket.

I was wondering whether to go upstairs or whether to follow Maxim to the library. Frith took the coat to the flower-room. I stood there, hesitating, biting my nails. Frith came back again. He looked surprised to see me still there.

"There is a good fire in the library now, Madam."

"Thank you, Frith," I said.

I walked slowly across the hall to the library. I opened the door and went in. Maxim was sitting in his chair, Jasper at his feet, the old dog in her basket. Maxim was not reading the paper, though it lay on the arm of the chair beside him. I went and knelt down by his side and put my face close to his.

"Don't be angry with me any more," I whispered.

He took my face in his hands, and looked down at me with his tired, strained eyes. "I'm not angry with you," he said.

"Yes," I said. "I've made you unhappy. It's the same as making you angry. You're all wounded and hurt and torn inside. I can't bear to see you like this. I love you so much."

"Do you?" he said. "Do you?" He held me very tight, and his eyes questioned me, dark and uncertain, the eyes of a child in pain, a child in fear.

"What is it, darling?" I said. "Why do you look like that?"

I heard the door open before he could answer, and I sank back on my heels, pretending to reach for a log to throw on the fire, while Frith came into the room followed by Robert, and the ritual of our tea began.

The performance of the day before was repeated, the placing of the table, the laying of the snow-white cloth, the putting down of cakes and crumpets, the silver kettle of hot water placed on its little flame, while Jasper, wagging his tail, his ears stretched back in anticipation, watched my face. Five minutes must have passed before we were alone again, and when I looked at Maxim I saw the colour had come back into his face, the tired, lost look was gone, and he was reaching for a sandwich.

"Having all that crowd to lunch was the trouble," he said. "Poor old Beatrice always does rub me up the wrong way. We used to scrap like dogs as children. I'm so fond of her too, bless her. Such a relief though that they don't live too near. Which reminds me, we'll have to go over and see Granny some time. Pour out my tea, sweetheart, and forgive me for being a bear to you."

It was over then. The episode was finished. We must not speak of it again. He smiled at me over his cup of tea, and then reached for the newspaper on the arm of his chair. The smile was my reward. Like a pat on the head to Jasper. Good dog then, lie down, don't worry me any more. I was Jasper again. I was back where I had been before. I took a piece of crumpet and divided it between the two dogs. I did not want it myself, I was not hungry. I felt very weary now, very tired in a dull, spent way. I looked at Maxim but he was reading his paper, he had folded it over to another page. My fingers were messy with the butter from the crumpet, and I felt in my pocket for a handkerchief. I drew it out, a tiny scrap of a thing, lace-edged. I stared at it, frowning, for it was not mine. I remembered then that Frith had picked it up from the stone floor of the hall. It must have fallen out of the pocket in the mackintosh. I turned it over in my hand. It was grubby, little bits of fluff from the pocket clung to it. It must have been in the mackintosh pocket for a long time. There was a monogram in the corner. A tall sloping R, with the letters de W interlaced. The R dwarfed the other letters, the tail of it ran down into the cambric, away from the laced edge. It was only a small handkerchief, quite a scrap of a thing. It had been rolled in a ball and put away in the pocket and forgotten.

I must have been the first person to put on that mackintosh since the handkerchief was used. She who had worn the coat then was tall, slim, broader than I about the shoulders, for I had found it big and over-long, and the sleeves had come below my wrists. Some of the buttons were missing. She had not bothered then to do it up. She had thrown it over her shoulders like a cape, or worn it loose, hanging open, her hands deep in the pockets.

There was a pink mark upon the handkerchief. The mark of lip-stick. She had rubbed her lips with the handkerchief, and then rolled it in a ball, and left it in the pocket. I wiped my fingers with the handkerchief, and as I did so I noticed that a dull scent clung about it still.

A scent I recognised, a scent I knew. I shut my eyes and tried to remember. It was something elusive, something faint and fragrant that I could not name. I had breathed it before, touched it surely, that very afternoon.

And then I knew that the vanished scent upon the handkerchief was the same as the crushed white petals of the azaleas in the Happy Valley.

CHAPTER ELEVEN

THE WEATHER WAS wet and cold for quite a week, as it often can be in the west country in early summer, and we did not go down to the beach again. I could see the sea from the terrace, and the lawns. It looked grey and uninviting, great rollers sweeping in to the bay past the beacon on the headland. I pictured them surging into the little cove and breaking with a roar upon the rocks, then running swift and strong to the shelving beach. If I stood on the terrace and listened I could hear the murmur of the sea below me, low and sullen. A dull, persistent sound that never ceased. And the gulls flew inland too, driven by the weather. They hovered above the house in circles, wheeling and crying, flapping their spread wings. I began to understand why some people could not bear the clamour of the sea. It has a mournful harping note sometimes, and the very persistence of it, that eternal roll and thunder and hiss, plays a jagged tune upon the nerves. I was glad our rooms were in the east wing and I could lean out of my window and look down upon the rose-garden. For sometimes I could not sleep, and getting softly out of bed in the quiet night I would wander to the window, and lean there, my arms upon the sill, and the air would be very peaceful, very still.

I could not hear the restless sea, and because I could not hear it my thoughts would be peaceful too. They would not carry me down that steep path through the woods to the grey cove and the deserted cottage. I did not want to think about the cottage. I remembered it too often in the day. The memory of it nagged at me whenever I saw the sea from the terrace. For I would see once more the blue spots on the china, the spun webs on the little masts of those model ships, and the rat holes on the sofa-bed. I would remember the pattering of the rain on the roof. And I thought of Ben, too, with his narrow watery blue eyes, his sly idiot's smile. These things disturbed me, I was not happy about them. I wanted to forget them but at the same time I wanted to know why they disturbed me, why they made me uneasy and unhappy. Somewhere, at the back of my mind, there was a frightened furtive seed of curiosity that grew slowly and stealthily, for all my denial of it, and I knew all the doubt and the anxiety of the child who has been told, "these things are not discussed, they are forbidden."

I could not forget the white, lost look in Maxim's eyes when we came up the path through the woods, and I could not forget his words, "Oh, God, what a fool I was to come back." It was all my fault, because I had gone down into the bay. I had opened up a road into the past again. And although Maxim had recovered, and was himself again, and we lived our lives together, sleeping, eating, walking, writing letters, driving to the village, working hour by hour through our day, I knew there was a barrier between us because of it.

He walked alone, on the other side, and I must not come to him. And I became nervous and fearful that some heedless word, some turn in a careless conversation should bring that expression back to his eyes again. I began to dread any mention of the sea, for the sea might lead to boats, to accidents, to drowning. . . . Even Frank Crawley, who came to lunch one day, put me in a little fever of fear when he said something about the sailing races in Kerrith harbour, three miles away. I looked steadily at my plate, a stab of sickness in my heart at once, but Maxim went on talking quite naturally, he did not seem to mind, while I sat in a sweat of uncertainty wondering what would happen and where the conversation would lead us.

It was during cheese, Frith had left the room, and I remember getting up and going to the side-board, and taking some more cheese, not wanting it, so as not to be at the table with them, listening; humming a little tune to myself so I could not hear. I was wrong of course, morbid, stupid, this was the hyper-sensitive behaviour of a neurotic, not the normal happy self I knew myself to be. But I could not help it. I did not know what to do. My shyness and gaucherie became worse, too, making me stolid and dumb when people came to the house. For we were called upon, I remember, during those first weeks, by people who lived near us in the county, and the receiving of them, and the shaking hands, and the spinning out of the formal half-hour became a worse ordeal than I first anticipated, because of this new fear of mine that they would talk about something that must not be discussed. The agony of those wheels on the drive, of that pealing bell, of my own first wild rush for flight to my own room. The scrambled dab of powder on my nose, the hasty comb through my hair, and then the inevitable knock on the door and the entrance of the cards on a silver salver.

"All right. I'll be down immediately." The clap of my heels on the stairs and across the hall, the opening of the library door or, worse still, that long, cold, lifeless drawing-room, and the strange woman waiting there, or two of them perhaps, or a husband and a wife.

"How do you do? I'm so sorry, Maxim is in the garden somewhere, Frith has gone to find him."

"We felt we must come and pay our respects to the bride."

A little laughter, a little flurry of chat, a pause, a glance round the room. "Manderley is looking as charming as ever. Don't you love it?"

"Oh, yes, rather . . ." And in my shyness and anxiety to please, those schoolgirl phrases would escape from me again, those words I never used except in moments like these, "Oh, ripping"; and "Oh, topping"; and "absolutely"; and "priceless"; even, I think, to one dowager who had carried a lorgnette "cheerio." My relief at Maxim's arrival would be tempered by the fear they might say something indiscreet, and I became dumb at once, a set smile on my lips, my hands in my lap. They would turn to Maxim then, talking of people and places I had not met or did not know, and now and again I would find their eyes upon me, doubtful, rather bewildered.

I could picture them saying to one another as they drove away, "My dear, what a dull girl. She scarcely opened her mouth"; and then the sentence I had first heard upon Beatrice's lips, haunting me ever since, a sentence I read in every eye, on every tongue—"She's so different to Rebecca."

Sometimes I would glean little snatches of information to add to my secret store. A word dropped here at random, a question, a passing phrase. And, if Maxim was not with me, the hearing of them would be a furtive, rather painful pleasure, guilty knowledge learnt in the dark.

I would return a call perhaps, for Maxim was punctilious in these matters and would not spare me, and if he did not come with me I must brave the formality alone, and there would be a pause in the conversation while I searched for something to say. "Will you be entertaining much at Manderley, Mrs. de Winter?" they would say and my answer would come, "I don't know, Maxim has not said much about it up to the present." "No, of course not, it's early yet. I believe the house was generally full of people in the old days." Another pause. "People from London, you know. There used to be tremendous parties." "Yes," I would say. "Yes, so I have heard." A further pause, and then the lowered voice that is always used about the dead or in a place of worship. "She was so tremendously popular, you know. Such a personality." "Yes," I would say. "Yes, of course." And after a moment or so I would glance at my watch under cover of my glove, and say "I'm afraid I ought to be going, it must be after four."

"Won't you stay for tea? We always have it quarter-past."

"No—no, really, thanks most awfully. I promised Maxim . . ." my sentence would go trailing off into nothing, but the meaning would be understood. We would both rise to our feet, both of us knowing I was not deceived about her offer to tea nor she in my mention of a promise to Maxim. I sometimes wondered what would happen if convention were denied, if, having got into the car and waved a hand to my hostess on the doorstep, I suddenly opened it again, and said "I don't think I'll go back after all. Let's go to your drawing-room again and sit down. I'll stay to dinner if you like or stop the night."

I used to wonder if convention and good county manners would brave the surprise, and whether a smile of welcome would be summoned to the frozen face. "But of course! How very delightful of you to suggest it." I used to wish I had the courage to try. But instead the door would slam, the car would go bowling away down the smooth gravel drive, and my late hostess would wander back to her room with a sigh of relief and become herself again. It was the wife of the bishop in the neighbouring cathedral town who said to me, "Will your husband revive the Manderley fancy dress ball, do you suppose? Such a lovely sight always, I shall never forget it."

I had to smile as though I knew all about it and say, "We have not decided. There have been so many things to do and to discuss."

"Yes, I suppose so. But I hope it won't be dropped. You must use your influence with him. There was not one last year of course. But I remember two years ago, the bishop and I went, and it was quite enchanting. Manderley so lends itself to anything like that. The hall looked wonderful. They danced there, and had the music in the gallery, it was all so in keeping. A tremendous thing to organise but everybody appreciated it so."

"Yes," I said. "Yes, I must ask Maxim about it."

I thought of the docketed pigeon-holes in the desk in the morning-room, I pictured the stack upon stack of invitation cards, the long list of names, the addresses, and I could see a woman sitting there at the desk and putting a V beside the names she wanted, and reaching for the invitation cards, dipping her pen in the ink, writing upon them swift and sure in that long, slanting hand.

"There was a garden party, too, we went to one summer," said the bishop's wife. "Everything always so beautifully done. The flowers at their best. A glorious day I remember. Tea was served at little tables in the rose-garden, such an attractive original idea. Of course, she was so clever . . ."

She stopped, turning a little pink, fearing a loss of tact, but I agreed with her at once to save embarrassment, and I heard myself saying boldly, brazenly, "Rebecca must have been a wonderful person."

I could not believe that I had said the name at last. I waited, wondering what would happen. I had said the name. I had said the word Rebecca aloud. It was a tremendous relief. It was as though I had taken a purge and rid myself of an intolerable pain. Rebecca. I had said it aloud.

I wondered if the bishop's wife saw the flush on my face, but she went on smoothly with the conversation, and I listened to her greedily, like an eavesdropper at a shuttered window.

"You never met her then?" she asked, and when I shook my head she hesitated a moment, a little uncertain of her ground. "We never knew her well personally, you know, the bishop was only inducted here four years ago, but of course she received us when we went to the ball and to the garden party. We dined there, too, one winter. Yes, she was a very lovely creature. So full of life."

"She seems to have been so good at everything too," I said, my voice just careless enough to show I did not mind, while I played with the fringe of my glove. "It's not often you get someone who is clever and beautiful and fond of sport."

"No, I suppose you don't," said the bishop's wife, "she was certainly very gifted. I can see her now, standing at the foot of the stairs on the night of of the ball, shaking hands with everybody, that cloud of dark hair against the very white skin, and her costume suited her so. Yes, she was very beautiful."

"She ran the house herself, too," I said smiling, as if to say, "I am quite at my ease, I often discuss her." "It must have taken a lot of time and thought. I'm afraid I leave it to the housekeeper."

"Oh, well, we can't all do everything. And you are very young, aren't you? No doubt in time, when you have settled down. Besides, you have your own hobby, haven't you? Someone told me you were fond of sketching."

"Oh, that," I said. "I don't know that I can count it for much."

"It's a nice little talent to have," said the bishop's wife; "it's not everyone that can sketch. You must not drop it. Manderley must be full of pretty spots to sketch."

"Yes," I said. "Yes, I suppose so," depressed by her words, having a sudden vision of myself wandering across the lawns with a camp-stool and a box of pencils under one arm, and my "little talent" as she described it, under the other. It sounded like a pet disease.

"Do you play any games, do you ride, or shoot?" she asked.

"No," I said, "I don't do anything like that. I'm fond of walking," I added, as a wretched anti-climax.

"The best exercise in the world," she said briskly, "the bishop and I walk a lot." I wondered if he went round and round the cathedral, in his shovel hat and his gaiters, with her on his arm. She began to talk about a walking holiday they had taken once, years ago, in the Pennines, how they had done an average of twenty miles a day, and I nodded my head, smiling politely, wondering about the Pennines, thinking they were something like the Andes, remembering afterwards, they were that chain of hills marked with a furry line in the middle of a pink England on my school atlas. And he all the time in his hat and gaiters.

The inevitable pause, the glance at the watch unnecessary, as her drawing-room clock chimed four in shrill tones, and my rise from the chair. "I'm so glad I found you in. I hope you will come and see us."

"We should love to. The bishop is always so busy, alas. Please remember me to your husband, and be sure and ask him to revive the ball."

"Yes, indeed I will." Lying, pretending I knew all about it; and in the car going home I sat in my corner, biting my thumb nail, seeing the great hall at Manderley thronged with people in fancy dress, the chatter, hum, and laughter of the moving crowd, the musicians in the gallery, supper in the drawing-room probably, long buffet tables against the wall, and I could see Maxim standing at the foot of the stairs, laughing, shaking hands, turning to someone who stood by his side, tall and slim, with dark hair, said the bishop's wife, dark hair against a white face, someone whose quick eyes saw to the comfort of her guests, who gave an order over her shoulder to a servant, someone who was never awkward, never without grace, who when she danced left a stab of perfume in the air like a white azalea.

"Will you be entertaining much at Manderley, Mrs. de Winter?" I heard the voice again, suggestive, rather inquisitive, in the voice of that woman I had called upon who lived the other side of Kerrith, and I saw her eye too, dubious, considering, taking in my clothes from top to toe, wondering, with that swift downward glance given to all brides, if I was going to have a baby.

I did not want to see her again. I did not want to see any of them again. They only came to call at Manderley because they were curious and prying. They liked to criticise my looks, my manners, my figure, they liked to watch how Maxim and I behaved to each other, whether we seemed fond of one another, so that they could go back afterwards and discuss us, saying, "Very different from the old days." They came because they wanted to compare me to Rebecca. . . . I would not return these calls any more, I decided, I should tell Maxim so. I did not mind if they thought me rude and ungracious. It would give them more to criticise, more to discuss. They could say I was ill-bred. "I'm not surprised," they would say, "after all, who was she?" And then a laugh and a shrug of the shoulder. "My dear, don't you know? He picked her up in Monte Carlo or somewhere, she hadn't a penny. She was a companion to some old woman." More laughter, more lifting of the eyebrows. "Nonsense, not really? How extraordinary men are. Maxim, of all people, who was so fastidious. How could he, after Rebecca?"

I did not mind. I did not care. They could say what they liked. As the car turned in at the lodge gates I leant forward in my seat to smile at the woman who lived there. She was bending down, picking flowers in the front garden. She straightened up as she heard the car, but she did not see me smile. I waved, and she stared at me blankly. I don't think she knew who I was. I leant back in my seat again. The car went on down the drive.

When we turned at one of the narrow bends I saw a man walking along the drive a little distance ahead. It was the agent, Frank Crawley. He stopped when he heard the car, and the chauffeur slowed down. Frank Crawley took off his hat and smiled when he saw me in the car. He seemed glad to see me. I smiled back at him. It was nice of him to be glad to see me. I liked Frank Crawley. I did not find him dull or uninteresting as Beatrice had done. Perhaps it was because I was dull myself. We were both dull. We neither of us had a word to say for ourselves. Like to like.

I tapped on the glass and told the chauffeur to stop.

"I think I'll get out and walk with Mr. Crawley," I said.

He opened the door for me. "Been paying calls, Mrs. de Winter?" he said.

"Yes, Frank," I said. I called him Frank because Maxim did, but he would always call me Mrs. de Winter. He was that sort of person. Even if we had been thrown on a desert island together, and lived there in intimacy for the rest of our lives, I should have been Mrs. de Winter.

"I've been calling on the bishop," I said, "and I found the bishop out but the bishop's lady was at home. She and the bishop are very fond of walking. Sometimes they do twenty miles a day, in the Pennines."

"I don't know that part of the world," said Frank Crawley, "they say the country round is very fine. An uncle of mine used to live there."

It was the sort of remark Frank Crawley always made. Safe, conventional, very correct.

"The bishop's wife wants to know when we are going to give a fancy dress ball at Manderley," I said, watching him out of the tail of my eye. "She came to the last one, she said, and enjoyed it very much. I did not know you have fancy dress dances here, Frank."

He hesitated a moment before replying. He looked a little troubled. "Oh, yes," he said after a moment, "the Manderley ball was generally an annual affair. Everyone in the county came. A lot of people from London too. Quite a big show."

"It must have taken a lot of organisation," I said.

"Yes," he said.

"I suppose," I said carelessly, "Rebecca did most of it?"

I looked straight ahead of me along the drive, but I could see his face was turned towards me, as though he wished to read my expression.

"We all of us worked pretty hard," he said quietly.

There was a funny reserve in his manner as he said this, a certain shyness that reminded me of my own. I wondered suddenly if he had been in love with Rebecca. His voice was the sort of voice I should have used in his circumstances, had this been so. The idea opened up a new field of possibilities. Frank Crawley being so shy, so dull. He would never have told anyone, least of all Rebecca.

"I'm afraid I should not be much use if we have a dance," I said, "I'm no earthly use at organising anything."

"There would be no need for you to do anything," he said, "you would just be your self and look decorative."

"That's very polite of you, Frank," I said, "but I'm afraid I should not be able to do that very well either."

"I think you would do it excellently," he said. Dear Frank Crawley, how tactful he was and considerate. I almost believed him. But he did not deceive me really.

"Will you ask Maxim about the ball?" I said.

"Why don't you ask him?" he answered.

"No," I said. "No, I don't like to."

We were silent then. We went on walking along the drive. Now that I had broken down my reluctance at saying Rebecca's name, first with the bishop's wife and now with Frank Crawley, the urge to continue was strong within me. It gave me a curious satisfaction, it acted upon me like a stimulant. I knew that in a moment or two I should have to say it again. "I was down on one of the beaches the other day," I said, "the one with the breakwater. Jasper was being infuriating, he kept barking at the poor man with the idiot's eyes."

"You must mean Ben," said Frank, his voice quite easy now, "he always potters about on the shore. He's quite a nice fellow, you need never be frightened of him. He would not hurt a fly."

"Oh, I wasn't frightened," I said. I waited a moment, humming a tune to give me confidence. "I'm afraid that cottage place is going to rack and ruin," I said lightly. "I had to go in, to find a piece of string or something to tie up Jasper. The china is mouldy and the books are being ruined. Why isn't something done about it? It seems such a pity."

I knew he would not answer at once. He bent down to tie up his shoe lace.

I pretended to examine a leaf on one of the shrubs. "I think if Maxim wanted anything done he would tell me," he said, still fumbling with his shoe.

"Are they all Rebecca's things?" I asked.

"Yes," he said.

I threw the leaf away and picked another, turning it over in my hands.

"What did she use the cottage for?" I asked, "it looked quite furnished. I thought from the outside it was just a boat-house."

"It was a boat-house originally," he said, his voice constrained again, difficult, the voice of someone who is uncomfortable about his subject. "Then—then she converted it like that, had furniture put, and china."

I thought it funny the way he called her "she." He did not say Rebecca or Mrs. de Winter, as I expected him to do.

"Did she use it a great deal?" I asked.

"Yes," he said. "Yes, she did. Moonlight picnics, and—and one thing and another."

We were walking again side by side, I still humming my little tune. "How jolly," I said brightly, "moonlight picnics must be great fun. Did you ever go to them?"

"Once or twice," he said. I pretended not to notice his manner, how quiet it had become, how reluctant to speak about these things.

"Why is the buoy there in the little harbour place?" I said.

"The boat used to be moored there," he said.

"What boat?" I asked.

"Her boat," he said.

A strange sort of excitement was upon me. I had to go on with my questions. He did not want to talk about it, I knew that, but although I was sorry for him and shocked at my own self I had to continue, I could not be silent.

"What happened to it?" I said, "was that the boat she was sailing when she drowned?"

"Yes," he said quietly, "it capsized and sank. She was washed overboard."

"What sort of size boat was it?" I asked.

"About three tons. It had a little cabin."

"What made it capsize?" I said.

"It can be very squally in the bay," he said.

I thought of that green sea, foam-flecked, that ran down channel beyond the headland. Did the wind come suddenly, I wondered, in a funnel from the beacon on the hill, and did the little boat heel to it, shivering, the white sail flat against a breaking sea?

"Could not someone have got out to her?" I said.

"Nobody saw the accident, nobody knew she had gone," he said.

I was very careful not to look at him. He might have seen the surprise in my face. I had always thought it happened in a sailing race, that other boats were there, the boats from Kerrith, and that people were watching, from the cliffs. I did not know she had been alone. Quite alone, out there in the bay.

"They must have known up at the house?" I said.

"No," he said. "She often went out alone like that. She would come back any time of the night, and sleep at the cottage on the beach."

"Was not she nervous?"

"Nervous?" he said, "no, she was not nervous of anything."

"Did—did Maxim mind her going off alone like that?"

He waited a minute, and then "I don't know," he said shortly. I had the impression he was being loyal to someone. Either to Maxim or to Rebecca, or perhaps even to himself. He was odd. I did not know what to make of it.

"She must have been drowned then, trying to swim to shore, after the boat sank?" I said.

"Yes," he said.

I knew how the little boat would quiver and plunge, the water gushing into the steering well, and how the sails would press her down, suddenly, horribly, in that gust of wind. It must have been very dark out there in the bay. The shore must have seemed very far away to anyone swimming there, in the water.

"How long afterwards was it that they found her?" I said.

"About two months," he said.

Two months. I thought drowned people were found after two days. I thought they would be washed up close to the shore, when the tide came.

"Where did they find her?" I asked.

"Near Edgecoombe, about forty miles up channel," he said.

I had spent a holiday at Edgecoombe once, when I was seven. It was a big place, with a pier, and donkeys. I remembered riding a donkey along the sands.

"How did they know it was her, after two months, how could they tell?" I said. I wondered why he paused before each sentence, as though he weighed his words. Had he cared for her then, had he minded so much?

"Maxim went up to Edgecoombe to identify her," he said.

Suddenly I did not want to ask him any more. I felt sick at myself, sick and disgusted. I was like a curious sight-seer standing on the fringe of a crowd after someone had been knocked down. I was like a poor person in a tenement building, when someone has died, asking if I might see the body. I hated myself. My questions had been degrading, shameful. Frank Crawley must despise me.

"It was a terrible time for all of you," I said rapidly, "I don't suppose you like being reminded about it. I just wondered if there was anything one could do to the cottage, that's all. It seems such a pity, all the furniture being spoilt by the damp."

He did not say anything. I felt hot and uncomfortable. He must have sensed that it was not concern for the empty cottage that had prompted me to all these questions, and now he was silent because he was shocked at me. Ours had been a comfortable, steady sort of friendship. I had felt him an ally. Perhaps I had destroyed all this, and he would never feel the same about me again.

"What a long drive this is," I said, "it always reminds me of the path in the forest in a Grimm's fairy tale, where the prince gets lost, you know. It's always longer than one expects, and the trees are so dark, and close."

"Yes, it is rather exceptional," he said.

I could tell by his manner he was still on his guard, as though waiting for a further question from me. There was an awkwardness between us that could not be ignored. Something had to be done about it, even if it covered me with shame.

"Frank," I said desperately, "I know what you are thinking. You can't understand why I asked all those questions just now. You think I'm morbid, and curious, in a rather beastly way. It's not that, I promise you. It's only that—that sometimes I feel myself at such a disadvantage. It's all very strange to me, living here at Manderley. Not the sort of life I've been brought up to. When I go returning these calls, as I did this afternoon, I know people are looking me up and down, wondering what sort of success I'm going to make of it. I can imagine them saying, 'What on earth does Maxim see in her?' And then, Frank, I begin to wonder myself, and I begin to doubt, and I have a fearful haunting feeling that I should never have married Maxim, that we are not going to be happy. You see, I know that all the time, whenever I meet anyone new, they are all thinking the same thing—How different she is to Rebecca."

I stopped breathless, already a little ashamed of my outburst, feeling that now at any rate I had burnt my boats for all time. He turned to me looking very concerned and troubled.

"Mrs. de Winter, please don't think that," he said. "For my part I can't tell you how delighted I am that you have married Maxim. It will make all the difference to his life. I am positive that you will make a great success of it. From my point of view it's—it's very refreshing and charming to find someone like yourself who is not entirely—er—" he blushed, searching for a word, "not entirely *au fait*, shall we say, with the ways at Manderley. And if the people around here give you the impression that they are criticising you, it's—well—it's most damnably offensive of them, that's all. I've never heard a word of criticism, and if I did I should take great care that it was never uttered again."

"That's very sweet of you, Frank," I said, "and what you say helps enormously. I dare say I've been very stupid. I'm not good at meeting people, I've never had to do it, and all the time I keep remembering how—how it must have been at Manderley before, when there was someone there who was born and bred to it, did it all naturally and without effort. And I realise, every day, that things I lack, confidence, grace, beauty, intelligence, wit—oh, all the qualities that mean most in a woman—she possessed. It doesn't help, Frank, it doesn't help."

He said nothing. He went on looking anxious, and distressed. He pulled out his handkerchief and blew his nose. "You must not say that," he said.

"Why not? It's true," I said.

"You have qualities that are just as important, far more so, in fact. It's perhaps cheek of me to say so, I don't know you very well. I'm a bachelor, I don't know very much about women, I lead a quiet sort of life down here at Manderley as you know, but I should say that kindliness, and sincerity, and if I may say so—modesty—are worth far more to a man, to a husband, than all the wit and beauty in the world."

He looked very agitated, and blew his nose again. I saw that I had upset him far more than I had upset myself, and the realisation of this calmed me and gave me a feeling of superiority. I wondered why he was making such a fuss. After all, I had not said so very much. I had only confessed my sense of insecurity, following as I did upon Rebecca. And she must have had these qualities that he presented to me as mine. She must have been kind and sincere, with all her friends, her boundless popularity. I was not sure what he meant by modesty. It was a word I had never understood. I always imagined it had something to do with minding meeting people in a passage on the way to a bathroom. . . . Poor Frank. And Beatrice had called him a dull man, with never a word to say for himself.

"Well," I said, rather embarrassed, "well, I don't know about all that. I don't think I'm very kind, or particularly sincere, and as for being modest, I don't think I've ever had much of a chance to be anything else. It was not very modest, of course, being married hurriedly like that, down in Monte Carlo, and being alone there in that hotel, beforehand, but perhaps you don't count that?"

"My dear Mrs. de Winter, you don't think I imagine for one moment that your meeting down there was not entirely above board?" he said in a low voice.

"No, of course not," I said gravely. Dear Frank. I think I had shocked him. What a Frank-ish expression, too, "above board." It made one think immediately of the sort of things that would happen below board.

"I'm sure," he began, and hesitated, his expression still troubled, "I'm sure that Maxim would be very worried, very distressed, if he knew how you felt. I don't think he can have any idea of it."

"You won't tell him?" I said hastily.

"No, naturally not, what do you take me for? But you see, Mrs. de Winter, I know Maxim pretty well, and I've seen him through many . . . moods. If he thought you were worrying about–well–about the past, it would distress him more than anything on earth, I can promise you that. He's looking very well, very fit, but Mrs. Lacy was quite right the other day when she said he had been on the verge of a breakdown last year, though it was tactless of her to say so in front of him. That's why you are so good for him. You are fresh and young–and sensible, you have nothing to do with all that time that has gone. Forget it, Mrs. de Winter, forget it, as he has done, thank heaven, and the rest of us. We none of us want to bring back the past, Maxim least of all. And it's up to you, you know, to lead us away from it. Not to take us back there again."

He was right, of course he was right. Dear good Frank, my friend, my ally. I had been selfish and hyper-sensitive, a martyr to my own inferiority complex. "I ought to have told you all this before," I said.

"I wish you had," he said, "I might have spared you some worry."

"I feel happier," I said, "much happier. And I've got you for my friend whatever happens, haven't I, Frank?"

"Yes, indeed," he said.

We were out of the dark wooded drive into the light again. The rhododendrons were upon us. Their hour would soon be over. Already they looked a little over-blown, a little faded. Next month the petals would fall one by one from the great faces, and the gardeners would come and sweep them away. Theirs was a brief beauty. Not lasting very long.

"Frank," I said, "before we put an end to this conversation, for ever let's say, will you promise to answer me one thing, quite truthfully?"

He paused, looking at me a little suspiciously. "That's not quite fair," he said, "you might ask me something that I should not be able to answer, something quite impossible."

"No," I said, "it's not that sort of question. It's not intimate or personal, or anything like that."

"Very well, I'll do my best," he said.

We came round the sweep of the drive and Manderley was before us, serene and peaceful in the hollow of the lawns, surprising me as it always did, with its perfect symmetry and grace, its great simplicity.

The sunlight flickered on the mullioned windows, and there was a soft rusted glow about the stone walls where the lichen clung. A thin column of smoke curled from the library chimney. I bit my thumb nail, watching Frank out of the tail of my eye.

"Tell me," I said, my voice casual, not caring a bit, "tell me, was Rebecca very beautiful?"

Frank waited a moment. I could not see his face. He was looking away from me towards the house. "Yes," he said slowly, "yes, I suppose she was the most beautiful creature I ever saw in my life."

We went up the steps then to the hall, and I rang the bell for tea.

CHAPTER TWELVE

I DID NOT SEE much of Mrs. Danvers. She kept very much to herself. She still rang the house telephone to the morning-room every day and submitted the menu to me as a matter of form, but that was the limit of our intercourse. She had engaged a maid for me, Clarice, the daughter of somebody on the estate, a nice quiet well-mannered girl, who, thank heaven, had never been in service before and had no alarming standards. I think she was the only person in the house who stood in awe of me. To her I was the mistress, I was Mrs. de Winter. The possible gossip of the others could not affect her. She had been away for some time, brought up by an aunt fifteen miles away, and in a sense she was as new to Manderley as I was. I felt at ease with her. I did not mind saying "Oh, Clarice, would you mend my stocking?"

The housemaid, Alice, had been so superior. I used to sneak my chemises and nightgowns out of my drawer and mend them myself rather than ask her to do them. I had seen her once, with one of my chemises over her arm, examining the plain material with its small edging of lace. I shall never forget her expression. She looked almost shocked, as though her own personal pride had received a blow. I had never thought about my underclothes before. As long as they were clean and neat I had not thought the material or the existence of lace mattered. Brides one read about had trousseaux, dozens of sets at a time, and I had never bothered. Alice's face taught me a lesson. I wrote quickly to a shop in London and asked for a catalogue of under-linen. By the time I had made my choice Alice was looking after me no longer and Clarice was installed instead. It seemed such a waste buying new underclothes for Clarice that I put the catalogue away in a drawer and never wrote to the shop after all.

I often wondered whether Alice told the others, and if my underclothes became a topic of conversation in the servants' hall, something rather dreadful, to be discussed in low tones when the men were nowhere about. She was too superior for it to be made a joking question. Phrases like "Chemise to you" would never be bandied between her and Frith for instance.

No, my underclothes were more serious than that. More like a divorce case heard *in camera*. . . . At any rate I was glad when Alice surrendered me to Clarice. Clarice would never know real lace from false. It was considerate of Mrs. Danvers to have engaged her. She must have thought we would be fit company, one for the other. Now that I knew the reason for Mrs. Danvers' dislike and resentment it made things a little easier. I knew it was not just me personally she hated, but what I represented. She would have felt the same towards anyone who had taken Rebecca's place. At least that was what I understood from Beatrice the day she came to lunch.

"Did not you know?" she had said, "she simply adored Rebecca."

The words had shocked me at the time. Somehow I had not expected them. But when I thought it over I began to lose my first fear of Mrs. Danvers. I began to be sorry for her. I could imagine what she must feel. It must hurt her every time she heard me called "Mrs. de Winter." Every morning when she took up the house telephone and spoke to me, and I answered "Yes, Mrs. Danvers," she must be thinking of another voice. When she passed through the rooms and saw traces of me about the place, a beret on a window seat, a bag of knitting on a chair, she must think of another one, who had done these things before. Even as I did. I, who had never known Rebecca. Mrs. Danvers knew how she walked and how she spoke. Mrs. Danvers knew the colour of her eyes, her smile, the texture of her hair. I knew none of these things, I had never asked about them, but sometimes I felt Rebecca was as real to me as she was to Mrs. Danvers.

Frank had told me to forget the past, and I wanted to forget it. But Frank did not have to sit in the morning-room as I did, every day, and touch the pen she had held between her fingers. He did not have to rest his hands on the blotter, and stare in front of him at her writing on the pigeon-holes. He did not have to look at the candlesticks on the mantelpiece, the clock, the vase in which the flowers stood, the pictures on the walls and remember, every day, that they belonged to her, she had chosen them, they were not mine at all. Frank did not have to sit at her place in the dining-room, hold the knife and fork that she had held, drink from her glass. He did not throw a coat over his shoulders which had been hers, nor find her handkerchief in the pocket. He did not notice, every day, as I did, the blind gaze of the old dog in its basket in the library, who lifted its head when it heard my footstep, the footstep of a woman, and sniffing the air drooped its head again, because I was not the one she sought.

Little things, meaningless and stupid in themselves, but they were there for me to see, for me to hear, for me to feel. Dear God, I did not want to think about Rebecca. I wanted to be happy, to make Maxim happy, and I wanted us to be together. There was no other wish in my heart but that. I could not help it if she came to me in thoughts, in dreams. I could not help it if I felt like a guest in Manderley, my home, walking where she had trodden, resting where she had lain. I was like a guest, biding my time, waiting for the return of the hostess. Little sentences, little reproofs reminding me every hour, every day.

"Frith," I said, coming into the library on a summer morning, my arms full of lilac, "Frith, where can I find a tall vase for these? They are all too small in the flower-room."

"The white alabaster vase in the drawing-room was always used for the lilac, Madam."

"Oh, wouldn't it be spoilt? It might get broken."

"Mrs. de Winter always used the alabaster vase, Madam."

"Oh, oh, I see."

Then the alabaster vase was brought for me, already filled with water, and as I put the sweet lilac in the vase and arranged the sprigs, one by one, the mauve warm scent filling the room, mingling with the smell of the new-mown lawn outside coming from the open window, I thought: "Rebecca did this. She took the lilac, as I am doing, and put the sprigs one by one in the white vase. I'm not the first to do it. This is Rebecca's vase, this is Rebecca's lilac." She must have wandered out into the garden as I did, in that floppy garden hat I had seen once at the back of a cupboard in the flower-room, hidden under some old cushions, and crossed the lawn to the lilac bushes, whistling perhaps, humming a tune, calling to the dogs to follow her, carrying in her hands the scissors that I carried now.

"Frith, could you move that book-stand from the table in the window, and I will put the lilac there?"

"Mrs. de Winter always had the alabaster vase on the table behind the sofa, Madam."

"Oh, well . . ." I hesitated, the vase in my hands, Frith's face impassive. He would obey me of course if I said I preferred to put the vase on the smaller table by the window. He would move the book-stand at once.

"All right," I said, "perhaps it would look better on the larger table." And the alabaster vase stood, as it had always done, on the table behind the sofa. . . .

Beatrice remembered her promise of a wedding present. A large parcel arrived one morning, almost too large for Robert to carry. I was sitting in the morning-room, having just read the menu for the day. I have always had a childish love of parcels. I snipped the string excitedly, and tore off the dark brown paper. It looked like books. I was right. It was books. Six big volumes. *A History of Painting*. And a sheet of note-paper in the first volume saying "I hope this is the sort of thing you like," and signed "Love from Beatrice." I could see her going into the shop in Wigmore Street and buying them. Looking about her in her abrupt, rather masculine way. "I want a set of books for someone who is keen on Art," she would say, and the attendant would answer, "Yes, Madam, will you come this way." She would finger the volumes a little suspiciously. "Yes, that's about the price. It's for a wedding present. I want them to look good. Are these all about Art?" "Yes, this is the standard work on the subject," the assistant would say. And then Beatrice must have written her note, and paid her cheque, and given the address "Mrs. de Winter, Manderley."

It was nice of Beatrice. There was something rather sincere and pathetic about her going off to a shop in London and buying me these books because she knew I was fond of painting. She imagined me, I expect, sitting down on a wet day and looking solemnly at the illustrations, and perhaps getting a sheet of drawing-paper and a paint-box and copying one of the pictures. Dear Beatrice. I had a sudden, stupid desire to cry. I gathered up the heavy volumes and looked round the morning-room for somewhere to put them. They were out of place in that fragile delicate room. Never mind, it was my room now, after all. I arranged them in a row on the top of the desk. They swayed dangerously, leaning one against the other. I stood back a bit, to watch the effect. Perhaps I moved too quickly, and it disturbed them. At any rate the foremost one fell, and the others slid after it. They upset a little china cupid who had hitherto stood alone on the desk except for the candlesticks. He fell to the ground, hitting the waste-paper basket as he did so, and broke into fragments. I glanced hurriedly at the door, like a guilty child. I knelt on the floor and swept up the pieces into my hand. I found an envelope to put them in. I hid the envelope at the back of one of the drawers in the desk. Then I took the books off to the library and found room for them on the shelves.

Maxim laughed when I showed them to him with pride.

"Dear old Bee," he said, "you must have had a success with her. She never opens a book if she can help it."

"Did she say anything about—well—what she thought of me?" I asked.

"The day she came to lunch? No, I don't think so."

"I thought she might have written or something."

"Beatrice and I don't correspond unless there's a major event in the family. Writing letters is a waste of time," said Maxim.

I supposed I was not a major event. Yet if I had been Beatrice, and had a brother, and the brother married, surely one would have said something, expressed an opinion, written two words? Unless of course one had taken a dislike to the wife, or thought her unsuitable. Then of course it would be different. Still, Beatrice had taken the trouble to go up to London and to buy the books for me. She would not have done that if she disliked me.

It was the following day I remember, when Frith, who had brought in the coffee after lunch to the library, waited a moment, hovering behind Maxim, and said,

"Could I speak to you, sir?" Maxim glanced up from his paper.

"Yes, Frith, what is it?" he said, rather surprised. Frith wore a stiff solemn expression, his lips pursed. I thought at once his wife had died.

"It's about Robert, sir. There has been a slight unpleasantness between him and Mrs. Danvers. Robert is very upset."

"Oh, Lord," said Maxim, making a face at me. I bent down to fondle Jasper, my unfailing habit in moments of embarrassment.

"Yes, sir. It appears Mrs. Danvers has accused Robert of secreting a valuable ornament from the morning-room. It is Robert's business to bring in the fresh flowers to the morning-room and place the vases. Mrs. Danvers went in this morning after the flowers had been done, and noticed one of the ornaments was missing. It was there yesterday, she said. She accused Robert of either taking the ornament or breaking it and concealing the breakage. Robert denied both accusations most emphatically, and came to me nearly in tears, sir. You may have noticed he was not himself at lunch."

"I wondered why he handed me the cutlets without giving me a plate," murmured Maxim. "I did not know Robert was so sensitive. Well, I suppose someone else did it. One of the maids."

"No, sir. Mrs. Danvers went into the room before the girl had done the room. Nobody had been there since Madam yesterday, and Robert first thing with the flowers. It makes it very unpleasant for Robert and myself, sir."

"Yes, of course it does. Well, you had better ask Mrs. Danvers to come here and we'll get to the bottom of it. What ornament was it, anyway?"

"The china cupid, sir, that stands on the writing-table."

"Oh! Oh, Lord. That's one of our treasures, isn't it? It will have to be found. Get hold of Mrs. Danvers at once."

"Very good, sir."

Frith left the room and we were alone again. "What a confounded nuisance," said Maxim, "that cupid is worth a hell of a lot. How I loathe servants' rows too. I wonder why they come to me about it. That's your job, sweetheart."

I looked up from Jasper, my face red as fire. "Darling," I said, "I meant to tell you before, but—but I forgot. The fact is I broke that cupid when I was in the morning-room yesterday."

"You broke it? Well, why the devil didn't you say so when Frith was here?"

"I don't know. I didn't like to. I was afraid he would think me a fool."

"He'll think you much more of a fool now. You'll have to explain to him and Mrs. Danvers."

"Oh, no, please, Maxim, you tell them. Let me go upstairs."

"Don't be a little idiot. Anyone would think you were afraid of them."

"I am afraid of them. At least, not afraid, but . . ."

The door opened, and Frith ushered Mrs. Danvers into the room. I looked nervously at Maxim. He shrugged his shoulders, half-amused, half-angry.

"It's all a mistake, Mrs. Danvers. Apparently Mrs. de Winter broke the cupid herself and forgot to say anything," said Maxim.

They all looked at me. It was like being a child again. I was still aware of my guilty flush. "I'm so sorry," I said, watching Mrs. Danvers, "I never thought Robert would get into trouble."

"Is it possible to repair the ornament, Madam?" said Mrs. Danvers. She did not seem to be surprised that I was the culprit. She looked at me with her white skull's face and her dark eyes. I felt she had known it was me all along and had accused Robert to see if I would have the courage to confess.

"I'm afraid not," I said, "it smashed in little pieces."

"What did you do with the pieces?" said Maxim.

It was like being a prisoner, giving evidence. How paltry and mean my actions sounded, even to myself. "I put them all into an envelope," I said.

"Well, what did you do with the envelope?" said Maxim lighting a cigarette, his tone a mixture of amusement and exasperation.

"I put it at the back of one of the drawers in the writing-desk," I said.

"It looks as though Mrs. de Winter thought you would put her in prison, doesn't it, Mrs. Danvers?" said Maxim; "perhaps you would find the envelope and send the pieces up to London. If they are too far gone to mend it can't be helped. All right, Frith. Tell Robert to dry his tears."

Mrs. Danvers lingered when Frith had gone. "I will apologise to Robert of course," she said, "but the evidence pointed so strongly to him. It did not occur to me that Mrs. de Winter had broken the ornament herself. Perhaps, if such a thing should happen again, Mrs. de Winter will tell me personally, and I will have the matter attended to? It would save everybody a lot of unpleasantness."

"Naturally," said Maxim impatiently, "I can't think why she didn't do so yesterday. I was just going to tell her when you came into the room."

"Perhaps Mrs. de Winter was not aware of the value of the ornament?" said Mrs. Danvers, turning her eyes upon me.

"Yes," I said wretchedly. "Yes, I was afraid it was valuable. That's why I swept the pieces up so carefully."

"And hid them at the back of a drawer where no one would find them, eh?" said Maxim, with a laugh, and a shrug of the shoulders. "Is not that the sort of thing the between-maid is supposed to do, Mrs. Danvers?"

"The between-maid at Manderley would never be allowed to touch the valuable things in the morning-room, sir," said Mrs. Danvers.

"No, I can't see you letting her," said Maxim.

"It's very unfortunate," said Mrs. Danvers, "I don't think we have ever had any breakages in the morning-room before. We were always so particular. I've done the dusting in there myself since—last year. There was no one I could trust. When Mrs. de Winter was alive we used to do the valuables together."

"Yes, well—it can't be helped," said Maxim. "All right, Mrs. Danvers."

She went out of the room, and I sat on the window seat, looking out of the window. Maxim picked up his paper again. Neither of us spoke.

"I'm awfully sorry, darling," I said, after a moment, "it was very careless of me. I can't think how it happened. I was just arranging those books on the desk, to see if they would stand, and the cupid slipped."

"My sweet child, forget it. What does it matter?"

"It does matter. I ought to have been more careful. Mrs. Danvers must be furious with me."

"What the devil has she got to be furious about? It's not her bit of china."

"No, but she takes such a pride in it all. It's so awful to think nothing in there has ever been broken before. It had to be me."

"Better you than the luckless Robert."

"I wish it had been Robert. Mrs. Danvers will never forgive me."

"Damn Mrs. Danvers," said Maxim, "she's not God Almighty, is she? I can't understand you. What do you mean by saying you are afraid of her?"

"I did not mean afraid exactly. I don't see much of her. It's not that. I can't really explain."

"You do such extraordinary things," said Maxim; "fancy not getting hold of her when you broke the thing and saying, 'Here, Mrs. Danvers, get this mended.' She'd understand that. Instead of which you scrape up the remains in an envelope and hide 'em at the back of a drawer. Just like a between-maid, as I said, and not the mistress of a house."

"I am like a between-maid," I said slowly, "I know I am, in lots of ways. That's why I have so much in common with Clarice. We are on the same sort of footing. And that's why she likes me. I went and saw her mother the other day. And do you know what she said? I asked her if she thought Clarice was happy with us, and she said, 'Oh, yes, Mrs. de Winter. Clarice seems quite happy. She says, "It's not like being with a lady, Mum, it's like being with one of ourselves."' Do you suppose she meant it as a compliment or not?"

"God knows," said Maxim, "remembering Clarice's mother I should take it as a direct insult. Her cottage is generally a shambles and smells of boiled cabbage. At one time she had nine children under eleven, and she herself used to patter about in that patch of garden with no shoes and a stocking round her head. We nearly gave her notice to quit. Why Clarice looks as neat and clean as she does I can't imagine."

"She's been living with an aunt," I said, feeling rather subdued. "I know my flannel skirt has a dirty mark down the front, but I've never walked bare-foot with a stocking round my head." I knew now why Clarice did not disdain my underclothes as Alice had done. "Perhaps that's why I prefer calling on Clarice's mother to calling on people like the bishop's wife?" I went on, "the bishop's wife never said I was like one of themselves."

"If you wear that grubby skirt when you call on her I don't suppose she does," said Maxim.

"Of course I didn't call on her in my old skirt, I wore a frock," I said, "and anyway I don't think much of people who just judge one by one's clothes."

"I hardly think the bishop's wife cares twopence about clothes," said Maxim, "but she may have been rather surprised if you sat on the extreme edge of the chair and answered 'Yes' and 'No' like someone after a new job, which you did the only time we returned a call together."

"I can't help being shy."

"I know you can't, sweetheart. But you don't make an effort to conquer it."

"I think that's very unfair," I said. "I try every day, every time I go out or meet anyone new. I'm always making efforts. You don't understand. It's all very well for you, you're used to that sort of thing. I've not been brought up to it."

"Rot," said Maxim, "it's not a question of bringing up, as you put it. It's a matter of application. You don't think I like calling on people, do you? It bores me stiff. But it has to be done, in this part of the world."

"We're not talking about boredom," I said, "there's nothing to be afraid of in being bored. If I was just bored it would be different. I hate people looking me up and down as though I were a prize cow."

"Who looks you up and down?"

"All the people down here. Everybody."

"What does it matter if they do? It gives them some interest in life."

"Why must I be the one to supply the interest, and have all the criticism?"

"Because life at Manderley is the only thing that ever interests anybody down here."

"What a slap in the eye I must be to them then."

Maxim did not answer. He went on looking at his paper.

"What a slap in the eye I must be to them," I repeated. And then "I suppose that's why you married me," I said, "you knew I was dull and quiet and inexperienced, so that there would never be any gossip about me."

Maxim threw his paper on the ground and got up from his chair. "What do you mean?" he said.

His face was dark and queer, and his voice was rough, not his voice at all.

"I—I don't know," I said, leaning back against the window, "I don't mean anything. Why do you look like that?"

"What do you know about any gossip down here?" he said.

"I don't," I said, scared by the way he looked at me, "I only said it because—because of something to say. Don't look at me like that. Maxim, what have I said; what's the matter?"

"Who's been talking to you?" he said slowly.

"No one. No one at all."

"Why did you say what you did?"

"I tell you, I don't know. It just came to my head. I was angry, cross. I do hate calling on these people, I can't help it. And you criticised me for being shy. I didn't mean it. Really, Maxim, I didn't. Please believe me."

"It was not a particularly attractive thing to say, was it?" he said.

"No," I said. "No, it was rude, hateful."

He stared at me moodily, his hands in his pockets, rocking backwards and forwards on his heels. "I wonder if I did a very selfish thing in marrying you," he said. He spoke slowly, thoughtfully.

I felt very cold, rather sick. "How do you mean?" I said.

"I'm not much of a companion to you, am I?" he said. "There are too many years between us. You ought to have waited, and then married a boy of your own age. Not someone like myself, with half his life behind him."

"That's ridiculous," I said hurriedly, "you know age doesn't mean anything in marriage. Of course we are companions."

"Are we? I don't know," he said.

I knelt up on the window seat and put my arms round his shoulders. "Why do you say these things to me?" I said, "you know I love you more than anything in the world. There has never been anyone but you. You are my father and my brother and my son. All those things."

"It was my fault," he said, not listening. "I rushed you into it. I never gave you a chance to think it over."

"I did not want to think it over," I said, "there was no other choice. You don't understand, Maxim. When one loves a person . . ."

"Are you happy here?" he said, looking away from me, out of the window. "I wonder sometimes. You've got thinner. Lost your colour."

"Of course I'm happy," I said, "I love Manderley, I love the garden, I love everything. I don't mind calling on people. I just said that to be tiresome. I'll call on people every day, if you want me to. I don't mind what I do. I've never for one moment regretted marrying you, surely you must know that?"

He patted my cheek in his terrible absent way, and bent down, and kissed the top of my head. "Poor lamb, you don't have much fun, do you? I'm afraid I'm very difficult to live with."

"You're not difficult," I said eagerly, "you are easy, very easy. Much easier than I thought you would be. I used to think it would be dreadful to be married, that one's husband would drink, or use awful language, or grumble if the toast was soft at breakfast, and be rather unattractive altogether, smell possibly. You don't do any of those things."

"Good God, I hope not," said Maxim, and he smiled.

I seized advantage of his smile, I smiled too, and took his hands and kissed them. "How absurd to say we are not companions," I said, "why, look how we sit here every evening, you with a book or a paper, and me with my knitting. Just like cups of tea. Just like old people, married for years and years. Of course we are companions. Of course we are happy. You talk as though you thought we had made a mistake. You don't mean it like that, do you, Maxim? You know our marriage is a success, a wonderful success?"

"If you say so, then it's all right," he said.

"No, but you think it too, don't you, darling? It's not just me? We are happy, aren't we? Terribly happy?"

He did not answer. He went on staring out of the window while I held his hands. My throat felt dry and tight, and my eyes were burning. Oh, God, I thought, this is like two people in a play, in a moment the curtain will come down, we shall bow to the audience, and go off to our dressing-rooms. This can't be a real moment in the lives of Maxim and myself. I sat down on the window seat, and let go of his hands. I heard myself speaking in a hard cool voice. "If you don't think we are happy it would be much better if you would admit it. I don't want you to pretend anything. I'd much rather go away. Not live with you any more." It was not really happening of course. It was the girl in the play talking, not me to Maxim. I pictured the type of girl who would play the part. Tall and slim, rather nervy.

"Well, why don't you answer me?" I said.

He took my face in his hands and looked at me, just as he had before, when Frith had come into the room with tea, the day we went to the beach.

"How can I answer you?" he said. "I don't know the answer myself. If you say we are happy, let's leave it at that. It's something I know nothing about. I take your word for it. We are happy. All right then, that's agreed!" He kissed me again, and then walked away across the room. I went on sitting by the window, stiff and straight, my hands in my lap.

"You say all this because you are disappointed in me," I said. "I'm gauche and awkward, I dress badly, I'm shy with people. I warned you in Monte Carlo how it would be. You think I'm not right for Manderley."

"Don't talk nonsense," he said. "I've never said you dressed badly, or were gauche. It's your imagination. As for being shy, you'll get over that. I've told you so before."

"We've argued in a circle," I said, "we've come right back to where we started. This all began because I broke the cupid in the morning-room. If I hadn't broken the cupid none of this would have happened. We'd have drunk our coffee, and gone out into the garden."

"Oh, damn that infernal cupid," said Maxim wearily. "Do you really think I care whether it's in ten thousand pieces or not?"

"Was it very valuable?"

"Heaven knows. I suppose so. I've really forgotten."

"Are all those things in the morning-room valuable?"

"Yes, I believe so."

"Why were all the most valuable things put in the morning-room?"

"I don't know. I suppose they looked well there."

"Were they always there? When your mother was alive?"

"No. No, I don't think they were. They were scattered about the house. The chairs were in a lumber room I believe."

"When was the morning-room furnished as it is now?"

"When I was married."

"I suppose the cupid was put there then?"

"I suppose so."

"Was that found in a lumber room?"

"No. No, I don't think it was. As a matter of fact I believe it was a wedding present. Rebecca knew a lot about china."

I did not look at him. I began to polish my nails. He had said the word quite naturally, quite calmly. It had been no effort to him. After a minute I glanced at him swiftly. He was standing by the mantelpiece, his hands in his pockets. He was staring straight in front of him. He is thinking about Rebecca, I said to myself. He is thinking how strange it was that a wedding present to me should have been the cause of destroying a wedding present to Rebecca. He is thinking about the cupid. He is remembering who gave it to Rebecca. He is going over in his mind how the parcel came and how pleased she was. Rebecca knew a lot about china. Perhaps he came into the room, and she was kneeling on the floor, wrenching open the little crate in which the cupid was packed. She must have glanced up at him, and smiled. "Look, Max," she would have said, "look what we've been sent." And she then would have plunged her hand down into the shavings and brought out the cupid who stood on one foot, his bow in his hand. "We'll have it in the morning-room," she must have said, and he must have knelt down beside her, and they must have looked at the cupid together.

I went on polishing my nails. They were scrubby, like a schoolboy's nails. The cuticles grew up over the half moons. The thumb was bitten nearly to the quick. I looked at Maxim again. He was still standing in front of the fireplace.

"What are you thinking about?" I said.

My voice was steady and cool. Not like my heart, thumping inside me. Not like my mind, bitter and resentful. He lit a cigarette, surely the twenty-fifth that day, and we had only just finished lunch; he threw the match into the empty grate, he picked up the paper.

"Nothing very much, why?" he said.

"Oh, I don't know," I said, "you looked so serious, so far away."

He whistled a tune absently, the cigarette twisting in his fingers. "As a matter of fact I was wondering if they had chosen the Surrey side to play Middlesex at the Oval," he said.

He sat down in the chair again and folded the paper. I looked out of the window. Presently Jasper came to me and climbed on my lap.

CHAPTER THIRTEEN

MAXIM HAD TO GO up to London at the end of June to some public dinner. A man's dinner. Something to do with the county. He was away for two days and I was left alone. I dreaded his going. When I saw the car disappear round the sweep in the drive I felt exactly as though it were to be a final parting and I should never see him again. There would be an accident of course and later on in the afternoon, when I came back from my walk, I should find Frith white and frightened waiting for me with a message. The doctor would have rung up from some cottage hospital. "You must be very brave," he would say, "I am afraid you must be prepared for a great shock."

And Frank would come, and we would go to the hospital together. Maxim would not recognise me. I went through the whole thing as I was sitting at lunch, I could see the crowd of local people clustering round the churchyard at the funeral, and myself leaning on Frank's arm. It was so real to me that I could scarcely eat any lunch, and I kept straining my ears to hear the telephone should it ring.

I sat out in the garden under the chestnut tree in the afternoon, with a book on my lap, but I scarcely read at all. When I saw Robert come across the lawn I knew it was the telephone and I felt physically sick. "A message from the club, Madam, to say Mr. de Winter arrived ten minutes ago."

I shut up my book. "Thank you, Robert. How quickly he got up."

"Yes, Madam. A very good run."

"Did he ask to speak to me, or leave any special message?"

"No, Madam. Just that he had arrived safely. It was the porter speaking."

"All right, Robert. Thanks very much."

The relief was tremendous. I did not feel sick any more. The pain had gone. It was like coming ashore after a channel crossing. I began to feel rather hungry, and when Robert had gone back into the house I crept into the dining-room through the long window and stole some biscuits from the sideboard. I had six of them. Bath Olivers. And then an apple as well. I had no idea I was so empty. I went and ate them in the woods, in case one of the servants should see me on the lawn from the windows, and then go and tell the cook that they did not think Mrs. de Winter cared for the food prepared in the kitchen, as they had just seen her filling herself with fruit and biscuits. The cook would be offended, and perhaps go to Mrs. Danvers.

Now that Maxim was safe in London, and I had eaten my biscuits, I felt very well and curiously happy. I was aware of a sense of freedom, as though I had no responsibilities at all. It was rather like a Saturday when one was a child. No lessons, and no prep. One could do as one liked. One put on an old skirt and a pair of sand-shoes and played Hares and Hounds on the common with the children who lived next door.

I had just the same feeling. I had not felt like this all the time I had been at Manderley. It must be because Maxim had gone to London.

I was rather shocked at myself. I could not understand it at all. I had not wanted him to go. And now this lightness of heart, this spring in my step, this childish feeling that I wanted to run across the lawn, and roll down the bank. I wiped the biscuit crumbs from my mouth and called to Jasper. Perhaps I was just feeling like this because it was a lovely day. . . .

We went through the Happy Valley to the little cove. The azaleas were finished now, the petals lay brown and crinkled on the moss. The bluebells had not faded yet, they made a solid carpet in the woods above the valley, and the young bracken was shooting up, curling and green. The moss smelt rich and deep, and the bluebells were earthy, bitter. I lay down in the long grass beside the bluebells with my hands behind my head, and Jasper at my side. He looked down at me panting, his face foolish, the saliva dripping from his tongue and his heavy jowl. There were pigeons somewhere in the trees above. It was very peaceful and quiet. I wondered why it was that places are so much lovelier when one is alone. How commonplace and stupid it would be if I had a friend now, sitting beside me, someone I had known at school, who would say "By-the-way, I saw old Hilda the other day. You remember her, the one who was so good at tennis. She's married, with two children." And the bluebells beside us unnoticed, and the pigeons overhead unheard. I did not want anyone with me. Not even Maxim. If Maxim had been there I should not be lying as I was now, chewing a piece of grass, my eyes shut. I should have been watching him, watching his eyes, his expression. Wondering if he liked it, if he was bored. Wondering what he was thinking. Now I could relax, none of these things mattered. Maxim was in London. How lovely it was to be alone again. No, I did not mean that. It was disloyal, wicked. It was not what I meant. Maxim was my life and my world. I got up from the bluebells and called sharply to Jasper. We set off together down the valley to the beach. The tide was out, the sea very calm and remote. It looked like a great placid lake out there in the bay. I could not imagine it rough now, any more than I could imagine winter in summer. There was no wind, and the sun shone on the lapping water where it ran into the little pools in the rocks. Jasper scrambled up the rocks immediately, glancing back at me, one ear blown back against his head, giving him an odd rakish appearance.

"Not that way, Jasper," I said.

He cared nothing for me of course. He loped off, deliberately disobedient. "What a nuisance he is," I said aloud, and I scrambled up the rocks after him, pretending to myself I did not want to go to the other beach. "Oh, well," I thought, "it can't be helped. After all, Maxim is not with me. It's nothing to do with me."

I splashed through the pools on the rocks, humming a tune. The cove looked different when the tide was out. Less formidable. There was only about three foot of water in the tiny harbour. A boat would just float there comfortably I supposed, at dead low water. The buoy was still there. It was painted white and green, I had not noticed that before. Perhaps because it had been raining the colouring was indistinct. There was no one on the beach. I walked across the shingle to the other side of the cove, and climbed the low stone wall of the jetty-arm. Jasper ran on ahead as though it was his custom. There was a ring in the wall and an iron ladder descending to the water. That's where the dinghy would be tied, I supposed, and one would climb to it from the ladder. The buoy was just opposite, about thirty feet away. There was something written on it. I craned my neck sideways to read the lettering. "Je Reviens." What a funny name. Not like a boat. Perhaps it had been a French boat though, a fishing boat. Fishing boats sometimes had names like that. "Happy Return," "I'm Here," those sort of names. "Je Reviens"—"I come back." Yes, I supposed it was quite a good name for a boat. Only it had not been right for that particular boat which would never come back again.

It must be cold sailing out there in the bay, beyond the beacon away on the headland. The sea was calm in the bay, but even to-day, when it was so still, out there round the headland there was a ripple of white foam on the surface of the water where the tide was racing. A small boat would heel to the wind when she rounded the headland and came out of the land-locked bay. The sea would splash inboard perhaps, run down the deck. The person at the tiller would wipe the spray out of her eyes and hair, glance up at the straining mast. I wondered what colour the boat had been. Green and white perhaps, like the buoy. Not very big, Frank had said, with a little cabin.

Jasper was sniffing at the iron ladder. "Come away," I said. "I don't want to go in after you." I went back along the harbour wall to the beach. The cottage did not seem so remote and sinister at the edge of the wood as it had done before. The sun made such a difference. No rain to-day, pattering on the roof. I walked slowly up the beach towards it. After all, it was only a cottage, with nobody living in it. There was nothing to be frightened of. Nothing at all. Any place seemed damp and sinister when it had been uninhabited for a certain time. Even new bungalows and places. Besides, they had had moonlight picnics and things here. Week-end visitors probably used to come and bathe, and then go for a sail in the boat. I stood looking into the neglected garden choked with nettles. Someone ought to come and tidy it up. One of the gardeners. There was no need to leave it like this. I pushed the little gate and went to the door of the cottage. It was not entirely closed. I was certain I had closed it the last time. Jasper began growling, sniffing under the door.

"Don't, Jasper," I said. He went on sniffing deeply, his nose thrust to the lintel. I pushed the door open and looked inside. It was very dark. Like it had been before. Nothing was changed. The cobwebs still clung to the rigging of the model boats. The door into the boat store at the end of the room was open though. Jasper growled again, and there was a sound of something falling. Jasper barked furiously, and darting between my legs into the room he tore to the open door of the store. I followed him, heart beating, and then stood uncertainly in the middle of the room. "Jasper, come back, don't be a fool," I said. He stood in the doorway, still barking furiously, an hysterical note in his voice. Something was there then, inside the store. Not a rat. He would have gone for a rat. "Jasper, Jasper. Come here," I said. He would not come. I went slowly to the door of the store.

"Is there anybody there?" I said.

No one answered. I bent down to Jasper, putting my hand on his collar, and looked round the edge of the door. Someone was sitting in the corner against the wall. Someone, who from his crouching position, was even more frightened than I. It was Ben. He was trying to hide behind one of the sails. "What is the matter, do you want something?" I said. He blinked at me stupidly, his mouth slightly open.

"I'm not doing nothing," he said.

"Quiet, Jasper," I scolded, putting my hand over his muzzle, and I took my belt off and ran it through his collar as a leash.

"What do you want, Ben?" I said, a little bolder this time.

He did not answer. He watched me with his sly idiot's eyes.

"I think you had better come out," I said. "Mr. de Winter doesn't like people walking in and out of here."

He shambled to his feet grinning furtively, wiping his nose with the back of his hand. The other hand he kept behind his back. "What have you got, Ben?" I said. He obeyed me like a child, showing me the other hand. There was a fishing line in it. "I'm not doing nothing," he repeated.

"Does that line belong here?" I asked.

"Eh?" he said.

"Listen, Ben," I said, "you can take that line if you want to, but you mustn't do it again. It's not honest, taking people's things."

He said nothing. He blinked at me and wriggled.

"Come along," I said firmly. I went into the main room and he followed me. Jasper had stopped barking, and was now sniffing at Ben's heels. I did not want to stop any longer in the cottage. I walked quickly out into the sunshine, Ben shuffling behind me. Then I shut the door.

"You had better go home," I said to Ben.

He held the fishing line clutched to his heart like a treasure. "You won't put me to the asylum, will you?" he said.

I saw then that he was trembling with fright. His hands were shaking, and his eyes were fixed on mine in supplication, like a dumb thing.

"Of course not," I said gently.

"I done nothing," he repeated, "I never told no one. I don't want to be put to the asylum." A tear rolled down his dirty face.

"That's all right, Ben," I said, "no one will put you away. But you must not go to the cottage again."

I turned away, and he came after me, pawing at my hand.

"Here," he said. "Here I got something for you."

He smiled foolishly, he beckoned with his finger, and turned towards the beach. I went with him, and he bent down and picked up a flat stone by a rock. There was a little heap of shells under the stone. He chose one, and presented it to me. "That's yourn," he said.

"Thank you, it's very pretty," I said.

He grinned again, rubbing his ear, his fright forgotten. "You've got angel's eyes," he said.

I glanced down at the shell, again, rather taken aback. I did not know what to say.

"You're not like the other one," he said.

"Who do you mean?" I said. "What other one?"

He shook his head. His eyes were sly again. He laid his finger against his nose. "Tall and dark she was," he said. "She gave you the feeling of a snake. I seen her here with me own eyes. By night she'd come. I seen her." He paused, watching me intently. I did not say anything. "I looked in on her once," he said, "and she turned on me, she did. 'You don't know me, do you?' she said. 'You've never seen me here, and you won't again. If I catch you looking at me through the windows here I'll have you put to the asylum,' she said. 'You wouldn't like that, would you? They're cruel to people in the asylum,' she said. 'I won't say nothing, Ma'am,' I said. And I touched me cap, like this here." He pulled at his sou'wester. "She's gone now, ain't she?" he said anxiously.

"I don't know who you mean," I said slowly, "no one is going to put you in the asylum. Good afternoon, Ben."

I turned away and walked up the beach to the path dragging Jasper by his belt. Poor wretch, he was potty of course. He did not know what he was talking about. It was hardly likely that anyone would threaten him with the asylum. Maxim had said he was quite harmless, and so had Frank. Perhaps he had heard himself discussed once, amongst his own people, and the memory of it lingered, like an ugly picture in the mind of a child. He would have a child's mentality too, regarding likes and dislikes. He would take a fancy to a person for no reason, and be friendly one day perhaps and sullen the next. He had been friendly with me because I had said he could keep the fishing line. To-morrow if I met him he might not know me. It was absurd to notice anything said by an idiot. I glanced back over my shoulder at the cove. The tide had begun to turn and was swirling slowly round the arm of the harbour wall. Ben had disappeared over the rocks. The beach was deserted again. I could just see the stone chimney of the cottage through a gap in the dark trees. I had a sudden unaccountable desire to run. I pulled at Jasper's leash and panted up the steep narrow path through the woods not looking back any more. Had I been offered all the treasures in the world I could not have turned and gone down to the cottage or the beach again. It was as though someone waited down there, in the little garden where the nettles grew. Someone who watched and listened.

Jasper barked as we ran together. He thought it was some new kind of game. He kept trying to bite the belt and worry it. I had not realised how closely the trees grew together here, their roots stretching across the path like tendrils ready to trip one. They ought to clear all this, I thought as I ran, catching my breath, Maxim should get the men on to it. There is no sense or beauty in this undergrowth. That tangle of shrubs there should be cut down to bring light to the path. It was dark, much too dark. That naked eucalyptus tree stifled by brambles looked like the white bleached limb of a skeleton, and there was a black earthy stream running beneath it, choked with the muddied rains of years, trickling silently to the beach below. The birds did not sing here as they did in the valley. It was quiet in a different way. And even as I ran and panted up the path I could hear the wash of the sea as the tide crept into the cove. I understood why Maxim disliked the path and the cove. I disliked it too. I had been a fool to come this way. I should have stayed on the other beach, on the white shingle, and come home by the Happy Valley.

I was glad to come out on to the lawn and see the house there in the hollow, solid and secure. The woods were behind me. I would ask Robert to bring me my tea under the chestnut tree. I glanced at my watch. It was earlier than I thought, not yet four. I would have to wait a bit. It was not the routine at Manderley to have tea before half-past. I was glad Frith was out. Robert would not make such a performance of bringing the tea out into the garden. As I wandered across the lawn to the terrace my eye was caught by a gleam of sunshine on something metal showing through the green of the rhododendron leaves at the turn in the drive. I shaded my eyes with my hand to see what it was. It looked like the radiator of a car. I wondered if someone had called. If they had though, they would have driven up to the house, not left their car concealed like that from the house, at the turn of the drive, by the shrubs. I went a little closer. Yes, it was a car all right. I could see the wings now and the hood. What a funny thing. Visitors never did that as a rule. And the tradesmen went round the back way by the old stables and the garage. It was not Frank's Morris. I knew that well. This was a long, low car, a sports car. I wondered what I had better do. If it was a caller Robert would have shown them into the library or the drawing-room. If the drawing-room they would be able to see me as I came across the lawn. I did not want to face a caller dressed like this. I should have to ask them to stay to tea. I hesitated, at the edge of the lawn. For no reason, perhaps because the sunlight flickered a moment on the glass, I looked up at the house, and as I did so I noticed with surprise that the shutters of one of the windows in the west wing had been opened up. Somebody stood by the window. A man. And then he must have caught sight of me because he drew back abruptly, and a figure behind him put up an arm and closed the shutters.

The arm belonged to Mrs. Danvers. I recognised the black sleeve. I wondered for a minute if it was a public day and she was showing the rooms. It could not be so though because Frith always did that, and Frith was out. Besides, the rooms in the west wing were not shown to the public. I had not even been into them myself yet. No, I knew it was not a public day. The public never came on a Tuesday. Perhaps it was something to do with a repair in one of the rooms. It was odd though the way the man had been looking out and directly he saw me he whipped back into the room and the shutters were closed. And the car too, drawn up behind the rhododendrons, so that it could not be seen from the house. Still, that was up to Mrs. Danvers. It was nothing to do with me. If she had friends she took to the west wing it was not exactly my affair. I had never known it to happen before though. Odd that it should occur on the only day Maxim was from home.

I strolled rather self-consciously across the lawn to the house, aware that they might be watching me still from a chink in the shutters.

I went up the steps and through the big front door to the hall. There was no sign of a strange cap or stick, and no card on the salver. Evidently this was not an official visitor. Well, it was not my affair. I went into the flower-room and washed my hands in the basin to save going upstairs. It would be awkward if I met them face to face on the stairs or somewhere. I remembered I had left my knitting in the morning-room before lunch, and I went along through the drawing-room to fetch it, the faithful Jasper at my heels. The morning-room door was open. And I noticed that my bag of knitting had been moved. I had left it on the divan, and it had been picked up and pushed behind a cushion. There was the imprint of a person on the fabric of the divan where my knitting had been before. Someone had sat down there recently, and picked up my knitting because it had been in the way. The chair by the desk had also been moved. It looked as though Mrs. Danvers entertained her visitors in the morning-room when Maxim and I were out of the way. I felt rather uncomfortable. I would rather not know. Jasper was sniffing round the divan and wagging his tail. He was not suspicious of the visitor anyway. I took my bag of knitting and went out. As I did so the door in the large drawing-room that led to the stone passage and the back premises opened, and I heard voices. I darted back into the morning-room again, just in time. I had not been seen. I waited behind the door frowning at Jasper who stood in the doorway looking at me, his tongue hanging out, wagging his tail. The little wretch would give me away. I stood very still, holding my breath.

Then I heard Mrs. Danvers speak. "I expect she has gone to the library," she said. "She's come home early for some reason. If she has gone to the library you will be able to go through the hall without her seeing you. Wait here while I go and see."

I knew they were talking about me. I began to feel more uncomfortable than ever. It was so furtive, the whole business. And I did not want to catch Mrs. Danvers in the wrong. Then Jasper turned his head sharply towards the drawing-room. He trotted out, wagging his tail.

"Hullo, you little tyke," I heard the man say. Jasper began to bark excitedly. I looked round desperately for somewhere to hide. Hopeless of course. And then I heard a footstep quite close to my ear, and the man came into the room. He did not see me at first because I was behind the door, but Jasper made a dive at me, still barking with delight.

The man wheeled round suddenly and saw me. I have never seen anyone look more astonished. I might have been the burglar and he the master of the house.

"I beg your pardon," he said, looking me up and down.

He was a big, hefty fellow, good-looking in a rather flashy, sunburnt way. He had the hot, blue eyes usually associated with heavy drinking and loose living. His hair was reddish like his skin. In a few years he would run to fat, his neck bulging over the back of his collar. His mouth gave him away, it was too soft, too pink. I could smell the whisky in his breath from where I stood. He began to smile. The sort of smile he would give to every woman.

"I hope I haven't startled you," he said.

I came out from behind the door looking no doubt as big a fool as I felt. "No, of course not," I said, "I heard voices, I was not quite sure who it was. I did not expect any callers this afternoon."

"What a shame," he said heartily, "it's too bad of me to butt in on you like this. I hope you'll forgive me. The fact is I just popped in to see old Danny, she's a very old friend of mine."

"Oh, of course, it's quite all right," I said.

"Dear old Danny," he said, "she's so anxious, bless her, not to disturb anyone. She didn't want to worry you."

"Oh, it does not matter at all," I said. I was watching Jasper, who was jumping up and pawing at the man in delight.

"This little beggar hasn't forgotten me, has he?" he said. "Grown into a jolly little beast. He was quite a youngster when I saw him last. He's too fat though. He needs more exercise."

"I've just taken him for a long walk," I said.

"Have you really? How sporting of you," he said. He went on patting Jasper and smiling at me in a familiar way. Then he pulled out his cigarette case. "Have one?" he said.

"I don't smoke," I told him.

"Don't you really?" He took one himself and lighted it.

I never minded those things, but it seemed odd to me, in somebody else's room. It was surely rather bad manners? Not polite to me.

"How's old Max?" he said.

I was surprised at his tone. It sounded as though he knew him well. It was queer, to hear Maxim talked of as Max. No one called him that.

"He's very well, thank you," I said, "he's gone up to London."

"And left the bride all alone? Why, that's too bad. Isn't he afraid someone will come and carry you off?"

He laughed, opening his mouth. I did not like his laugh. There was something offensive about it. I did not like him either. Just then Mrs. Danvers came into the room. She turned her eyes upon me and I felt quite cold. Oh, God, I thought, how she must hate me.

"Hullo, Danny, there you are," said the man, "all your precautions were in vain. The mistress of the house was hiding behind the door." And he laughed again. Mrs. Danvers did not say anything. She just went on looking at me. "Well, aren't you going to introduce me?" he said, "after all, it's the usual thing to do, isn't it, to pay one's respects to a bride?"

"This is Mr. Favell, Madam," said Mrs. Danvers. She spoke quietly, rather unwillingly. I don't think she wanted to introduce him to me.

"How do you do," I said, and then, with an effort to be polite, "Won't you stay to tea?"

He looked very amused. He turned to Mrs. Danvers.

"Now isn't that a charming invitation?" he said. "I've been asked to stay to tea. By heaven, Danny, I've a good mind to."

I saw her flash a look of warning at him. I felt very uneasy. It was all wrong, this situation. It ought not to be happening at all.

"Well, perhaps you're right," he said, "it would have been a lot of fun, all the same. I suppose I had better be going, hadn't I? Come and have a look at my car." He still spoke in a familiar rather offensive way. I did not want to go and look at his car. I felt very awkward and embarrassed. "Come on," he said, "it's a jolly good little car. Much faster than anything poor old Max ever has."

I could not think of an excuse. The whole business was so forced and stupid. I did not like it. And why did Mrs. Danvers have to stand there looking at me with that smouldering look in her eyes?

"Where is the car?" I said feebly.

"Round the bend in the drive. I didn't drive to the door. I was afraid of disturbing you. I had some idea you probably rested in the afternoon."

I said nothing. The lie was too obvious. We all walked out through the drawing-room and into the hall. I saw him glance over his shoulder and wink at Mrs. Danvers. She did not wink in return. I hardly expected she would. She looked very hard and grim. Jasper frolicked out on the drive. He seemed delighted with the sudden appearance of this visitor whom he appeared to know so well.

"I left my cap in the car I believe," said the man, pretending to glance round the hall. "As a matter of fact, I didn't come in this way. I slipped round and bearded Danny in her den. Coming out to see the car too?"

He looked enquiringly at Mrs. Danvers. She hesitated, watching me out of the tail of her eye.

"No," she said. "No, I don't think I'll come out now. Good-bye, Mr. Jack."

He seized her hand and shook it heartily. "Good-bye, Danny, take care of yourself. You know where to get in touch with me always. It's done me a power of good to see you again." He walked out on to the drive, Jasper dancing at his heels, and I followed him slowly, feeling very uncomfortable still.

"Dear old Manderley," he said, looking up at the windows, "the place hasn't changed much. I suppose Danny sees to that. What a wonderful woman she is, eh?"

"Yes, she's very efficient," I said.

"And what do you think of it all? Like being buried down here?"

"I'm very fond of Manderley," I said stiffly.

"Weren't you living somewhere down in the south of France when Max met you? Monte, wasn't it? I used to know Monte well."

"Yes, I was in Monte Carlo," I said.

We had come to his car now. A green sports thing, typical of its owner.

"What do you think of it?" he said.

"Very nice," I said politely.

"Come for a run to the lodge gates?" he said.

"No, I don't think I will," I said. "I'm rather tired."

"You don't think it would look too good for the mistress of Manderley to be seen driving with someone like me, is that it?" he said, and he laughed, shaking his head at me.

"Oh, no," I said, turning rather red. "No, really."

He went on looking me up and down in his amused way with those familiar, unpleasant blue eyes. I felt like a bar-maid.

"Oh, well," he said, "we mustn't lead the bride astray, must we, Jasper? It wouldn't do at all." He reached for his cap, and an enormous pair of motoring gloves. He threw his cigarette away on the drive.

"Good-bye," he said, holding out his hand, "it's been a lot of fun meeting you."

"Good-bye," I said.

"By-the-way," he said carelessly, "it would be very sporting and grand of you if you did not mention this little visit of mine to Max. He doesn't exactly approve of me, I'm afraid; I don't know why, and it might get poor old Danny into trouble."

"No," I said awkwardly. "No, all right."

"That's very sporting of you. Sure you won't change your mind and come for a run?"

"No, I don't think I will, if you don't mind."

"Bye-bye, then. Perhaps I'll come and look you up one day. Get down, Jasper, you devil, you'll scratch my paint. I say, I call it a damn shame Max going up to London and leaving you alone like this."

"I don't mind. I like being alone," I said.

"Do you, by Jove? What an extraordinary thing. It's all wrong, you know. Against nature. How long have you been married? Three months, isn't it?"

"About that," I said.

"I say, I wish I'd got a bride of three months waiting for me at home! I'm a poor lonesome bachelor." He laughed again, and pulled his cap down over his eyes. "Fare you well," he said, starting up the engine, and the car shot down the drive snorting explosive fury from the exhaust, while Jasper stood looking after it, his ears drooping, his tail between his legs.

"Oh, come on, Jasper," I said, "don't be so idiotic." I walked slowly back to the house. Mrs. Danvers had disappeared. I stood in the hall and rang the bell. Nothing happened for about five minutes. I rang. Presently Alice appeared, her face rather aggrieved. "Yes, Madam?" she said.

"Oh, Alice," I said, "isn't Robert there? I rather fancied my tea out under the chestnut tree."

"Robert went to the post this afternoon, and isn't back yet, Madam," said Alice. "Mrs. Danvers gave him to understand you would be late for tea. Frith is out too of course. If you want your tea now I can get it for you. I don't think it's quite half-past four yet."

"Oh, it doesn't matter, Alice, I'll wait till Robert comes back," I said. I supposed when Maxim was away things automatically became slack. I had never known Frith and Robert to be out at the same time. It was Frith's day of course. And Mrs. Danvers had sent Robert to the post. And I myself was understood to have gone for a long walk. That man Favell had chosen his time well to pay his call on Mrs. Danvers. It was almost too well chosen. There was something not right about it, I was certain of that. And then he had asked me not to say anything to Maxim. It was all very awkward. I did not want to get Mrs. Danvers into trouble or make any sort of scene. More important still I did not want to worry Maxim.

I wondered who he was, this man Favell. He had called Maxim "Max." No one ever called him Max. I had seen it written once, on the fly-leaf of a book, the letters thin and slanting, curiously pointed, the tail of the M very definite, very long. I thought there was only one person who had ever called him Max. . . .

As I stood there in the hall, undecided about my tea, wondering what to do, the thought suddenly came to me that perhaps Mrs. Danvers was dishonest, that all this time she was engaged in some business behind Maxim's back, and coming back early as I had to-day I had discovered her and this man, an accomplice, who had then bluffed his way out by pretending to be familiar with the house and with Maxim. I wondered what they had been doing in the west wing. Why had they closed the shutters when they saw me on the lawn? I was filled with vague disquiet. Frith and Robert had been away. The maids were generally in their bedrooms changing during the afternoon. Mrs. Danvers would have the run of the place. Supposing this man was a thief, and Mrs. Danvers was in his pay? There were valuable things in the west wing. I had a sudden rather terrifying impulse to creep upstairs now to the west wing and go into those rooms and see for myself.

Robert was not yet back. I would just have time before tea. I hesitated, glancing at the gallery. The house seemed very still and quiet. The servants were all in their own quarters beyond the kitchen. Jasper lapped noisily at his drinking bowl below the stairs, the sound echoing in the great stone hall. I began to walk upstairs. My heart was beating in a queer excited way.

CHAPTER FOURTEEN

I FOUND MYSELF in the corridor where I had stood that first morning. I had not been there since, nor had I wished to go. The sun streamed in from the window in the alcove and made gold patterns on the dark panelling.

There was no sound at all. I was aware of the same musty, unused smell that had been before. I was uncertain which way to go. The plan of the rooms was not familiar to me. I remembered then that last time Mrs. Danvers had come out of a door here, just behind me, and it seemed to me that the position of the room would make it the one I wanted, whose windows looked out upon the lawns to the sea. I turned the handle of the door and went inside. It was dark of course, because of the shutters. I felt for the electric light switch on the wall and turned it on. I was standing in a little ante-room, a dressing-room I judged, with big wardrobes round the wall, and at the end of this room was another door, open, leading to a larger room. I went through to this room, and turned on the light. My first impression was one of shock because the room was fully furnished, as though in use.

I had expected to see chairs and tables swathed in dust-sheets, and dust-sheets too over the great double bed against the wall. Nothing was covered up. There were brushes and combs on the dressing-table, scent, and powder. The bed was made up, I saw the gleam of white linen on the pillow-case, and the tip of a blanket beneath the quilted coverlet. There were flowers on the dressing-table and on the table beside the bed. Flowers too on the carved mantelpiece. A satin dressing-gown lay on a chair, and a pair of bedroom slippers beneath. For one desperate moment I thought that something had happened to my brain, that I was seeing back into Time, and looking upon the room as it used to be, before she died. . . . In a minute Rebecca herself would come back into the room, sit down before the looking-glass at her dressing-table, humming a tune, reach for her comb and run it through her hair. If she sat there I should see her reflection in the glass, and she would see me too, standing like this by the door. Nothing happened. I went on standing there, waiting for something to happen. It was the clock ticking on the wall that brought me to reality again. The hands stood at twenty-five past four. My watch said the same. There was something sane and comforting about the ticking of the clock. It reminded me of the present, and that tea would soon be ready for me on the lawn. I walked slowly into the middle of the room. No, it was not used. It was not lived in any more. Even the flowers could not destroy the musty smell. The curtains were drawn and the shutters were closed. Rebecca would never come back to the room again. Even if Mrs. Danvers did put the flowers on the mantelpiece and the sheets upon the bed, they would not bring her back. She was dead. She had been dead now for a year. She lay buried in the crypt of the church with all the other dead de Winters.

I could hear the sound of the sea very plainly. I went to the window and swung back the shutter. Yes, I was standing at the same window where Favell and Mrs. Danvers had stood, half an hour ago. The long shaft of daylight made the electric light look false and yellow. I opened the shutter a little more. The daylight cast a white beam upon the bed. It shone upon the nightdress case, lying on the pillow. It shone on the glass top of the dressing-table, on the brushes, and on the scent bottles.

The daylight gave an even greater air of reality to the room. When the shutter was closed and it had been lit by electricity the room had more the appearance of a setting on the stage. The scene set between performances. The curtain having fallen for the night, the evening over, and the first act set for to-morrow's matinée. But the daylight made the room vivid and alive. I forgot the musty smell and the drawn curtains of the other windows. I was a guest again. An uninvited guest. I had strolled into my hostess's bedroom by mistake. Those were her brushes on the dressing-table, that was her dressing-gown and slippers laid out upon the chair.

I realised for the first time since I had come into the room that my legs were trembling, weak as straw. I sat down on the stool by the dressing-table. My heart no longer beat in a strange excited way. It felt as heavy as lead. I looked about me in the room with a sort of dumb stupidity. Yes, it was a beautiful room. Mrs. Danvers had not exaggerated that first evening. It was the most beautiful room in the house. That exquisite mantelpiece, the ceiling, the carved bedstead and the curtain hangings, even the clock on the wall and the candlesticks upon the dressing-table beside me, all were things I would have loved and almost worshipped had they been mine. They were not mine though. They belonged to somebody else. I put out my hand and touched the brushes. One was more worn than its fellow. I understood it well. There was always one brush that had the greater use. Often you forgot to use the other, and when they were taken to be washed there was one that was still quite clean and untouched. How white and thin my face looked in the glass, my hair hanging lank and straight. Did I always look like this? Surely I had more colour as a rule? The reflection stared back at me, sallow and plain.

I got up from the stool and went and touched the dressing-gown on the chair. I picked up the slippers and held them in my hand. I was aware of a growing sense of horror, of horror turning to despair. I touched the quilt on the bed, traced with my fingers the monogram on the nightdress case, R de W, interwoven and interlaced. The letters were corded and strong against the golden satin material. The nightdress was inside the case, thin as gossamer, apricot in colour. I touched it, drew it out from the case, put it against my face. It was cold, quite cold. But there was a dim mustiness about it still where the scent had been. The scent of the white azalea. I folded it, and put it back into the case, and as I did so I noticed with a sick dull aching in my heart that there were creases in the nightdress, the texture was ruffled, it had not been touched or laundered since it was last worn.

On a sudden impulse I moved away from the bed and went back to the little ante-room where I had seen the wardrobes. I opened one of them. It was as I thought. The wardrobe was full of clothes. There were evening dresses here, I caught the shimmer of silver over the top of the white bags that enfolded them. There was a piece of gold brocade. There, next to it, was velvet, wine-coloured, and soft. There was a train of white satin, dripping on the floor of the wardrobe. Peeping out from a piece of tissue paper on a shelf above was an ostrich feather fan.

The wardrobe smelt stuffy, queer. The azalea scent, so fragrant and delicate in the air, had turned stale inside the wardrobe, tarnishing the silver dresses and the brocade, and the breath of it wafted towards me now from the open doors, faded and old. I shut the doors. I went back into the bedroom once again. The gleam of light from the shutter still shone white and clear on the golden coverlet of the bed, picking out clearly and distinctly the tall sloping R of the monogram.

Then I heard a step behind me and turning round I saw Mrs. Danvers.

I shall never forget the expression on her face. Triumphant, gloating, excited in a strange unhealthy way. I felt very frightened.

"Is anything the matter, Madam?" she said.

I tried to smile at her and could not. I tried to speak.

"Are you feeling unwell?" she said, coming nearer to me, speaking very softly. I backed away from her. I believe if she had come any closer to me I should have fainted. I felt her breath on my face.

"I'm all right, Mrs. Danvers," I said, after a moment, "I did not expect to see you. The fact is, I was looking up at the windows from the lawn. I noticed one of the shutters was not quite closed. I came up to see if I could fasten it."

"I will fasten it," she said, and she went silently across the room and clamped back the shutter. The daylight had gone. The room looked unreal again in the false yellow light. Unreal and ghastly.

Mrs. Danvers came back and stood beside me. She smiled, and her manner instead of being still and unbending as it usually was became startlingly familiar, fawning even.

"Why did you tell me the shutter was open?" she said. "I closed it before I left the room. You opened it yourself, didn't you, now? You wanted to see the room. Why have you never asked me to show it to you before? I was ready to show it to you every day. You had only to ask me."

I wanted to run away, but I could not move. I went on watching her eyes.

"Now you are here, let me show you everything," she said, her voice ingratiating and sweet as honey, horrible, false. "I know you want to see it all, you've wanted to for a long time, and you were too shy to ask. It's a lovely room, isn't it? The loveliest room you have ever seen."

She took hold of my arm, and walked me towards the bed. I could not resist her, I was like a dumb thing. The touch of her hand made me shudder. And her voice was low and intimate, a voice I hated and feared.

"That was her bed. It's a beautiful bed, isn't it? I keep the golden coverlet on it always, it was her favourite. Here is her nightdress inside the case. You've been touching it, haven't you? This was the nightdress she was wearing for the last time, before she died. Would you like to touch it again?" She took the nightdress from the case and held it before me. "Feel it, hold it," she said, "how soft and light it is, isn't it? I haven't washed it since she wore it for the last time. I put it out like this, and the dressing-gown and slippers, just as I put them out for her the night she never came back, the night she was drowned." She folded up the nightgown and put it back in the case. "I did everything for her, you know," she said, taking my arm again, leading me to the dressing-gown and slippers. "We tried maid after maid but not one of them suited. 'You maid me better than anyone, Danny,' she used to say, 'I won't have anyone but you.' Look, this is her dressing-gown. She was much taller than you, you can see by the length. Put it up against you. It comes down to your ankles. She had a beautiful figure. These are her slippers. 'Throw me my slips, Danny,' she used to say. She had little feet for her height. Put your hands inside the slippers. They are quite small and narrow, aren't they?"

She forced the slippers over my hands, smiling all the while, watching my eyes. "You never would have thought she was so tall, would you?" she said, "these slippers would fit a tiny foot. She was so slim too. You would forget her height, until she stood beside you. She was every bit as tall as me. But lying there in bed she looked quite a slip of a thing, with her mass of dark hair, standing out from her face like a halo."

She put the slippers back on the floor, and laid the dressing-gown on the chair. "You've seen her brushes, haven't you?" she said, taking me to the dressing-table, "there they are, just as she used them, unwashed and untouched. I used to brush her hair for her every evening. 'Come on, Danny, hair-drill,' she would say, and I'd stand behind her by the stool here, and brush away for twenty minutes at a time. She only wore it short the last few years, you know. It came down below the waist, when she was first married. Mr. de Winter used to brush it for her then. I've come into this room time and time again and seen him, in his shirt sleeves, with the two brushes in his hand. 'Harder, Max, harder,' she would say, laughing up at him, and he would do as she told him. They would be dressing for dinner, you see, and the house filled with guests. 'Here, I shall be late,' he would say, throwing the brushes to me, and laughing back at her. He was always laughing and gay then."

She paused, her hand still resting on my arm.

"Everyone was angry with her when she cut her hair," she said, "but she did not care. 'It's nothing to do with anyone but myself,' she would say. And of course short hair was much easier for riding and sailing. She was painted on horseback, you know. A famous artist did it. The picture hung in the Academy. Did you ever see it?"

I shook my head. "No," I said. "No."

"I understood it was the picture of the year," she went on, "but Mr. de Winter did not care for it, and would not have it at Manderley. I don't think he considered it did her justice. You would like to see her clothes, wouldn't you?" She did not wait for my answer. She led me to the little ante-room and opened the wardrobes, one by one.

"I keep her furs in here," she said, "the moths have not got to them yet, and I doubt if they ever will. I'm too careful. Feel that sable wrap. That was a Christmas present from Mr. de Winter. She told me the cost once, but I've forgotten it now. This chinchilla she wore in the evenings mostly. Round her shoulders, very often, when the evenings were cold. This wardrobe here is full of her evening clothes. You opened it, didn't you? The latch is not quite closed. I believe Mr. de Winter liked her to wear silver mostly. But of course she could wear anything, stand any colour. She looked beautiful in this velvet. Put it against your face. It's soft, isn't it? You can feel it, can't you? The scent is still fresh, isn't it? You could almost imagine she had only just taken it off. I would always know when she had been before me in a room. There would be a little whiff of her scent in the room. These are her underclothes, in this drawer. This pink set here she had never worn. She was wearing slacks of course and a shirt when she died. They were torn from her body in the water though. There was nothing on the body when it was found, all those weeks afterwards."

Her fingers tightened on my arm. She bent down to me, her skull's face close, her dark eyes searching mine. "The rocks had battered her to bits, you know," she whispered, "her beautiful face unrecognisable, and both arms gone. Mr. de Winter identified her. He went up to Edgecoombe to do it. He went quite alone. He was very ill at the time but he would go. No one could stop him. Not even Mr. Crawley."

She paused, her eyes never leaving my face. "I shall always blame myself for the accident," she said, "it was my fault for being out that evening. I had gone into Kerrith for the afternoon and stayed there late, as Mrs. de Winter was up in London and not expected back until much later. That's why I did not hurry back. When I came in, about half-past nine, I heard she had returned just before seven, had her dinner, and then went out again. Down to the beach of course. I felt worried then. It was blowing up from the southwest. She would never have gone if I'd been in. She always listened to me. 'I wouldn't go out this evening, it's not fit,' I should have said, and she would have answered me 'All right, Danny, you old fusspot.' And we would have sat up here talking no doubt, she telling me all she had done up in London, like she always did."

My arm was bruised and numb from the pressure of her fingers. I could see how tightly the skin was stretched across her face, showing the cheek-bones. There were little patches of yellow beneath her ears.

"Mr. de Winter had been dining with Mr. Crawley down at his house," she went on. "I don't know what time he got back, I dare say it was after eleven. But it began to blow quite hard, just before midnight, and she had not come back. I went downstairs, but there were no lights under the library door. I came upstairs again and knocked on the dressing-room door. Mr. de Winter answered at once, 'Who is it, what do you want?' he said. I told him I was worried about Mrs. de Winter not being back. He waited a moment, and then he came and opened the door in his dressing-gown. 'She's spending the night down at the cottage I expect,' he said. 'I should go to bed if I were you. She won't come back here to sleep if it goes on like this.' He looked tired, and I did not like to disturb him. After all, she spent many nights at the cottage, and had sailed in every sort of weather. She might not even have gone for a sail, but just wanted the night at the cottage as a change after London. I said good night to Mr. de Winter and went back to my room. I did not sleep though. I kept wondering what she was doing."

She paused again. I did not want to hear any more. I wanted to get away from her, away from the room.

"I sat on my bed until half-past five," she said, "then I couldn't wait there any longer. I got up and put on my coat and went down through the woods to the beach. It was getting light, but there was still a misty sort of rain falling, although the wind had dropped. When I got to the beach I saw the buoy there in the water and the dinghy, but the boat had gone. . . ." It seemed to me that I could see the cove in the grey morning light, feel the thin drizzle on my face, and peering through the mist could make out, shadowy and indistinct, the low dark outline of the buoy.

Mrs. Danvers loosened the pressure on my arm. Her hand fell back again to her side. Her voice lost all expression, became the hard mechanical voice of every day.

"One of the life-buoys was washed up at Kerrith in the afternoon," she said, "and another was found the next day by some crabbers on the rocks below the headland. Bits and pieces of rigging too would come in with the tide." She turned away from me, and closed the chest of drawers. She straightened one of the pictures on the wall. She picked up a piece of fluff from the carpet. I stood watching her, not knowing what to do.

"You know now," she said, "why Mr. de Winter does not use these rooms any more. Listen to the sea."

Even with the windows closed and the shutters fastened I could hear it; a low sullen murmur as the waves broke on the white shingle in the cove. The tide would be coming in fast now and running up the beach nearly to the stone cottage.

"He has not used these rooms since the night she was drowned," she said. "He had his things moved out from the dressing-room. We made up one of the rooms at the end of the corridor. I don't think he slept much even there. He used to sit in the arm-chair. There would be cigarette-ash all round it in the morning. And in the daytime Frith would hear him in the library pacing up and down. Up and down, up and down."

I too could see the ash on the floor beside the chair. I too could hear his footsteps; one, two, one, two, backwards and forwards across the library. . . . Mrs. Danvers closed the door softly between the bedroom and the ante-room where we were standing, and put out the light. I could not see the bed any more, nor the nightdress case upon the pillow, nor the dressing-table, nor the slippers by the chair. She crossed the ante-room and put her hand on the knob of the door and stood waiting for me to follow her.

"I come to the rooms and dust them myself every day," she said. "If you want to come again you have only to tell me. Ring me on the house telephone. I shall understand. I don't allow the maids up here. No one ever comes but me."

Her manner was fawning again, intimate and unpleasant. The smile on her face was a false, unnatural thing. "Sometimes when Mr. de Winter is away, and you feel lonely, you might like to come up to these rooms and sit here. You have only to tell me. They are such beautiful rooms. You would not think she had been gone now for so long, would you, not by the way the rooms are kept? You would think she had just gone out for a little while and would be back in the evening."

I forced a smile. I could not speak. My throat felt dry and tight.

"It's not only this room," she said. "It's in many rooms in the house. In the morning-room, in the hall, even in the little flower-room. I feel her everywhere. You do too, don't you?"

She stared at me curiously. Her voice dropped to a whisper. "Sometimes, when I walk along the corridor here I fancy I hear her just behind me. That quick, light footstep. I could not mistake it anywhere. And in the minstrels' gallery above the hall. I've seen her leaning there, in the evenings in the old days, looking down at the hall below and calling to the dogs. I can fancy her there now from time to time. It's almost as though I catch the sound of her dress sweeping the stairs as she comes down to dinner." She paused. She went on looking at me, watching my eyes. "Do you think she can see us, talking to one another now?" she said slowly. "Do you think the dead come back and watch the living?"

I swallowed. I dug my nails into my hands.

"I don't know," I said. "I don't know." My voice sounded high-pitched and unnatural. Not my voice at all.

"Sometimes I wonder," she whispered. "Sometimes I wonder if she comes back here to Manderley and watches you and Mr. de Winter together."

We stood there by the door, staring at one another. I could not take my eyes away from hers. How dark and sombre they were in that white skull's face of hers, how malevolent, how full of hatred. Then she opened the door into the corridor. "Robert is back now," she said. "He came back a quarter of an hour ago. He has orders to take your tea out under the chestnut tree."

She stepped aside for me to pass. I stumbled out on to the corridor, not looking where I was going. I did not speak to her, I went down the stairs blindly, and turned the corner and pushed through the door that led to my own rooms in the east wing. I shut the door of my room and turned the key, and put the key in my pocket.

Then I lay down on my bed and closed my eyes. I felt deadly sick.

CHAPTER FIFTEEN

MAXIM RANG up the next morning to say he would be back about seven. Frith took the message. Maxim did not ask to speak to me himself. I heard the telephone ring while I was at breakfast and I thought perhaps Frith would come into the dining-room and say "Mr. de Winter on the telephone, Madam." I had put down my napkin and had risen to my feet. And then Frith came back into the dining-room and gave me the message.

He saw me push back my chair and go to the door. "Mr. de Winter has rung off, Madam," he said, "there was no message. Just that he would be back about seven."

I sat down in my chair again and picked up my napkin. Frith must have thought me eager and stupid rushing across the dining-room.

"All right, Frith. Thank you," I said.

I went on eating my eggs and bacon, Jasper at my feet, the old dog in her basket in the corner. I wondered what I should do with my day. I had slept badly; perhaps because I was alone in the room. I had been restless, waking up often, and when I glanced at my clock I saw the hands had scarcely moved. When I did fall asleep I had varied, wandering dreams. We were walking through woods, Maxim and I, and he was always just a little ahead of me. I could not keep up with him. Nor could I see his face. Just his figure, striding away in front of me all the time. I must have cried while I slept, for when I woke in the morning the pillow was damp. My eyes were heavy too, when I looked in the glass. I looked plain, unattractive. I rubbed a little rouge on my cheeks in a wretched attempt to give myself colour. But it made me worse. It gave me a false clown look. Perhaps I did not know the best way to put it on. I noticed Robert staring at me as I crossed the hall and went in to breakfast.

About ten o'clock as I was crumbling some pieces for the birds on the terrace the telephone rang again. This time it was for me. Frith came and said Mrs. Lacy wanted to speak to me.

"Good morning, Beatrice," I said.

"Well, my dear, how are you?" she said, her telephone voice typical of herself, brisk, rather masculine, standing no nonsense, and then not waiting for my answer, "I thought of motoring over this afternoon and looking up Gran. I'm lunching with people about twenty miles from you. Shall I come and pick you up and we'll go together? It's time you met the old lady, you know."

"I'd like to very much, Beatrice," I said.

"Splendid. Very well, then, I'll come along for you about half-past three. Giles saw Maxim at the dinner. Poor food, he said, but excellent wine. All right, my dear, see you later."

The click of the receiver, and she was gone. I wandered back into the garden. I was glad she had rung up and suggested the plan of going over to see the grandmother. It made something to look forward to, and broke the monotony of the day. The hours had seemed so long until seven o'clock. I did not feel in my holiday mood to-day, and I had no wish to go off with Jasper to the Happy Valley and come to the cove and throw stones in the water. The sense of freedom had departed, and the childish desire to run across the lawns in sand-shoes. I went and sat down with a book and *The Times* and my knitting in the rose-garden, domestic as a matron, yawning in the warm sun while the bees hummed amongst the flowers.

I tried to concentrate on the bald newspaper columns, and later to lose myself in the racy plot of the novel in my hands. I did not want to think of yesterday afternoon and Mrs. Danvers. I tried to forget that she was in the house at this moment, perhaps looking down on me from one of the windows. And now and again, when I looked up from my book or glanced across the garden, I had the feeling I was not alone.

There were so many windows in Manderley, so many rooms that were never used by Maxim and myself that were empty now, dust-sheeted, silent, rooms that had been occupied in the old days when his father and his grandfather had been alive, when there had been much entertaining, many servants. It would be easy for Mrs. Danvers to open those doors softly, and close them again, and then steal quietly across the shrouded room and look down upon me from behind the drawn curtains.

I should not know. Even if I turned in my chair and looked up to the windows I would not see her. I remembered a game I had played as a child that my friends next-door had called "Grandmother's Steps" and myself "Old Witch." You had to stand at the end of the garden with your back turned to the rest, and one by one they crept nearer to you, advancing in short furtive fashion. Every few minutes you turned to look at them, and if you saw one of them moving the offender had to retire to the back line, and begin again. But there was always one a little bolder than the rest, who came up very close, whose movement was impossible to detect, and as you waited there, your back turned, counting the regulation Ten, you knew, with a fatal terrifying certainty, that before long, before even the Ten was counted, this bold player would pounce upon you from behind, unheralded, unseen, with a scream of triumph. I felt as tense and expectant as I did then. I was playing "Old Witch" with Mrs. Danvers.

Lunch was a welcome break to the long morning. The calm efficiency of Frith, and Robert's rather foolish face, helped me more than my book and my newspaper had done. And at half-past three, punctual to the moment, I heard the sound of Beatrice's car round the sweep of the drive and pull up at the steps before the house. I ran out to meet her, ready dressed, my gloves in my hand. "Well, my dear, here I am, what a splendid day, isn't it?" She slammed the door of the car and came up the steps to meet me. She gave me a hard swift kiss, brushing me somewhere near the ear.

"You don't look well," she said immediately, looking me up and down, "much too thin in the face, and no colour. What's wrong with you?"

"Nothing," I said humbly, knowing the fault of my face too well, "I'm not a person who ever has much colour."

"Oh, bosh," she replied, "you looked quite different when I saw you before."

"I expect the brown of Italy has worn off," I said, getting into the car.

"H'mph," she said shortly, "you're as bad as Maxim. Can't stand any criticism about your health. Slam the door hard or it doesn't shut." We started off down the drive, swerving at the corner, going rather too fast. "You're not by any chance starting an infant, are you?" she said, turning her hawk-brown eyes upon me.

"No," I said awkwardly. "No, I don't think so."

"No morning sickness or anything like that?"

"No."

"Oh, well—of course it doesn't always follow. I never turned a hair when Roger was born. Felt as fit as a fiddle the whole nine months. I played golf the day before he arrived. There's nothing to be embarrassed about in the facts of nature, you know. If you have any suspicions you had better tell me."

"No, really, Beatrice," I said, "there's nothing to tell."

"I must say I do hope you will produce a son and heir before long. It would be so terribly good for Maxim. I hope you are doing nothing to prevent it."

"Of course not," I said. What an extraordinary conversation.

"Oh, don't be shocked," she said, "you must never mind what I say. After all, brides of to-day are up to everything. It's a damn nuisance if you want to hunt and you land yourself with an infant your first season. Quite enough to break a marriage up if you are both keen. Wouldn't matter in your case. Babies needn't interfere with sketching. How is the sketching, by-the-way?"

"I'm afraid I don't seem to do much," I said.

"Oh, really? Nice weather too, for sitting out of doors. You only need a camp-stool and a box of pencils, don't you? Tell me, were you interested in those books I sent you?"

"Yes, of course," I said. "It was a lovely present, Beatrice."

She looked pleased. "Glad you liked them," she said.

The car sped along. She kept her foot permanently on the accelerator, and took every corner at an acute angle. Two motorists we passed looked out of their windows outraged as she swept by, and one pedestrian in a lane waved his stick at her. I felt rather hot for her. She did not seem to notice though. I crouched lower in my seat.

"Roger goes up to Oxford next term," she said, "heaven knows what he'll do with himself. Awful waste of time I think, and so does Giles, but we couldn't think what else to do with him. Of course he's just like Giles and myself. Thinks of nothing but horses. What on earth does this car in front think it's doing? Why don't you put out your hand, my good man? Really, some of these people on the road to-day ought to be shot."

We swerved into a main road, narrowly avoiding the car ahead of us. "Had any people down to stay?" she asked.

"No, we've been very quiet," I said.

"Much better, too," she said, "awful bore, I always think, those big parties. You won't find it alarming if you come to stay with us. Very nice lot of people all around, and we all know one another frightfully well. We dine in one another's houses, and have our bridge, and don't bother with outsiders. You do play bridge, don't you?"

"I'm not very good, Beatrice."

"Oh, we shan't mind that. As long as you can play. I've no patience with people who won't learn. What on earth can one do with them between tea and dinner in the winter, and after dinner? One can't just sit and talk."

I wondered why. However, it was simpler not to say anything.

"It's quite amusing now Roger is a reasonable age," she went on, "because he brings his friends to stay, and we have really good fun. You ought to have been with us last Christmas. We had charades. My dear, it was the greatest fun. Giles was in his element. He adores dressing-up, you know, and after a glass or two of champagne he's the funniest thing you've ever seen. We often say he's missed his vocation and ought to have been on the stage." I thought of Giles, and his large moon face, his horn spectacles. I felt the sight of him being funny after champagne would embarrass me. "He and another man, a great friend of ours, Dickie Marsh, dressed up as women and sang a duet.

What exactly it had to do with the word in the charade nobody knew, but it did not matter. We all roared."

I smiled politely. "Fancy, how funny," I said.

I saw them all rocking from side to side in Beatrice's drawing-room. All these friends who knew one another so well. Roger would look like Giles. Beatrice was laughing again at the memory. "Poor Giles," she said. "I shall never forget his face when Dick squirted the soda syphon down his back. We were all in fits."

I had an uneasy feeling we might be asked to spend the approaching Christmas with Beatrice. Perhaps I could have influenza.

"Of course our acting was never very ambitious," she said. "It was just a lot of fun amongst ourselves. At Manderley now, there is scope for a really fine show. I remember a pageant they had there, some years ago. People from London came down to do it. Of course that type of thing needs terrific organisation."

"Yes," I said.

She was silent for a while, and drove without speaking.

"How is Maxim?" she said, after a moment.

"Very well, thanks," I said.

"Quite cheerful and happy?"

"Oh, yes. Yes, rather."

A narrow village street engaged her attention. I wondered whether I should tell her about Mrs. Danvers. About the man Favell. I did not want her to make a blunder though, and perhaps tell Maxim.

"Beatrice," I said, deciding upon it, "have you ever heard of someone called Favell? Jack Favell?"

"Jack Favell," she repeated. "Yes, I do know the name. Wait a minute. Jack Favell. Of course. An awful bounder. I met him once, ages ago."

"He came to Manderley yesterday to see Mrs. Danvers," I said.

"Really? Oh, well, perhaps he would. . . ."

"Why?" I said.

"I rather think he was Rebecca's cousin," she said.

I was very surprised. That man her relation? It was not my idea of the sort of cousin Rebecca would have. Jack Favell her cousin. "Oh," I said. "Oh, I hadn't realised that."

"He probably used to go to Manderley a lot," said Beatrice. "I don't know. I couldn't tell you. I was very seldom there." Her manner was abrupt. It gave me the impression she did not want to pursue the subject.

"I did not take to him much," I said.

"No," said Beatrice. "I don't blame you."

I waited, but she did not say any more. I thought it wiser not to tell her how Favell had asked me to keep the visit a secret. It might lead to some complication. Besides, we were just coming to our destination. A pair of white gates and a smooth gravel drive.

"Don't forget the old lady is nearly blind," said Beatrice, "and she's not very bright these days. I telephoned to the nurse that we were coming so everything will be all right."

The house was large, red-bricked, and gabled. Late Victorian I supposed. Not an attractive house. I could tell in a glance it was the sort of house that was aggressively well-kept by a big staff. And all for one old lady who was nearly blind.

A trim parlour-maid opened the door.

"Good afternoon, Norah, how are you?" said Beatrice.

"Very well, thank you, Madam. I hope you are keeping well?"

"Oh, yes, we are all flourishing. How has the old lady been, Norah?"

"Rather mixed, Madam. She has one good day, and then a bad. She's not too bad in herself, you know. She will be pleased to see you I'm sure." She glanced curiously at me.

"This is Mrs. Maxim," said Beatrice.

"Yes, Madam. How do you do," said Norah.

We went through a narrow hall and a drawing-room crowded with furniture to a verandah facing a square clipped lawn. There were many bright geraniums in stone vases on the steps of the verandah. In the corner was a bath chair. Beatrice's grandmother was sitting there, propped up with pillows and surrounded by shawls. When we came close to her I saw that she had a strong, rather uncanny, resemblance to Maxim. That was what Maxim would look like, if he was very old, if he was blind. The nurse by her side got up from her chair and put a mark in the book she was reading aloud. She smiled at Beatrice.

"How are you, Mrs. Lacy?" she said.

Beatrice shook hands with her and introduced me. "The old lady looks all right," she said. "I don't know how she does it, at eighty-six. Here we are, Gran," she said, raising her voice, "arrived safe and sound."

The grandmother looked in our direction. "Dear Bee," she said, "how sweet of you to come and visit me. We're so dull here, nothing for you to do."

Beatrice leant over her and kissed her. "I've brought Maxim's wife over to see you," she said, "she wanted to come and see you before, but she and Maxim have been so busy."

Beatrice prodded me in the back. "Kiss her," she murmured. I too bent down and kissed her on the cheek.

The grandmother touched my face with her fingers. "You nice thing," she said, "so good of you to come. I'm very pleased to see you, dear. You ought to have brought Maxim with you."

"Maxim is in London," I said, "he's coming back to-night."

"You must bring him next time," she said. "Sit down, dear, in this chair, where I can see you. And Bee, come the other side. How is dear Roger? He's a naughty boy, he doesn't come and see me."

"He shall come during August," shouted Beatrice; "he's leaving Eton, you know, he's going up to Oxford."

"Oh, dear, he'll be quite a young man, I shan't know him."

"He's taller than Giles now," said Beatrice.

She went on, telling her about Giles, and Roger, and the horses, and the dogs. The nurse brought out some knitting, and clicked her needles sharply. She turned to me, very bright, very cheerful.

"How are you liking Manderley, Mrs. de Winter?"

"Very much, thank you," I said.

"It's a beautiful spot, isn't it?" she said, the needles jabbing one another. "Of course we don't get over there now, she's not up to it. I am so sorry, I used to love our days at Manderley."

"You must come over yourself sometime," I said.

"Thank you, I should love to. Mr. de Winter is well I suppose?"

"Yes, very well."

"You spent your honeymoon in Italy, didn't you? We were so pleased with the picture post-card Mr. de Winter sent."

I wondered whether she used "we" in the royal sense, or if she meant that Maxim's grandmother and herself were one.

"Did he send one? I don't remember."

"Oh, yes, it was quite an excitement. We love anything like that. We keep a scrap-book you know, and paste anything to do with the family inside it. Anything pleasant, that is."

"How nice," I said.

I caught snatches of Beatrice's conversation on the other side. "We had to put old Marksman down," she was saying. "You remember old Marksman? The best hunter I ever had."

"Oh, dear, not old Marksman?" said her grandmother.

"Yes, poor old man. Got blind in both eyes, you know."

"Poor Marksman," echoed the old lady.

I thought perhaps it was not very tactful to talk about blindness, and I glanced at the nurse. She was still busy clicking her needles.

"Do you hunt, Mrs. de Winter?" she said.

"No, I'm afraid I don't," I said.

"Perhaps you will come to it. We are all very fond of hunting in this part of the world."

"Yes."

"Mrs. de Winter is very keen on art," said Beatrice to the nurse. "I tell her there are heaps of spots in Manderley that would make very jolly pictures."

"Oh, rather," agreed the nurse, pausing a moment from the fury of knitting. "What a nice hobby. I had a friend who was a wonder with her pencil. We went to Provence together one Easter and she did such pretty sketches."

"How nice," I said.

"We're talking about sketching," shouted Beatrice to her grandmother, "you did not know we had an artist in the family, did you?"

"Who's an artist?" said the old lady. "I don't know any."

"Your new grand-daughter," said Beatrice; "you ask her what I gave her for a wedding present."

I smiled, waiting to be asked. The old lady turned her head in my direction. "What's Bee talking about?" she said. "I did not know you were an artist. We've never had any artists in the family."

"Beatrice was joking," I said; "of course I'm not an artist really. I like drawing as a hobby. I've never had any lessons. Beatrice gave me some lovely books as a present."

"Oh," she said, rather bewildered. "Beatrice gave you some books, did she? Rather like taking coals to Newcastle, wasn't it? There are so many books in the library at Manderley." She laughed heartily. We all joined in her joke. I hoped the subject would be left at that, but Beatrice had to harp on it. "You don't understand, Gran," she said. "They weren't ordinary books. They were volumes on Art. Six of 'em."

The nurse leant forward to add her tribute. "Mrs. Lacy is trying to explain that Mrs. de Winter is very fond of sketching as a hobby. So she gave her six fine volumes all about painting as a wedding present."

"What a funny thing to do," said the grandmother. "I don't think much of books for a wedding present. Nobody ever gave me any books when I was married. I should never have read them if they had."

She laughed again. Beatrice looked rather offended. I smiled at her to show my sympathy. I don't think she saw. The nurse resumed her knitting.

"I want my tea," said the old lady querulously, "isn't it half-past four yet? Why doesn't Norah bring the tea?"

"What? Hungry again after our big lunch?" said the nurse, rising to her feet and smiling brightly at her charge.

I felt rather exhausted, and wondered, rather shocked at my callous thought, why old people were sometimes such a strain. Worse than young children or puppies because one had to be polite. I sat with my hands in my lap ready to agree with what anybody said. The nurse was thumping the pillows and arranging the shawls.

Maxim's grandmother suffered her in patience. She closed her eyes as though she too were tired. She looked more like Maxim than ever. I knew how she must have looked when she was young, tall and handsome, going round to the stables at Manderley with sugar in her pockets, holding her trailing skirt out of the mud. I pictured the nipped-in waist, the high collar, I heard her ordering the carriage for two o'clock. That was all finished now for her, all gone. Her husband had been dead for forty years, her son for fifteen. She had to live here in this bright, red-gabled house with the nurse until it was time for her to die. I thought how little we know about the feelings of old people. Children we understand, their fears and hopes and make-believe. I was a child yesterday. I had not forgotten. But Maxim's grandmother, sitting there in her shawl with her poor blind eyes, what did she feel, what was she thinking? Did she know that Beatrice was yawning and glancing at her watch? Did she guess that we had come to visit her because we felt it right, it was a duty, so that when she got home afterwards Beatrice would be able to say, "Well, that clears my conscience for three months"?

Did she ever think about Manderley? Did she remember sitting at the dining-room table, where I sat? Did she too have tea under the chestnut tree? Or was it all forgotten and laid aside, and was there nothing left behind that calm, pale face of hers but little aches and little strange discomforts, a blurred thankfulness when the sun shone, a tremor when the wind blew cold?

I wished that I could lay my hands upon her face and take the years away. I wished I could see her young, as she was once, with colour in her cheeks and chestnut hair, alert and active as Beatrice by her side, talking as she did about hunting, hounds, and horses. Not sitting there with her eyes closed while the nurse thumped the pillows behind her head.

"We've got a treat to-day, you know," said the nurse, "water-cress sandwiches for tea. We love water-cress, don't we?"

"Is it water-cress day?" said Maxim's grandmother, raising her head from the pillows, and looking towards the door. "You did not tell me that. Why does not Norah bring in the tea?"

"I wouldn't have your job, Sister, for a thousand a day," said Beatrice *sotto voce* to the nurse.

"Oh, I'm used to it, Mrs. Lacy," smiled the nurse; "it's very comfortable here, you know. Of course we have our bad days but they might be a great deal worse. She's very easy, not like some patients. The staff are obliging too, that's really the main thing. Here comes Norah."

The parlour-maid brought out a little gate-legged table and a snowy cloth.

"What a time you've been, Norah," grumbled the old lady.

"It's only just turned the half-hour, Madam," said Norah in a special voice, bright and cheerful like the nurse. I wondered if Maxim's grandmother realised that people spoke to her in this way. I wondered when they had done so for the first time, and if she had noticed then. Perhaps she had said to herself, "They think I'm getting old, how very ridiculous," and then little by little she had become accustomed to it, and now it was as though they had always done so, it was part of her background. But the young woman with the chestnut hair and the narrow waist who gave sugar to the horses, where was she?

We drew our chairs to the gate-legged table and began to eat the water-cress sandwiches. The nurse prepared special ones for the old lady.

"There, now, isn't that a treat?" she said.

I saw a slow smile pass over the calm, placid face. "I like water-cress day," she said.

The tea was scalding, much too hot to drink. The nurse drank hers in tiny sips.

"Boiling water to-day," she said, nodding at Beatrice. "I have such trouble about it. They will let the tea stew. I've told them time and time again about it. They will not listen."

"Oh, they're all the same," said Beatrice. "I've given it up as a bad job."

The old lady stirred hers with a spoon, her eyes very far and distant. I wished I knew what she was thinking about.

"Did you have fine weather in Italy?" said the nurse.

"Yes, it was very warm," I said.

Beatrice turned to her grandmother. "They had lovely weather in Italy for their honeymoon, she says. Maxim got quite sunburnt."

"Why isn't Maxim here to-day?" said the old lady.

"We told you, darling, Maxim had to go to London," said Beatrice impatiently. "Some dinner you know. Giles went too."

"Oh, I see. Why did you say Maxim was in Italy?"

"He was in Italy, Gran. In April. They're back at Manderley now." She glanced at the nurse, shrugging her shoulders.

"Mr. and Mrs. de Winter are in Manderley now," repeated the nurse.

"It's been lovely there this month," I said, drawing nearer to Maxim's grandmother. "The roses are in bloom now. I wish I had brought you some."

"Yes, I like roses," she said vaguely, and then peering closer at me with her dim blue eyes, "Are you staying at Manderley too?"

I swallowed. There was a slight pause. Then Beatrice broke in with her loud, impatient voice, "Gran, darling, you know perfectly well she lives there now. She and Maxim are married."

I noticed the nurse put down her cup of tea and glance swiftly at the old lady. She had relaxed against the pillows, plucking at her shawl, and her mouth began to tremble. "You talk too much, all of you. I don't understand." Then she looked across at me, a frown on her face, and began shaking her head. "Who are you, my dear, I haven't seen you before? I don't know your face. I don't remember you at Manderley. Bee, who is this child? Why did not Maxim bring Rebecca? I'm so fond of Rebecca. Where is dear Rebecca?"

There was a long pause, a moment of agony. I felt my cheeks grow scarlet. The nurse got to her feet very quickly and went to the bath chair.

"I want Rebecca," repeated the old lady, "what have you done with Rebecca?" Beatrice rose clumsily from the table, shaking the cups and saucers. She too had turned very red, and her mouth twitched.

"I think you had better go, Mrs. Lacy," said the nurse, rather pink and flustered. "She's looking a little tired, and when she wanders like this it sometimes lasts a few hours. She does get excited like this from time to time. It's very unfortunate it should happen to-day. I'm sure you will understand, Mrs. de Winter?" She turned apologetically to me.

"Of course," I said quickly, "it's much better we should go."

Beatrice and I groped for our bags and gloves. The nurse had turned to her patient again. "Now, what's all this about? Don't you want your nice watercress sandwich that I've cut for you?"

"Where is Rebecca? Why did not Maxim come and bring Rebecca?" replied the thin, tired, querulous voice.

We went through the drawing-room to the hall and let ourselves out of the front door. Beatrice started up the car without a word. We drove down the smooth gravel drive and out of the white gates.

I stared straight in front of me down the road. I did not mind for myself. I should not have cared if I had been alone. I minded for Beatrice.

The whole thing had been so wretched and awkward for Beatrice.

She spoke to me when we turned out of the village. "My dear," she began. "I'm so dreadfully sorry. I don't know what to say."

"Don't be absurd, Beatrice," I said hurriedly, "it doesn't matter a bit. It's absolutely all right."

"I had no idea she would do that," said Beatrice. "I would never have dreamt of taking you to see her. I'm so frightfully sorry."

"There's nothing to be sorry about. Please don't say any more."

"I can't make it out. She knew all about you. I wrote and told her, and so did Maxim. She was so interested in the wedding abroad."

"You forget how old she is," I said. "Why should she remember that? She doesn't connect me with Maxim. She only connects him with Rebecca." We went on driving in silence. It was a relief to be in the car again. I did not mind the jerky motion and the swaying corners.

"I'd forgotten she was so fond of Rebecca," said Beatrice slowly, "I was a fool not to expect something like this. I don't believe she ever took it in properly about the accident. Oh, Lord, what a ghastly afternoon. What on earth will you think of me?"

"Please, Beatrice, don't. I tell you I don't mind."

"Rebecca made a great fuss of her always. And she used to have the old lady over to Manderley. Poor darling Gran was much more alert then. She used to rock with laughter at whatever Rebecca said. Of course she was always very amusing, and the old lady loved that. She had an amazing gift, Rebecca I mean, of being attractive to people; men, women, children, dogs. I suppose the old lady has never forgotten her. My dear, you won't thank me for this afternoon."

"I don't mind, I don't mind," I repeated mechanically. If only Beatrice could leave the subject alone. It did not interest me. What did it matter after all? What did anything matter?

"Giles will be very upset," said Beatrice. "He will blame me for taking you over. 'What an idiotic thing to do, Bee.' I can hear him saying it. I shall get into a fine row."

"Don't say anything about it," I said. "I would much rather it was forgotten. The story will only get repeated and exaggerated."

"Giles will know something is wrong from my face. I never have been able to hide anything from him."

I was silent. I knew how the story would be tossed about in their immediate circle of friends. I could imagine the little crowd at Sunday lunch. The round eyes, the eager ears, and the gasps and exclamations—

"My Lord, how awful, what on earth did you do?" and then, "How did she take it? How terribly embarrassing for everyone!"

The only thing that mattered to me was that Maxim should never come to hear of it. One day I might tell Frank Crawley, but not yet, not for quite a while.

It was not long before we came to the high-road at the top of the hill. In the distance I could see the first grey roofs of Kerrith, while to the right, in a hollow, lay the deep woods of Manderley and the sea beyond.

"Are you in a frightful hurry to get home?" said Beatrice.

"No," I said. "I don't think so. Why?"

"Would you think me a perfect pig if I dropped you at the lodge gates? If I drive like hell now I shall just be in time to meet Giles by the London train, and it will save him taking the station taxi."

"Of course," I said. "I can walk down the drive."

"Thanks awfully," she said gratefully.

I felt the afternoon had been too much for her. She wanted to be alone again, and did not want to face another belated tea at Manderley.

I got out of the car at the lodge gates and we kissed good-bye.

"Put on some weight next time I see you," she said, "it doesn't suit you to be so thin. Give Maxim my love, and forgive me for to-day." She vanished in a cloud of dust and I turned in down the drive.

I wondered if it had altered much since Maxim's grandmother had driven down it in her carriage. She had ridden here as a young woman, she had smiled at the woman at the lodge as I did now. And in her day the lodge-keeper's wife had curtseyed, sweeping the path with her full wide skirt. This woman nodded to me briefly, and then called to her little boy who was grubbing with some kittens at the back. Maxim's grandmother had bowed her head to avoid the sweeping branches of the trees, and the horse had trotted down the twisting drive where I now walked. The drive had been wider then, and smoother too, better kept. The woods did not encroach upon it.

I did not think of her as she was now, lying against those pillows, with that shawl around her. I saw her when she was young, and when Manderley was her home. I saw her wandering in the gardens with a small boy, Maxim's father, clattering behind her on his hobby horse. He would wear a stiff Norfolk jacket and a round white collar. Picnics to the cove would be an expedition, a treat that was not indulged in very often. There would be a photograph somewhere, in an old album—all the family sitting very straight and rigid round a table-cloth set upon the beach, the servants in the background beside a huge lunch-basket. And I saw Maxim's grandmother when she was older too, a few years ago. Walking on the terrace at Manderley, leaning on a stick. And someone walked beside her, laughing, holding her arm. Someone tall and slim and very beautiful, who had a gift, Beatrice said, of being attractive to people. Easy to like, I supposed, easy to love.

When I came to the end of the long drive at last I saw that Maxim's car was standing in front of the house. My heart lifted, I ran quickly into the hall. His hat and gloves were lying on the table. I went towards the library, and as I came near I heard the sound of voices, one raised louder than the other, Maxim's voice. The door was shut. I hesitated a moment before going in.

"You can write and tell him from me to keep away from Manderley in future, do you hear? Never mind who told me, that's of no importance. I happen to know his car was seen here yesterday afternoon. If you want to meet him you can meet him outside Manderley. I won't have him inside the gates, do you understand? Remember, I'm warning you for the last time."

I slipped away from the door to the stairs. I heard the door of the library open. I ran swiftly up the stairs and hid in the gallery. Mrs. Danvers came out of the library, shutting the door behind her. I crouched against the wall of the gallery so that I should not be seen. I had caught one glimpse of her face. It was grey with anger, distorted, horrible.

She passed up the stairs swiftly and silently and disappeared through the door leading to the west wing.

I waited a moment. Then I went slowly downstairs to the library. I opened the door and went in. Maxim was standing by the window, some letters in his hand. His back was turned to me. For a moment I thought of creeping out again, and going upstairs to my room and sitting there. He must have heard me though, for he swung round impatiently.

"Who is it now?" he said.

I smiled, holding out my hands. "Hullo!" I said.

"Oh, it's you. . . ."

I could tell in a glance that something had made him very angry. His mouth was hard, his nostrils white and pinched. "What have you been doing with yourself?" he said. He kissed the top of my head and put his arm round my shoulder. I felt as if a very long time had passed since he had left me yesterday.

"I've been to see your grandmother," I said. "Beatrice drove me over this afternoon."

"How was the old lady?"

"All right."

"What's happened to Bee?"

"She had to get back to meet Giles."

We sat down together on the window seat. I took his hand in mine. "I hated you being away, I've missed you terribly," I said.

"Have you?" he said.

We did not say anything for a bit. I just held his hand.

"Was it hot up in London?" I said.

"Yes, pretty awful. I always hate the place."

I wondered if he would tell me what had happened just now in the library with Mrs. Danvers. I wondered who had told him about Favell.

"Are you worried about something?" I said.

"I've had a long day," he said, "that drive twice in twenty-four hours is too much for anyone."

He got up and wandered away, lighting a cigarette. I knew then that he was not going to tell me about Mrs. Danvers.

"I'm tired too," I said slowly, "it's been a funny sort of day."

CHAPTER SIXTEEN

IT WAS ONE Sunday, I remember, when we had an invasion of visitors during the afternoon, that the subject of the fancy dress ball was first brought up.

Frank Crawley had come over to lunch, and we were all three of us looking forward to a peaceful afternoon under the chestnut tree when we heard the fatal sound of a car rounding the sweep in the drive. It was too late to warn Frith, the car itself came upon us standing on the terrace with cushions and papers under our arms.

We had to come forward and welcome the unexpected guests. As it often happens in such cases, these were not to be the only visitors. Another car arrived about half-an-hour afterwards, followed by three local people who had walked from Kerrith, and we found ourselves, with the peace stripped from our day, entertaining group after group of dreary acquaintances, doing the regulation walk in the grounds, the tour of the rose-garden, the stroll across the lawns, and the formal inspection of the Happy Valley.

They stayed for tea of course, and instead of a lazy nibbling of cucumber sandwiches under the chestnut tree, we had the paraphernalia of a stiff tea in the drawing-room, which I always loathed. Frith in his element of course, directing Robert with a lift of his eyebrows, and myself rather hot and flustered with a monstrous silver tea-pot and kettle that I never knew how to manage. I found it very difficult to gauge the exact moment when it became imperative to dilute the tea with the boiling water, and more difficult still to concentrate on the small talk that was going on at my side.

Frank Crawley was invaluable at a moment like this. He took the cups from me and handed them to people, and when my answers seemed more than usually vague owing to my concentration on the silver tea-pot he quietly and unobtrusively put in his small wedge to the conversation, relieving me of responsibility. Maxim was always at the other end of the room, showing a book to a bore, or pointing out a picture, playing the perfect host in his own inimitable way, and the business of tea was a side-issue that did not matter to him. His own cup of tea grew cold, left on a side table behind some flowers, and I, steaming behind my kettle, and Frank, gallantly juggling with scones and angel cake, were left to minister to the common wants of the herd. It was Lady Crowan, a tiresome gushing woman who lived in Kerrith, who introduced the matter. There was one of those pauses in conversation that happen in every tea-party, and I saw Frank's lips about to form the inevitable and idiotic remark about an angel passing overhead, when Lady Crowan, balancing a piece of cake on the edge of her saucer, looked up at Maxim who happened to be beside her.

"Oh, Mr. de Winter," she said, "there is something I've been wanting to ask you for ages. Now tell me, is there any chance of you reviving the Manderley fancy dress ball?" She put her head on one side as she spoke, flashing her too prominent teeth in what she supposed was a smile. I lowered my head instantly, and became very busy with the emptying of my own tea-cup, screening myself behind the cosy.

It was a moment or two before Maxim replied, and when he did his voice was quite calm and matter-of-fact. "I haven't thought about it," he said, "and I don't think anyone else has."

"Oh, but I assure you we have all thought of it so much," continued Lady

Crowan. "It used to make the summer for all of us in this part of the world. You have no idea of the pleasure it used to give. Can't I persuade you to think about it again?"

"Well, I don't know," said Maxim drily. "It was all rather a business to organise. You had better ask Frank Crawley, he'd have to do it."

"Oh, Mr. Crawley, do be on my side," she persisted, and one or two of the others joined in. "It would be a most popular move, you know, we all miss the Manderley gaiety."

I heard Frank's quiet voice beside me. "I don't mind organising the ball if Maxim has no objection to giving it. It's up to him and Mrs. de Winter. It's nothing to do with me."

Of course I was bombarded at once. Lady Crowan moved her chair so that the cosy no longer hid me from view. "Now, Mrs. de Winter, you get round your husband. You are the person he will listen to. He should give the ball in your honour as the bride."

"Yes, of course," said somebody else, a man. "We missed the fun of the wedding you know, it's a shame to deprive us of all excitement. Hands up for the Manderley fancy dress ball. There you see, de Winter? Carried unanimously." There was much laughter and clapping of hands.

Maxim lit a cigarette and his eyes met mine over the tea-pot.

"What do you think about it?" he said.

"I don't know," I said uncertainly. "I don't mind."

"Of course she longs to have a ball in her honour," gushed Lady Crowan. "What girl wouldn't? You'd look sweet, Mrs. de Winter, dressed as a little Dresden shepherdess, your hair tucked under a big three-cornered hat."

I thought of my clumsy hands and feet and the slope of my shoulders. A fine Dresden shepherdess I should make! What an idiot the woman was. I was not surprised when nobody agreed with her, and once more I was grateful to Frank for turning the conversation away from me.

"As a matter of fact, Maxim, someone was talking about it the other day. 'I suppose we shall be having some sort of celebration for the bride, shan't we, Mr. Crawley?' he said. 'I wish Mr. de Winter would give a ball again. It was rare fun for all of us.' It was Tucker, at the Home farm," he added, to Lady Crowan. "Of course they do adore a show of any kind. 'I don't know,' I told him. 'Mr. de Winter hasn't said anything to me.' "

"There you are," said Lady Crowan triumphantly to the drawing-room in general. "What did I say? Your own people are asking for a ball. If you don't care for us surely you care about them."

Maxim still watched me doubtfully over the tea-pot. It occurred to me that perhaps he thought I could not face it, that being shy, as he knew only too well, I should find myself unable to cope. I did not want him to think that. I did not want him to feel I should let him down.

"I think it would be rather fun," I said.

Maxim turned away, shrugging his shoulders. "That settles it of course," he said. "All right, Frank, you will have to go ahead with the arrangements. Better get Mrs. Danvers to help you. She will remember the form."

"That amazing Mrs. Danvers is still with you then?" said Lady Crowan.

"Yes," said Maxim shortly, "have some more cake, will you? Or have you finished? Then let's all go into the garden."

We wandered out on to the terrace, everyone discussing the prospect of the ball and suitable dates, and then, greatly to my relief, the car parties decided it was time to take their departure, and the walkers went too, on being offered a lift. I went back into the drawing-room and had another cup of tea which I thoroughly enjoyed now that the burden of entertaining had been taken from me, and Frank came too, and we crumbled up the remains of the scones and ate them, feeling like conspirators.

Maxim was throwing sticks for Jasper on the lawn. I wondered if it was the same in every home, this feeling of exuberance when visitors had gone. We did not say anything about the ball for a little while, and then, when I had finished my cup of tea and wiped my sticky fingers on a handkerchief, I said to Frank, "What do you truthfully think about this fancy dress business?"

Frank hesitated, half glancing out of the window at Maxim on the lawn. "I don't know," he said. "Maxim did not seem to object, did he? I thought he took the suggestion very well."

"It was difficult for him to do anything else," I said. "What a tiresome person Lady Crowan is. Do you really believe all the people round here are talking and dreaming of nothing but a fancy dress ball at Manderley?"

"I think they would all enjoy a show of some sort," said Frank. "We're very conventional down here, you know, about these things. I don't honestly think Lady Crowan was exaggerating when she said something should be done in your honour. After all, Mrs. de Winter, you are a bride."

How pompous and stupid it sounded. I wished Frank would not always be so terribly correct.

"I'm not a bride," I said. "I did not even have a proper wedding. No white dress or orange blossom or trailing bridesmaids. I don't want any silly dance given in my honour."

"It's a very fine sight, Manderley *en fête*," said Frank. "You'll enjoy it, you see. You won't have to do anything alarming. You just receive the guests and there's nothing in that. Perhaps you'll give me a dance?"

Dear Frank. I loved his little solemn air of gallantry.

"You shall have as many dances as you like," I said. "I shan't dance with anyone except you and Maxim."

"Oh, but that would not look right at all," said Frank seriously. "People would be very offended. You must dance with the people who ask you." I turned away to hide my smile. It was a joy to me the way he never knew when his leg had been pulled.

"Do you think Lady Crowan's suggestion about the Dresden shepherdess was a good one?" I said slyly.

He considered me solemnly without the trace of a smile. "Yes, I do," he said. "I think you'd look very well indeed."

I burst into laughter. "Oh, Frank, dear, I do love you," I said, and he turned rather pink, a little shocked I think at my impulsive words, and a little hurt too that I was laughing at him.

"I don't see that I've said anything funny," he said stiffly.

Maxim came in at the window, Jasper dancing at his heels. "What's all the excitement about?" he said.

"Frank is being so gallant," I said. "He thinks Lady Crowan's idea of my dressing up as a Dresden shepherdess is nothing to laugh at."

"Lady Crowan is a damned nuisance," said Maxim. "If she had to write out all the invitations and organise the affair she would not be so enthusiastic. It's always been the same though. The locals look upon Manderley as if it was a pavilion on the end of a pier, and expect us to put up a turn for their benefit. I suppose we shall have to ask the whole county."

"I've got the records in the office," said Frank. "It won't really entail much work. Licking the stamps is the longest job."

"We'll give that to you to do," said Maxim, smiling at me.

"Oh, we'll do that in the office," said Frank. "Mrs. de Winter need not bother her head about anything at all."

I wondered what they would say if I suddenly announced my intention of running the whole affair. Laugh, I suppose, and then begin talking of something else. I was glad, of course, to be relieved of responsibility, but it rather added to my sense of humility to feel that I was not even capable of licking stamps. I thought of the writing-desk in the morning-room, the docketed pigeon-holes all marked in ink by that slanting pointed hand.

"What will you wear?" I said to Maxim.

"I never dress up," said Maxim. "It's the one perquisite allowed to the host, isn't it, Frank?"

"I can't really go as a Dresden shepherdess," I said, "what on earth shall I do? I'm not much good at dressing-up."

"Put a ribbon round your hair and be Alice-in-Wonderland," said Maxim lightly; "you look like it now, with your finger in your mouth."

"Don't be so rude," I said. "I know my hair is straight, but it isn't as straight as that. I tell you what. I'll give you and Frank the surprise of your lives, and you won't know me."

"As long as you don't black your face and pretend to be a monkey I don't mind what you do," said Maxim.

"All right, that's a bargain," I said. "I'll keep my costume a secret to the last minute, and you won't know anything about it. Come on, Jasper, we don't care what they say, do we?" I heard Maxim laughing as I went out into the garden, and he said something to Frank which I did not catch.

I wished he would not always treat me as a child, rather spoilt, rather irresponsible, someone to be petted from time to time when the mood came upon him, but more often forgotten, more often patted on the shoulder and told to run away and play. I wished something would happen to make me look wiser, more mature. Was it always going to be like this? He away ahead of me, with his own moods that I did not share, his secret troubles that I did not know? Would we never be together, he a man and I a woman, standing shoulder to shoulder, hand in hand, with no gulf between us? I did not want to be a child. I wanted to be his wife, his mother. I wanted to be old.

I stood on the terrace, biting my nails, looking down towards the sea, and as I stood there I wondered for the twentieth time that day whether it was by Maxim's orders that those rooms in the west wing were kept furnished and untouched. I wondered if he went, as Mrs. Danvers did, and touched the brushes on the dressing-table, opened the wardrobe doors and put his hands amongst the clothes.

"Come on, Jasper," I shouted, "run, run with me, come on, can't you?" and I tore across the grass, savagely, angrily, the bitter tears behind my eyes, with Jasper leaping at my heels and barking hysterically.

The news soon spread about the fancy dress ball. My little maid Clarice, her eyes shining with excitement, talked of nothing else. I gathered from her that the servants in general were delighted. "Mr. Frith says it will be like old times," said Clarice eagerly. "I heard him saying so to Alice in the passage this morning. What will you wear, Madam?"

"I don't know, Clarice, I can't think," I said.

"Mother said I was to be sure and tell her," said Clarice. "She remembers the last ball they gave at Manderley, and she has never forgotten it. Will you be hiring a costume from London, do you think?"

"I haven't made up my mind, Clarice," I said. "But I tell you what. When I do decide, I shall tell you and nobody else. It will be a dead secret between us both."

"Oh, Madam, how exciting," breathed Clarice. "I don't know how I am going to wait for the day."

I was curious to know Mrs. Danvers' reaction to the news. Since that afternoon I dreaded even the sound of her voice down the house telephone, and by using Robert as mediator between us I was spared this last ordeal. I could not forget the expression on her face when she left the library after that interview with Maxim. I thanked God she had not seen me crouching in the gallery. And I wondered, too, if she thought that it was I who told Maxim about Favell's visit to the house. If so, she would hate me more than ever. I shuddered now when I remembered the touch of her hand on my arm, and that dreadful soft, intimate pitch of her voice close to my ear. I did not want to remember anything about that afternoon. That was why I did not speak to her, not even on the house telephone.

The preparations went on for the ball. Everything seemed to be done down at the estate office. Maxim and Frank were down there every morning. As Frank had said, I did not have to bother my head about anything. I don't think I licked one stamp. I began to get in a panic about my costume. It seemed so feeble not to be able to think of anything, and I kept remembering all the people who would come, from Kerrith and round about, the bishop's wife who had enjoyed herself so much the last time, Beatrice and Giles, that tiresome Lady Crowan, and many more people I did not know and who had never seen me, they would every one of them have some criticism to offer, some curiosity to know what sort of effort I should make. At last, in desperation, I remembered the books that Beatrice had given me for a wedding present, and I sat down in the library one morning turning over the pages as a last hope, passing from illustration to illustration in a sort of frenzy. Nothing seemed suitable, they were all so elaborate and pretentious, those gorgeous costumes of velvet and silk in the reproductions given of Rubens, Rembrandt and others. I got hold of a piece of paper and a pencil and copied one or two of them, but they did not please me, and I threw the sketches into the waste-paper basket in disgust, thinking no more about them.

In the evening, when I was changing for dinner, there was a knock at my bedroom door. I called "Come in," thinking it was Clarice. The door opened and it was not Clarice. It was Mrs. Danvers. She held a piece of paper in her hand. "I hope you will forgive me disturbing you," she said, "but I was not sure whether you meant to throw these drawings away. All the waste-paper baskets are always brought to me to check, at the end of the day, in case of mislaying anything of value. Robert told me this was thrown into the library basket."

I had turned quite cold all over at the sight of her, and at first I could not find my voice. She held out the paper for me to see. It was the rough drawing I had done during the morning.

"No, Mrs. Danvers," I said, after a moment, "it doesn't matter throwing that away. It was only a rough sketch. I don't want it."

"Very good," she said, "I thought it better to enquire from you personally to save any misunderstanding."

"Yes," I said. "Yes, of course." I thought she would turn and go, but she went on standing there by the door.

"So you have not decided yet what you will wear?" she said. There was a hint of derision in her voice, a trace of odd satisfaction. I supposed she had heard of my efforts through Clarice in some way.

"No," I said. "No, I haven't decided."

She continued watching me, her hand on the handle of the door.

"I wonder you don't copy one of the pictures in the gallery," she said.

I pretended to file my nails. They were too short and too brittle, but the action gave me something to do and I did not have to look at her.

"Yes, I might think about that," I said. I wondered privately why such an idea had never come to me before. It was an obvious and very good solution to my difficulty. I did not want her to know this though. I went on filing my nails.

"All the pictures in the gallery would make good costumes," said Mrs. Danvers, "especially that one of the young lady in white, with her hat in her hand. I wonder Mr. de Winter does not make it a period ball, everyone dressed more or less the same, to be in keeping. I never think it looks right to see a clown dancing with a lady in powder and patches."

"Some people enjoy the variety," I said. "They think it makes it all the more amusing."

"I don't like it myself," said Mrs. Danvers. Her voice was surprisingly normal and friendly, and I wondered why it was she had taken the trouble to come up with my discarded sketch herself. Did she want to be friends with me at last? Or did she realise that it had not been me at all who had told Maxim about Favell, and this was her way of thanking me for my silence?

"Has not Mr. de Winter suggested a costume for you?" she said.

"No," I said, after a moment's hesitation. "No, I want to surprise him and Mr. Crawley. I don't want them to know anything about it."

"It's not for me to make a suggestion, I know," she said, "but when you do decide, I should advise you to have your dress made in London. There is no one down here can do that sort of thing well. Voce, in Bond Street, is a good place I know."

"I must remember that," I said.

"Yes," she said, and then, as she opened the door, "I should study the pictures in the gallery, Madam, if I were you, especially the one I mentioned. And you need not think I will give you away. I won't say a word to anyone."

"Thank you, Mrs. Danvers," I said. She shut the door very gently behind her. I went on with my dressing, puzzled at her attitude, so different from our last encounter, and wondering whether I had the unpleasant Favell to thank for it.

Rebecca's cousin. Why should Maxim dislike Rebecca's cousin? Why had he forbidden him to come to Manderley? Beatrice had called him a bounder. She had not said much about him. And the more I considered him the more I agreed with her. Those hot blue eyes, that loose mouth, and the careless familiar laugh. Some people would consider him attractive. Girls in sweet shops giggling behind the counter, and girls who gave one programmes in a cinema. I knew how he would look at them, smiling, and half whistling a tune under his breath. The sort of look and the type of whistle that would make one feel uncomfortable. I wondered how well he knew Manderley. He seemed quite at home, and Jasper certainly recognised him, but these two facts did not fit in with Maxim's words to Mrs. Danvers. And I could not connect him with my idea of Rebecca. Rebecca, with her beauty, her charm, her breeding, why did she have a cousin like Jack Favell? It was wrong, out of all proportion. I decided he must be the skeleton in the family cupboard, and Rebecca, with her generosity, had taken pity on him from time to time and invited him to Manderley, perhaps when Maxim was from home, knowing his dislike. There had been some argument about it probably, Rebecca defending him, and ever after this perhaps a slight awkwardness whenever his name was mentioned.

As I sat down to dinner in the dining-room in my accustomed place, with Maxim at the head of the table, I pictured Rebecca sitting where I sat now, picking up her fork for the fish, and then the telephone ringing and Frith coming into the room and saying "Mr. Favell on the 'phone, Madam, wishing to speak to you," and Rebecca would get up from her chair with a quick glance at Maxim, who would not say anything, who would go on eating his fish. And when she came back, having finished her conversation, and sat down in her place again, Rebecca would begin talking about something different, in a gay, careless way, to cover up the little cloud between them. At first

Maxim would be glum, answering in monosyllables, but little by little she would win his humour back again, telling him some story of her day, about someone she had seen in Kerrith, and when they had finished the next course he would be laughing again, looking at her and smiling, putting out his hand to her across the table.

"What the devil are you thinking about?" said Maxim.

I started, the colour flooding my face, for in that brief moment, sixty seconds in time perhaps, I had so identified myself with Rebecca that my own dull self did not exist, had never come to Manderley. I had gone back in thought and in person to the days that were gone.

"Do you know you were going through the most extraordinary antics instead of eating your fish?" said Maxim, "first you listened, as though you heard the telephone, and then your lips moved, and you threw half a glance at me. And you shook your head, and smiled, and shrugged your shoulders. All in about a second. Are you practising your appearance for the fancy dress ball?" He looked across at me, laughing, and I wondered what he would say if he really knew my thoughts, my heart, and my mind, and that for one second he had been the Maxim of another year, and I had been Rebecca. "You look like a little criminal," he said, "what is it?"

"Nothing," I said quickly, "I wasn't doing anything."

"Tell me what you were thinking?"

"Why should I? You never tell me what you are thinking about."

"I don't think you've ever asked me, have you?"

"Yes, I did once."

"I don't remember."

"We were in the library."

"Very probably. What did I say?"

"You told me you were wondering who had been chosen to play for Surrey against Middlesex."

Maxim laughed again. "What a disappointment to you. What did you hope I was thinking?"

"Something very different."

"What sort of thing?"

"Oh, I don't know."

"No, I don't suppose you do. If I told you I was thinking about Surrey and Middlesex I was thinking about Surrey and Middlesex. Men are simpler than you imagine, my sweet child. But what goes on in the twisted tortuous minds of women would baffle anyone. Do you know, you did not look a bit like yourself just now? You had quite a different expression on your face."

"I did? What sort of expression?"

"I don't know that I can explain. You looked older suddenly, deceitful. It was rather unpleasant."

"I did not mean to."

"No, I don't suppose you did."

I drank some water, watching him over the rim of my glass.

"Don't you want me to look older?" I said.

"No."

"Why not?"

"Because it would not suit you."

"One day I shall. It can't be helped. I shall have grey hair, and lines and things."

"I don't mind that."

"What do you mind then?"

"I don't want you to look like you did just now. You had a twist to your mouth and a flash of knowledge in your eyes. Not the right sort of knowledge."

I felt very curious, rather excited. "What do you mean, Maxim? What isn't the right sort of knowledge?"

He did not answer for a moment. Frith had come back into the room and was changing the plates. Maxim waited until Frith had gone behind the screen and through the Service door before speaking again.

"When I met you first you had a certain expression on your face," he said slowly, "and you have it still. I'm not going to define it, I don't know how to. But it was one of the reasons why I married you. A moment ago, when you were going through that curious little performance, the expression had gone. Something else had taken its place."

"What sort of thing? Explain to me, Maxim," I said eagerly.

He considered me a moment, his eyebrows raised, whistling softly. "Listen, my sweet. When you were a little girl, were you ever forbidden to read certain books, and did your father put those books under lock and key?"

"Yes," I said.

"Well, then. A husband is not so very different from a father after all. There is a certain type of knowledge I prefer you not to have. It's better kept under lock and key. So that's that. And now eat up your peaches, and don't ask me any more questions, or I shall put you in the corner."

"I wish you would not treat me as if I was six," I said.

"How do you want to be treated?"

"Like other men treat their wives."

"Knock you about, do you mean?"

"Don't be absurd. Why must you make a joke of everything?"

"I'm not joking. I'm very serious."

"No, you're not. I can tell by your eyes. You're playing with me all the time, just as if I was a silly little girl."

"Alice-in-Wonderland. That was a good idea of mine. Have you bought your sash and your hair-ribbon yet?"

"I warn you. You'll get the surprise of your life when you do see me in my fancy dress."

"I'm sure I shall. Get on with your peach and don't talk with your mouth full. I've got a lot of letters to write after dinner." He did not wait for me to finish. He got up and strolled about the room, and asked Frith to bring the coffee in the library. I sat still, sullenly, being as slow as I could, hoping to keep things back and irritate him, but Frith took no notice of me and my peach, he brought the coffee at once and Maxim went off to the library by himself.

When I had finished I went upstairs to the minstrels' gallery to have a look at the pictures. I knew them well of course by now, but had never studied them with a view to reproducing one of them as a fancy dress. Mrs. Danvers was right of course. What an idiot I had been not to think of it before. I always loved the girl in white, with a hat in her hand. It was a Raeburn, and the portrait was of Caroline de Winter, a sister of Maxim's great-great-grandfather. She married a great Whig politician, and was a famous London beauty for many years, but this portrait was painted before that, when she was still unmarried. The white dress should be easy to copy. Those puffed sleeves, the flounce, and the little bodice. The hat might be rather difficult, and I should have to wear a wig. My straight hair would never curl in that way. Perhaps that Voce place in London that Mrs. Danvers had told me about would do the whole thing. I would send them a sketch of the portrait and tell them to copy it faithfully, sending my measurements.

What a relief it was to have decided at last! Quite a weight off my mind. I began almost to look forward to the ball. Perhaps I should enjoy it after all, almost as much as little Clarice.

I wrote to the shop in the morning, enclosing a sketch of the portrait, and I had a very favourable reply, full of honour at my esteemed order, and saying the work would be put in hand right away, and they would manage the wig as well.

Clarice could hardly contain herself for excitement, and I, too, began to get party fever as the great day approached. Giles and Beatrice were coming for the night, but nobody else, thank heaven, although a lot of people were expected to dinner first. I had imagined we should have to hold a large house-party for the occasion, but Maxim decided against it. "Having the dance alone is quite enough effort," he said; and I wondered whether he did it for my sake alone, or whether a large crowd of people really bored him as he said. I had heard so much of the Manderley parties in the old days, with people sleeping in bathrooms and on sofas because of the squash. And here we were alone in the vast house, with only Beatrice and Giles to count as guests.

The house began to wear a new, expectant air. Men came to lay the floor for dancing in the great hall, and in the drawing-room some of the furniture was moved so that the long buffet tables could be placed against the wall. Lights were put up on the terrace, and in the rose-garden too, wherever one walked there would be some sign of preparation for the ball. Workmen from the estate were everywhere, and Frank came to lunch nearly every day. The servants talked of nothing else, and Frith stalked about as though the whole of the evening would depend on him alone. Robert rather lost his head, and kept forgetting things, napkins at lunch, and handing vegetables. He wore a harassed expression, like someone who has got to catch a train. The dogs were miserable. Jasper trailed about the hall with his tail between his legs, and nipped every workman on sight. He used to stand on the terrace, barking idiotically, and then dash madly to one corner of the lawn and eat grass in a sort of frenzy. Mrs. Danvers never obtruded herself, but I was aware of her continually. It was her voice I heard in the drawing-room when they came to put the tables, it was she who gave directions for the laying of the floor in the hall. Whenever I came upon the scene she had always just disappeared; I would catch a glimpse of her skirt brushing the door, or hear the sound of her footsteps on the stairs. I was a lay-figure, no use to man or beast. I used to stand about doing nothing except get in the way. "Excuse me, Madam," I would hear a man say, just behind me, and he would pass, with a smile of apology, carrying two chairs on his back, his face dripping with perspiration.

"I'm awfully sorry," I would say, getting quickly to one side, and then as a cover to my idleness, "Can I help you? What about putting those chairs in the library?" The man would look bewildered. "Mrs. Danvers' orders, Madam, was that we were to take the chairs round to the back, to be out of the way."

"Oh," I said, "yes, of course. How silly of me. Take them round to the back, as she said." And I would walk quickly away murmuring something about finding a piece of paper and pencil, in a vain attempt to delude the man into thinking I was busy, while he went on across the hall, looking rather astonished, and I would feel I had not deceived him for a moment.

The great day dawned misty and over-cast, but the glass was high and we had no fears. The mist was a good sign. It cleared about eleven, as Maxim had foretold, and we had a glorious still summer's day without a cloud in the blue sky. All the morning the gardeners were bringing flowers into the house, the last of the white lilac, and great lupins and delphiniums, five foot high, roses in hundreds, and every sort of lily.

Mrs. Danvers showed herself at last; quietly, calmly, she told the gardeners where to put the flowers, and she herself arranged them, stacking the vases with quick, deft fingers. I watched her in fascination, the way she did vase after vase, carrying them herself through the flower-room to the drawing-room and the various corners of the house, massing them in just the right numbers and profusion, putting colour where colour was needed, leaving the walls bare where severity paid.

Maxim and I had lunch with Frank at his bachelor establishment next-door to the office to be out of the way. We were all three in the rather hearty, cheerful humour of people before a funeral. We made pointless jokes about nothing at all, our minds eternally on the thought of the next few hours. I felt very much the same as I did the morning I was married. The same stifled feeling that I had gone too far now to turn back.

The evening had got to be endured. Thank heaven Messrs. Voce had sent my dress in time. It looked perfect, in its folds of tissue paper. And the wig was a triumph. I had tried it on after breakfast, and was amazed at the transformation. I looked quite attractive, quite different altogether. Not me at all. Someone much more interesting, more vivid and alive. Maxim and Frank kept asking me about my costume.

"You won't know me," I told them, "you will both get the shock of your lives."

"You are not going to dress up as a clown, are you?" said Maxim gloomily. "No frightful attempt to be funny?"

"No, nothing like that," I said, full of importance.

"I wish you had kept to Alice-in-Wonderland," he said.

"Or Joan of Arc with your hair," said Frank shyly.

"I never thought of that," I said blankly, and Frank went rather pink. "I'm sure we shall all like whatever you wear," he said in his most pompous Frankish voice.

"Don't encourage her, Frank," said Maxim. "She's so full of her precious disguise already there's no holding her. Bee will put you in your place, that's one comfort. She'll soon tell you if she doesn't like your dress. Dear old Bee always looks just wrong on these occasions, bless her. I remember her once as Madame Pompadour and she tripped up going in to supper and her wig came adrift. 'I can't stand this damned thing,' she said, in that blunt voice of hers, and chucked it on a chair and went through the rest of the evening with her own cropped hair. You can imagine what it looked like, against a pale blue satin crinoline, or whatever the dress was. Poor old Giles did not cope that year. He came as a cook, and sat about in the bar all night looking perfectly miserable. I think he felt Bee had let him down."

"No, it wasn't that," said Frank, "he'd lost his front teeth trying out a new mare, don't you remember, and he was so shy about it he wouldn't open his mouth."

"Oh, was that it? Poor Giles. He generally enjoys dressing-up."

"Beatrice says he loves playing charades," I said. "She told me they always have charades at Christmas."

"I know," said Maxim, "that's why I've never spent Christmas with her."

"Have some more asparagus, Mrs. de Winter, and another potato?"

"No, really, Frank, I'm not hungry, thank you."

"Nerves," said Maxim, shaking his head. "Never mind, this time to-morrow it will all be over."

"I sincerely hope so," said Frank seriously. "I was going to give orders that all cars should stand by for five a.m."

I began to laugh weakly, the tears coming into my eyes. "Oh, dear," I said, "let's send wires to everybody not to come."

"Come on, be brave and face it," said Maxim. "We need not give another one for years. Frank, I have an uneasy feeling we ought to be going up to the house. What do you think?"

Frank agreed, and I followed them unwillingly, reluctant to leave the cramped, rather uncomfortable little dining-room that was so typical of Frank's bachelor establishment, and which seemed to me to-day the embodiment of peace and quietude. When we came to the house we found that the band had arrived, and were standing about in the hall rather pink in the face and self-conscious, while Frith, more important than ever, offered refreshments. The band were to be our guests for the night, and after we had welcomed them and exchanged a few slightly obvious jokes proper to the occasion, the band were borne off to their quarters, to be followed by a tour of the grounds.

The afternoon dragged, like the last hour before a journey when one is packed up and keyed to departure, and I wandered from room to room almost as lost as Jasper, who trailed reproachfully at my heels.

There was nothing I could do to help, and it would have been wiser on my part to have kept clear of the house altogether and taken the dog and myself for a long walk. By the time I decided upon this it was too late, Maxim and Frank were demanding tea, and when tea was over Beatrice and Giles arrived. The evening had come upon us all too soon.

"This is like old times," said Beatrice, kissing Maxim, and looking about her. "Congratulations to you for remembering every detail. The flowers are exquisite," she added, turning to me. "Did you do them?"

"No," I said, rather ashamed, "Mrs. Danvers is responsible for everything."

"Oh. Well, after all . . ." Beatrice did not finish her sentence, she accepted a light for her cigarette from Frank, and once it was lit she appeared to have forgotten what she was going to say.

"Have you got Mitchell's to do the catering as usual?" asked Giles.

"Yes," said Maxim. "I don't think anything has been altered, has it, Frank? We had all the records down at the office. Nothing has been forgotten, and I don't think we have left anyone out."

"What a relief to find only ourselves," said Beatrice. "I remember once arriving about this time, and there were about twenty-five people in the place already. All going to stop the night.

"What's everyone going to wear? I suppose Maxim, as always, refuses to play?"

"As always," said Maxim.

"Such a mistake I think. The whole thing would go with much more swing if you did."

"Have you ever known a ball at Manderley not to go with a swing?"

"No, my dear boy, the organisation is too good. But I do think the host ought to give the lead himself."

"I think it's quite enough if the hostess makes the effort," said Maxim. "Why should I make myself hot and uncomfortable and a damn fool into the bargain?"

"Oh, but that's absurd. There's no need to look a fool. With your appearance, my dear Maxim, you could get away with any costume. You don't have to worry about your figure like poor Giles."

"What is Giles going to wear to-night?" I asked, "or is it a dead secret?"

"No, rather not," beamed Giles, "as a matter of fact it's a pretty good effort. I got our local tailor to rig it up. I'm coming as an Arabian sheik."

"Good God," said Maxim.

"It's not at all bad," said Beatrice warmly. "He stains his face of course, and leaves off his glasses. The head-dress is authentic. We borrowed it off a friend who used to live in the East, and the rest the tailor copied from some paper. Giles looks very well in it."

"What are you going to be, Mrs. Lacy?" said Frank.

"Oh, I'm afraid I haven't coped much," said Beatrice. "I've got some sort of eastern get-up to go with Giles, but I don't pretend it's genuine. Strings of beads, you know, and a veil over my face."

"It sounds very nice," I said politely.

"Oh, it's not bad. Comfortable to wear, that's one blessing. I shall take off the veil if I get too hot. What are you wearing?"

"Don't ask her," said Maxim. "She won't tell any of us. There has never been such a secret. I believe she even wrote to London for it."

"My dear," said Beatrice, rather impressed, "don't say you have gone a bust and will put us all to shame? Mine is only home-made, you know."

"Don't worry," I said, laughing, "it's quite simple really. But Maxim would tease me, and I've promised to give him the surprise of his life."

"Quite right too," said Giles, "Maxim is too superior altogether. The fact is he's jealous, wishes he was dressing up like the rest of us, and doesn't like to say so."

"Heaven forbid," said Maxim.

"What are you doing, Crawley?" asked Giles.

Frank looked rather apologetic. "I've been so busy I'm afraid I've left things to the last moment. I hunted up an old pair of trousers last night, and a striped football jersey, and thought of putting a patch over one eye and coming as a pirate."

"Why on earth didn't you write to us and borrow a costume?" said Beatrice. "There's one of a Dutchman that Roger had last winter in Switzerland. It would have suited you excellently."

"I refuse to allow my agent to walk about as a Dutchman," said Maxim. "He'd never get rents out of anybody again. Let him stick to his pirate. It might frighten some of them."

"Anything less like a pirate," murmured Beatrice in my ear.

I pretended not to hear. Poor Frank, she was always rather down on him.

"How long will it take me to paint my face?" asked Giles.

"Two hours at least," said Beatrice. "I should begin thinking about it if I were you. How many shall we be at dinner?"

"Sixteen," said Maxim, "counting ourselves. No strangers. You know them all."

"I'm beginning to get dress fever already," said Beatrice. "What fun it all is. I'm so glad you decided to do this again, Maxim."

"You've got her to thank for it," said Maxim, nodding at me.

"Oh, it's not true," I said. "It was all the fault of Lady Crowan."

"Nonsense," said Maxim, smiling at me, "you know you're as excited as a child at its first party."

"I'm not."

"I'm longing to see your dress," said Beatrice.

"It's nothing out of the way. Really it's not," I insisted.

"Mrs. de Winter says we shan't know her," said Frank.

Everybody looked at me and smiled. I felt pleased and flushed and rather happy. People were being nice. They were all so friendly. It was suddenly fun, the thought of the dance, and that I was to be the hostess.

The dance was being given for me, in my honour, because I was the bride. I sat on the table in the library, swinging my legs, while the rest of them stood round, and I had a longing to go upstairs and put on my dress, try the wig in front of the looking-glass, turn this way and that before the long mirror on the wall. It was new, this sudden unexpected sensation of being important, of having Giles, and Beatrice, and Frank and Maxim all looking at me and talking about my dress. All wondering what I was going to wear. I thought of the soft white dress in its folds of tissue paper, and how it would hide my flat dull figure, my rather sloping shoulders. I thought of my own lank hair covered by the sleek and gleaming curls.

"What's the time?" I said carelessly, yawning a little, pretending I did not care. "I wonder if we ought to think about going upstairs . . . ?"

As we crossed the great hall on the way to our rooms I realised for the first time how the house lent itself to the occasion, and how beautiful the rooms were looking. Even the drawing-room, formal and cold to my consideration when we were alone, was a blaze of colour now, flowers in every corner, red roses in silver bowls on the white cloth of the supper table, the long windows open to the terrace, where, as soon as it was dusk, the fairy lights would shine. The band had stacked their instruments ready in the minstrels' gallery above the hall, and the hall itself wore a strange, waiting air; there was a warmth about it I had never known before, due to the night itself, so still and clear, to the flowers beneath the pictures, to our own laughter as we hovered on the wide stone stairs.

The old austerity had gone. Manderley had come alive in a fashion I would not have believed possible. It was not the still quiet Manderley I knew. There was a certain significance about it now that had not been before. A reckless air, rather triumphant, rather pleasing. It was as if the house remembered other days, long, long ago, when the hall was a banqueting hall indeed, with weapons and tapestry hanging upon the walls, and men sat at a long narrow table in the centre laughing louder than we laughed now, calling for wine, for song, throwing great pieces of meat upon the flags to the slumbering dogs. Later, in other years, it would still be gay, but with a certain grace and dignity, and Caroline de Winter, whom I should represent to-night, would walk down the wide stone stairs in her white dress to dance the minuet. I wished we could sweep away the years and see her. I wished we did not have to degrade the house with our modern jig-tunes, so out-of-place and unromantic. They would not suit Manderley. I found myself in sudden agreement with Mrs. Danvers. We should have made it a period ball, not the hotch-potch of humanity it was bound to be, with Giles, poor fellow, well-meaning and hearty in his guise of Arabian sheik. I found Clarice waiting for me in my bedroom, her round face scarlet with excitement. We giggled at one another like schoolgirls, and I bade her lock my door. There was much sound of tissue paper, rustling and mysterious. We spoke to one another softly like conspirators, we walked on tip-toe. I felt like a child again on the eve of Christmas. This padding to and fro in my room with bare feet, the little furtive bursts of laughter, the stifled exclamations, reminded me of hanging up my stocking long ago. Maxim was safe in his dressing-room, and the way through was barred against him. Clarice alone was my ally and favoured friend. The dress fitted perfectly. I stood still, hardly able to restrain my impatience while Clarice hooked me up with fumbling fingers.

"It's handsome, Madam," she kept saying, leaning back on her heels to look at me. "It's a dress fit for the Queen of England."

"What about under the left shoulder there?" I said, anxiously. "That strap of mine, is it going to show?"

"No, Madam, nothing shows."

"How is it? How do I look?" I did not wait for her answer, I twisted and turned in front of the mirror, I frowned, I smiled. I felt different already, no longer hampered by my appearance. My own dull personality was submerged at last. "Give me the wig," I said excitedly, "careful, don't crush it, the curls mustn't be flat. They are supposed to stand out from the face." Clarice stood behind my shoulder, I saw her round face beyond mine in the reflection of the looking-glass, her eyes shining, her mouth a little open. I brushed my own hair sleek behind my ears. I took hold of the soft gleaming curls with trembling fingers, laughing under my breath, looking up at Clarice.

"Oh, Clarice," I said, "what will Mr. de Winter say?"

I covered my own mousy hair with the curled wig trying to hide my triumph, trying to hide my smile. Somebody came and hammered on the door.

"Who's there?" I called in panic, "you can't come in."

"It's me, my dear, don't alarm yourself," said Beatrice, "how far have you got? I want to look at you."

"No, no," I said, "you can't come in, I'm not ready."

The flustered Clarice stood beside me, her hand full of hair-pins, while I took them from her one by one, controlling the curls that had become fluffed in the box.

"I'll come down when I am ready," I called. "Go on down, all of you. Don't wait for me. Tell Maxim he can't come in."

"Maxim's down," she said. "He came along to us. He said he hammered on your bathroom door and you never answered. Don't be too long, my dear, we are all so intrigued. Are you sure you don't want any help?"

"No," I shouted impatiently, losing my head, "go away, go on down."

Why did she have to come and bother just at this moment? It fussed me. I did not know what I was doing. I jabbed with a hair-pin, flattening it against a curl. I heard no more from Beatrice, she must have gone along the passage. I wondered if she was happy in her eastern robes and if Giles had succeeded in painting his face. How absurd it was, the whole thing. Why did we do it, I wondered, why were we such children?

I did not recognise the face that stared at me in the glass. The eyes were larger surely, the mouth narrower, the skin white and clear? The curls stood away from the head in a little cloud. I watched this self that was not me at all and then smiled; a new, slow smile.

"Oh, Clarice!" I said. "Oh, Clarice!" I took the skirt of my dress in my hands and curtseyed to her, the flounces sweeping the ground. She giggled excitedly, rather embarrassed, flushed though, very pleased. I paraded up and down in front of my glass watching my reflection.

"Unlock the door," I said. "I'm going down. Run ahead and see if they are there." She obeyed me, still giggling, and I lifted my skirts off the ground and followed her along the corridor.

She looked back at me and beckoned. "They've gone down," she whispered, "Mr. de Winter, and Major and Mrs. Lacy. Mr. Crawley has just come. They are all standing in the hall." I peered through the archway at the head of the big staircase, and looked down on the hall below.

Yes, there they were. Giles, in his white Arab dress, laughing loudly, showing the knife at his side, Beatrice swathed in an extraordinary green garment and hung about the neck with trailing beads, poor Frank self-conscious and slightly foolish in his striped jersey and sea-boots, Maxim, the only normal one of the party, in his evening clothes.

"I don't know what she's doing," he said, "she's been up in her bedroom for hours. What's the time, Frank? The dinner crowd will be upon us before we know where we are."

The band were changed, and in the gallery already. One of the men was tuning his fiddle. He played a scale softly, and then plucked at a string. The light shone on the picture of Caroline de Winter.

Yes, the dress had been copied exactly from my sketch of the portrait. The puffed sleeve, the sash and the ribbon, the wide floppy hat I held in my hand. And my curls were her curls, they stood out from my face as hers did in the picture. I don't think I have ever felt so excited before, so happy and so proud. I waved my hand at the man with the fiddle, and then put my finger to my lips for silence. He smiled and bowed. He came across the gallery to the archway where I stood.

"Make the drummer announce me," I whispered, "make him beat the drum, you know how they do, and then call out Miss Caroline de Winter. I want to surprise them below." He nodded his head, he understood. My heart fluttered absurdly, and my cheeks were burning. What fun it was, what mad ridiculous childish fun! I smiled at Clarice still crouching in the corridor, I picked up my skirt in my hands. Then the sound of the drum echoed in the great hall, startling me for a moment, who had waited for it, who knew that it would come. I saw them look up surprised and bewildered from the hall below.

"Miss Caroline de Winter," shouted the drummer.

I came forward to the head of the stairs and stood there, smiling, my hat in my hand, like the girl in the picture. I waited for the clapping and the laughter that would follow as I walked slowly down the stairs. Nobody clapped, nobody moved.

They all stared at me like dumb things. Beatrice uttered a little cry and put her hand to her mouth. I went on smiling, I put one hand on the banister.

"How do you do, Mr. de Winter," I said.

Maxim had not moved. He stared up at me, his glass in his hand. There was no colour in his face. It was ashen white. I saw Frank go to him as though he would speak, but Maxim shook him off. I hesitated, one foot already on the stairs. Something was wrong, they had not understood. Why was Maxim looking like that? Why did they all stand like dummies, like people in a trance?

Then Maxim moved forward to the stairs, his eyes never leaving my face.

"What the hell do you think you are doing?" he said. His eyes blazed in anger. His face was still ashen white.

I could not move, I went on standing there, my hand on the banister.

"It's the picture," I said, terrified at his eyes, at his voice. "It's the picture, the one in the gallery."

There was a long silence. We went on staring at each other. Nobody moved in the hall. I swallowed, my hand moved to my throat. "What is it?" I said. "What have I done?"

If only they would not stare at me like that with dull blank faces. If only somebody would say something. When Maxim spoke again I did not recognise his voice. It was still and quiet, icy cold, not a voice I knew.

"Go and change," he said, "it does not matter what you put on. Find an ordinary evening frock, anything will do. Go now, before anybody comes."

I could not speak, I went on staring at him. His eyes were the only living things in the white mask of his face.

"What are you standing there for?" he said, his voice harsh and queer. "Didn't you hear what I said?"

I turned and ran blindly through the archway to the corridors beyond. I caught a glimpse of the astonished face of the drummer who had announced me. I brushed past him, stumbling, not looking where I went. Tears blinded my eyes. I did not know what was happening. Clarice had gone. The corridor was deserted. I looked about me stunned and stupid like a haunted thing. Then I saw that the door leading to the west wing was open wide, and that someone was standing there.

It was Mrs. Danvers. I shall never forget the expression on her face, loathsome, triumphant. The face of an exulting devil. She stood there, smiling at me.

And then I ran from her, down the long narrow passage to my own room, tripping, stumbling over the flounces of my dress.

CHAPTER SEVENTEEN

CLARICE WAS WAITING for me in my bedroom. She looked pale and scared. As soon as she saw me she burst into tears. I did not say anything. I began tearing at the hooks of my dress, ripping the stuff. I could not manage them properly, and Clarice came to help me, still crying noisily.

"It's all right, Clarice, it's not your fault," I said, and she shook her head, the tears running down her cheeks.

"Your lovely dress, Madam," she said, "your lovely white dress."

"It doesn't matter," I said. "Can't you find the hook? There it is, at the back. And another one somewhere, just below."

She fumbled with the hooks, her hands trembling, making worse trouble with it than I did myself, and all the time catching at her breath.

"What will you wear instead, Madam?" she said.

"I don't know," I said. "I don't know." She had managed to unfasten the hooks, and I struggled out of the dress. "I think I'd rather like to be alone, Clarice," I said, "would you be a dear and leave me? Don't worry, I shall manage all right. Forget what's happened. I want you to enjoy the party."

"Can't I press out a dress for you, Madam?" she said, looking up at me with swollen streaming eyes. "It won't take me a moment."

"No," I said, "don't bother, I'd rather you went, and Clarice . . ."

"Yes, Madam?"

"Don't—don't say anything about what's just happened."

"No, Madam." She burst into another torrent of weeping.

"Don't let the others see you like that," I said. "Go to your bedroom and do something to your face. There's nothing to cry about, nothing at all." Somebody knocked on the door. Clarice threw me a quick frightened glance.

"Who is it?" I said. The door opened and Beatrice came into the room. She came to me at once, a strange rather ludicrous figure in her eastern drapery, the bangles jangling on her wrists.

"My dear," she said, "my dear," and held out her hands to me.

Clarice slipped out of the room. I felt tired suddenly, and unable to cope. I went and sat down on the bed. I put my hand up to my head and took off the curled wig. Beatrice stood watching me.

"Are you all right?" she said. "You look very white."

"It's the light," I said. "It never gives one any colour."

"Sit down for a few minutes and you'll be all right," she said, "wait, I'll get you a glass of water."

She went into the bathroom, her bangles jangling with her every movement, and then she came back, the glass of water in her hands.

I drank some to please her, not wanting it a bit. It tasted warm from the tap; she had not let it run.

"Of course I knew at once it was just a terrible mistake," she said. "You could not possibly have known, why should you?"

"Known what?" I said.

"Why, the dress, you poor dear, the picture you copied of the girl in the gallery. It was what Rebecca did at the last fancy dress ball at Manderley. Identical. The same picture, the same dress. You stood there on the stairs, and for one ghastly moment I thought . . ."

She did not go on with her sentence, she patted me on the shoulder. "You poor child, how wretchedly unfortunate, how were you to know?"

"I ought to have known," I said stupidly, staring at her, too stunned to understand. "I ought to have known."

"Nonsense, how could you know? It was not the sort of thing that could possibly enter any of our heads. Only it was such a shock, you see. We none of us expected it, and Maxim . . ."

"Yes, Maxim?" I said.

"He thinks, you see, it was deliberate on your part. You had some bet that you would startle him, didn't you? Some foolish joke. And of course, he doesn't understand. It was such a frightful shock for him. I told him at once you could not have done such a thing, and that it was sheer appalling luck that you had chosen that particular picture."

"I ought to have known," I repeated again. "It's all my fault, I ought to have seen. I ought to have known."

"No, no. Don't worry, you'll be able to explain the whole thing to him quietly. Everything will be quite all right. The first lot of people were arriving just as I came upstairs to you. They are having drinks. Everything's all right. I've told Frank and Giles to make up a story about your dress not fitting, and you are very disappointed."

I did not say anything. I went on sitting on the bed with my hands in my lap.

"What can you wear instead?" said Beatrice, going to my wardrobe and flinging open the doors. "Here, what's this blue? It looks charming. Put this on. Nobody will mind. Quick, I'll help you."

"No," I said. "No, I'm not coming down."

Beatrice stared at me in great distress, my blue frock over her arm.

"But, my dear, you must," she said in dismay. "You can't possibly not appear."

"No, Beatrice, I'm not coming down. I can't face them, not after what's happened."

"But nobody will know about the dress," she said. "Frank and Giles will never breathe a word. We've got the story all arranged. The shop sent the wrong dress, and it did not fit, so you are wearing an ordinary evening dress instead. Everyone will think it perfectly natural. It won't make any difference to the evening."

"You don't understand," I said. "I don't care about the dress. It's not that at all. It's what has happened, what I did. I can't come down now, Beatrice, I can't."

"But, my dear, Giles and Frank understand perfectly. They are full of sympathy. And Maxim too. It was just the first shock. . . . I'll try and get him alone a minute, I'll explain the whole thing."

"No!" I said. "No!"

She put my blue frock down beside me on the bed. "Everyone will be arriving," she said, very worried, very upset. "It will look so extraordinary if you don't come down. I can't say you've suddenly got a headache."

"Why not?" I said wearily. "What does it matter? Make anything up. Nobody will mind, they don't any of them know me."

"Come now, my dear," she said, patting my hand, "try and make the effort. Put on this charming blue. Think of Maxim. You must come down for his sake."

"I'm thinking about Maxim all the time," I said.

"Well then, surely . . . ?"

"No," I said, tearing at my nails, rocking backwards and forwards on the bed. "I can't, I can't."

Somebody else knocked on the door. "Oh, dear, who on earth is that?" said Beatrice, walking to the door. "What is it?"

She opened the door. Giles was standing just outside.

"Everyone has turned up, Maxim sent me up to find out what's happening?" he said.

"She says she won't come down," said Beatrice. "What on earth are we going to say?"

I caught sight of Giles peering at me through the open door.

"Oh, Lord, what a frightful mix-up," he whispered. He turned away embarrassed when he noticed that I had seen him.

"What shall I say to Maxim?" he asked Beatrice. "It's five past eight now."

"Say she's feeling rather faint, but will try and come down later. Tell them not to wait dinner. I'll be down directly, I'll make it all right."

"Yes, right you are." He half glanced in my direction again, sympathetic but rather curious, wondering why I sat there on the bed, and his voice was low, as it might be after an accident, when people are waiting for the doctor.

"Is there anything else I can do?" he said.

"No," said Beatrice, "go down now, I'll follow in a minute."

He obeyed her, shuffling away in his Arabian robes. This is the sort of moment, I thought, that I shall laugh at years afterwards, that I shall say "Do you remember how Giles was dressed as an Arab, and Beatrice had a veil over her face, and jangling bangles on her wrists?" And time will mellow it, make it a moment for laughter. But now it was not funny, now I did not laugh. It was not the future, it was the present. It was too vivid and too real. I sat on the bed, plucking at the eiderdown, pulling a little feather out of a slit in one corner.

"Would you like some brandy?" said Beatrice, making a last effort. "I know it's only Dutch courage, but it sometimes works wonders."

"No," I said. "No, I don't want anything."

"I shall have to go down. Giles says they are waiting dinner. Are you sure it's all right for me to leave you?"

"Yes. And thank you, Beatrice."

"Oh, my dear, don't thank me. I wish I could do something." She stooped swiftly to my looking-glass and dabbed her face with powder. "God, what a sight I look," she said, "this damn veil is crooked I know. However it can't be helped." She rustled out of the room, closing the door behind her. I felt I had forfeited her sympathy by my refusal to go down. I had shown the white feather. She had not understood. She belonged to another breed of men and women, another race than I. They had guts, the women of her race. They were not like me. If it had been Beatrice who had done this thing instead of me she would have put on her other dress and gone down again to welcome her guests. She would have stood by Giles's side, and shaken hands with people, a smile on her face. I could not do that. I had not the pride, I had not the guts. I was badly bred.

I kept seeing Maxim's eyes blazing in his white face, and behind him Giles, and Beatrice and Frank standing like dummies, staring at me.

I got up from my bed and went and looked out of the window. The gardeners were going round to the lights in the rose-garden, testing them to see if they all worked. The sky was pale, with a few salmon clouds of evening streaking to the west. When it was dusk the lamps would all be lit. There were tables and chairs in the rose-garden for the couples who wanted to sit out. I could smell the roses from my window. The men were talking to one another and laughing. "There's one here gone," I heard a voice call out; "can you get me another small bulb? One of the blue ones, Bill." He fixed the light into position. He whistled a popular tune of the moment with easy confidence, and I thought how to-night perhaps the band would play the same tune in the minstrels' gallery above the hall. "That's got it," said the man, switching the light on and off, "they're all right here. No others gone. We'd better have a look at those on the terrace." They went off round the corner of the house, still whistling the song. I wished I could be the man. Later in the evening he would stand with his friend in the drive and watch the cars drive up to the house, his hands in his pockets, his cap on the back of his head. He would stand in a crowd with the other people from the estate, and then drink cider at the long table arranged for them in one corner of the terrace. "Like the old days, isn't it?" he would say. But his friend would shake his head, puffing at his pipe. "This new one's not like our Mrs. de Winter, she's different altogether." And a woman next them in the crowd would agree, other people too, all saying "That's right," and nodding their heads.

"Where is she to-night? She's not been on the terrace once."

"I can't say, I'm sure. I've not seen her."

"Mrs. de Winter used to be here, there, and everywhere."

"Aye, that's right."

And the woman would turn to her neighbours nodding mysteriously.

"They say she's not appearing to-night at all."

"Go on."

" 'Tis true. Ask Mary here."

"That's right. One of the servants from the house told me Mrs. de Winter hasn't come down from her room all the evening."

"What's wrong with the maid, is she bad?"

"No, sulky I reckon. They say her dress didn't please her."

A squeal of laughter and a murmur from the little crowd.

"Did you ever hear of such a thing? It's a shame for Mr. de Winter."

"I wouldn't stand for it, not from a chit like her."

"Maybe it's not true at all."

"It's true all right. They're full of it up at the house." One to the other.

This one to the next. A smile, a wink, a shrug of the shoulder. One group, and then another group. And then spreading to the guests who walked on the terrace and strolled across the lawns. The couple who in three hours' time would sit in those chairs beneath me in the rose-garden.

"Do you suppose it's true what I heard?"

"What did you hear?"

"Why, that there's nothing wrong with her at all, they've had a colossal row, and she won't appear!"

"I say!" A lift of the eyebrows, a long whistle.

"I know. Well, it does look rather odd, don't you think? What I mean is, people don't suddenly for no reason have violent headaches. I call the whole thing jolly fishy."

"I thought he looked a bit grim."

"So did I."

"Of course I have heard before the marriage is not a wild success."

"Oh, really?"

"H'm. Several people have said so. They say he's beginning to realise he's made a big mistake. She's nothing to look at, you know."

"No, I've heard there's nothing much to her. Who was she?"

"Oh, no one at all. Some pick-up in the south of France, a nursery gov., or something."

"Good Lord!"

"I know. And when you think of Rebecca . . ."

I went on staring at the empty chairs. The salmon sky had turned to grey. Above my head was the evening star. In the woods beyond the rose-garden the birds were making their last little rustling noises before nightfall. A lone gull flew across the sky. I went away from the window, back to the bed again. I picked up the white dress I had left on the floor and put it back in the box with the tissue paper. I put the wig back in its box too. Then I looked in one of my cupboards for the little portable iron I used to have in Monte Carlo for Mrs. Van Hopper's dresses. It was lying at the back of a shelf with some woollen jumpers I had not worn for a long time. The iron was one of those universal kinds that go on any voltage and I fitted it to the plug in the wall. I began to iron the blue dress that Beatrice had taken from the wardrobe, slowly, methodically, as I used to iron Mrs. Van Hopper's dresses in Monte Carlo.

When I had finished I laid the dress ready on the bed. Then I cleaned the make-up off my face that I had put on for the fancy dress. I combed my hair, and washed my hands. I put on the blue dress and the shoes that went with it. I might have been my old self again, going down to the lounge of the hotel with Mrs. Van Hopper. I opened the door of my room and went along the corridor. Everything was still and silent. There might not have been a party at all. I tip-toed to the end of the passage and turned the corner. The door to the west wing was closed. There was no sound of anything at all. When I came to the archway by the gallery and the staircase I heard the murmur and hum of conversation coming from the dining-room. They were still having dinner. The great hall was deserted. There was nobody in the gallery either. The band must be having their dinner too. I did not know what arrangements had been made for them. Frank had done it—Frank or Mrs. Danvers.

From where I stood I could see the picture of Caroline de Winter facing me in the gallery. I could see the curls framing her face, and I could see the smile on her lips. I remembered the bishop's wife who had said to me that day I called, "I shall never forget her, dressed all in white, with that cloud of dark hair." I ought to have remembered that, I ought to have known. How queer the instruments looked in the gallery, the little stands for the music, the big drum. One of the men had left his handkerchief on a chair. I leant over the rail and looked down at the hall below. Soon it would be filled with people, like the bishop's wife had said, and Maxim would stand at the bottom of the stairs shaking hands with them, as they came into the hall. The sound of their voices would echo to the ceiling, and then the band would play from the gallery where I was leaning now, the man with the violin smiling, swaying to the music.

It would not be quiet like this any more. A board creaked in the gallery. I swung round, looking at the gallery behind me. There was nobody there. The gallery was empty, just as it had been before. A current of air blew in my face though, somebody must have left a window open in one of the passages. The hum of voices continued in the dining-room. I wondered why the board creaked when I had not moved at all. The warmth of the night perhaps, a swelling somewhere in the old wood. The draught still blew in my face though. A piece of music on one of the stands fluttered to the floor. I looked towards the archway above the stairs. The draught was coming from there. I went beneath the arch again, and when I came out on to the long corridor I saw that the door to the west wing had blown open and swung back against the wall. It was dark in the west passage, none of the lights had been turned on. I could feel the wind blowing on my face from an open window. I fumbled for a switch on the wall and could not find one. I could see the window in an angle of the passage, the curtain blowing softly, backwards and forwards. The grey evening light cast queer shadows on the floor. The sound of the sea came to me through the open window, the soft hissing sound of the ebb-tide leaving the shingle.

I did not go and shut the window. I stood there shivering a moment in my thin dress, listening to the sea as it sighed and left the shore. Then I turned quickly and shut the door of the west wing behind me, and came out again through the archway by the stairs.

The murmur of voices had swollen now and was louder than before. The door of the dining-room was open. They were coming out of dinner. I could see Robert standing by the open door, and there was a scraping of chairs, a babble of conversation, and of laughter.

I walked slowly down the stairs to meet them.

When I look back at my first party at Manderley, my first and my last, I can remember little isolated things standing alone out of the vast blank canvas of the evening. The background was hazy, a sea of dim faces none of whom I knew, and there was the slow drone of the band harping out a waltz that never finished, that went on and on. The same couples swung by in rotation, with the same fixed smiles, and to me, standing with Maxim at the bottom of the stairs to welcome the late-comers, these dancing couples seemed like marionettes twisting and turning on a piece of string, held by some invisible hand.

There was a woman, I never knew her name, never saw her again, but she wore a salmon-coloured gown hooped in crinoline form, a vague gesture to some past century but whether seventeenth, eighteenth, or nineteenth I could not tell, and every time she passed me it coincided with a sweeping bar of the waltz to which she dipped and swayed, smiling as she did so in my direction. It happened again and again until it became automatic, a matter of routine, like those promenades on board ship when we meet the same people bent on exercise like ourselves, and know with deadly certainty that we will pass them by the bridge.

I can see her now, the prominent teeth, the gay spot of rouge placed high upon her cheek-bones, and her smile, vacant, happy, enjoying her evening. Later I saw her by the supper table, her keen eyes searching the food, and she heaped a plate high with salmon and lobster mayonnaise and went off into a corner. There was Lady Crowan too, monstrous in purple, disguised as I know not what romantic figure of the past, it might have been Marie Antoinette or Nell Gwyn, for all I knew, or a strange erotic combination of the two, and she kept exclaiming in excited high-pitch tones, a little higher than usual because of the champagne she had consumed, "You all have me to thank for this, not the de Winters at all."

I remember Robert dropping a tray of ices, and the expression of Frith's face when he saw Robert was the culprit and not one of the minions hired for the occasion. I wanted to go to Robert and stand beside him and say "I know how you feel. I understand. I've done worse than you to-night." I can feel now the stiff, set smile on my face that did not match the misery in my eyes. I can see Beatrice, dear friendly tactless Beatrice, watching me from her partner's arms, nodding encouragement, the bangles jangling on her wrists, the veil slipping continually from her over-heated forehead. I can picture myself once more whirled round the room in a desperate dance with Giles, who with dog-like sympathy and kind warm heart would take no refusal, but must steer me through the stamping crowd as he would one of his own horses at a meet. "That's a jolly pretty dress you're wearing," I can hear him say, "it makes all these people look damn silly," and I blessed him for his pathetic simple gesture of understanding and sincerity, thinking, dear Giles, that I was disappointed in my dress, that I was worrying about my appearance that I cared.

It was Frank who brought me a plate of chicken and ham that I could not eat, and Frank who stood by my elbow with a glass of champagne I would not drink.

"I wish you would," he said quietly, "I think you need it," and I took three sips of it to please him. The black patch over his eye gave him a pale odd appearance, it made him look older, different. There seemed to be lines on his face I had not seen before.

He moved amongst the guests like another host, seeing to their comfort, that they were supplied with drink, and food, and cigarettes, and he danced too in solemn painstaking fashion, walking his partners round the room with a set face. He did not wear his pirate costume with abandon, and there was something rather tragic about the side-whiskers he had fluffed under the scarlet handkerchief on his head. I thought of him standing before the looking-glass in his bare bachelor bedroom curling them round his fingers. Poor Frank. Dear Frank. I never asked, I never knew, how much he hated the last fancy dress ball ever given at Manderley.

The band played on, and the swaying couples twisted like bobbing marionettes, to and fro, to and fro, across the great hall and back again, and it was not I who watched them at all, not someone with feelings, made of flesh and blood, but a dummy-stick of a person in my stead, a prop who wore a smile screwed to its face. The figure who stood beside it was wooden too. His face was a mask, his smile was not his own. The eyes were not the eyes of the man I loved, the man I knew. They looked through me and beyond me, cold, expressionless, to some place of pain and torture I could not enter, to some private, inward hell I could not share.

He never spoke to me. He never touched me. We stood beside one another, the host and the hostess, and we were not together. I watched his courtesy to his guests. He flung a word to one, a jest to another, a smile to a third, a call over his shoulder to a fourth, and no one but myself could know that every utterance he made, every movement, was automatic and the work of a machine. We were like two performers in a play, but we were divided, we were not acting with one another. We had to endure it alone, we had to put up this show, this miserable, sham performance for the sake of all these people I did not know and did not want to see again.

"I hear your wife's frock never turned up in time," said someone with a mottled face and a sailor's pigtail, and he laughed, and dug Maxim in the ribs. "Damn shame, what? I should sue the shop for fraud. Same thing happened to my wife's cousin once."

"Yes, it was unfortunate," said Maxim.

"I tell you what," said the sailor, turning to me, "you ought to say you are a forget-me-not. They're blue, aren't they? Jolly little flowers, forget-me-nots. That's right, isn't it, de Winter? Tell your wife she must call herself a 'forget-me-not.'" He swept away, roaring with laughter, his partner in his arms. "Pretty good idea, what? A forget-me-not." Then Frank again hovering just behind me, another glass in his hand, lemonade this time. "No, Frank, I'm not thirsty."

"Why don't you dance? Or come and sit down a moment, there's a corner in the terrace."

"No, I'm better standing. I don't want to sit down."

"Can't I get you something, a sandwich, a peach?"

"No, I don't want anything."

There was the salmon lady again, she forgot to smile at me this time. She was flushed after her supper. She kept looking up into her partner's face. He was very tall, very thin, he had a chin like a fiddle.

The Destiny waltz, the Blue Danube, the Merry Widow, one-two-three, one-two-three, round-and-round, one-two-three, one-two-three, round-and-round. The salmon lady, a green lady, Beatrice again, her veil pushed back off her forehead, Giles, his face streaming with perspiration, and that sailor once more, with another partner, they stopped beside me, I did not know her, she was dressed as a Tudor woman, any Tudor woman, she wore a ruffle round her throat and a black velvet dress.

"When are you coming to see us?" she said, as though we were old friends, and I answered, "Soon of course, we were talking about it the other day," wondering why I found it so easy to lie suddenly, no effort at all. "Such a delightful party, I do congratulate you," she said, and "Thank you very much," I said. "It's fun, isn't it?"

"I hear they sent you the wrong dress?"

"Yes, absurd, wasn't it?"

"These shops are all the same. No depending on them. But you look delightfully fresh in that pretty blue. Much more comfortable than this hot velvet. Don't forget, you must both come and dine at the Palace soon."

"We should love to."

What did she mean, where, what palace? Were we entertaining royalty? She swept on to the Blue Danube in the arms of the sailor, her velvet frock brushing the ground like a carpet-sweeper, and it was not until long afterwards, in the middle of some night, when I could not sleep, that I remembered the Tudor woman was the bishop's wife who liked walking in the Pennines.

What was the time? I did not know. The evening dragged on, hour after hour, the same faces and the same tunes. Now and again the bridge people crept out of the library like hermits to watch the dancers, and then returned again. Beatrice, her draperies trailing behind her, whispered in my ear,

"Why don't you sit down? You look like death."

"I'm all right."

Giles, the make-up running on his face, poor fellow, and stifling in his Arab blanket, came up to me and said, "Come and watch the fireworks on the terrace."

I remember standing on the terrace and staring up at the sky as the foolish rockets burst and fell. There was little Clarice in a corner with some boy off the estate, she was smiling happily, squealing with delight as a squib spluttered at her feet. She had forgotten her tears.

"Hullo, this will be a big-un." Giles, his large face upturned, his mouth open. "Here she comes. Bravo, jolly fine show."

The slow hiss of the rocket as it sped into the air, the burst of the explosion, the stream of little emerald stars. A murmur of approval from the crowd, cries of delight, and a clapping of hands.

The salmon lady well to the front, her face eager with expectation, a remark for every star that fell. "Oh, what a beauty . . . look at that one now, I say, how pretty. . . . Oh, that one didn't burst . . . take care, it's coming our way . . . what are those men doing over there?" . . . Even the hermits left their lair and came to join the dancers on the terrace. The lawns were black with people. The bursting stars shone on their upturned faces.

Again and again the rockets sped into the air like arrows, and the sky became crimson and gold. Manderley stood out like an enchanted house, every window aflame, the grey walls coloured by the falling stars. A house bewitched, carved out of the dark woods. And when the last rocket burst and the cheering died away the night that had been fine before seemed dull and heavy in contrast, the sky became a pall. The little groups on the lawns and in the drive broke up and scattered. The guests crowded the long windows in the terrace back to the drawing-room again. It was anti-climax, the aftermath had come. We stood about with blank faces. Someone gave me a glass of champagne. I heard the sound of cars starting up in the drive.

"They're beginning to go," I thought. "Thank God, they're beginning to go." The salmon lady was having some more supper. It would take time yet to clear the hall. I saw Frank make a signal to the band. I stood in the doorway between the drawing-room and the hall beside a man I did not know.

"What a wonderful party it's been," he said.

"Yes," I said.

"I've enjoyed every minute of it," he said.

"I'm so glad," I said.

"Molly was wild with fury at missing it," he said.

"Was she?" I said.

The band began to play Auld Lang Syne. The man seized my hand and started swinging it up and down. "Here," he said, "come on, some of you." Somebody else swung my other hand, and more people joined us. We stood in a great circle singing at the top of our voices. The man who had enjoyed his evening and said Molly would be wild at missing it was dressed as a Chinese mandarin, and his false nails got caught up in his sleeve as we swung our hands up and down. He roared with laughter. We all laughed. "Should auld acquaintance be forgot," we sang.

The hilarious gaiety changed swiftly at the closing bars, and the drummer rattled his sticks in the inevitable prelude to God Save the King. The smiles left our faces as though wiped clean by a sponge. The mandarin sprung to attention, his hands stiff to his sides. I remember wondering vaguely if he was in the Army. How queer he looked with his long poker face, and his drooping mandarin moustache. I caught the salmon lady's eye. God Save the King had taken her unawares, she was still holding a plate heaped with chicken in aspic. She held it stiffly out in front of her like a church collection. All animation had gone from her face. As the last note of God Save the King died away she relaxed again, and attacked her chicken in a sort of frenzy, chattering over her shoulder to her partner. Somebody came and wrung me by the hand.

"Don't forget, you're dining with us on the fourteenth of next month."

"Oh, are we?" I stared at him blankly.

"Yes, we've got your sister-in-law to promise too."

"Oh. Oh, what fun."

"Eight-thirty, and black tie. So looking forward to seeing you."

"Yes. Yes rather."

People began to form up in queues to say good-bye. Maxim was at the other side of the room. I put on my smile again which had worn thin after Auld Lang Syne.

"The best evening I've spent for a long time."

"I'm so glad."

"Many thanks for a grand party."

"I'm so glad."

"Here we are, you see, staying to the bitter end."

"Yes, I'm so glad."

Was there no other sentence in the English language? I bowed and smiled like a dummy, my eyes searching for Maxim above their heads. He was caught up in a knot of people by the library. Beatrice too was surrounded, and Giles had led a team of stragglers to the buffet table in the drawing-room. Frank was out in the drive seeing that people got their cars. I was hemmed in by strangers.

"Good-bye, and thanks tremendously."

"I'm so glad."

The great hall began to empty. Already it wore that drab deserted air of a vanished evening and the dawn of a tired day. There was a grey light on the terrace, I could see the shapes of the blown firework stands taking form on the lawns.

"Good-bye, a wonderful party."

"I'm so glad."

Maxim had gone out to join Frank in the drive. Beatrice came up to me, pulling off her jangling bracelets. "I can't stand these things a moment longer. Heavens, I'm dead beat. I don't believe I've missed a dance. Anyway, it was a tremendous success."

"Was it?" I said.

"My dear, hadn't you better go to bed? You look worn out. You've been standing nearly all the evening. Where are the men?"

"Out on the drive."

"I shall have some coffee, and eggs and bacon. What about you?"

"No, Beatrice, I don't think I will."

"You looked very charming in your blue. Everyone said so. And nobody had an inkling about–about the other thing, so you mustn't worry."

"No."

"If I were you I should have a good long lie to-morrow morning. Don't attempt to get up. Have your breakfast in bed."

"Yes, perhaps."

"I'll tell Maxim you've gone up, shall I?"

"Please, Beatrice."

"All right, my dear. Sleep well." She kissed me swiftly, patting my shoulder at the same time, and then went off to find Giles in the supper-room. I walked slowly up the stairs, one step at a time. The band had turned the lights off in the gallery, and had gone down to have eggs and bacon too. Pieces of music lay about the floor. One chair had been upturned. There was an ash-tray full of the stubs of their cigarettes. The aftermath of the party. I went along the corridor to my room. It was getting lighter every moment, and the birds had started singing. I did not have to turn on the light to undress. A little chill wind blew in from the open window. It was rather cold. Many people must have used the rose-garden during the evening, for all the chairs were moved, and dragged from their places. There was a tray of empty glasses on one of the tables. Someone had left a bag behind on a chair. I pulled the curtains to darken the room, but the grey morning light found its way through the gaps at the sides.

I got into bed, my legs very weary, a niggling pain in the small of my back. I lay back and closed my eyes, thankful for the cool white comfort of clean sheets. I wished my mind would rest like my body, relax, and pass to sleep. Not hum round in the way it did, jigging to music, whirling in a sea of faces. I pressed my hands over my eyes but they would not go.

I wondered how long Maxim would be. The bed beside me looked stark and cold. Soon there would be no shadows in the room at all, the walls and the ceiling and the floor would be white with the morning. The birds would sing their songs, louder, gayer, less subdued. The sun would make a yellow pattern on the curtain. My little bed-side clock ticked out the minutes one by one. The hand moved round the dial. I lay on my side watching it. It came to the hour and passed it again. It started afresh on its journey. But Maxim did not come.

CHAPTER EIGHTEEN

I THINK I fell asleep a little after seven. It was broad daylight I remember, there was no longer any pretence that the drawn curtains hid the sun. The light streamed in at the open window and made patterns on the wall. I heard the men below in the rose-garden clearing away the tables and the chairs, and taking down the chain of fairy lights. Maxim's bed was still bare and empty. I lay across my bed, my arms over my eyes, a strange, mad position and the least likely to bring sleep, but I drifted to the border-line of the unconscious and slipped over it at last. When I awoke it was past eleven, and Clarice must have come in and brought me my tea without my hearing her, for there was a tray by my side, and a stone-cold tea-pot, and my clothes had been tidied, my blue frock put away in the wardrobe.

I drank my cold tea, still blurred and stupid from my short heavy sleep, and stared at the blank wall in front of me. Maxim's empty bed brought me to realisation with a queer shock to my heart, and the full anguish of the night before was upon me once again. He had not come to bed at all. His pyjamas lay folded on the turned-down sheet untouched. I wondered what Clarice had thought when she came into the room with my tea. Had she noticed? Would she have gone out and told the other servants, and would they all discuss it over their breakfast? I wondered why I minded that, and why the thought of the servants talking about it in the kitchen should cause me such distress. It must be that I had a small mean mind, a conventional, petty hatred of gossip.

That was why I had come down last night in my blue dress and had not stayed hidden in my room. There was nothing brave or fine about it, it was a wretched tribute to convention. I had not come down for Maxim's sake, for Beatrice's, for the sake of Manderley. I had come down because I did not want the people at the ball to think I had quarrelled with Maxim. I didn't want them to go home and say, "Of course you know they don't get on. I hear he's not at all happy." I had come for my own sake, my own poor personal pride. As I sipped my cold tea I thought with a tired bitter feeling of despair that I would be content to live in one corner of Manderley and Maxim in the other as long as the outside world should never know. If he had no more tenderness for me, never kissed me again, did not speak to me except on matters of necessity, I believed I could bear it if I were certain that nobody knew of this but our two selves. If we could bribe servants not to tell, play our part before relations, before Beatrice, and then when we were alone sit apart in our separate rooms, leading our separate lives.

It seemed to me, as I sat there in bed, staring at the wall, at the sunlight coming in at the window, at Maxim's empty bed, that there was nothing quite so shaming, so degrading, as a marriage that had failed. Failed after three months, as mine had done. For I had no illusions left now, I no longer made any effort to pretend. Last night had shown me too well. My marriage was a failure. All the things that people would say about it if they knew were true. We did not get on. We were not companions. We were not suited to one another. I was too young for Maxim, too inexperienced, and more important still, I was not of his world. The fact that I loved him in a sick, hurt, desperate way, like a child or a dog, did not matter. It was not the sort of love he needed. He wanted something else that I could not give him, something he had had before. I thought of the youthful almost hysterical excitement and conceit with which I had gone into this marriage, imagining I would bring happiness to Maxim who had known much greater happiness before. Even Mrs. Van Hopper, with her cheap views and common outlook, had known I was making a mistake. "I'm afraid you will regret it," she said. "I believe you are making a big mistake."

I would not listen to her, I thought her hard and cruel. But she was right. She was right in everything. That last mean thrust thrown at me before she said good-bye, "You don't flatter yourself he's in love with you, do you? He's lonely, he can't bear that great empty house," was the sanest, most truthful statement she had ever made in her life. Maxim was not in love with me, he had never loved me. Our honeymoon in Italy had meant nothing at all to him, nor our living here together. What I had thought was love for me, for myself as a person, was not love. It was just that he was a man, and I was his wife and was young, and he was lonely. He did not belong to me at all, he belonged to Rebecca. He still thought about Rebecca. He would never love me because of Rebecca. She was in the house still as Mrs. Danvers had said, she was in that room in the west wing, she was in the library, in the morning-room, in the gallery above the hall. Even in the little flower-room, where her mackintosh still hung. And in the garden, and in the woods, and down in the stone cottage on the beach. Her footsteps sounded in the corridors, her scent lingered on the stairs. The servants obeyed her orders still, the food we ate was the food she liked. Her favourite flowers filled the rooms. Her clothes were in the wardrobes in her room, her brushes were on the table, her shoes beneath the chair, her nightdress on her bed. Rebecca was still mistress of Manderley. Rebecca was still Mrs. de Winter. I had no business here at all. I had come blundering like a poor fool on ground that was preserved. "Where is Rebecca?" Maxim's grandmother had cried, "I want Rebecca. What have you done with Rebecca?" She did not know me, she did not care about me? Why should she? I was a stranger to her. I did not belong to Maxim or to Manderley. And Beatrice at our first meeting, looking me up and down, frank, direct, "You're so very different from Rebecca." Frank, reserved, embarrassed when I spoke of her, hating those questions I had poured upon him, even as I had hated them myself, and then answering that final one as we came towards the house, his voice grave and quiet, "Yes, she was the most beautiful creature I have ever seen."

Rebecca, always Rebecca. Wherever I walked in Manderley, wherever I sat, even in my thoughts and in my dreams, I met Rebecca. I knew her figure now, the long slim legs, the small and narrow feet. Her shoulders, broader than mine, the capable clever hands. Hands that could steer a boat, could hold a horse. Hands that arranged flowers, made the models of ships, and wrote "Max from Rebecca" on the fly-leaf of a book. I knew her face too, small and oval, the clear white skin, the cloud of dark hair. I knew the scent she wore, I could guess her laughter and her smile. If I heard it, even among a thousand others, I should recognise her voice. Rebecca, always Rebecca. I should never be rid of Rebecca.

Perhaps I haunted her as she haunted me; she looked down on me from the gallery as Mrs. Danvers had said, she sat beside me when I wrote my letters at her desk. That mackintosh I wore, that handkerchief I used. They were hers. Perhaps she knew and had seen me take them. Jasper had been her dog, and he ran at my heels now. The roses were hers and I cut them. Did she resent me and fear me as I resented her? Did she want Maxim alone in the house again? I could fight the living but I could not fight the dead. If there was some woman in London that Maxim loved, someone he wrote to, visited, dined with, slept with, I could fight with her. We would stand on common ground. I should not be afraid. Anger and jealousy were things that could be conquered. One day the woman would grow old or tired or different, and Maxim would not love her any more. But Rebecca would never grow old. Rebecca would always be the same. And her I could not fight. She was too strong for me.

I got out of bed and pulled the curtains. The sun streamed into the room. The men had cleared the mess away from the rose-garden. I wondered if people were talking about the ball in the way they do the day after a party.

"Did you think it quite up to their usual standard?"

"Oh, I think so."

"The band dragged a bit I thought."

"The supper was damn good."

"Fireworks weren't bad."

"Bee Lacy is beginning to look old."

"Who wouldn't in that get-up?"

"I thought he looked rather ill."

"He always does."

"What do you think of the bride?"

"Not much. Rather dull."

"I wonder if it's a success."

"Yes, I wonder . . ."

Then I noticed for the first time there was a note under my door. I went and picked it up. I recognised the square hand of Beatrice. She had scribbled it in pencil after breakfast. "*I knocked at your door but had no answer so gather you've taken my advice and are sleeping off last night. Giles is anxious to get back early as they have rung up from home to say he's wanted to take somebody's place in a cricket match, and it starts at two. How he is going to see the ball after all the champagne he put away last night heaven only knows! I'm feeling a bit weak in the legs, but slept like a top. Frith says Maxim was down to an early breakfast, and there's now no sign of him! So please give him our love, and many thanks to you both for our evening, which we thoroughly enjoyed. Don't think any more about the dress.* (This last was heavily underlined.) *Yours affectionately, Bee,*" and a postscript, "*You must both come over and see us soon.*"

She had scribbled nine-thirty a.m. at the top of the paper, and it was now nearly half-past eleven. They had been gone about two hours. They would be home by now, Beatrice with her suit-case unpacked, going out into her garden and taking up her ordinary routine, and Giles preparing for his match, renewing the whipping on his bat.

In the afternoon Beatrice would change into a cool frock and a shady hat and watch Giles play cricket. They would have tea afterwards in a tent, Giles very hot and red in the face, Beatrice laughing and talking to her friends. "Yes, we went over for the dance at Manderley, it was great fun. I wonder Giles was able to run a yard." Smiling at Giles, patting him on the back. They were both middle-aged and unromantic. They had been married for twenty years and had a grown-up son who was going to Oxford. They were very happy. Their marriage was a success. It had not failed after three months as mine had done.

I could not go on sitting in my bedroom any longer. The maids would want to come and do the room. Perhaps Clarice would not have noticed about Maxim's bed after all. I rumpled it, to make it look as though he had slept there. I did not want the housemaids to know, if Clarice had not told them.

I had a bath and dressed, and went downstairs. The men had taken up the floor already in the hall and the flowers had been carried away. The music stands were gone from the gallery. The band must have caught an early train. The gardeners were sweeping the lawns and the drive clear of the spent fireworks. Soon there would be no trace left of the fancy dress ball at Manderley. How long the preparations had seemed, and how short and swift the clearance now.

I remembered the salmon lady standing by the drawing-room door with her plate of chicken, and it seemed to me a thing I must have fancied, or something that had happened very long ago. Robert was polishing the table in the dining-room. He was normal again, stolid, dull, not the fey excited creature of the past few weeks.

"Good morning, Robert," I said.

"Good morning, Madam."

"Have you see Mr. de Winter anywhere?"

"He went out soon after breakfast, Madam, before Major and Mrs. Lacy were down. He has not been in since."

"You don't know where he went?"

"No, Madam, I could not say."

I wandered back again into the hall. I went through the drawing-room to the morning-room. Jasper rushed at me and licked my hands in a frenzy of delight as if I had been away for a long time. He had spent the evening on Clarice's bed and I had not seen him since tea-time yesterday. Perhaps the hours had been as long for him as they had for me.

I picked up the telephone and asked for the number of the estate office. Perhaps Maxim was with Frank. I felt I must speak to him, even if it was only for two minutes. I must explain to him that I had not meant to do what I had done last night. Even if I never spoke to him again. I must tell him that. The clerk answered the telephone, and told me that Maxim was not there.

"Mr. Crawley is here, Mrs. de Winter," said the clerk, "would you speak to him?" I would have refused, but he gave me no chance, and before I could put down the receiver I heard Frank's voice.

"Is anything the matter?" It was a funny way to begin a conversation. The thought flashed through my mind. He did not say good morning, or did you sleep well? Why did he ask if something was the matter?

"Frank, it's me," I said, "where's Maxim?"

"I don't know, I haven't seen him. He's not been in this morning."

"Not been to the office?"

"No."

"Oh! Oh, well, it doesn't matter."

"Did you see him at breakfast?" said Frank.

"No, I did not get up."

"How did he sleep?"

I hesitated, Frank was the only person I did not mind knowing. "He did not come to bed last night."

There was silence at the other end of the line, as though Frank was thinking hard for an answer.

"Oh," he said at last, very slowly. "Oh, I see," and then, after a minute, "I was afraid something like that would happen."

"Frank," I said desperately, "what did he say last night when everyone had gone? What did you all do?"

"I had a sandwich with Giles and Mrs. Lacy," said Frank. "Maxim did not come. He made some excuse and went into the library. I came back home almost at once. Perhaps Mrs. Lacy can tell you."

"She's gone," I said, "they went after breakfast. She sent up a note. She had not seen Maxim, she said."

"Oh," said Frank. I did not like it. I did not like the way he said it. It was sharp, ominous.

"Where do you think he's gone?" I said.

"I don't know," said Frank, "perhaps he's gone for a walk." It was the sort of voice doctors used to relatives at a nursing-home when they came to enquire.

"Frank, I must see him," I said. "I've got to explain about last night."

Frank did not answer. I could picture his anxious face, the lines on his forehead.

"Maxim thinks I did it on purpose," I said, my voice breaking in spite of myself, and the tears that had blinded me last night and I had not shed came coursing down my cheeks sixteen hours too late. "Maxim thinks I did it as a joke, a beastly damnable joke!"

"No," said Frank. "No."

"He does, I tell you. You didn't see his eyes, as I did. You didn't stand beside him all the evening, watching him, as I did. He didn't speak to me, Frank. He never looked at me again. We stood there together the whole evening and we never spoke to one another."

"There was no chance," said Frank. "All those people. Of course I saw, don't you think I know Maxim well enough for that? Look here . . ."

"I don't blame him," I interrupted. "If he believes I played that vile hideous joke he has a right to think what he likes of me, and never talk to me again, never see me again."

"You mustn't talk like that," said Frank. "You don't know what you're saying. Let me come up and see you. I think I can explain."

What was the use of Frank coming to see me, and us sitting in the morning-room together, Frank smoothing me down, Frank being tactful, Frank being kind? I did not want kindness from anybody now. It was too late.

"No," I said. "No, I don't want to go over it and over it again. It's happened, it can't be altered now. Perhaps it's a good thing, it's made me realise something I ought to have known before, that I ought to have suspected when I married Maxim."

"What do you mean?" said Frank.

His voice was sharp, queer. I wondered why it should matter to him about Maxim not loving me. Why did he not want me to know?

"About him and Rebecca," I said, and as I said her name it sounded strange and sour like a forbidden word, a relief to me no longer, not a pleasure, but hot and shaming as a sin confessed.

Frank did not answer for a moment. I heard him draw in his breath at the other end of the wire.

"What do you mean?" he said again, shorter and sharper than before. "What do you mean?"

"He doesn't love me, he loves Rebecca," I said. "He's never forgotten her, he thinks about her still, night and day. He's never loved me, Frank. It's always Rebecca, Rebecca, Rebecca."

I heard Frank give a startled cry but I did not care how much I shocked him now. "Now you know how I feel," I said, "now you understand."

"Look here," he said, "I've got to come and see you, I've got to, do you hear? It's vitally important, I can't talk to you down the telephone. Mrs. de Winter? Mrs. de Winter?"

I slammed down the receiver, and got up from the writing-desk. I did not want to see Frank. He could not help me over this. No one could help me but myself. My face was red and blotchy from crying. I walked about the room biting the corner of my handkerchief, tearing at the edge.

The feeling was strong within me that I should never see Maxim again. It was certainty, born of some strange instinct. He had gone away and would not come back. I knew in my heart that Frank believed this too and would not admit it to me on the telephone. He did not want to frighten me. If I rang him up again at the office now I should find that he had gone. The clerk would say "Mr. Crawley has just gone out, Mrs. de Winter," and I could see Frank, hatless, climbing into his small, shabby Morris, driving off in search of Maxim.

I went and stared out of the window at the little clearing where the satyr played his pipes. The rhododendrons were all over now. They would not bloom again for another year. The tall shrubs looked dark and drab now that the colour had gone. A fog was rolling up from the sea, and I could not see the woods beyond the bank. It was very hot, very oppressive. I could imagine our guests of last night saying to one another, "What a good thing this fog kept off for yesterday, we should never have seen the fireworks." I went out of the morning-room and through the drawing-room to the terrace. The sun had gone in now behind a wall of mist. It was as though a blight had fallen upon Manderley taking the sky away and the light of the day. One of the gardeners passed me with a barrow full of bits of paper, and litter, and the skins of fruit left on the lawns by the people last night. "Good morning," I said.

"Good morning, Madam."

"I'm afraid the ball last night has made a lot of work for you," I said.

"That's all right, Madam," he said. "I think everyone enjoyed themselves good and hearty, and that's the main thing, isn't it?"

"Yes, I suppose so," I said.

He looked across the lawns to the clearing in the woods where the valley sloped to the sea. The dark trees loomed thin and indistinct.

"It's coming up very thick," he said.

"Yes," I said.

"A good thing it wasn't like this last night," he said.

"Yes," I said.

He waited a moment, and then he touched his cap and went off trundling his barrow. I went across the lawns to the edge of the woods. The mist in the trees had turned to moisture and dripped upon my bare head like a thin rain. Jasper stood by my feet dejected, his tail downcast, his pink tongue hanging from his mouth. The clammy oppression of the day made him listless and heavy. I could hear the sea from where I stood, sullen and slow, as it broke in the coves below the woods. The white fog rolled on past me towards the house smelling of damp salt and sea-weed. I put my hand on Jasper's coat. It was wringing wet. When I looked back at the house I could not see the chimneys or the contour of the walls, I could only see the vague substance of the house, the windows in the west wing, and the flower tubs on the terrace. The shutter had been pulled aside from the window of the large bedroom in the west wing, and someone was standing there, looking down upon the lawns. The figure was shadowy and indistinct and for one moment of shock and fear I believed it to be Maxim. Then the figure moved, I saw the arm reach up to fold the shutter, and I knew it was Mrs. Danvers. She had been watching me then as I stood at the edge of the woods bathed in that white wall of fog. She had seen me walk slowly from the terrace to the lawns. She may have listened to my conversation with Frank on the telephone from the connecting line in her own room. She would know that Maxim had not been with me last night. She would have heard my voice, known about my tears. She knew the part I had played through the long hours, standing by Maxim's side in my blue dress at the bottom of the stairs, and that he had not looked at me nor spoken to me. She knew because she had meant it to happen. This was her triumph, hers and Rebecca's.

I thought of her as I had seen her last night watching me through the open door to the west wing, and that diabolical smile on her white skull's face, and I remembered that she was a living breathing woman like myself, she was made of flesh and blood. She was not dead, like Rebecca. I could speak to her, but I could not speak to Rebecca.

I walked back across the lawns on sudden impulse to the house. I went through the hall and up the great stairs, I turned in under the archway by the gallery, I passed through the door to the west wing, and so along the dark silent corridor to Rebecca's room. I turned the handle of the door and went inside.

Mrs. Danvers was still standing by the window, and the shutter was folded back.

"Mrs. Danvers," I said. "Mrs. Danvers." She turned to look at me, and I saw her eyes were red and swollen with crying, even as mine were, and there were dark shadows in her white face.

"What is it?" she said, and her voice was thick and muffled from the tears she had shed, even as mine had been.

I had not expected to find her so. I had pictured her smiling as she had smiled last night, cruel and evil. Now she was none of these things, she was an old woman who was ill and tired.

I hesitated, my hand still on the knob of the open door, and I did not know what to say to her now or what to do.

She went on staring at me with those red, swollen eyes and I could not answer her. "I left the menu on the desk as usual," she said. "Do you want something changed?" Her words gave me courage, and I left the door and came to the middle of the room.

"Mrs. Danvers," I said, "I have not come to talk about the menu. You know that, don't you?"

She did not answer me. Her left hand opened and shut.

"You've done what you wanted, haven't you?" I said, "you meant this to happen, didn't you? Are you pleased now, are you happy?"

She turned her head away, and looked out of the window as she had done when I first came into the room. "Why did you ever come here?" she said. "Nobody wanted you at Manderley. We were all right until you came. Why did not you stay where you were out in France?"

"You seem to forget I love Mr. de Winter," I said.

"If you loved him you would never have married him," she said.

I did not know what to say. The situation was mad, unreal. She kept talking in that choked muffled way with her head turned from me.

"I thought I hated you but I don't now," she said, "it seems to have spent itself, all the feeling I had."

"Why should you hate me?" I asked, "what have I ever done to you that you should hate me?"

"You tried to take Mrs. de Winter's place," she said.

Still she would not look at me. She stood there sullen, her head turned from me. "I had nothing changed," I said. "Manderley went on as it had always been. I gave no orders, I left everything to you. I would have been friends with you, if you had let me, but you set yourself against me from the first. I saw it in your face, the moment I shook hands with you."

She did not answer, and her hand kept opening and shutting against her dress. "Many people marry twice, men and women," I said. "There are thousands of second marriages taking place every day. You talk as though my marrying Mr. de Winter was a crime, a sacrilege against the dead. Haven't we as much right to be happy as anyone else?"

"Mr. de Winter is not happy," she said, turning to look at me at last, "any fool can see that. You have only to look at his eyes. He's still in hell, and he's looked like that ever since she died."

"It's not true," I said. "It's not true. He was happy when we were in France together, he was younger, much younger, and laughing and gay."

"Well, he's a man isn't he?" she said. "No man denies himself on a honeymoon does he? Mr. de Winter's not forty-six yet."

She laughed contemptuously, and shrugged her shoulders.

"How dare you speak to me like that, how dare you?" I said.

I was not afraid of her any more. I went up to her, shook her by the arm. "You made me wear that dress last night," I said, "I should never have thought of it but for you. You did it because you wanted to hurt Mr. de Winter, you wanted to make him suffer. Hasn't he suffered enough without your playing that vile hideous joke upon him? Do you think his agony and pain will bring Mrs. de Winter back again?"

She shook herself clear of me, the angry colour flooded her dead white face. "What do I care for his suffering?" she said, "he's never cared about mine. How do you think I've liked it, watching you sit in her place, walk in her footsteps, touch the things that were hers? What do you think it's meant to me all these months knowing that you wrote at her desk in the morning-room, using the very pen that she used, speaking down the house telephone where she used to speak, every morning of her life to me, ever since she first came to Manderley. What do you think it meant to me to hear Frith and Robert and the rest of the servants talking about you as 'Mrs. de Winter'? 'Mrs. de Winter has gone out for a walk.' 'Mrs. de Winter wants the car this afternoon at three o'clock.' 'Mrs. de Winter won't be in to tea till five o'clock.' And all the while my Mrs. de Winter, my lady with her smile and her lovely face and brave ways, the real Mrs. de Winter, lying dead and cold and forgotten in the church crypt. If he suffers then he deserves to suffer, marrying a young girl like you not ten months afterwards. Well, he's paying for it now, isn't he? I've seen his face, I've seen his eyes. He's made his own hell and there's no one but himself to thank for it. He knows she sees him, he knows she comes by night and watches him. And she doesn't come kindly, not she, not my lady. She was never one to stand mute and still and be wronged. 'I'll see them in hell, Danny,' she'd say, 'I'll see them in hell first.' 'That's right, my dear,' I'd tell her, 'no one will put upon you. You were born into this world to take what you could out of it,' and she did, she didn't care, she wasn't afraid. She had all the courage and the spirit of a boy, had my Mrs. de Winter. She ought to have been a boy, I often told her that. I had the care of her as a child. You knew that, didn't you?"

"No!" I said, "no. Mrs. Danvers, what's the use of all this? I don't want to hear any more, I don't want to know. Haven't I got feelings as well as you? Can't you understand what it means to me, to hear her mentioned, to stand here and listen while you tell me about her?"

She did not hear me, she went on raving like a madwoman, a fanatic, her long fingers twisting and tearing the black stuff of her dress.

"She was lovely then," she said. "Lovely as a picture, men turning to stare at her when she passed, and she not twelve years old. She knew then, she used to wink at me like the little devil she was. 'I'm going to be a beauty, aren't I, Danny?' she said, and 'We'll see about that, my love, we'll see about that,' I told her. She had all the knowledge then of a grown person, she'd enter into conversation with men and women as clever and full of tricks as someone of eighteen. She twisted her father round her little finger, and she'd have done the same with her mother, had she lived. Spirit, you couldn't beat my lady for spirit. She drove a four-in-hand on her fourteenth birthday, and her cousin, Mr. Jack, got up on the box beside her and tried to take the reins from her hands. They fought it out there together, for three minutes, like a couple of wild cats, and the horses galloping to glory. She won though, my lady won. She cracked her whip over his head and down he came, head-over-heels, cursing and laughing. They were a pair, I tell you, she and Mr. Jack. They sent him in the Navy, but he wouldn't stand the discipline, and I don't blame him. He had too much spirit to obey orders, like my lady."

I watched her, fascinated, horrified; a queer ecstatic smile was on her lips making her older than ever, making her skull's face vivid and real. "No one got the better of her, never, never," she said. "She did what she liked, she lived as she liked. She had the strength of a little lion too. I remember her at sixteen getting up on one of her father's horses, a big brute of an animal too, that the groom said was too hot for her to ride. She stuck to him, all right. I can see her now, with her hair flying out behind her, slashing at him, drawing blood, digging the spurs into his side, and when she got off his back he was trembling all over, full of froth and blood. 'That will teach him, won't it, Danny?' she said, and walked off to wash her hands as cool as you please. And that's how she went at life, when she grew up. I saw her, I was with her. She cared for nothing and for no one. And then she was beaten in the end. But it wasn't a man, it wasn't a woman. The sea got her. The sea was too strong for her. The sea got her in the end."

She broke off, her mouth working strangely, and dragging at the corners. She began to cry noisily, harshly, her mouth open and her eyes dry.

"Mrs. Danvers," I said. "Mrs. Danvers." I stood before her helplessly, not knowing what to do. I mistrusted her no longer, I was afraid of her no more, but the sight of her sobbing there, dry-eyed, made me shudder, made me ill. "Mrs. Danvers," I said, "you're not well, you ought to be in bed. Why don't you go to your room and rest? Why don't you go to bed?"

She turned on me fiercely. "Leave me alone, can't you?" she said. "What's it to do with you if I show my grief? I'm not ashamed of it, I don't shut myself up in my room to cry. I don't walk up and down, up and down, in my room like Mr. de Winter, with the door locked on me."

"What do you mean?" I said. "Mr. de Winter does not do that."

"He did," she said, "after she died. Up and down, up and down, in the library. I heard him. I watched him too, through the key-hole, more than once. Backwards and forwards, like an animal in a cage."

"I don't want to hear," I said. "I don't want to know."

"And then you say you made him happy on his honeymoon," she said, "made him happy, you, a young ignorant girl, young enough to be his daughter. What do you know about life, what do you know about men? You come here and think you can take Mrs. de Winter's place. You. You take my lady's place. Why, even the servants laughed at you when you came to Manderley. Even the little scullery-maid you met in the back passage there on your first morning. I wonder what Mr. de Winter thought when he got you back here at Manderley, after his precious honeymoon was over. I wonder what he thought when he saw you sitting at the dining-room table for the first time."

"You'd better stop this, Mrs. Danvers," I said; "you'd better go to your room."

"Go to my room," she mimicked, "go to my room. The mistress of the house thinks I had better go to my room. And after that, what then? You'll go running to Mr. de Winter and saying, 'Mrs. Danvers has been unkind to me. Mrs. Danvers has been rude.' You'll go running to him like you did before when Mr. Jack came to see me."

"I never told him," I said.

"That's a lie," she said, "who else told him, if you didn't? No one else was here. Frith and Robert were out, and none of the other servants knew. I made up my mind then I'd teach you a lesson, and him too. Let him suffer, I say. What do I care? What's his suffering to me? Why shouldn't I see Mr. Jack here at Manderley? He's the only link I have left now with Mrs. de Winter. 'I'll not have him here,' he said, 'I'm warning you, it's the last time.' He's not forgotten to be jealous, has he?"

I remembered crouching in the gallery when the library door was open. I remembered Maxim's voice raised in anger, using the words that Mrs. Danvers had just repeated. Jealous. Maxim jealous. . . .

"He was jealous while she lived, and now he's jealous when she's dead," said Mrs. Danvers. "He forbids Mr. Jack the house now like he did then. That shows you he's not forgotten her, doesn't it? Of course he was jealous. So was I. So was everyone who knew her. She didn't care. She only laughed. 'I shall live as I please, Danny,' she told me, 'and the whole world won't stop me.' A man had only to look at her once and be mad about her. I've seen them here, staying in the house, men she'd meet up in London and bring for week-ends. She would take them bathing from the boat, she would have a picnic supper at her cottage in the cove. They made love to her of course, who would not? She laughed, she would come back and tell me what they had said, and what they'd done. She did not mind, it was like a game to her. Like a game. Who wouldn't be jealous? They were all jealous, all mad for her. Mr. de Winter, Mr. Jack, Mr. Crawley, everyone who knew her, everyone who came to Manderley."

"I don't want to know," I said. "I don't want to know."

Mrs. Danvers came close to me, she put her face near to mine. "It's no use, is it?" she said. "You'll never get the better of her. She's still mistress here, even if she is dead. She's the real Mrs. de Winter, not you. It's you that's the shadow and the ghost. It's you that's forgotten and not wanted and pushed aside. Well, why don't you leave Manderley to her? Why don't you go?"

I backed away from her towards the window, my old fear and horror rising up in me again. She took my arm and held it like a vice.

"Why don't you go?" she said. "We none of us want you. He doesn't want you, he never did. He can't forget her. He wants to be alone in the house again, with her. It's you that ought to be lying there in the church crypt, not her. It's you who ought to be dead, not Mrs. de Winter."

She pushed me towards the open window. I could see the terrace below me grey and indistinct in the white wall of fog. "Look down there," she said. "It's easy, isn't it? Why don't you jump? It wouldn't hurt, not to break your neck. It's a quick, kind way. It's not like drowning. Why don't you try it? Why don't you go?"

The fog filled the open window, damp and clammy, it stung my eyes, it clung to my nostrils. I held on to the window-sill with my hands.

"Don't be afraid," said Mrs. Danvers. "I won't push you. I won't stand by you. You can jump of your own accord. What's the use of your staying here at Manderley? You're not happy. Mr. de Winter doesn't love you. There's not much for you to live for, is there? Why don't you jump now and have done with it? Then you won't be unhappy any more."

I could see the flower tubs on the terrace and the blue of the hydrangeas clumped and solid. The paved stones were smooth and grey. They were not jagged and uneven. It was the fog that made them look so far away. They were not far really, the window was not so very high.

"Why don't you jump?" whispered Mrs. Danvers. "Why don't you try?"

The fog came thicker than before and the terrace was hidden from me. I could not see the flower tubs any more, nor the smooth paved stones. There was nothing but the white mist about me, smelling of sea-weed dank and chill. The only reality was the window-sill beneath my hands and the grip of Mrs. Danvers on my left arm. If I jumped I should not see the stones rise up to meet me, the fog would hide them from me. The pain would be sharp and sudden as she said. The fall would break my neck. It would not be slow, like drowning. It would soon be over. And Maxim did not love me. Maxim wanted to be alone again, with Rebecca.

"Go on," whispered Mrs. Danvers. "Go on, don't be afraid."

I shut my eyes. I was giddy from staring down at the terrace, and my fingers ached from holding to the ledge. The mist entered my nostrils and lay upon my lips rank and sour. It was stifling, like a blanket, like an anaesthetic. I was beginning to forget about being unhappy, and about loving Maxim. I was beginning to forget Rebecca. Soon I would not have to think about Rebecca any more. . . .

As I relaxed my hands and sighed, the white mist and the silence that was part of it was shattered suddenly, was rent in two by an explosion that shook the window where we stood. The glass shivered in its frame. I opened my eyes. I stared at Mrs. Danvers. The burst was followed by another, and yet a third and fourth. The sound of the explosions stung the air and the birds rose unseen from the woods around the house and made an echo with their clamour.

"What is it?" I said stupidly. "What has happened?"

Mrs. Danvers relaxed her grip upon my arm. She stared out of the window into the fog. "It's the rockets," she said; "there must be a ship gone ashore there in the bay."

We listened, staring into the white fog together. And then we heard the sound of footsteps running on the terrace beneath us.

CHAPTER NINETEEN

IT WAS MAXIM. I could not see him but I could hear his voice. He was shouting for Frith as he ran. I heard Frith answer from the hall and come out on to the terrace. Their figures loomed out of the mist beneath us.

"She's ashore all right," said Maxim. "I was watching her from the headland and I saw her come right into the bay, and head for the reef. They'll never shift her, not with these tides. She must have mistaken the bay for Kerrith harbour. It's like a wall out there, in the bay. Tell them in the house to stand by with food and drink in case these fellows want anything, and ring through to the office to Mr. Crawley and tell him what's happened. I'm going back to the cove to see if I can do anything. Get me some cigarettes, will you?"

Mrs. Danvers drew back from the window. Her face was expressionless once more, the cold white mask that I knew.

"We had better go down," she said, "Frith will be looking for me to make arrangements. Mr. de Winter may bring the men back to the house as he said. Be careful of your hands, I'm going to shut the window." I stepped back into the room still dazed and stupid, not sure of myself or of her. I watched her close the window and fasten the shutters, and draw the curtains in their place.

"It's a good thing there is no sea running," she said, "there wouldn't have been much chance for them then. But on a day like this there's no danger. The owners will lose their ship though if she's run on the reef as Mr. de Winter said."

She glanced round the room to make certain that nothing was disarranged or out of place. She straightened the cover on the double bed. Then she went to the door and held it open for me. "I will tell them in the kitchen to serve cold lunch in the dining-room after all," she said, "and then it won't matter what time you come for it. Mr. de Winter may not want to rush back at one o'clock if he's busy down there in the cove."

I stared at her blankly and then passed out of the open door, stiff and wooden like a dummy.

"When you see Mr. de Winter, Madam, will you tell him it will be quite all right if he wants to bring the men back from the ship. There will be a hot meal ready for them any time."

"Yes," I said. "Yes, Mrs. Danvers."

She turned her back on me and went along the corridor to the Service staircase, a weird gaunt figure in her black dress, the skirt just sweeping the ground like the full, wide skirts of thirty years ago. Then she turned the corner of the corridor and disappeared.

I walked slowly along the passage to the door by the archway, my mind still blunt and slow as though I had just woken from a long sleep. I pushed through the door and went down the stairs with no set purpose before me. Frith was crossing the hall towards the dining-room. When he saw me he stopped, and waited until I came down into the hall.

"Mr. de Winter was in a few moments ago, Madam," he said. "He took some cigarettes, and then went back again to the beach. It appears there is a ship gone ashore."

"Yes," I said.

"Did you hear the rockets, Madam?" said Frith.

"Yes, I heard the rockets," I said.

"I was in the pantry with Robert and we both thought at first that one of the gardeners had let off a firework left over from last night," said Frith, "and I said to Robert, 'What do they want to do that for in this weather? Why don't they keep them for the kiddies on Saturday night?' And then the next one came, and then the third. 'That's not fireworks,' says Robert, 'that's a ship in distress.' 'I believe you're right,' I said, and I went out to the hall and there was Mr. de Winter calling me from the terrace."

"Yes," I said.

"Well, it's hardly to be wondered at in this fog, Madam. That's what I said to Robert just now. It's difficult to find your way on the road, let alone on the water."

"Yes," I said.

"If you want to catch Mr. de Winter he went straight across the lawn only two minutes ago," said Frith.

"Thank you, Frith," I said.

I went out on to the terrace. I could see the trees taking shape beyond the lawns. The fog was lifting, it was rising in little clouds to the sky above. It whirled above my head in wreaths of smoke. I looked up at the windows above my head. They were tightly closed, and the shutters were fastened. They looked as though they would never open, never be thrown wide.

It was by the large window in the centre that I had stood five minutes before. How high it seemed above my head, how lofty and remote. The stones were hard and solid under my feet. I looked down at my feet and then up again to the shuttered window, and as I did so I became aware suddenly that my head was swimming and I felt hot. A little trickle of perspiration ran down the back of my neck. Black dots jumped about in the air in front of me. I went into the hall again and sat down on a chair. My hands were quite wet. I sat very still, holding my knees.

"Frith," I called, "Frith, are you in the dining-room?"

"Yes, Madam?" He came out at once, and crossed the hall towards me.

"Don't think me very odd, Frith, but I rather think I'd like a small glass of brandy."

"Certainly, Madam."

I went on holding my knees and sitting very still. He came back with a liqueur glass on a silver salver.

"Do you feel a trifle unwell, Madam?" said Frith. "Would you like me to call Clarice?"

"No, I'll be all right, Frith," I said. "I felt a bit hot, that's all."

"It's a very warm morning, Madam. Very warm indeed. Oppressive, one might almost say."

"Yes, Frith. Very oppressive."

I drank the brandy and put the glass back on the silver salver.

"Perhaps the sound of those rockets alarmed you," said Frith, "they went off so very sudden."

"Yes, they did," I said.

"And what with the hot morning and standing about all last night you are not perhaps feeling quite like yourself, Madam," said Frith.

"No, perhaps not," I said.

"Will you lie down for half-an-hour? It's quite cool in the library."

"No. No, I think I'll go out in a moment or two. Don't bother, Frith."

"No. Very good, Madam."

He went away and left me alone in the hall. It was quiet sitting there, quiet and cool. All trace of the party had been cleared away. It might never have happened. The hall was as it had always been, grey and silent and austere, with the portraits and the weapons on the wall. I could scarcely believe that last night I had stood there in my blue dress at the bottom of the stairs, shaking hands with five hundred people. I could not believe that there had been music stands in the minstrels' gallery, and a band playing there, a man with a fiddle, a man with a drum. I got up and went out on to the terrace again.

The fog was rising, lifting to the tops of the trees. I could see the woods at the end of the lawns. Above my head a pale sun tried to penetrate the heavy sky. It was hotter than ever. Oppressive, as Frith had said. A bee hummed by me in search of scent, bumbling, noisy, and then creeping inside a flower was suddenly silent. On the grass banks above the lawns the gardener started his mowing machine. A startled linnet fled from the whirring blades towards the rose-garden. The gardener bent to the handles of the machine and walked slowly along the bank scattering the short-tipped grass and the pin-point daisy heads. The smell of the sweet warm grass came towards me on the air, and the sun shone down upon me full and strong from out of the white mist. I whistled for Jasper but he did not come. Perhaps he had followed Maxim when he went down to the beach. I glanced at my watch. It was after half-past twelve, nearly twenty to one. This time yesterday Maxim and I were standing with Frank in the little garden in front of his house, waiting for his housekeeper to serve lunch.

Twenty-four hours ago. They were teasing me, baiting me about my dress. "You'll both get the surprise of your lives," I had said.

I felt sick with shame at the memory of my words. And then I realised for the first time that Maxim had not gone away as I had feared. The voice

I had heard on the terrace was calm and practical. The voice I knew. Not the voice of last night when I stood at the head of the stairs. Maxim had not gone away. He was down there in the cove somewhere. He was himself, normal and sane. He had just been for a walk as Frank had said. He had been on the headland, he had seen the ship closing in towards the shore. All my fears were without foundation. Maxim was safe. Maxim was all right. I had just experienced something that was degrading and horrible and mad, something that I did not fully understand even now, that I had no wish to remember, that I wanted to bury forever more deep in the shadows of my mind with the old forgotten terrors of childhood; but even this did not matter as long as Maxim was all right.

Then I, too, went down the steep twisting path through the dark woods to the beach below.

The fog had almost gone and when I came to the cove I could see the ship at once, lying about two miles off-shore with her bows pointed towards the cliffs. I went along the breakwater and stood at the end of it, leaning against the rounded wall. There was a crowd of people on the cliffs already who must have walked along the coast-guard path from Kerrith. The cliffs and the headland were part of Manderley but the public had always used the right-of-way along the cliffs. Some of them were scrambling down the cliff face to get a closer view of the stranded ship. She lay at an awkward angle, her stern tilted, and there were a number of rowing-boats already pulling round her. The life-boat was standing off. I saw someone stand up in her and shout through a megaphone. I could not hear what he was saying. It was still misty out in the bay, and I could not see the horizon. Another motor-boat chugged into the light with some men aboard. The motor-boat was dark grey. I could see someone in uniform. That would be the harbour-master from Kerrith, and the Lloyd's agent with him. Another motor-boat followed, a party of holiday-makers from Kerrith aboard. They circled round and round the stranded steamer chatting excitedly. I could hear their voices echoing across the still water.

I left the breakwater and the cove and climbed up the path over the cliffs towards the rest of the people. I did not see Maxim anywhere. Frank was there, talking to one of the coast-guards. I hung back when I saw him, momentarily embarrassed. Barely an hour ago I had been crying to him, down the telephone. I was not sure what I ought to do. He saw me at once and waved his hand. I went over to him and the coast-guard. The coast-guard knew me.

"Come to see the fun, Mrs. de Winter?" he said smiling. "I'm afraid it will be a hard job. The tugs may shift her but I doubt it. She's hard and fast where she is on that ledge."

"What will they do?" I said.

"They'll send a diver down directly to see if she's broken her back," he replied. "There's the fellow there in the red stocking cap. Like to see through these glasses?"

I took his glasses and looked at the ship. I could see a group of men staring over her stern. One of them was pointing at something. The man in the lifeboat was still shouting through the megaphone.

The harbour-master from Kerrith had joined the group of men in the stern of the stranded ship. The diver in his stocking cap was sitting in the grey motor-boat belonging to the harbour-master.

The pleasure-boat was still circling round the ship. A woman was standing up taking a snapshot. A group of gulls had settled on the water and were crying foolishly, hoping for scraps.

I gave the glasses back to the coast-guard.

"Nothing seems to be happening," I said.

"They'll send him down directly," said the coast-guard. "They'll argue a bit first no doubt like all foreigners. Here come the tugs."

"They'll never do it," said Frank. "Look at the angle she's lying at. It's much shallower there than I thought."

"That reef runs out quite a way," said the coast-guard, "you don't notice it in the ordinary way, going over that piece of water in a small boat. But a ship with her depth would touch all right."

"I was down in the first cove by the valley when they fired the rockets," said Frank. "I could scarcely see three yards in front of me where I was. And then the things went off out of the blue."

I thought how alike people were in a moment of common interest. Frank was Frith all over again, giving his version of the story, as though it mattered, as though we cared. I knew that he had gone down to the beach to look for Maxim. I knew that he had been frightened, as I had been. And now all this was forgotten and put aside, our conversation down the telephone, our mutual anxiety, his insistence that he must see me. All because a ship had gone ashore in the fog.

A small boy came running up to us. "Will the sailors be drowned?" he asked.

"Not them. They're all right, sonny," said the coast-guard. "The sea's as flat as the back of my hand. No one's going to be hurt this time."

"If it had happened last night we should never have heard them," said Frank. "We must have let off more than fifty rockets at our show, besides all the smaller things."

"We'd have heard all right," said the coast-guard. "We'd have seen the flash and known the direction. There's the diver, Mrs. de Winter. See him putting on his helmet?"

"I want to see the diver," said the small boy.

"There he is," said Frank, bending and pointing, "that chap there putting on the helmet. They're going to lower him into the water."

"Won't he be drowned?" said the child.

"Divers don't drown," said the coast-guard. "They have air pumped into them all the time. Watch him disappear. There he goes."

The surface of the water was disturbed a minute and then was clear again.

"He's gone," said the small boy.

"Where's Maxim?" I said.

"He's taken one of the crew into Kerrith," said Frank, "the fellow lost his head and jumped for it apparently when the ship struck. We found him clinging on to one of the rocks here under the cliff. He was soaked to the skin of course and shaking like a jelly. Couldn't speak a word of English of course. Maxim went down to him, and found him bleeding like a pig from a scratch on the rocks. He spoke to him in German. Then he hailed one of the motor-boats from Kerrith that was hanging around like a hungry shark, and he's gone off with him to get him bandaged by a doctor. If he's lucky he'll just catch old Phillips sitting down to lunch."

"When did he go?" I said.

"He went just before you turned up," said Frank, "about five minutes ago. I wonder you didn't see the boat. He was sitting in the stern with this German fellow."

"He must have gone while I was climbing up the cliff," I said.

"Maxim is splendid at anything like this," said Frank. "He always gives a hand if he can. You'll find he will invite the whole crew back to Manderley, and feed them, and give them beds into the bargain."

"That's right," said the coast-guard. "He'd give the coat off his back for any of his own people, I know that. I wish there was more like him in the county."

"Yes, we could do with them," said Frank.

We went on staring at the ship. The tugs were standing off still, but the life-boat had turned and gone back towards Kerrith.

"It's not their turn to-day," said the coast-guard.

"No," said Frank, "and I don't think it's a job for the tugs either. It's the ship-breaker who's going to make money this time."

The gulls wheeled overhead, mewing like hungry cats; some of them settled on the ledges of the cliff, while others, bolder, rode the surface of the water beside the ship.

The coast-guard took off his cap and mopped his forehead.

"Seems kind of airless, doesn't it?" he said.

"Yes," I said.

The pleasure-boat with the camera people went chugging off towards Kerrith. "They've got fed up," said the coast-guard.

"I don't blame them," said Frank. "I don't suppose anything will happen for hours. The diver will have to make his report before they try and shift her."

"That's right," said the coast-guard.

"I don't think there's much sense in hanging about here," said Frank, "we can't do anything. I want my lunch."

I did not say anything. He hesitated. I felt his eyes upon me.

"What are you going to do?" he said.

"I think I shall stay here a bit," I said. "I can have lunch any time. It's cold. It doesn't matter. I want to see what the diver's going to do." Somehow I could not face Frank just at the moment. I wanted to be alone, or with someone I did not know, like the coast-guard.

"You won't see anything," said Frank; "there won't be anything to see. Why not come back and have some lunch with me?"

"No," I said. "No, really . . ."

"Oh, well," said Frank, "you know where to find me if you do want me. I shall be at the office all the afternoon."

"All right," I said.

He nodded to the coast-guard and went off down the cliff towards the cove. I wondered if I had offended him. I could not help it. All these things would be settled some day, one day. So much seemed to have happened since I spoke to him on the telephone and I did not want to think about anything any more. I just wanted to sit there on the cliff and stare at the ship.

"He's a good sort, Mr. Crawley," said the coast-guard.

"Yes," I said.

"He'd give his right hand for Mr. de Winter too," he said.

"Yes, I think he would," I said.

The small boy was still hopping round on the grass in front of us.

"When's the diver coming up again?" he said.

"Not yet, sonny," said the coast-guard.

A woman in a pink striped frock and a hair-net came across the grass towards us. "Charlie? Charlie? where are you?" she called.

"Here's your mother coming to give you what-for," said the coast-guard.

"I've seen the diver, Mum," shouted the boy.

The woman nodded to us and smiled. She did not know me. She was a holiday-maker from Kerrith. "The excitement all seems to be over, doesn't it?" she said; "they are saying down on the cliff there the ship will be there for days."

"They're waiting for the diver's report," said the coast-guard.

"I don't know how they get them to go down under the water like that," said the woman, "they ought to pay them well."

"They do that," said the coast-guard.

"I want to be a diver, Mum," said the small boy.

"You must ask your Daddy, dear," said the woman, laughing at us. "It's a lovely spot up here, isn't it?" she said to me. "We brought a picnic lunch never thinking it would turn foggy and we'd have a wreck into the bargain. We were just thinking of going back to Kerrith when the rockets went off under our noses it seemed. I nearly jumped out of my skin. 'Why, whatever's that?' I said to my husband. 'That's a distress signal,' he said, 'let's stop and see the fun.' There's no dragging him away, he's as bad as my little boy. I don't see anything in it myself."

"No, there's not much to see now," said the coast-guard.

"Those are nice-looking woods over there, I suppose they're private," said the woman.

The coast-guard coughed awkwardly, and glanced at me. I began eating a piece of grass and looked away.

"Yes, that's all private in there," he said.

"My husband says all these big estates will be chopped up in time and bungalows built," said the woman. "I wouldn't mind a nice little bungalow up here facing the sea. I don't know that I'd care for this part of the world in the winter though."

"No, it's very quiet here winter times," said the coast-guard.

I went on chewing my piece of grass. The little boy kept running round in circles. The coast-guard looked at his watch. "Well, I must be getting on," he said, "good afternoon!" He saluted me, and turned back along the path towards Kerrith. "Come on, Charlie, come and find Daddy," said the woman.

She nodded to me in friendly fashion, and sauntered off to the edge of the cliff, the little boy running at her heels. A thin man in khaki shorts and a striped blazer waved to her. They sat down by a clump of gorse bushes, and the woman began to undo paper packages.

I wished I could lose my own identity and join them. Eat hard-boiled eggs and potted meat sandwiches, laugh rather loudly, enter their conversation, and then wander back with them during the afternoon to Kerrith and paddle on the beach, run races across the stretch of sand, and so to their lodgings and have shrimps for tea. Instead of which I must go back alone through the woods to Manderley and wait for Maxim. And I did not know what we should say to one another, how he would look at me, what would be his voice. I went on sitting there on the cliff. I was not hungry, I did not think about lunch.

More people came and wandered over the cliffs to look at the ship. It made an excitement for the afternoon. There was nobody I knew. They were all holiday-makers from Kerrith. The sea was glassy calm. The gulls no longer wheeled overhead, they had settled on the water a little distance from the ship. More pleasure-boats appeared during the afternoon. It must be a field day for Kerrith boat-men. The diver came up and then went down again. One of the tugs steamed away while the other still stood by. The harbour-master went back in his grey motor-boat, taking some men with him, and the diver who had come to the surface for the second time. The crew of the ship leant against the side throwing scraps to the gulls, while visitors in pleasure-boats rowed slowly round the ship. Nothing happened at all. It was dead low water now, and the ship was heeled at an angle, the propeller showing clean. Little ridges of white cloud formed in the western sky and the sun became pallid. It was still very hot. The woman in the pink striped frock with the little boy got up and wandered off along the path towards Kerrith, the man in the shorts following with the picnic basket.

I glanced at my watch. It was after three o'clock. I got up and went down the hill to the cove. It was quiet and deserted as always. The shingle was dark and grey. The water in the little harbour was glassy like a mirror. My feet made a queer crunching noise as I crossed the shingle. The ridges of white cloud now covered all the sky above my head, and the sun was hidden. When I came to the further side of the cove I saw Ben crouching by a little pool between two rocks scraping winkles into his hand. My shadow fell upon the water as I passed, and he looked up and saw me.

"G'day," he said, his mouth opening in a grin.

"Good afternoon," I said.

He scrambled to his feet and opened a dirty handkerchief he had filled with winkles.

"You eat winkles?" he said.

I did not want to hurt his feelings. "Thank you," I said.

He emptied about a dozen winkles into my hand, and I put them in the two pockets of my skirt. "They'm all right with bread-an'-butter," he said, "you must boil 'em first."

"Yes, all right," I said.

He stood there grinning at me. "Seen the steamer?" he said.

"Yes," I said, "she's gone ashore, hasn't she?"

"Eh?" he said.

"She's run aground," I repeated. "I expect she's got a hole in her bottom."

His face went blank and foolish. "Aye," he said, "she's down there all right. She'll not come back again."

"Perhaps the tugs will get her off when the tide makes," I said.

He did not answer. He was staring out towards the stranded ship. I could see her broadside on from here, the red under-water section showing against the black of the top-sides, and the single funnel leaning rakishly towards the cliffs beyond. The crew were still leaning over her side feeding the gulls and staring into the water. The rowing boats were pulling back to Kerrith.

"She's a Dutchman, ain't she?" said Ben.

"I don't know," I said. "German or Dutch."

"She'll break up there where she's to," he said.

"I'm afraid so," I said.

He grinned again, and wiped his nose with the back of his hand.

"She'll break up bit by bit," he said, "she'll not sink like a stone like the little 'un." He chuckled to himself, picking his nose. I did not say anything. "The fishes have eaten her up by now, haven't they?" he said.

"Who?" I said.

He jerked his thumb towards the sea. "Her," he said, "the other one."

"Fishes don't eat steamers, Ben," I said.

"Eh?" he said. He stared at me, foolish and blank once more.

"I must go home now," I said; "good afternoon."

I left him and walked towards the path through the woods. I did not look at the cottage. I was aware of it on my right hand, grey and quiet. I went straight to the path and up through the trees. I paused to rest half-way and looking through the trees I could still see the stranded ship leaning towards the shore. The pleasure-boats had all gone. Even the crew had disappeared below. The ridges of cloud covered the whole sky. A little wind sprang from nowhere and blew into my face. A leaf fell on to my hand from the tree above. I shivered for no reason. Then the wind went again, it was hot and sultry as before. The ship looked desolate there upon her side, with no one on her decks, and her thin black funnel pointing to the shore. The sea was so calm that when it broke upon the shingle in the cove it was like a whisper, hushed and still. I turned once more to the steep path through the woods, my legs reluctant, my head heavy, a strange sense of foreboding in my heart.

The house looked very peaceful as I came upon it from the woods and crossed the lawns. It seemed sheltered and protected, more beautiful than I had ever seen it. Standing there, looking down upon it from the banks, I realised, perhaps for the first time, with a funny feeling of bewilderment and pride that it was my home, I belonged there, and Manderley belonged to me. The trees and the grass and the flower tubs on the terrace were reflected in the mullioned windows. A thin column of smoke rose in the air from one of the chimneys. The new-cut grass on the lawn smelt sweet as hay. A blackbird was singing on the chestnut tree. A yellow butterfly winged his foolish way before me to the terrace.

I went into the hall and through to the dining-room. My place was still laid, but Maxim's had been cleared away. The cold meat and salad awaited me on the side-board. I hesitated, and then rang the dining-room bell. Robert came in from behind the screen.

"Has Mr. de Winter been in?" I said.

"Yes, Madam," said Robert; "he came in just after two, and had a quick lunch, and then went out again. He asked for you and Frith said he thought you must have gone down to see the ship."

"Did he say when he would be back again?" I asked.

"No, Madam."

"Perhaps he went to the beach by another way," I said; "I may have missed him."

"Yes, Madam," said Robert.

I looked at the cold meat and the salad. I felt empty but not hungry. I did not want cold meat now. "Will you be taking lunch?" said Robert.

"No," I said. "No, you might bring me some tea, Robert, in the library. Nothing like cakes or scones. Just tea and bread-and-butter."

"Yes, Madam."

I went and sat on the window seat in the library. It seemed funny without Jasper. He must have gone with Maxim. The old dog lay asleep in her basket. I picked up *The Times* and turned the pages without reading it. It was queer this feeling of marking time, like sitting in a waiting-room at a dentist's. I knew I should never settle to my knitting or to a book. I was waiting for something to happen, something unforeseen. The horror of my morning and the stranded ship and not having any lunch had all combined to give birth to a latent sense of excitement at the back of my mind that I did not understand. It was as though I had entered into a new phase of my life and nothing would be quite the same again. The girl who had dressed for the fancy dress ball the night before had been left behind. It had all happened a very long time ago. This self who sat on the window seat was new, was different. . . . Robert brought in my tea, and I ate my bread-and-butter hungrily. He had brought scones as well, and some sandwiches, and an angel cake. He must have thought it derogatory to bring bread-and-butter alone, nor was it Manderley routine. I was glad of the scones and the angel cake. I remembered I had only had cold tea at half-past eleven, and no breakfast. Just after I had drunk my third cup Robert came in again.

"Mr. de Winter is not back yet, is he, Madam?" he said.

"No," I said. "Why? Does someone want him?"

"Yes, Madam," said Robert, "it's Captain Searle, the harbour-master of Kerrith, on the telephone. He wants to know if he can come up and see Mr. de Winter personally."

"I don't know what to say," I said. "He may not be back for ages."

"No, Madam."

"You'd better tell him to ring again at five o'clock," I said. Robert went out of the room and came back again in a few minutes.

"Captain Searle would like to see you, if it would be convenient, Madam," said Robert. "He says the matter is rather urgent. He tried to get Mr. Crawley, but there was no reply."

"Yes, of course I must see him if it's urgent," I said. "Tell him to come along at once if he likes. Has he got a car?"

"Yes, I believe so, Madam."

Robert went out of the room. I wondered what I should say to Captain Searle. His business must be something to do with the stranded ship. I could not understand what concern it was of Maxim's. It would have been different if the ship had gone ashore in the cove. That was Manderley property. They might have to ask Maxim's permission to blast away rocks or whatever it was that was done to move a ship. But the open bay and the ledge of rock under the water did not belong to Maxim. Captain Searle would waste his time talking to me about it all.

He must have got into his car right away after talking to Robert because in less than quarter-of-an-hour he was shown into the room.

He was still in his uniform as I had seen him through the glasses in the early afternoon. I got up from the window seat and shook hands with him. "I'm sorry my husband isn't back yet, Captain Searle," I said; "he must have gone down to the cliffs again, and he went into Kerrith before that. I haven't seen him all day."

"Yes, I heard he'd been to Kerrith but I missed him there," said the harbour-master. "He must have walked back across the cliffs when I was in my boat. And I can't get hold of Mr. Crawley either."

"I'm afraid the ship has disorganised everybody," I said. "I was out on the cliffs and went without my lunch, and I know Mr. Crawley was there earlier on. What will happen to her? Will tugs get her off do you think?"

Captain Searle made a great circle with his hands. "There's a hole that deep in her bottom," he said, "she'll not see Hamburg again. Never mind the ship. Her owner and Lloyd's agent will settle that between them. No, Mrs. de Winter, it's not the ship that's brought me here. Indirectly of course she's the cause of my coming. The fact is, I've got some news for Mr. de Winter, and I hardly know how to break it to him." He looked at me very straight with his bright blue eyes.

"What sort of news, Captain Searle?"

He brought a large white handkerchief out of his pocket and blew his nose. "Well, Mrs. de Winter, it's not very pleasant for me to tell you either. The last thing I want to do is to cause distress or pain to you and your husband. We're all very fond of Mr. de Winter in Kerrith, you know, and the family has always done a lot of good. It's hard on him and hard on you that we can't let the past lie quiet. But I don't see how we can under the circumstances." He paused, and put his handkerchief back in his pocket. He lowered his voice, although we were alone in the room.

"We sent the diver down to inspect the ship's bottom," he said, "and while he was down there he made a discovery. It appears he found the hole in the ship's bottom and was working round to the other side to see what further damage there was when he came across the hull of a little sailing boat, lying on her side, quite intact and not broken up at all. He's a local man, of course, and he recognised the boat at once. It was the little boat belonging to the late Mrs. de Winter."

My first feeling was one of thankfulness that Maxim was not there to hear. This fresh blow coming swiftly upon my masquerade of the night before was ironic, and rather horrible.

"I'm so sorry," I said slowly, "it's not the sort of thing one expected would happen, is it necessary to tell Mr. de Winter? Couldn't the boat be left there, as it is, it's not doing any harm, is it?"

"It would be left, Mrs. de Winter, in the ordinary way. I'm the last man in the world to want to disturb it. And I'd give anything, as I said before, to spare Mr. de Winter's feelings. But that wasn't all, Mrs. de Winter. My man poked round the little boat and he made another, more important discovery. The cabin door was tightly closed, it was not stove in, and the portlights were closed too. He broke one of the ports with a stone from the sea bed, and looked into the cabin. It was full of water, the sea must have come through some hole in the bottom, there seemed no damage elsewhere. And then he got the fright of his life, Mrs. de Winter."

Captain Searle paused, he looked over his shoulder as though one of the servants might hear him. "There was a body in there, lying on the cabin floor," he said quietly. "It was dissolved of course, there was no flesh on it. But it was a body all right. He saw the head and the limbs. He came up to the surface then and reported it direct to me. And now you understand, Mrs. de Winter, why I've got to see your husband."

I stared at him, bewildered at first, then shocked, then rather sick.

"She was supposed to be sailing alone," I whispered, "there must have been someone with her then, all the time, and no one ever knew?"

"It looks like it," said the harbour-master.

"Who could it have been?" I said. "Surely relatives would know if anyone had been missing? There was so much about it at the time, it was all in the papers. Why should one of them be in the cabin and Mrs. de Winter herself be picked up many miles away, months afterwards?"

Captain Searle shook his head. "I can't tell any more than you," he said. "All we know is that the body is there, and it has got to be reported. There'll be publicity, I'm afraid, Mrs. de Winter. I don't know how we're going to avoid it. It's very hard on you and Mr. de Winter. Here you are, settled down quietly, wanting to be happy, and this has to happen."

I knew now the reason for my sense of foreboding. It was not the stranded ship that was sinister, nor the crying gulls, nor the thin black funnel pointing to the shore. It was the stillness of the black water, and the unknown things that lay beneath. It was the diver going down into those cool quiet depths and stumbling upon Rebecca's boat, and Rebecca's dead companion. He had touched the boat, had looked into the cabin, and all the while I sat on the cliffs and had not known.

"If only we did not have to tell him," I said. "If only we could keep the whole thing from him."

"You know I would if it were possible, Mrs. de Winter," said the harbour-master, "but my personal feelings have to go, in a matter like this. I've got to do my duty. I've got to report that body." He broke off short as the door opened, and Maxim came into the room.

"Hullo," he said, "what's happening? I didn't know you were here, Captain Searle. Is anything the matter?"

I could not stand it any longer. I went out of the room like the coward I was and shut the door behind me. I had not even glanced at Maxim's face. I had the vague impression that he looked tired, untidy, hatless.

I went and stood in the hall by the front door. Jasper was drinking noisily from his bowl. He wagged his tail when he saw me and went on drinking. Then he loped towards me, and stood up, pawing at my dress. I kissed the top of his head and went and sat on the terrace. The moment of crisis had come, and I must face it. My old fears, my diffidence, my shyness, my hopeless sense of inferiority, must be conquered now and thrust aside. If I failed now I should fail forever. There would never be another chance. I prayed for courage in a blind despairing way, and dug my nails into my hands. I sat there for five minutes staring at the green lawns and the flower tubs on the terrace. I heard the sound of a car starting up in the drive. It must be Captain Searle. He had broken his news to Maxim and had gone. I got up from the terrace and went slowly through the hall to the library. I kept turning over in my pockets the winkles that Ben had given me. I clutched them tight in my hands.

Maxim was standing by the window. His back was turned to me. I waited by the door. Still he did not turn round. I took my hands out of my pockets and went and stood beside him. I reached out for his hand and laid it against my cheek. He did not say anything. He went on standing there.

"I'm so sorry," I whispered, "so terribly, terribly sorry." He did not answer. His hand was icy cold. I kissed the back of it, and then the fingers, one by one. "I don't want you to bear this alone," I said. "I want to share it with you. I've grown up, Maxim, in twenty-four hours. I'll never be a child again."

He put his arm round me and pulled me to him very close. My reserve was broken, and my shyness too. I stood there with my face against his shoulder. "You've forgiven me, haven't you?" I said.

He spoke to me at last. "Forgiven you?" he said. "What have I got to forgive you for?"

"Last night," I said; "you thought I did it on purpose."

"Ah, that," he said, "I'd forgotten. I was angry with you, wasn't I?"

"Yes," I said.

He did not say any more. He went on holding me close to his shoulder. "Maxim," I said, "can't we start all over again? Can't we begin from to-day, and face things together? I don't want you to love me, I won't ask impossible things. I'll be your friend and your companion, a sort of boy. I don't ever want more than that."

He took my face between his hands and looked at me. For the first time I saw how thin his face was, how lined and drawn. And there were great shadows beneath his eyes.

"How much do you love me?" he said.

I could not answer. I could only stare back at him, at his dark tortured eyes, and his pale drawn face.

"It's too late, my darling, too late," he said. "We've lost our little chance of happiness."

"No, Maxim. No," I said.

"Yes," he said. "It's all over now. The thing has happened."

"What thing?" I said.

"The thing I've always foreseen. The thing I've dreamt about, day after day, night after night. We're not meant for happiness, you and I." He sat down on the window seat, and I knelt in front of him, my hands on his shoulders.

"What are you trying to tell me?" I said.

He put his hands over mine and looked into my face. "Rebecca has won," he said.

I stared at him, my heart beating strangely, my hands suddenly cold beneath his hands.

"Her shadow between us all the time," he said. "Her damned shadow keeping us from one another. How could I hold you like this, my darling, my little love, with the fear always in my heart that this would happen? I remembered her eyes as she looked at me before she died. I remembered that slow treacherous smile. She knew this would happen even then. She knew she would win in the end."

"Maxim," I whispered, "what are you saying, what are you trying to tell me?"

"Her boat," he said, "they've found it. The diver found it this afternoon."

"Yes," I said. "I know. Captain Searle came to tell me. You are thinking about the body, aren't you, the body the diver found in the cabin?"

"Yes," he said.

"It means she was not alone," I said. "It means there was somebody sailing with Rebecca at the time. And you have to find out who it was. That's it, isn't it, Maxim?"

"No," he said. "No, you don't understand."

"I want to share this with you, darling," I said. "I want to help you."

"There was no one with Rebecca, she was alone," he said.

I knelt there watching his face, watching his eyes.

"It's Rebecca's body lying there on the cabin floor," he said.

"No," I said. "No."

"The woman buried in the crypt is not Rebecca," he said. "It's the body of some unknown woman, unclaimed, belonging nowhere. There never was an accident. Rebecca was not drowned at all. I killed her. I shot Rebecca in the cottage in the cove. I carried her body to the cabin, and took the boat out that night and sunk it there, where they found it to-day. It's Rebecca who's lying dead there on the cabin floor. Will you look into my eyes and tell me that you love me now?"

CHAPTER TWENTY

IT WAS VERY QUIET in the library. The only sound was that of Jasper licking his foot. He must have caught a thorn in his pads, for he kept biting and sucking at the skin. Then I heard the watch on Maxim's wrist ticking close to my ear. The little normal sounds of every day. And for no reason the stupid proverb of my school-days ran through my mind, "Time and Tide wait for no man." The words repeated themselves over and over again. "Time and Tide wait for no man." These were the only sounds then, the ticking of Maxim's watch and Jasper licking his foot on the floor beside me.

When people suffer a great shock, like death, or the loss of a limb, I believe they don't feel it just at first. If your hand is taken from you you don't know, for a few minutes, that your hand is gone. You go on feeling the fingers. You stretch and beat them on the air, one by one, and all the time there is nothing there, no hand, no fingers. I knelt there by Maxim's side, my body against his body, my hands upon his shoulders, and I was aware of no feeling at all, no pain and no fear, there was no horror in my heart. I thought how I must take the thorn out of Jasper's foot and I wondered if Robert would come in and clear the tea-things. It seemed strange to me that I should think of these things, Jasper's foot, Maxim's watch, Robert and the tea-things. I was shocked at my lack of emotion and this queer cold absence of distress. Little by little the feeling will come back to me, I said to myself, little by little I shall understand. What he has told me and all that has happened will tumble into place like pieces of a jig-saw puzzle. They will fit themselves into a pattern. At the moment I am nothing, I have no heart, and no mind, and no senses, I am just a wooden thing in Maxim's arms. Then he began to kiss me. He had not kissed me like this before. I put my hands behind his head and shut my eyes.

"I love you so much," he whispered. "So much."

This is what I have wanted him to say every day and every night, I thought, and now he is saying it at last. This is what I imagined in Monte Carlo, in

Italy, here in Manderley. He is saying it now. I opened my eyes and looked at a little patch of curtain above his head. He went on kissing me, hungry, desperate, murmuring my name. I kept on looking at the patch of curtain, and saw where the sun had faded it, making it lighter than the piece above. How calm I am, I thought. How cool. Here I am looking at the piece of curtain, and Maxim is kissing me. For the first time he is telling me he loves me.

Then he stopped suddenly, he pushed me away from him, and got up from the window seat. "You see, I was right," he said. "It's too late. You don't love me now. Why should you?" He went and stood over by the mantelpiece. "We'll forget that," he said, "it won't happen again."

Realisation flooded me at once, and my heart jumped in quick and sudden panic. "It's not too late," I said swiftly, getting up from the floor and going to him, putting my arms about him; "you're not to say that, you don't understand. I love you more than anything in the world. But when you kissed me just now I felt stunned and shaken, I could not feel anything. I could not grasp anything. It was just as though I had no more feeling left in me at all."

"You don't love me," he said, "that's why you did not feel anything. I know. I understand. It's come too late for you, hasn't it?"

"No," I said.

"This ought to have happened four months ago," he said. "I should have known. Women are not like men."

"I want you to kiss me again," I said, "please, Maxim."

"No," he said, "it's no use now."

"We can't lose each other now," I said. "We've got to be together always, with no secrets, no shadows. Please, darling, please."

"There's no time," he said. "We may only have a few hours, a few days. How can we be together now that this has happened? I've told you they've found the boat. They've found Rebecca."

I stared at him stupidly, not understanding. "What will they do?" I said.

"They'll identify her body," he said, "there's everything to tell them, there in the cabin. The clothes she had, the shoes, the rings on her fingers. They'll identify her body; and then they will remember the other one, the woman buried up there, in the crypt."

"What are you going to do?" I whispered.

"I don't know," he said. "I don't know."

The feeling was coming back to me, little by little, as I knew it would. My hands were cold no longer. They were clammy, warm. I felt a wave of colour come into my face, my throat. My cheeks were burning hot. I thought of Captain Searle, the diver, the Lloyd's agent, all those men on the stranded ship leaning against the side, staring down into the water. I thought of the shopkeepers in Kerrith, of errand boys whistling in the street, of the vicar walking out of church, of Lady Crowan cutting roses in her garden, of the woman in the pink dress and her little boy on the cliffs. Soon they would know. In a few hours. By breakfast-time to-morrow. "They've found Mrs. de Winter's boat, and they say there is a body in the cabin." A body in the cabin. Rebecca was lying there on the cabin floor. She was not in the crypt at all.

Some other woman was lying in the crypt. Maxim had killed Rebecca. Rebecca had not been drowned at all. Maxim had killed her. He had shot her in the cottage in the woods. He had carried her body to the boat, and sunk the boat there in the bay. That grey, silent cottage, with the rain pattering on the roof. The jig-saw pieces came tumbling thick and fast upon me. Disjointed pictures flashed one by one through my bewildered mind. Maxim sitting in the car beside me in the south of France. "Something happened nearly a year ago that altered my whole life. I had to begin living all over again. . . ." Maxim's silence, Maxim's moods. The way he never talked about Rebecca. The way he never mentioned her name. Maxim's dislike of the cove, of the stone cottage. "If you had my memories you would not go there either." The way he climbed the path through the woods not looking behind him. Maxim pacing up and down the library after Rebecca died. Up and down. Up and down. "I came away in rather a hurry," he said to Mrs. Van Hopper, a line, thin as gossamer, between his brows. "They say he can't get over his wife's death." The fancy dress dance last night, and I coming down to the head of the stairs, in Rebecca's dress. "I killed Rebecca," Maxim had said. "I shot Rebecca in the cottage in the woods." And the diver had found her lying there, on the cabin floor. . . .

"What are we going to do?" I said. "What are we going to say?"

Maxim did not answer. He stood there by the mantelpiece, his eyes wide and staring, looking in front of him, not seeing anything.

"Does anyone know?" I said, "anyone at all?"

He shook his head. "No," he said.

"No one but you and me?" I asked.

"No one but you and me," he said.

"Frank," I said suddenly, "are you sure Frank does not know?"

"How could he?" said Maxim, "there was nobody there but myself. It was dark . . ." He stopped. He sat down on a chair, he put his hand up to his forehead. I went and knelt beside him. He sat very still a moment. I took his hands away from his face and looked into his eyes. "I love you," I whispered, "I love you. Will you believe me now?" He kissed my face and my hands. He held my hands very tightly like a child who would gain confidence.

"I thought I should go mad," he said, "sitting here, day after day, waiting for something to happen. Sitting down at the desk there, answering those terrible letters of sympathy. The notices in the papers, the interviews, all the little aftermath of death. Eating and drinking, trying to be normal, trying to be sane. Frith, the servants, Mrs. Danvers. Mrs. Danvers, who I had not the courage to turn away, because with her knowledge of Rebecca she might have suspected, she might have guessed. . . . Frank, always by my side, discreet, sympathetic. 'Why don't you get away?' he used to say, 'I can manage here. You ought to get away.' And Giles, and Bee, poor dear tactless Bee. 'You're looking frightfully ill, can't you go and see a doctor?' I had to face them, all these people, knowing every word I uttered was a lie."

I went on holding his hands very tight. I leant close to him, quite close. "I nearly told you, once," he said, "that day Jasper ran to the cove, and you went to the cottage for some string. We were sitting here, like this, and then Frith and Robert came in with the tea."

"Yes," I said. "I remember. Why didn't you tell me? The time we've wasted when we might have been together. All these weeks and days."

"You were so aloof," he said, "always wandering into the garden with Jasper, going off on your own. You never came to me like this."

"Why didn't you tell me?" I whispered. "Why didn't you tell me?"

"I thought you were unhappy, bored," he said. "I'm so much older than you. You seemed to have more to say to Frank than you ever had to me. You were funny with me, awkward, shy."

"How could I come to you when I knew you were thinking about Rebecca?" I said. "How could I ask you to love me when I knew you loved Rebecca still?"

He pulled me close to him and searched my eyes.

"What are you talking about, what do you mean?" he said.

I knelt up straight beside him. "Whenever you touched me I thought you were comparing me to Rebecca," I said. "Whenever you spoke to me or looked at me, walked with me in the garden, sat down to dinner, I felt you were saying to yourself, 'This I did with Rebecca, and this, and this.'" He stared at me bewildered as though he did not understand.

"It was true, wasn't it?" I said.

"Oh, my God," he said. He pushed me away, he got up and began walking up and down the room, clasping his hands.

"What is it? What's the matter?" I said.

He whipped round and looked at me as I sat there huddled on the floor. "You thought I loved Rebecca?" he said. "You thought I killed her, loving her? I hated her, I tell you, our marriage was a farce from the very first. She was vicious, damnable, rotten through and through. We never loved each other, never had one moment of happiness together. Rebecca was incapable of love, of tenderness, of decency. She was not even normal."

I sat on the floor, clasping my knees, staring at him.

"She was clever of course," he said. "Damnably clever. No one would guess meeting her that she was not the kindest, most generous, most gifted person in the world. She knew exactly what to say to different people, how to match her mood to theirs. Had she met you, she would have walked off into the garden with you, arm-in-arm, calling to Jasper, chatting about flowers, music, painting, whatever she knew to be your particular hobby; and you would have been taken in, like the rest. You would have sat at her feet and worshipped her."

Up and down he walked, up and down across the library floor.

"When I married her I was told I was the luckiest man in the world," he said. "She was so lovely, so accomplished, so amusing. Even Gran, the most difficult person to please in those days, adored her from the first. 'She's got the three things that matter in a wife,' she told me; 'breeding, brains, and beauty.' And I believed her, or forced myself to believe her. But all the time

I had a seed of doubt at the back of my mind. There was something about her eyes. . . ."

The jig-saw pieces came together piece by piece, and the real Rebecca took shape and form before me, stepping from her shadow world like a living figure from a picture frame. Rebecca slashing at her horse; Rebecca seizing life with her two hands; Rebecca, triumphant, leaning down from the minstrels' gallery with a smile on her lips.

Once more I saw myself standing on the beach beside poor startled Ben. "You're kind," he said, "not like the other one. You won't put me to the asylum, will you?" There was someone who walked through the woods by night, someone tall and slim. She gave you the feeling of a snake. . . .

Maxim was talking though. Maxim was walking up and down the library floor. "I found her out at once," he was saying, "five days after we were married. You remember that time I drove you in the car, to the hills above Monte Carlo? I wanted to stand there again, to remember. She sat there, laughing, her black hair blowing in the wind; she told me about herself, told me things I shall never repeat to a living soul. I knew then what I had done, what I had married. Beauty, brains, and breeding. Oh, my God."

He broke off abruptly. He went and stood by the window, looking out upon the lawns. He began to laugh. He stood there laughing. I could not bear it, it made me frightened, ill. I could not stand it.

"Maxim!" I cried. "Maxim."

He lit a cigarette, and stood there smoking, not saying anything. Then he turned away again, and paced up and down the room once more. "I nearly killed her then," he said. "It would have been so easy. One false step, one slip. You remember the precipice. I frightened you, didn't I? You thought I was mad. Perhaps I was. Perhaps I am. It doesn't make for sanity, does it, living with the devil."

I sat there watching him, up and down, up and down.

"She made a bargain with me up there, on the side of the precipice," he said. " 'I'll run your house for you,' she told me, 'I'll look after your precious Manderley for you, make it the most famous show-place in all the country, if you like. And people will visit us, and envy us, and talk about us; they'll say we are the luckiest, happiest, handsomest couple in all England. What a leg-pull, Max,' she said, 'what a God-damn triumph!' She sat there on the hillside, laughing, tearing a flower to bits in her hands."

Maxim threw his cigarette away, a quarter smoked, into the empty grate.

"I did not kill her," he said, "I watched her, I said nothing, I let her laugh. We got into the car together and drove away. And she knew I would do as she suggested, come here to Manderley, throw the place open, entertain, have our marriage spoken of as the success of the century. She knew I would sacrifice pride, honour, personal feeling, every damned quality on earth, rather than stand before our little world after a week of marriage and have them know the things about her that she had told me then. She knew I would never stand in a divorce court and give her away, have fingers pointing at us, mud flung at us in the newspapers, all the people who belong down here whispering when my name was mentioned, all the trippers from Kerrith trooping to the lodge gates, peering into the grounds and saying, 'That's where he lives, in there. That's Manderley. That's the place that belongs to the chap who had that divorce case we read about. Do you remember what the judge said about his wife . . . ?' "

He came and stood before me. He held out his hands. "You despise me, don't you?" he said. "You can't understand my shame, and loathing, and disgust."

I did not say anything. I held his hands against my heart. I did not care about his shame. None of the things that he had told me mattered to me at all. I clung to one thing only, and repeated it to myself, over and over again. Maxim did not love Rebecca. He had never loved her, never, never. They had never known one moment's happiness together. Maxim was talking, and I listened to him, but his words meant nothing to me. I did not really care.

"I thought about Manderley too much," he said. "I put Manderley first, before anything else. And it does not prosper, that sort of love. They don't preach about it in the churches. Christ said nothing about stones, and bricks, and walls, the love that a man can bear for his plot of earth, his soil, his little kingdom. It does not come into the Christian creed."

"My darling," I said, "my Maxim, my love." I laid his hands against my face, I put my lips against them.

"Do you understand?" he said, "do you, do you?"

"Yes," I said, "my sweet, my love." But I looked away from him so he should not see my face. What did it matter whether I understood him or not? My heart was light like a feather floating in the air. He had never loved Rebecca.

"I don't want to look back on those years," he said slowly. "I don't want even to tell you about them. The shame and the degradation. The lie we lived, she and I. The shabby, sordid farce we played together. Before friends, before relations, even before the servants, before faithful, trusting creatures like old Frith. They all believed in her down here, they all admired her, they never knew how she laughed at them behind their backs, jeered at them, mimicked them. I can remember days when the place was full for some show or other, a garden party, a pageant, and she walked about with a smile like an angel on her face, her arm through mine, giving prizes afterwards to a little troop of children; and then the day afterwards she would be up at dawn driving to London, streaking to that flat of hers by the river like an animal to its hole in the ditch, coming back here at the end of the week, after five unspeakable days. Oh, I kept to my side of the bargain all right. I never gave her away. Her blasted taste made Manderley the thing it is to-day. The gardens, the shrubs, even the azaleas in the Happy Valley, do you think they existed when my father was alive? God, the place was a wilderness, lovely yes, wild and lonely with a beauty of its own, yes, but crying out for skill and care and the money that he would never give to it, that I would not have thought of giving to it—but for Rebecca. Half the stuff you see here in the rooms was never here originally. The drawing-room as it is to-day, the morning-room—that's all Rebecca. Those chairs that Frith points out so proudly to the visitors on the public day, and that panel of tapestry—Rebecca again. Oh, some of the things were here admittedly, stored away in back rooms, my father knew nothing about furniture or pictures, but the majority was bought by Rebecca. The beauty of Manderley that you see to-day, the Manderley that people talk about and photograph and paint, it's all due to her, to Rebecca."

I did not say anything. I held him close. I wanted him to go on talking like this, that his bitterness might loosen and come away, carrying with it all the pent-up hatred and disgust and muck of the lost years.

"And so we lived," he said, "month after month, year after year. I accepted everything—because of Manderley. What she did in London did not touch me—because it did not hurt Manderley. And she was careful those first years, there was never a murmur about her, never a whisper. Then little by little she began to grow careless. You know how a man starts drinking? He goes easy at first, just a little at a time, a bad bout perhaps every five months or so. And then the period between grows less and less. Soon it's every month, every fortnight, every few days. There's no margin of safety left and all his secret cunning goes. It was like that with Rebecca. She began to ask her friends down here. She would have one or two of them and mix them up at a week-end party so that at first I was not quite sure, not quite certain. She would have picnics down at her cottage in the cove. I came back once, having been away shooting in Scotland, and found her there, with half-a-dozen of them, people I had never seen before. I warned her, and she shrugged her shoulders. 'What the hell's it got to do with you?' she said. I told her she could see her friends in London, but Manderley was mine. She must stick to that part of the bargain. She smiled, she did not say anything. Then she started on Frank, poor shy faithful Frank. He came to me one day and said he wanted to leave Manderley and take another job. We argued for two hours, here in the library, and then I understood. He broke down and told me. She never left him alone, he said, she was always going down to his house, trying to get him to the cottage. Dear, wretched Frank, who had not understood, who had always thought we were the normal happy married couple we pretended to be.

"I accused Rebecca of this, and she flared up at once, cursing me, using every filthy word in her particular vocabulary. We had a sickening, loathsome scene. She went up to London after that and stayed there for a month. When she came back again she was quiet at first, I thought she had learnt her lesson. Bee and Giles came for a week-end. And I realised then what I had sometimes suspected before, that Bee did not like Rebecca. I believe, in her funny, abrupt, downright way, she saw through her, guessed something was wrong. It was a tricky, nervy sort of week-end. Giles went out sailing with Rebecca. Bee and I lazed on the lawn. And when they came back I could tell by Giles's rather hearty jovial manner and by a look in Rebecca's eye that she had started on him, as she had done on Frank. I saw Bee watching

Giles at dinner, who laughed louder than usual, talked a little too much. And all the while Rebecca sitting there at the head of the table, looking like an angel."

They were all fitting into place, the jig-saw pieces. The odd strained shapes that I had tried to piece together with my fumbling fingers and they had never fitted. Frank's odd manner when I spoke about Rebecca. Beatrice, and her rather diffident negative attitude. The silence that I had always taken for sympathy and regret was a silence born of shame and embarrassment. It seemed incredible to me now that I had never understood. I wondered how many people there were in the world who suffered, and continued to suffer, because they could not break out from their own web of shyness and reserve, and in their blindness and folly built up a great distorted wall in front of them that hid the truth. This was what I had done. I had built up false pictures in my mind and sat before them. I had never had the courage to demand the truth. Had I made one step forward out of my own shyness Maxim would have told me these things four months, five months ago.

"That was the last week-end Bee and Giles ever spent at Manderley," said Maxim. "I never asked them alone again. They came officially, to garden-parties, and dances. Bee never said a word to me or I to her. But I think she guessed my life, I think she knew. Even as Frank did. Rebecca grew cunning again. Her behaviour was faultless, outwardly. But if I happened to be away when she was here at Manderley I could never be certain what might happen. There had been Frank, and Giles. She might get hold of one of the workmen on the estate, someone from Kerrith, anyone. . . . And then the bomb would have to fall. The gossip, the publicity I dreaded."

It seemed to me I stood again by the cottage in the woods, and I heard the drip-drip of the rain upon the roof. I saw the dust on the model ships, the rat holes on the divan. I saw Ben with his poor staring idiot's eyes. "You'll not put me to the asylum, will you?" And I thought of the dark steep path through the woods, and how, if a woman stood there behind the trees, her evening dress would rustle in the thin night breeze.

"She had a cousin," said Maxim slowly, "a fellow who had been abroad, and was living in England again. He took to coming here, if ever I was away. Frank used to see him. A fellow called Jack Favell."

"I know him," I said, "he came here the day you went to London."

"You saw him too?" said Maxim, "why didn't you tell me? I heard it from Frank, who saw his car turn in at the lodge gates."

"I did not like to," I said, "I thought it would remind you of Rebecca."

"Remind me?" whispered Maxim. "Oh, God, as if I needed reminding."

He stared in front of him, breaking off from his story, and I wondered if he was thinking, as I was, of that flooded cabin beneath the waters in the bay.

"She used to have this fellow Favell down to the cottage," said Maxim, "she would tell the servants she was going to sail, and would not be back before the morning. Then she would spend the night down there with him.

Once again I warned her. I said if I found him here, anywhere on the estate, I'd shoot him. He had a black, filthy record. . . . The very thought of him walking about the woods in Manderley, in places like the Happy Valley, made me mad. I told her I would not stand for it. She shrugged her shoulders. She forgot to blaspheme. And I noticed she was looking paler than usual, nervy, rather haggard. I wondered then what the hell would happen to her when she began to look old, feel old. Things drifted on. Nothing very much happened. Then one day she went up to London, and came back again the same day, which she did not do as a rule. I did not expect her. I dined that night with Frank at his house, we had a lot of work on at the time."

He was speaking now in short, jerky sentences. I had his hands very tightly between my two hands.

"I came back after dinner, about half-past ten, and I saw her scarf and gloves lying on a chair in the hall. I wondered what the devil she had come back for. I went into the morning-room but she was not there. I guessed she had gone off there then, down to the cove. And I knew then I could not stand this life of lies and filth and deceit any longer. The thing had got to be settled, one way or the other. I thought I'd take a gun and frighten the fellow, frighten them both. I went down right away to the cottage. The servants never knew I had come back to the house at all. I slipped out into the garden and through the woods. I saw the light in the cottage window, and I went straight in. To my surprise Rebecca was alone. She was lying on the divan with an ash-tray full of cigarette stubs beside her. She looked ill, queer.

"I began at once about Favell and she listened to me without a word. 'We've lived this life of degradation long enough, you and I,' I said. 'This is the end, do you understand? What you do in London does not concern me. You can live with Favell there, or with anyone you like. But not here. Not at Manderley.'

"She said nothing for a moment. She stared at me, and then she smiled. 'Suppose it suits me better to live here, what then?' she said.

" 'You know the conditions,' I said, 'I've kept my part of our dirty, damnable bargain, haven't I? But you've cheated. You think you can treat my house and my home like your own sink in London. I've stood enough, but my God, Rebecca, this is your last chance.'

"I remember she squashed out her cigarette in the tub by the divan, and then she got up, and stretched herself, her arms above her head.

" 'You're right, Max,' she said. 'It's time I turned over a new leaf.'

"She looked very pale, very thin. She began walking up and down the room, her hands in the pockets of her trousers. She looked like a boy in her sailing kit, a boy with a face like a Botticelli angel.

" 'Have you ever thought,' she said, 'how damned hard it would be for you to make a case against me? In a court of law, I mean. If you wanted to divorce me. Do you realise that you've never had one shred of proof against me, from the very first? All your friends, even the servants, believe our marriage to be a success.'

" 'What about Frank?' I said. 'What about Beatrice?'

"She threw back her head and laughed. 'What sort of a story could Frank tell against mine?' she said. 'Don't you know me well enough for that? As for Beatrice, wouldn't it be the easiest thing in the world for her to stand in a witness box as the ordinary jealous woman whose husband once lost his head and made a fool of himself? Oh, no, Max, you'd have a hell of a time trying to prove anything against me.'

"She stood watching me, rocking on her heels, her hands in her pockets and a smile on her face. 'Do you realise that I could get Danny, as my personal maid, to swear anything I asked her to swear, in a court of law? And that the rest of the servants, in blind ignorance, would follow her example and swear too? They think we live together at Manderley as husband and wife, don't they? And so does everyone, your friends, all our little world. Well, how are you going to prove that we don't?'

"She sat down on the edge of the table, swinging her legs, watching me.

"'Haven't we acted the parts of a loving husband and wife rather too well?' she said. I remember watching that foot of hers in its striped sandal swinging backwards and forwards, and my eyes and my brain began to burn in a strange quick way.

"'We could make you look very foolish, Danny and I,' she said softly. 'We could make you look so foolish that no one would believe you, Max, nobody at all.' Still that foot of hers, swinging to and fro, that damned foot in its blue and white striped sandal.

"Suddenly she slipped off the table and stood in front of me, smiling still, her hands in her pockets.

"'If I had a child, Max,' she said, 'neither you, nor anyone in the world, would ever prove that it was not yours. It would grow up here in Manderley, bearing your name. There would be nothing you could do. And when you died Manderley would be his. You could not prevent it. The property's entailed. You would like an heir, wouldn't you, for your beloved Manderley? You would enjoy it, wouldn't you, seeing my son lying in his pram under the chestnut tree, playing leap-frog on the lawn, catching butterflies in the Happy Valley? It would give you the biggest thrill of your life, wouldn't it, Max, to watch my son grow bigger day by day, and to know that when you died, all this would be his?'

"She waited a minute, rocking on her heels, and then she lit a cigarette and went and stood by the window. She began to laugh. She went on laughing. I thought she would never stop. 'God, how funny,' she said, 'how supremely, wonderfully funny. Well, you heard me say I was going to turn over a new leaf, didn't you? Now you know the reason. They'll be happy, won't they, all these smug locals, all your blasted tenants? "It's what we've always hoped for, Mrs. de Winter," they will say. I'll be the perfect mother, Max, like I've been the perfect wife. And none of them will ever guess, none of them will ever know.'

"She turned round and faced me, smiling, one hand in her pocket, the other holding her cigarette. When I killed her she was smiling still. I fired at her heart. The bullet passed right through. She did not fall at once. She stood there, looking at me, that slow smile on her face, her eyes wide open . . ."

Maxim's voice had sunk low, so low, that it was like a whisper. The hand that I held between my own was cold. I did not look at him. I watched Jasper's sleeping body on the carpet beside me, the little thump of his tail, now and then, upon the floor.

"I'd forgotten," said Maxim, and his voice was slow now, tired, without expression, "that when you shot a person there was so much blood."

There was a hole there on the carpet beneath Jasper's tail. The burnt hole from a cigarette. I wondered how long it had been there. Some people said ash was good for the carpets.

"I had to get water from the cove," said Maxim. "I had to keep going backwards and forwards to the cove for water. Even by the fireplace, where she had not been, there was a stain. It was all round her where she lay on the floor. It began to blow too. There was no catch on the window. The window kept banging backwards and forwards, while I knelt there on the floor, with that dishcloth, and the bucket beside me."

And the rain on the roof, I thought, he does not remember the rain on the roof. It pattered thin and light and very fast.

"I carried her out to the boat," he said, "it must have been half-past eleven by then, nearly twelve. It was quite dark. There was no moon. The wind was squally, from the west. I carried her down to the cabin and left her there. Then I had to get under way, with the dinghy astern, and beat out of the little harbour against the tide. The wind was with me but it came in puffs, and I was in the lee there, under cover of the headland. I remember I got the main-sail jammed half-way up the mast. I had not done it, you see, for a long time. I never went out with Rebecca.

"And I thought of the tide, how swift it ran and strong into the little cove. The wind blew down from the headland like a funnel. I got the boat out into the bay. I got her out there, beyond the beacon, and I tried to go about, to clear the ridge of rocks. The little jib fluttered. I could not sheet it in. A puff of wind came and the sheet tore out of my hands, went twisting round the mast. The sail thundered and shook. It cracked like a whip above my head. I could not remember what one had to do. I could not remember. I tried to reach that sheet and it blew above me in the air. Another blast of wind came straight ahead. We began to drift sideways, closer to the ridge. It was dark, so damned dark I couldn't see anything on the black, slippery deck. Somehow I blundered down into the cabin. I had a spike with me. If I didn't do it now it would be too late. We were getting so near to the ridge, and in six or seven minutes, drifting like this, we should be out of deep water. I opened the sea-cocks. The water began to come in. I drove the spike into the bottom boards. One of the planks split right across. I took the spike out and began to drive in another plank. The water came up over my feet. I left Rebecca lying there, on the floor. I fastened both the scuttles. I bolted the door. When I came up on deck I saw we were within twenty yards of the ridge. I threw some of the loose stuff on the deck into the water.

There was a life-buoy, a pair of sweeps, a coil of rope. I climbed into the dinghy. I pulled away, and lay back on the paddles, and watched. The boat was drifting still. She was sinking too. Sinking by the head. The jib was still shaking and cracking like a whip. I thought someone must hear it, someone walking the cliffs late at night, some fisherman from Kerrith away beyond me in the bay, whose boat I could not see. The boat was smaller, like a black shadow on the water. The mast began to shiver, began to crack. Suddenly she heeled right over and as she went the mast broke in two, split right down the centre. The life-buoy and the sweeps floated away from me on the water. The boat was not there any more. I remember staring at the place where she had been. Then I pulled back to the cove. It started raining."

Maxim waited. He stared in front of him still. Then he looked at me, sitting beside him on the floor.

"That's all," he said, "there's no more to tell. I left the dinghy on the buoy, as she would have done. I went back and looked at the cottage. The floor was wet with the salt water. She might have done it herself. I walked up the path through the woods. I went into the house. Up the stairs to the dressing-room. I remember undressing. It began to blow and rain very hard. I was sitting there, on the bed, when Mrs. Danvers knocked on the door. I went and opened it, in my dressing-gown, and spoke to her. She was worried about Rebecca. I told her to go back to bed. I shut the door again. I went back and sat by the window in my dressing-gown, watching the rain, listening to the sea as it broke there, in the cove."

We sat there together without saying anything. I went on holding his cold hands. I wondered why Robert did not come to clear the tea.

"She sank too close in," said Maxim. "I meant to take her right out in the bay. They would never have found her there. She was too close in."

"It was the ship," I said; "it would not have happened but for the ship. No one would have known."

"She was too close in," said Maxim.

We were silent again. I began to feel very tired.

"I knew it would happen one day," said Maxim, "even when I went up to Edgecoombe and identified that body as hers, I knew it meant nothing, nothing at all. It was only a question of waiting, of marking time. Rebecca would win in the end. Finding you has not made any difference has it? Loving you does not alter things at all. Rebecca knew she would win in the end. I saw her smile, when she died."

"Rebecca is dead," I said. "That's what we've got to remember. Rebecca is dead. She can't speak, she can't bear witness. She can't harm you any more."

"There's her body," he said, "the diver has seen it. It's lying there, on the cabin floor."

"We've got to explain it," I said. "We've got to think out a way to explain it. It's got to be the body of someone you don't know. Someone you've never seen before."

"Her things will be there still," he said. "The rings on her fingers. Even if her clothes have rotted in the water there will be something there to tell them. It's not like a body lost at sea, battered against rocks. The cabin is untouched. She must be lying there on the floor as I left her. The boat has been there, all these months. No one has moved anything. There is the boat, lying on the sea-bed where she sank."

"A body rots in water, doesn't it?" I whispered; "even if it's lying there, undisturbed, the water rots it, doesn't it?"

"I don't know," he said. "I don't know."

"How will you find out, how will you know?" I said.

"The diver is going down again at five-thirty to-morrow morning," said Maxim. "Searle has made all the arrangements. They are going to try to raise the boat. No one will be about. I'm going with them. He's sending his boat to pick me up in the cove. Five-thirty to-morrow morning."

"And then?" I said, "if they get it up, what then?"

"Searle's going to have his big lighter anchored there, just out in the deep water. If the boat's wood has not rotted, if it still holds together, his crane will be able to lift it on to the lighter. They'll go back to Kerrith then. Searle says he will moor the lighter at the head of that disused creek half-way up Kerrith harbour. It drives out very easily. It's mud there at low water and the trippers can't row up there. We shall have the place to ourselves. He says we'll have to let the water drain out of the boat, leaving the cabin bare. He's going to get hold of a doctor."

"What will he do?" I said. "What will the doctor do?"

"I don't know," he said.

"If they find out it's Rebecca you must say the other body was a mistake," I said. "You must say that body in the crypt was a mistake, a ghastly mistake. You must say that when you went to Edgecoombe you were ill, you did not know what you were doing. You were not sure, even then. You could not tell. It was a mistake, just a mistake. You will say that, won't you?"

"Yes," he said. "Yes."

"They can't prove anything against you," I said. "Nobody saw you that night. You had gone to bed. They can't prove anything. No one knows but you and I. No one at all. Not even Frank. We are the only two people in the world to know, Maxim. You and I."

"Yes," he said, "yes."

"They will think the boat capsized and sank when she was in the cabin," I said, "they will think she went below for a rope, for something, and while she was there the wind came from the headland, and the boat heeled over, and Rebecca was trapped. They'll think that, won't they?"

"I don't know," he said. "I don't know."

Suddenly the telephone began ringing in the little room behind the library.

CHAPTER TWENTY-ONE

MAXIM WENT into the little room and shut the door. Robert came in a few minutes afterwards to clear away the tea. I stood up, my back turned to him so that he should not see my face. I wondered when they would begin to know, on the estate, in the servants' hall, in Kerrith itself. I wondered how long it took for news to trickle through.

I could hear the murmur of Maxim's voice in the little room beyond. I had a sick expectant feeling at the pit of my stomach. The sound of the telephone ringing seemed to have woken every nerve in my body. I had sat there on the floor beside Maxim in a sort of dream, his hand in mine, my face against his shoulder. I had listened to his story and part of me went with him like a shadow in his tracks. I too had killed Rebecca, I too had sunk the boat there in the bay. I had listened beside him to the wind and water. I had waited for Mrs. Danvers' knocking on the door. All this I had suffered with him, all this and more beside. But the rest of me sat there on the carpet, unmoved and detached, thinking and caring for one thing only, repeating a phrase over and over again, "He did not love Rebecca, he did not love Rebecca." Now, at the ringing of the telephone, these two selves merged and became one again. I was the self that I had always been, I was not changed. But something new had come upon me that had not been before. My heart, for all its anxiety and doubt, was light and free. I knew then that I was no longer afraid of Rebecca. I did not hate her any more. Now that I knew her to have been evil and vicious and rotten I did not hate her any more. She could not hurt me. I could go to the morning-room and sit down at her desk and touch her pen and look at her writing on the pigeon-holes, and I should not mind. I could go to her room in the west wing, stand by the window even as I had done this morning, and I should not be afraid. Rebecca's power had dissolved into the air, like the mist had done. She would never haunt me again. She would never stand behind me on the stairs, sit beside me in the dining-room, lean down from the gallery and watch me standing in the hall. Maxim had never loved her. I did not hate her any more. Her body had come back, her boat had been found with its queer prophetic name, Je Reviens, but I was free of her forever.

I was free now to be with Maxim, to touch him, and hold him, and love him. I would never be a child again. It would not be I, I, I any longer, it would be we, it would be us. We would be together. We would face this trouble together, he and I. Captain Searle, and the diver, and Frank, and Mrs. Danvers, and Beatrice, and the men and women of Kerrith reading their newspapers, could not break us now. Our happiness had not come too late. I was not young any more. I was not shy. I was not afraid. I would fight for Maxim. I would lie and perjure and swear, I would blaspheme and pray. Rebecca had not won. Rebecca had lost.

Robert had taken away the tea and Maxim came back into the room.

"It was Colonel Julyan," he said, "he's just been talking to Searle. He's coming out with us to the boat to-morrow. Searle has told him."

"Why Colonel Julyan, why?" I said.

"He's the magistrate for Kerrith. He has to be present."

"What did he say?"

"He asked me if I had any idea whose body it could be."

"What did you say?"

"I said I did not know. I said we believed Rebecca to be alone. I said I did not know of any friend."

"Did he say anything after that?"

"Yes."

"What did he say?"

"He asked me if I thought it possible that I made a mistake when I went up to Edgecoombe."

"He said that? He said that already?"

"Yes."

"And you?"

"I said it might be possible. I did not know."

"He'll be with you then to-morrow when you look at the boat? He, and Captain Searle, and a doctor."

"Inspector Welch too."

"Inspector Welch?"

"Yes."

"Why? Why Inspector Welch?"

"It's the custom, when a body has been found."

I did not say anything. We stared at one another. I felt the little pain come again at the pit of my stomach.

"They may not be able to raise the boat," I said.

"No," he said.

"They couldn't do anything then about the body, could they?" I said.

"I don't know," he said.

He glanced out of the window. The sky was white and overcast as it had been when I came away from the cliffs. There was no wind though. It was still and quiet.

"I thought it might blow from the south-west about an hour ago but the wind has died away again," he said.

"Yes," I said.

"It will be a flat calm to-morrow for the diver," he said.

The telephone began ringing again from the little room. There was something sickening about the shrill urgent summons of the bell. Maxim and I looked at one another. Then he went into the room to answer it, shutting the door behind him as he had done before. The queer nagging pain had not left me yet. It returned again in greater force with the ringing of the bell. The feel of it took me back across the years to my childhood. This was the pain I had known when I was very small and the maroons had sounded in the streets of London, and I had sat, shivering, not understanding, under a little cupboard beneath the stairs. It was the same feeling, the same pain.

Maxim came back into the library. "It's begun," he said slowly.

"What do you mean, what's happened?" I said, grown suddenly cold.

"It was a reporter," he said, "the fellow from the *County Chronicle*. Was it true, he said, that the boat belonging to the late Mrs. de Winter had been found?"

"What did you say?"

"I said, Yes, a boat had been found, but that was all we know. It might not be her boat at all."

"Was that all he said?"

"No. He asked if I could confirm the rumour that a body had been found in the cabin."

"No!"

"Yes. Someone must have been talking. Not Searle, I know that. The diver, one of his friends. You can't stop these people. The whole story will be all over Kerrith by breakfast time to-morrow."

"What did you say, about the body?"

"I said I did not know. I had no statement to make. And I should be obliged if he did not ring me up again."

"You will irritate them. You will have them against you."

"I can't help that. I don't make statements to newspapers. I won't have those fellows ringing up and asking questions."

"We might want them on our side," I said.

"If it comes to fighting, I'll fight alone," he said. "I don't want a newspaper behind me."

"The reporter will ring up someone else," I said. "He will get on to Colonel Julyan or Captain Searle."

"He won't get much change out of them," said Maxim.

"If only we could do something," I said, "all these hours ahead of us, and we sit here, idle, waiting for to-morrow morning."

"There's nothing we can do," said Maxim.

We went on sitting in the library. Maxim picked up a book but I know he did not read. Now and again I saw him lift his head and listen, as though he heard the telephone again. But it did not ring again. No one disturbed us. We dressed for dinner as usual. It seemed incredible to me that this time last night I had been putting on my white dress, sitting before the mirror at my dressing-table, arranging the curled wig. It was like an old forgotten nightmare, something remembered months afterwards with doubt and disbelief. We had dinner. Frith served us, returned from his afternoon. His face was solemn, expressionless. I wondered if he had been in Kerrith, if he had heard anything.

After dinner we went back again to the library. We did not talk much. I sat on the floor at Maxim's feet, my head against his knees. He ran his fingers through my hair. Different from his old abstracted way. It was not like stroking Jasper any more. I felt his finger tips on the scalp of my head. Sometimes he kissed me. Sometimes he said things to me. There were no shadows between us any more, and when we were silent it was because the silence came to us of our own asking. I wondered how it was I could be so happy when our little world about us was so black. It was a strange sort of happiness. Not what I had dreamt about or expected. It was not the sort of happiness I had imagined in the lonely hours. There was nothing feverish or urgent about this. It was a quiet, still happiness. The library windows were open wide, and when we did not talk or touch one another we looked out at the dark dull sky.

It must have rained in the night for when I woke the next morning, just after seven, and got up, and looked out of the window, I saw the roses in the garden below were folded and drooping, and the grass banks leading to the woods were wet and silver. There was a little smell in the air of mist and damp, the smell that comes with the first fall of the leaf. I wondered if autumn would come upon us two months before her time. Maxim had not woken me when he got up at five. He must have crept from his bed and gone through the bathroom to his dressing-room without a sound. He would be down there now, in the bay, with Colonel Julyan, and Captain Searle, and the men from the lighter. The lighter would be there, the crane and the chain, and Rebecca's boat coming to the surface. I thought about it calmly, coolly, without feeling. I pictured them all down there in the bay, and the little dark hull of the boat rising slowly to the surface, sodden, dripping, the grass-green sea-weed and the shells clinging to her sides. When they lifted her on to the lighter the water would stream from her sides, back into the sea again. The wood of the little boat would look soft and grey, pulpy in places. She would smell of mud and rust, and that dark black weed that grows deep beneath the sea beside rocks that are never uncovered. Perhaps the name-board still hung upon her stern. Je Reviens. The lettering green and faded. The nails rusted through. And Rebecca herself was there, lying on the cabin floor.

I got up and had my bath and dressed, and went down to breakfast at nine o'clock as usual. There were a lot of letters on my plate. Letters from people thanking us for the dance. I skimmed through them, I did not read them all. Frith wanted to know whether to keep the breakfast hot for Maxim. I told him I did not know when he would be back. He had to go out very early, I said. Frith did not say anything. He looked very solemn, very grave. I wondered again if he knew.

After breakfast I took my letters along to the morning-room. The room smelt fusty, the windows had not been opened. I flung them wide, letting in the cool fresh air. The flowers on the mantelpiece were drooping, many of them dead. The petals lay on the floor. I rang the bell, and Maud, the under-housemaid, came into the room.

"This room has not been touched this morning," I said, "even the windows were shut. And the flowers are dead. Will you please take them away."

She looked nervous and apologetic. "I'm very sorry, Madam," she said. She went to the mantelpiece and took the vases.

"Don't let it happen again," I said.

"No, Madam," she said. She went out of the room, taking the flowers with her. I had not thought it would be so easy to be severe. I wondered why it had seemed hard for me before. The menu for the day lay on the writing-desk. Cold salmon and mayonnaise, cutlets in aspic, galantine of chicken, soufflé. I recognised them all from the buffet-supper of the night of the ball. We were evidently still living on the remains. This must be the cold lunch that was put out in the dining-room yesterday and I had not eaten. The staff were taking things easily it seemed. I put a pencil through the list and rang for Robert. "Tell Mrs. Danvers to order something hot," I said. "If there's still a lot of cold stuff to finish we don't want it in the dining-room."

"Very good, Madam," he said.

I followed him out of the room and went to the little flower-room for my scissors. Then I went into the rose-garden and cut some young buds. The chill had worn away from the air. It was going to be as hot and airless as yesterday had been. I wondered if they were still down in the bay or whether they had gone back to the creek in Kerrith harbour. Presently I should hear. Presently Maxim would come back and tell me. Whatever happened I must be calm and quiet. Whatever happened I must not be afraid. I cut my roses and took them back into the morning-room. The carpet had been dusted, and the fallen petals removed. I began to arrange the flowers in the vases that Robert had filled with water. When I had nearly finished there was a knock on the door.

"Come in," I said.

It was Mrs. Danvers. She had the menu list in her hand. She looked pale and tired. There were great rings round her eyes.

"Good morning, Mrs. Danvers," I said.

"I don't understand," she began, "why you sent the menu out and the message by Robert. Why did you do it?"

I looked across at her, a rose in my hand.

"Those cutlets and that salmon were sent in yesterday," I said. "I saw them on the side-board. I should prefer something hot to-day. If they won't eat the cold in the kitchen you had better throw the stuff away. So much waste goes on in this house anyway that a little more won't make any difference."

She stared at me. She did not say anything. I put the rose in the vase with the others.

"Don't tell me you can't think of anything to give us, Mrs. Danvers," I said. "You must have menus for all occasions in your room."

"I'm not used to having messages sent to me by Robert," she said. "If Mrs. de Winter wanted anything changed she would ring me personally on the house telephone."

"I'm afraid it does not concern me very much what Mrs. de Winter used to do," I said. "I am Mrs. de Winter now, you know. And if I choose to send a message by Robert I shall do so."

Just then Robert came into the room. "The *County Chronicle* on the telephone, Madam," he said.

"Tell the *County Chronicle* I'm not at home," I said.

"Yes, Madam," he said. He went out of the room.

"Well, Mrs. Danvers, is there anything else?" I said.

She went on staring at me. Still she did not say anything. "If you have nothing else to say you had better go and tell the cook about the hot lunch," I said. "I'm rather busy."

"Why did the *County Chronicle* want to speak to you?" she said.

"I haven't the slightest idea, Mrs. Danvers," I said.

"Is it true," she said slowly, "the story Frith brought back with him from Kerrith last night, that Mrs. de Winter's boat has been found?"

"Is there such a story?" I said. "I'm afraid I don't know anything about it."

"Captain Searle, the Kerrith harbour-master, called here yesterday, didn't he?" she said. "Robert told me, Robert showed him in. Frith says the story in Kerrith is that the diver who went down about the ship there in the bay found Mrs. de Winter's boat."

"Perhaps so," I said. "You had better wait until Mr. de Winter himself comes in and ask him about it."

"Why was Mr. de Winter up so early?" she asked.

"That was Mr. de Winter's business," I said.

She went on staring at me. "Frith said the story goes that there was a body in the cabin of the little boat," she said. "Why should there be a body there? Mrs. de Winter always sailed alone."

"It's no use asking me, Mrs. Danvers," I said. "I don't know any more than you do."

"Don't you?" she said slowly. She kept on looking at me. I turned away, I put the vase back on the table by the window.

"I will give the orders about the lunch," she said. She waited a moment. I did not say anything. Then she went out of the room. She can't frighten me any more, I thought. She has lost her power with Rebecca. Whatever she said or did now it could not matter to me or hurt me. I knew she was my enemy and I did not mind. But if she should learn the truth about the body in the boat and become Maxim's enemy too—what then? I sat down in the chair. I put the scissors on the table. I did not feel like doing any more roses. I kept wondering what Maxim was doing. I wondered why the reporter from the *County Chronicle* had rung us up again. The old sick feeling came back inside me. I went and leant out of the window. It was very hot. There was thunder in the air. The gardeners began to mow the grass again. I could see one of the men with his machine walk backwards and forwards on the top of the bank. I could not go on sitting in the morning-room. I left my scissors and my roses and went out on to the terrace. I began to walk up and down. Jasper padded after me, wondering why I did not take him for a walk. I went on walking up and down the terrace. About half-past eleven Frith came out to me from the hall.

"Mr. de Winter on the telephone, Madam," he said.

I went through the library to the little room beyond. My hands were shaking as I lifted the receiver.

"Is that you?" he said, "it's Maxim. I'm speaking from the office. I'm with Frank."

"Yes?" I said.

There was a pause. "I shall be bringing Frank and Colonel Julyan back to lunch at one o'clock," he said.

"Yes," I said.

I waited. I waited for him to go on. "They were able to raise the boat," he said. "I've just got back from the creek."

"Yes," I said.

"Searle was there, and Colonel Julyan, and Frank, and the others," he said. I wondered if Frank was standing beside him at the telephone, and if that was the reason he was so cool, so distant.

"All right then," he said, "expect us about one o'clock."

I put back the receiver. He had not told me anything. I still did not know what had happened. I went back again to the terrace, telling Frith first that we should be four to lunch instead of two.

An hour dragged past, slow, interminable. I went upstairs and changed into a thinner frock. I came down again. I went and sat in the drawing-room and waited. At five minutes to one I heard the sound of a car in the drive, and then voices in the hall. I patted my hair in front of the looking-glass. My face was very white. I pinched some colour into my cheeks and stood up waiting for them to come into the room. Maxim came in, and Frank, and Colonel Julyan. I remembered seeing Colonel Julyan at the ball dressed as Cromwell. He looked shrunken now, different. A smaller man altogether.

"How do you do?" he said. He spoke quietly, gravely, like a doctor.

"Ask Frith to bring the sherry," said Maxim. "I'm going to wash."

"I'll have a wash too," said Frank. Before I rang the bell Frith appeared with the sherry. Colonel Julyan did not have any. I took some to give me something to hold. Colonel Julyan came and stood beside me by the window.

"This is a most distressing thing, Mrs. de Winter," he said gently. "I do feel for you and your husband most acutely."

"Thank you," I said. I began to sip my sherry. Then I put the glass back again on the table. I was afraid he would notice that my hand was shaking.

"What makes it so difficult was the fact of your husband identifying that first body, over a year ago," he said.

"I don't quite understand," I said.

"You did not hear then, what we found this morning?" he said.

"I knew there was a body. The diver found a body," I said.

"Yes," he said. And then, half glancing over his shoulder towards the hall: "I'm afraid it was her, without a doubt," he said, lowering his voice. "I can't go into details with you, but the evidence was sufficient for your husband and Doctor Phillips to identify."

He stopped suddenly, and moved away from me. Maxim and Frank had come back into the room.

"Lunch is ready, shall we go in," said Maxim.

I led the way into the hall, my heart like a stone, heavy, numb. Colonel Julyan sat on my right, Frank on my left. I did not look at Maxim. Frith and Robert began to hand the first course. We all talked about the weather.

"I see in *The Times* they had it well over eighty in London yesterday," said Colonel Julyan.

"Really?" I said.

"Yes. Must be frightful for the poor devils who can't get away."

"Yes, frightful," I said.

"Paris can be hotter than London," said Frank. "I remember staying a week-end in Paris in the middle of August, and it was quite impossible to sleep. There was not a breath of air in the whole city. The temperature was over ninety."

"Of course the French always sleep with their windows shut, don't they?" said Colonel Julyan.

"I don't know," said Frank. "I was staying in a hotel. The people were mostly Americans."

"You know France of course, Mrs. de Winter?" said Colonel Julyan.

"Not so very well," I said.

"Oh, I had the idea you had lived many years out there."

"No," I said.

"She was staying in Monte Carlo when I met her," said Maxim. "You don't call that France, do you?"

"No, I suppose not," said Colonel Julyan, "it must be very cosmopolitan. The coast is pretty though, isn't it?"

"Very pretty," I said.

"Not so rugged as this, eh? Still, I know which I'd rather have. Give me England every time, when it comes to settling down. You know where you are over here."

"I dare say the French feel that about France," said Maxim.

"Oh, no doubt," said Colonel Julyan.

We went on eating awhile in silence. Frith stood behind my chair. We were all thinking of one thing, but because of Frith we had to keep up our little performance. I supposed Frith was thinking about it too, and I thought how much easier it would be if we cast aside convention and let him join in with us, if he had anything to say. Robert came with the drinks. Our plates were changed. The second course was handed. Mrs. Danvers had not forgotten my wish for hot food. I took something out of a casserole covered in mushroom sauce.

"I think everyone enjoyed your wonderful party the other night," said Colonel Julyan.

"I'm so glad," I said.

"Does an immense amount of good locally, that sort of thing," he said.

"Yes, I suppose it does," I said.

"It's a universal instinct of the human species, isn't it, that desire to dress up in some sort of disguise?" said Frank.

"I must be very inhuman then," said Maxim.

"It's natural I suppose," said Colonel Julyan, "for all of us to wish to look different. We are all children in some ways."

I wondered how much pleasure it had given him to disguise himself as

Cromwell. I had not seen much of him at the ball. He had spent most of the evening in the morning-room, playing bridge.

"You don't play golf, do you, Mrs. de Winter?" said Colonel Julyan.

"No, I'm afraid I don't," I said.

"You ought to take it up," he said. "My eldest girl is very keen, and she can't find many young people to play with her. I gave her a small car for her birthday and she drives herself over to the north coast nearly every day. It gives her something to do."

"How nice," I said.

"She ought to have been the boy," he said. "My lad is different altogether. No earthly use at games. Always writing poetry. I suppose he'll grow out of it."

"Oh, rather," said Frank. "I used to write poetry myself when I was his age. Awful nonsense too. I never write any now."

"Good heavens, I should hope not," said Maxim.

"I don't know where my boy gets it from," said Colonel Julyan, "certainly not from his mother or from me."

There was another long silence. Colonel Julyan had a second dip into the casserole. "Mrs. Lacy looked very well the other night," he said.

"Yes," I said.

"Her dress came adrift as usual," said Maxim.

"Those eastern garments must be the devil to manage," said Colonel Julyan, "and yet they say, you know, they are far more comfortable and far cooler than anything you ladies wear in England."

"Really?" I said.

"Yes, so they say. It seems all that loose drapery throws off the hot rays of the sun."

"How curious," said Frank, "you'd think it would have just the opposite effect."

"No, apparently not," said Colonel Julyan.

"Do you know the East, sir?" said Frank.

"I know the far East," said Colonel Julyan. "I was in China for five years. Then Singapore."

"Isn't that where they make the curry?" I said.

"Yes, they gave us very good curry in Singapore," he said.

"I'm fond of curry," said Frank.

"Ah, it's not curry at all in England, it's hash," said Colonel Julyan.

The plates were cleared away. A soufflé was handed, and a bowl of fruit salad. "I suppose you are coming to the end of your raspberries," said Colonel Julyan. "It's been a wonderful summer for them, hasn't it? We've put down pots and pots of jam."

"I never think raspberry jam is a great success," said Frank, "there are always so many pips."

"You must come and try some of ours," said Colonel Julyan. "I don't think we have a great lot of pips."

"We're going to have a mass of apples this year at Manderley," said Frank.

"I was saying to Maxim a few days ago we ought to have a record season. We shall be able to send a lot up to London."

"Do you really find it pays?" said Colonel Julyan, "by the time you've paid your men for the extra labour, and then the packing, and carting, do you make any sort of profit worth while?"

"Oh, Lord yes," said Frank.

"How interesting. I must tell my wife," said Colonel Julyan.

The soufflé and the fruit salad did not take long to finish. Robert appeared with cheese and biscuits, and a few minutes later Frith came with the coffee and cigarettes. Then they both went out of the room and shut the door. We drank our coffee in silence. I gazed steadily at my plate.

"I was saying to your wife before luncheon, de Winter," began Colonel Julyan, resuming his first quiet confidential tone, "that the awkward part of this whole distressing business is the fact that you identified that original body."

"Yes, quite," said Maxim.

"I think the mistake was very natural under the circumstances," said Frank quickly. "The authorities wrote to Maxim, asking him to go up to Edgecoombe, presupposing before he arrived there that the body was hers. And Maxim was not well at the time. I wanted to go with him, but he insisted on going alone. He was not in a fit state to undertake anything of the sort."

"That's nonsense," said Maxim. "I was perfectly well."

"Well, it's no use going into all that now," said Colonel Julyan. "You made that first identification, and now the only thing to do is to admit the error. There seems to be no doubt about it this time."

"No," said Maxim.

"I wish you could be spared the formality and the publicity of an inquest," said Colonel Julyan, "but I'm afraid that's quite impossible."

"Naturally," said Maxim.

"I don't think it need take very long," said Colonel Julyan. "It's just a case of you re-affirming identification, and then getting Tabb, who you say converted the boat when your wife brought her from France, just to give his piece of evidence that the boat was sea-worthy and in good order when he last had her in his yard. It's just red-tape you know. But it has to be done. No, what bothers me is the wretched publicity of the affair. So sad and unpleasant for you and your wife."

"That's quite all right," said Maxim. "We understand."

"So unfortunate that wretched ship going ashore there," said Colonel Julyan, "but for that the whole matter would have rested in peace."

"Yes," said Maxim.

"The only consolation is that now we know poor Mrs. de Winter's death must have been swift and sudden, not the dreadful slow lingering affair we all believed it to be. There can have been no question of trying to swim."

"None," said Maxim.

"She must have gone down for something, and then the door jammed, and a squall caught the boat without anyone at the helm," said Colonel Julyan. "A dreadful thing."

"Yes," said Maxim.

"That seems to be the solution, don't you think, Crawley?" said Colonel Julyan, turning to Frank.

"Oh, yes, undoubtedly," said Frank.

I glanced up and I saw Frank looking at Maxim. He looked away again immediately but not before I had seen and understood the expression in his eyes. Frank knew. And Maxim did not know that he knew. I went on stirring my coffee. My hand was hot, damp.

"I suppose sooner or later we all make a mistake in judgement," said Colonel Julyan, "and then we are for it. Mrs. de Winter must have known how the wind comes down like a funnel in that bay, and that it was not safe to leave the helm of a small boat like that. She must have sailed alone over that spot scores of times. And then the moment came, she took a chance—and the chance killed her. It's a lesson to all of us."

"Accidents happen so easily," said Frank, "even to the most experienced people. Think of the number killed out hunting every season."

"Oh, I know. But then it's the horse falling generally that lets you down. If Mrs. de Winter had not left the helm of her boat the accident would never have happened. An extraordinary thing to do. I must have watched her many times in the handicap race on Saturdays from Kerrith, and I never saw her make an elementary mistake. It's the sort of thing a novice would do. In that particular place too, just by the ridge."

"It was very squally that night," said Frank, "something may have happened to the gear. Something may have jammed. And then she slipped down for a knife."

"Of course. Of course. Well, we shall never know. And I don't suppose we should be any the better for it if we did. As I said before, I wish I could stop this inquest but I can't. I'm trying to arrange it for Tuesday morning, and it will be as short as possible. Just a formal matter. But I'm afraid we shan't be able to keep the reporters out of it."

There was another silence. I judged the time had come to push back my chair.

"Shall we go into the garden?" I said.

We all stood up, and then I led the way to the terrace. Colonel Julyan patted Jasper.

"He's grown into a nice-looking dog," he said.

"Yes," I said.

"They make nice pets," he said.

"Yes," I said.

We stood about for a minute. Then he glanced at his watch.

"Thank you for your most excellent lunch," he said. "I have rather a busy afternoon in front of me, and I hope you will excuse me dashing away."

"Of course," I said.

"I'm so very sorry this should have happened. You have all my sympathy.

I consider it's almost harder for you than for your husband. However, once the inquest is over you must both forget all about it."

"Yes," I said, "yes, we must try to."

"My car is here in the drive. I wonder whether Crawley would like a lift. Crawley? I can drop you at your office if it's any use."

"Thank you, sir," said Frank.

He came and took my hand. "I shall be seeing you again," he said.

"Yes," I said.

I did not look at him. I was afraid he would understand my eyes. I did not want him to know that I knew. Maxim walked with them to the car. When they had gone he came back to me on the terrace. He took my arm. We stood looking down at the green lawns towards the sea and the beacon on the headland.

"It's going to be all right," he said. "I'm quite calm, quite confident. You saw how Julyan was at lunch, and Frank. There won't be any difficulty at the inquest. It's going to be all right."

I did not say anything. I held his arm tightly.

"There was never any question of the body being someone unknown," he said. "What we saw was enough for Doctor Phillips even to make the identification alone without me. It was straightforward, simple. There was no trace of what I'd done. The bullet had not touched the bone."

A butterfly sped past us on the terrace, silly and inconsequent.

"You heard what they said," he went on, "they think she was trapped there, in the cabin. The jury will believe that at the inquest too. Phillips will tell them so." He paused. Still I did not speak.

"I only mind for you," he said, "I don't regret anything else. If it had to come all over again I should not do anything different. I'm glad I killed Rebecca, I shall never have any remorse for that, never, never. But you. I can't forget what it has done to you. I was looking at you, thinking of nothing else all through lunch. It's gone forever, that funny, young, lost look that I loved. It won't come back again. I killed that too, when I told you about Rebecca. It's gone, in twenty-four hours. You are so much older. . . ."

CHAPTER TWENTY-TWO

THAT EVENING, when Frith brought in the local paper, there were great headlines right across the top of the page. He brought the paper and laid it down on the table. Maxim was not there, he had gone up early to change for dinner. Frith stood a moment, waiting for me to say something, and it seemed to me stupid and insulting to ignore a matter that must mean so much to everyone in the house.

"This is a very dreadful thing, Frith," I said.

"Yes, Madam, we are all most distressed outside," he said.

"It's so sad for Mr. de Winter," I said, "having to go through it all again."

"Yes, Madam. Very sad. Such a shocking experience, Madam, having to identify the second body having seen the first. I suppose there is no doubt then, that the remains in the boat are genuinely those of the late Mrs. de Winter?"

"I'm afraid not, Frith. No doubt at all."

"It seems so odd to us, Madam, that she should have let herself be trapped like that in the cabin. She was so experienced in a boat."

"Yes, Frith. That's what we all feel. But accidents will happen. And how it happened I don't suppose any of us will ever know."

"I suppose not, Madam. But it's a great shock, all the same. We are most distressed about it outside. And coming suddenly, just after the party. It doesn't seem right somehow, does it?"

"No, Frith."

"It seems there is to be an inquest, Madam?"

"Yes. A formality, you know."

"Of course, Madam. I wonder if any of us will be required to give evidence?"

"I don't think so."

"I shall be only too pleased to do anything that might help the family, Mr. de Winter knows that."

"Yes, Frith. I'm sure he does."

"I've told them outside not to discuss the matter, but it's very difficult to keep an eye on them, especially the girls. I can deal with Robert of course. I'm afraid the news has been a great shock to Mrs. Danvers."

"Yes, Frith. I rather expected it would."

"She went up to her room straight after lunch, and has not come down again. Alice took her a cup of tea and the paper a few minutes ago. She said Mrs. Danvers looked very ill indeed."

"It would be better really if she stayed where she is," I said. "It's no use her getting up and seeing to things if she is ill. Perhaps Alice would tell her that. I can very well manage the ordering. The cook and I between us."

"Yes, Madam. I don't think she is physically ill, Madam, it's just the shock of Mrs. de Winter being found. She was very devoted to Mrs. de Winter."

"Yes," I said. "Yes, I know."

Frith went out of the room after that, and I glanced quickly at the paper before Maxim came down. There was a great column, all down the front page, and an awful blurred photograph of Maxim that must have been taken at least fifteen years ago. It was dreadful, seeing it there on the front page staring at me. And the little line about myself at the bottom, saying who Maxim had married as his second wife, and how he had just given the fancy dress ball at Manderley. It sounded so crude and callous, in the dark print of the newspaper. Rebecca, whom they described as beautiful, talented, and loved by all who knew her, having been drowned a year ago, and then Maxim marrying again the following spring, bringing his bride straight to Manderley (so it said) and giving the big fancy dress ball in her honour. And then the following morning the body of his first wife being found, trapped in the cabin of her sailing boat, at the bottom of the bay.

It was true of course, though sprinkled with little inaccuracies that added to the story, making it strong meat for the hundreds of readers who wanted value for their pennies. Maxim sounded vile in it, a sort of satyr. Bringing back his "young bride," as it described me, to Manderley, and giving the dance, as though we wanted to display ourselves before the world.

I hid the paper under the cushion of the chair so that Maxim should not see it. But I could not keep the morning editions from him. The story was in our London papers too. There was a picture of Manderley, and the story underneath. Manderley was news, and so was Maxim. They talked about him as Max de Winter. It sounded racy, horrible. Each paper made great play of the fact that Rebecca's body had been found the day after the fancy dress ball, as though there was something deliberate about it. Both papers used the same word, "ironic." Yes, I supposed it was ironic. It made a good story. I watched Maxim at the breakfast table getting whiter and whiter as he read the papers, one after the other, and then the local one as well. He did not say anything. He just looked across at me, and I stretched out my hand to him. "Damn them," he whispered, "damn them, damn them."

I thought of all the things they could say, if they knew the truth. Not one column, but five or six. Placards in London. Newsboys shouting in the streets, outside the underground stations. That frightful word of six letters, in the middle of the placard, large and black.

Frank came up after breakfast. He looked pale and tired, as though he had not slept. "I've told the exchange to put all calls for Manderley through to the office," he said to Maxim. "It doesn't matter who it is. If reporters ring up I can deal with them. And anyone else too. I don't want either of you to be worried at all. We've had several calls already from locals. I gave the same answer to each. Mr. and Mrs. de Winter were grateful for all sympathetic enquiries, and they hoped their friends would understand that they were not receiving calls during the next few days. Mrs. Lacy rang up about eight-thirty. Wanted to come over at once."

"Oh, my God . . ." began Maxim.

"It's all right, I prevented her. I told her quite truthfully that I did not think she would do any good by coming over. That you did not want to see anyone but Mrs. de Winter. She wanted to know when they were holding the inquest but I told her it had not been settled. I don't know that we can stop her from coming to that, if she finds it in the papers."

"Those blasted reporters," said Maxim.

"I know," said Frank, "we all want to wring their necks, but you've got to see their point of view. It's their bread-and-butter, they've got to do the job for their paper. If they don't get a story the editor probably sacks them. If the editor does not produce a saleable edition the proprietor sacks him. And if the paper doesn't sell, the proprietor loses all his money. You won't have to see them or speak to them, Maxim. I'm going to do all that for you. All you have to concentrate on is your statement at the inquest."

"I know what to say," said Maxim.

"Of course you do, but don't forget old Horridge is the coroner. He's a sticky sort of chap, goes into details that are quite irrelevant, just to show the jury how thorough he is at his job. You must not let him rattle you."

"Why the devil should I be rattled? I have nothing to be rattled about."

"Of course not. But I've attended these coroner's inquests before, and it's so easy to get nervy and irritable. You don't want to put the fellow's back up."

"Frank's right," I said. "I know just what he means. The swifter and smoother the whole thing goes the easier it will be for everyone. Then, once the wretched thing is over we shall forget all about it, and so will everyone else, won't they, Frank?"

"Yes, of course," said Frank.

I still avoided his eye, but I was more convinced than ever that he knew the truth. He had always known it. From the very first. I remembered the first time I met him, that first day of mine at Manderley, when he, and Beatrice, and Giles had all been at lunch, and Beatrice had been tactless about Maxim's health. I remembered Frank, his quiet turning of the subject, the way he had come to Maxim's aid in his quiet unobtrusive manner if there was ever any question of difficulty. That strange reluctance of his to talk about Rebecca, his stiff, funny, pompous way of making conversation whenever we had approached anything like intimacy. I understood it all. Frank knew, but Maxim did not know that he knew. And Frank did not want Maxim to know that he knew. And we all stood there, looking at one another, keeping up these little barriers between us.

We were not bothered with the telephone again. All the calls were put through to the office. It was just a question of waiting now. Waiting until the Tuesday.

I saw nothing of Mrs. Danvers. The menu was sent through as usual, and I did not change it. I asked little Clarice about her. She said she was going about her work as usual but she was not speaking to anybody. She had all her meals alone in her sitting-room.

Clarice was wide-eyed, evidently curious, but she did not ask me any questions, and I was not going to discuss it with her. No doubt they talked of nothing else, out in the kitchen, and on the estate too, in the lodge, on the farms. I supposed all Kerrith was full of it. We stayed in Manderley, in the gardens close to the house. We did not even walk in the woods. The weather had not broken yet. It was still hot, oppressive. The air was full of thunder, and there was rain behind the white dull sky, but it did not fall. I could feel it, and smell it, pent up there, behind the clouds. The inquest was to be on the Tuesday afternoon at two o'clock.

We had lunch at a quarter-to-one. Frank came. Thank heaven Beatrice had telephoned that she could not get over. The boy Roger had arrived home with measles; they were all in quarantine. I could not help blessing the measles. I don't think Maxim could have borne it, with Beatrice sitting here, staying in the house, sincere, anxious, and affectionate, but asking questions all the time. Forever asking questions.

Lunch was a hurried, nervous meal. We none of us talked very much. I had that nagging pain again. I did not want anything to eat. I could not swallow. It was a relief when the farce of the meal was over, and I heard Maxim go out on to the drive and start up the car. The sound of the engine steadied me. It meant we had to go, we had to be doing something. Not just sitting at Manderley. Frank followed us in his own car. I had my hand on Maxim's knee all the way as he drove. He seemed quite calm. Not nervous in any way. It was like going with someone to a nursing-home, someone who was to have an operation. And not knowing what would happen. Whether the operation would be successful. My hands were very cold. My heart was beating in a funny, jerky way. And all the time that little nagging pain beneath my heart. The inquest was to be held at Lanyon, the market town six miles the other side of Kerrith. We had to park the cars in the big cobbled square by the market-place. Doctor Phillips' car was there already, and also Colonel Julyan's. Other cars too. I saw a passerby stare curiously at Maxim, and then nudge her companion's arm.

"I think I shall stay here," I said. "I don't think I'll come in with you after all."

"I did not want you to come," said Maxim. "I was against it from the first. You'd much better have stayed at Manderley."

"No," I said. "No, I'll be all right here, sitting in the car."

Frank came and looked in at the window. "Isn't Mrs. de Winter coming?" he said.

"No," said Maxim. "She wants to stay in the car."

"I think she's right," said Frank, "there's no earthly reason why she should be present at all. We shan't be long."

"It's all right," I said.

"I'll keep a seat for you," said Frank, "in case you should change your mind."

They went off together and left me sitting there. It was early-closing day. The shops looked drab and dull. There were not many people about. Lanyon was not much of a holiday centre anyway, it was too far inland. I sat looking at the silent shops. The minutes went by. I wondered what they were doing, the coroner, Frank, Maxim, Colonel Julyan. I got out of the car and began walking up and down the market square. I went and looked in a shop window. Then I walked up and down again. I saw a policeman watching me curiously. I turned up a side-street to avoid him.

Somehow, in spite of myself, I found I was coming to the building where the inquest was being held. There had been little publicity about the actual time, and because of this there was no crowd waiting, as I had feared and expected. The place seemed deserted. I went up the steps and stood just inside the door.

A policeman appeared from nowhere. "Do you want anything?" he said.

"No," I said. "No."

"You can't wait here," he said.

"I'm sorry," I said. I went back towards the steps into the street.

"Excuse me, Madam," he said, "aren't you Mrs. de Winter?"

"Yes," I said.

"Of course that's different," he said, "you can wait here if you like. Would you like to take a seat just inside this room?"

"Thank you," I said.

He showed me into a little bare room with a desk in it. It was like a waiting-room at a station. I sat there, with my hands on my lap. Five minutes passed. Nothing happened. It was worse than being outside, than sitting in the car. I got up and went into the passage. The policeman was still standing there.

"How long will they be?" I said.

"I'll go and enquire if you like," he said.

He disappeared along the passage. In a moment he came back again. "I don't think they will be very much longer," he said. "Mr. de Winter has just given his evidence. Captain Searle, and the diver, and Doctor Phillips have already given theirs. There's only one more to speak. Mr. Tabb, the boat-builder from Kerrith."

"Then it's nearly over," I said.

"I expect so, Madam," he said. Then he said, on a sudden thought, "Would you like to hear the remaining evidence? There is a seat there, just inside the door. If you slip in now nobody will notice you."

"Yes," I said. "Yes, I think I will."

It was nearly over. Maxim had finished giving his evidence. I did not mind hearing the rest. It was Maxim I had not wanted to hear. I had been nervous of listening to his evidence. That was why I had not gone with him and Frank in the first place. Now it did not matter. His part of it was over.

I followed the policeman, and he opened a door at the end of the passage. I slipped in, I sat down just by the door. I kept my head low so that I did not have to look at anybody. The room was smaller than I had imagined. Rather hot and stuffy. I had pictured a great bare room with benches, like a church. Maxim and Frank were sitting down at the other end. The coroner was a thin, elderly man in pince-nez. There were people there I did not know. I glanced at them out of the tail of my eye. My heart gave a jump suddenly as I recognised Mrs. Danvers. She was sitting right at the back. And Favell was beside her. Jack Favell, Rebecca's cousin. He was leaning forward, his chin in his hands, his eyes fixed on the coroner, Mr. Horridge. I had not expected him to be there. I wondered if Maxim had seen him. James Tabb, the boat-builder, was standing up now and the coroner was asking him a question.

"Yes, sir," answered Tabb, "I converted Mrs. de Winter's little boat. She was a French fishing boat originally, and Mrs. de Winter bought her for next to nothing over in Brittany, and had her shipped over. She gave me the job of converting her and doing her up like a little yacht."

"Was the boat in a fit state to put to sea?" said the coroner.

"She was when I fitted her out in April of last year," said Tabb. "Mrs. de Winter laid her up as usual at my yard in October, and then in March I had word from her to fit her up as usual, which I did. That would be Mrs. de Winter's fourth season with the boat since I did the conversion job for her."

"Had the boat ever been known to capsize before?" asked the coroner.

"No, sir. I should soon have heard of it from Mrs. de Winter had there been any question of it. She was delighted with the boat in every way, according to what she said to me."

"I suppose great care was needed to handle the boat?" said the coroner.

"Well, sir, everyone has to have their wits about them, when they go sailing boats, I won't deny it. But Mrs. de Winter's boat wasn't one of those cranky little crafts that you can't leave for a moment, like some of the boats you see in Kerrith. She was a stout sea-worthy boat, and could stand a lot of wind. Mrs. de Winter had sailed her in worse weather than she ever found that night. Why, it was only blowing in fits and starts at the time. That's what I've said all along. I couldn't understand Mrs. de Winter's boat being lost on a night like that."

"But surely, if Mrs. de Winter went below for a coat, as is supposed, and a sudden puff of wind was to come down from that headland, it would be enough to capsize the boat?" asked the coroner.

James Tabb shook his head. "No," he said stubbornly, "I don't see that it would."

"Well, I'm afraid that is what must have happened," said the coroner. "I don't think Mr. de Winter or any of us suggest that your workmanship was to blame for the accident at all. You fitted the boat out at the beginning of the season, you reported her sound and sea-worthy, and that's all I want to know. Unfortunately the late Mrs. de Winter relaxed her watchfulness for a moment and she lost her life, the boat sinking with her aboard. Such accidents have happened before. I repeat again we are not blaming you."

"Excuse me, sir," said the boat-builder, "but there is a little bit more to it than that. And if you would allow me I should like to make a further statement."

"Very well, go on," said the coroner.

"It's like this, sir. After the accident last year a lot of people in Kerrith made unpleasantness about my work. Some said I had let Mrs. de Winter start the season in a leaky, rotten boat. I lost two or three orders because of it. It was very unfair, but the boat had sunk, and there was nothing I could say to clear myself. Then that steamer went ashore, as we all know, and Mrs. de Winter's little boat was found, and brought to the surface. Captain Searle himself gave me permission yesterday to go and look at her, and I did. I wanted to satisfy myself that the work I had put into her was sound, in spite of the fact that she had been waterlogged for twelve months or more."

"Well, that was very natural," said the coroner, "and I hope you were satisfied."

"Yes, sir, I was. There was nothing wrong with that boat as regards the work I did to her. I examined every corner of her there on the lighter up the pill where Captain Searle had put her. She had sunk on sandy bottom, I asked the diver about that, and he told me so. She had not touched the ridge at all. The ridge was a clear five feet away. She was lying on sand, and there wasn't the mark of a rock on her."

He paused. The coroner looked at him expectantly.

"Well?" he said, "is that all you want to say?"

"No, sir," said Tabb emphatically, "it's not. What I want to know is this. Who drove the holes in her planking? Rocks didn't do it. The nearest rock was five feet away. Besides, they weren't the sort of marks made by a rock. They were holes. Done with a spike."

I did not look at him. I was looking at the floor. There was oil-cloth laid on the boards. Green oil-cloth. I looked at it.

I wondered why the coroner did not say something. Why did the pause last so long? When he spoke at last his voice sounded rather far away.

"What do you mean?" he said, "what sort of holes?"

"There were three of them altogether," said the boat-builder, "one right for'ard, by her chain locker, on her starboard planking, below the water-line. The other two close together amidships, underneath her floor-boards, in the bottom. The ballast had been shifted too. It was lying loose. And that's not all. The sea-cocks had been turned on."

"The sea-cocks? What are they?" asked the coroner.

"The fitting that plugs the pipes leading from a wash-basin or lavatory, sir. Mrs. de Winter had a little place fitted up right aft. And there was a sink for'ard, where the washing-up was done. There was a sea-cock there, and another in the lavatory. These are always kept tight closed when you're under way, otherwise the water would flow in. When I examined the boat yesterday both sea-cocks were turned full on."

It was hot, much too hot. Why didn't they open a window? We should be suffocated if we sat here with the air like this, and there were so many people, all breathing the same air, so many people.

"With those holes in her planking, sir, and the sea-cocks not closed, it wouldn't take long for a small boat like her to sink. Not much more than ten minutes, I should say. Those holes weren't there when the boat left my yard. I was proud of my work, and so was Mrs. de Winter. It's my opinion, sir, that the boat never capsized at all. She was deliberately scuttled."

I must try and get out of the door. I must try and go back to the waiting-room again. There was no air left in this place, and the person next to me was pressing close, close. . . . Someone in front of me was standing up, and they were talking, too, they were all talking. I did not know what was happening. I could not see anything. It was hot, so very hot. The coroner was asking everybody to be silent. And he said something about "Mr. de Winter." I could not see. That woman's hat was in front of me. Maxim was standing up now. I could not look at him. I must not look at him. I felt like this once before. When was it? I don't know. I don't remember. Oh, yes, with Mrs. Danvers. The time Mrs. Danvers stood with me by the window. Mrs. Danvers was in this place now, listening to the coroner. Maxim was standing up over there. The heat was coming up at me from the floor, rising in slow waves. It reached my hands, wet and slippery, it touched my neck, my chin, my face.

"Mr. de Winter, you heard the statement from James Tabb, who had the care of Mrs. de Winter's boat? Do you know anything of these holes driven in the planking?"

"Nothing whatever."

"Can you think of any reason why they should be there?"

"No, of course not."

"It's the first time you have heard them mentioned?"

"Yes."

"It's a shock to you, of course?"

"It was shock enough to learn that I made a mistake in identification over twelve months ago, and now I learn that my late wife was not only drowned in the cabin of her boat, but that holes were bored in the boat with the deliberate intent of letting in the water so that the boat should sink. Does it surprise you that I should be shocked?"

No, Maxim, no. You will put his back up. You heard what Frank said. You must not put his back up. Not that voice. Not that angry voice, Maxim. He won't understand. Please, darling, please. Oh, God, don't let Maxim lose his temper. Don't let him lose his temper.

"Mr. de Winter, I want you to believe that we all feel very deeply for you in this matter. No doubt you have suffered a shock, a very severe shock, in learning that your late wife was drowned in her own cabin, and not at sea as you supposed. And I am enquiring into the matter for you. I want, for your sake, to find out exactly how and why she died. I don't conduct this enquiry for my own amusement."

"That's rather obvious, isn't it?"

"I hope that it is. James Tabb has just told us that the boat which contained the remains of the late Mrs. de Winter had three holes hammered through her bottom. And that the sea-cocks were open. Do you doubt his statement?"

"Of course not. He's a boat-builder, he knows what he is talking about."

"Who looked after Mrs. de Winter's boat?"

"She looked after it herself."

"She employed no hand?"

"No, nobody at all."

"The boat was moored in the private harbour belonging to Manderley?"

"Yes."

"Any stranger who tried to tamper with the boat would be seen? There is no access to the harbour by public foot-path?"

"No, none at all."

"The harbour is quiet, is it not, and surrounded by trees?"

"Yes."

"A trespasser might not be noticed?"

"Possibly not."

"Yet James Tabb has told us, and we have no reason to disbelieve him, that a boat with those holes drilled in her bottom and the sea-cocks open could not float for more than ten or fifteen minutes."

"Quite."

"Therefore we can put aside the idea that the boat was tampered with maliciously before Mrs. de Winter went for her evening sail. Had that been the case the boat would have sunk at her moorings."

"No doubt."

"Therefore we must assume that whoever took the boat out that night drove in the planking and opened the sea-cocks."

"I suppose so."

"You have told us already that the door of the cabin was shut, the port-holes closed, and your wife's remains were on the floor. This was in your statement, and Doctor Phillips', and in Captain Searle's?"

"Yes."

"And now added to this is the information that a spike was driven through the bottom, and the sea-cocks were open. Does not this strike you, Mr. de Winter, as being very strange?"

"Certainly."

"You have no suggestion to make?"

"No, none at all."

"Mr. de Winter, painful as it may be, it is my duty to ask you a very personal question."

"Yes."

"Were relations between you and the late Mrs. de Winter perfectly happy?"

They had to come of course, those black spots in front of my eyes, dancing, flickering, stabbing the hazy air, and it was hot, so hot, with all those people, all those faces, and no open window; the door, from being near to me, was farther away than I had thought, and all the time the ground coming up to meet me.

And then, out of the queer mist around me, Maxim's voice, clear and strong, "Will someone take my wife outside? She is going to faint."

CHAPTER TWENTY-THREE

I WAS SITTING in the little room again. The room like a waiting-room at the station. The policeman was there, bending over me, giving me a glass of water, and someone's hand was on my arm, Frank's hand. I sat quite still, the floor, the walls, the figures of Frank and the policeman taking solid shape before me.

"I'm so sorry," I said, "such a stupid thing to do. It was so hot in that room, so very hot."

"It gets very airless in there," said the policeman, "there's been complaints about it often, but nothing's ever done. We've had ladies fainting in there before."

"Are you feeling better, Mrs. de Winter?" said Frank.

"Yes. Yes, much better. I shall be all right again. Don't wait with me."

"I'm going to take you back to Manderley."

"No."

"Yes. Maxim has asked me to."

"No. You ought to stay with him."

"Maxim told me to take you back to Manderley."

He put his arm through mine and helped me to get up. "Can you walk as far as the car or shall I bring it round?"

"I can walk. But I'd much rather stay. I want to wait for Maxim."

"Maxim may be a long time."

Why did he say that? What did he mean? Why didn't he look at me? He took my arm and walked with me along the passage to the door, and so down the steps into the street. Maxim may be a long time. . . .

We did not speak. We came to the little Morris car belonging to Frank. He opened the door, and helped me in. Then he got in himself and started up the engine. We drove away from the cobbled market-place, through the empty town, and out on to the road to Kerrith.

"Why will they be a long time? What are they going to do?"

"They may have to go over the evidence again." Frank looked straight in front of him along the hard white road.

"They've had all the evidence," I said. "There's nothing more anyone can say."

"You never know," said Frank, "the coroner may put his questions in a different way. Tabb has altered the whole business. The coroner will have to approach it now from another angle."

"What angle? How do you mean?"

"You heard the evidence? You heard what Tabb said about the boat? They won't believe in an accident any more."

"It's absurd, Frank, it's ridiculous. They should not listen to Tabb. How can he tell, after all these months, how holes came to be in a boat? What are they trying to prove?"

"I don't know."

"That coroner will go on and on harping at Maxim, making him lose his temper, making him say things he doesn't mean. He will ask question after question, Frank, and Maxim won't stand it, I know he won't stand it."

Frank did not answer. He was driving very fast. For the first time since I had known him he was at a loss for the usual conventional phrase. That meant he was worried, very worried. And usually he was such a slow careful driver, stopping dead at every cross-roads, peering to right and left, blowing his horn at every bend in the road.

"That man was there," I said, "that man who came once to Manderley to see Mrs. Danvers."

"You mean Favell?" said Frank. "Yes, I saw him."

"He was sitting there, with Mrs. Danvers."

"Yes, I know."

"Why was he there? What right had he to go to the inquest?"

"He was her cousin."

"It's not right that he and Mrs. Danvers should sit there, listening to that evidence. I don't trust them, Frank."

"No."

"They might do something; they might make mischief."

Again Frank did not answer. I realised that his loyalty to Maxim was such that he would not let himself be drawn into a discussion, even with me. He did not know how much I knew. Nor could I tell for certainty how much he knew. We were allies, we travelled the same road, but we could not look at one another. We neither of us dared risk a confession. We were turning in now at the lodge gates, and down the long twisting narrow drive to the house. I noticed for the first time how the hydrangeas were coming into bloom, their blue heads thrusting themselves from the green foliage behind. For all their beauty there was something sombre about them, funereal; they were like the wreaths, stiff and artificial, that you see beneath glass cases in a foreign churchyard. There they were, all the way along the drive, on either side of us, blue, monotonous, like spectators lined up in a street to watch us pass.

We came to the house at last and rounded the great sweep before the steps. "Will you be all right now?" said Frank. "You can lie down, can't you?"

"Yes," I said, "yes, perhaps."

"I shall go back to Lanyon," he said, "Maxim may want me."

He did not say anything more. He got quickly back into the car again and drove away. Maxim might want him. Why did he say Maxim might want him? Perhaps the coroner was going to question Frank as well. Ask him about that evening, over twelve months ago, when Maxim had dined with Frank. He would want to know the exact time that Maxim left his house. He would want to know if anybody saw Maxim when he returned to the house. Whether the servants knew that he was there. Whether anybody could prove that Maxim went straight up to bed and undressed. Mrs. Danvers might be questioned. They might ask Mrs. Danvers to give evidence. And Maxim beginning to lose his temper, beginning to go white. . . .

I went into the hall. I went upstairs to my room, and lay down upon my bed, even as Frank had suggested. I put my hands over my eyes. I kept seeing that room and all the faces. The lined, painstaking, aggravating face of the coroner, the gold pince-nez on his nose.

"I don't conduct this enquiry for my own amusement." His slow careful mind, easily offended. What were they all saying now? What was happening? Suppose in a little while Frank came back to Manderley, alone?

I did not know what happened. I did not know what people did. I remembered pictures of men in the papers, leaving places like that, and being taken away. Suppose Maxim was taken away? They would not let me go to him. They would not let me see him. I should have to stay here at Manderley day after day, night after night, waiting, as I was waiting now. People like Colonel Julyan being kind. People saying "You must not be alone. You must come to us." The telephone, the newspapers, the telephone again. "No, Mrs. de Winter can't see anyone. Mrs. de Winter has no story to give the *County Chronicle*." And another day. And another day. Weeks that would be blurred and non-existent. Frank at last taking me to see Maxim. He would look thin, queer, like people in hospital. . . .

Other women had been through this. Women I had read about in papers. They sent letters to the Home Secretary and it was not any good. The Home Secretary always said that justice must take its course. Friends sent petitions too, everybody signed them, but the Home Secretary could never do anything. And the ordinary people who read about it in the papers said why should the fellow get off, he murdered his wife, didn't he? What about the poor, murdered wife? This sentimental business about abolishing the death penalty simply encourages crime. This fellow ought to have thought about that before he killed his wife. It's too late now. He will have to hang for it, like any other murderer. And serve him right too. Let it be a warning to others.

I remember seeing a picture on the back of a paper once, of a little crowd collected outside a prison gate, and just after nine o'clock a policeman came and pinned a notice on the gate for the people to read. The notice said something about the sentence being carried out. "Sentence of death was carried out this morning at nine o'clock. The governor, the prison doctor, and the sheriff of the county were present." Hanging was quick. Hanging did not hurt. It broke your neck at once. No, it did not. Someone said once it did not always work. Someone who had known the governor of a prison. They put that bag over your head, and you stand on the little platform, and then the floor gives way beneath you. It takes exactly three minutes to go from the cell to the moment you are hanged. No, fifty seconds, someone said. No, that's absurd. It could not be fifty seconds. There's a little flight of steps down the side of the shed, down to the pit. The doctor goes down there to look. They die instantly. No, they don't. The body moves for some time, the neck is not always broken. Yes, but even so they don't feel anything. Someone said they did. Someone who had a brother who was a prison doctor said it was not generally known, because it would be such a scandal, but they did not always die at once. Their eyes are open, they stay open for quite a long time.

God, don't let me go on thinking about this. Let me think about something else. About other things. About Mrs. Van Hopper in America. She must be staying with her daughter now. They had that house on Long Island in the summer. I expect they played a lot of bridge. They went to the races. Mrs. Van Hopper was fond of the races. I wonder if she still wears that little yellow hat. It was too small for her. Much too small on that big face. Mrs. Van Hopper sitting about in the garden of that house on Long Island, with novels, and magazines, and papers on her lap. Mrs. Van Hopper putting up her lorgnette and calling to her daughter. "Look at this, Helen. They say

Max de Winter murdered his first wife. I always did think there was something peculiar about him. I warned that fool of a girl she was making a mistake, but she wouldn't listen to me. Well, she's cooked her goose now all right. I suppose they'll make her a big offer to go on the pictures."

Something was touching my hand. It was Jasper. It was Jasper, thrusting his cold damp nose in my hands. He had followed me up from the hall. Why did dogs make one want to cry? There was something so quiet and hopeless about their sympathy. Jasper, knowing something was wrong, as dogs always do. Trunks being packed. Cars being brought to the door. Dogs standing with drooping tails, dejected eyes. Wandering back to their baskets in the hall when the sound of the car dies away. . . .

I must have fallen asleep because I woke suddenly with a start, and heard that first crack of thunder in the air. I sat up. The clock said five. I got up and went to the window. There was not a breath of wind. The leaves hung listless on the trees, waiting. The sky was slatey grey. The jagged lightning split the sky. Another rumble in the distance. No rain fell. I went out into the corridor and listened. I could not hear anything. I went to the head of the stairs. There was no sign of anybody. The hall was dark because of the menace of thunder overhead. I went down and stood on the terrace. There was another burst of thunder. One spot of rain fell on my hand. One spot. No more. It was very dark. I could see the sea beyond the dip in the valley like a black lake. Another spot fell on my hand, and another crack of thunder came. One of the housemaids began shutting the windows in the rooms upstairs. Robert appeared and shut the windows of the drawing-room behind me.

"The gentlemen are not back yet, are they, Robert?" I asked.

"No, Madam, not yet. I thought you were with them, Madam."

"No. No, I've been back some time."

"Will you have tea, Madam?"

"No, no, I'll wait."

"It looks as though the weather was going to break at last, Madam."

"Yes."

No rain fell. Nothing since those two drops on my hand. I went back and sat in the library. At half-past five Robert came into the room.

"The car has just driven up to the door now, Madam," he said.

"Which car?" I said.

"Mr. de Winter's car, Madam," he said.

"Is Mr. de Winter driving it himself?"

"Yes, Madam."

I tried to get up but my legs were things of straw, they would not bear me. I stood leaning against the sofa. My throat was very dry. After a minute Maxim came into the room. He stood just inside the door.

He looked very tired, old. There were lines at the corner of his mouth I had never noticed before.

"It's all over," he said.

I waited. Still I could not speak or move towards him.

"Suicide," he said, "without sufficient evidence to show the state of mind of the deceased. They were all at sea of course, they did not know what they were doing."

I sat down on the sofa. "Suicide," I said, "but the motive? Where was the motive?"

"God knows," he said. "They did not seem to think a motive was necessary. Old Horridge, peering at me, wanting to know if Rebecca had any money troubles. Money troubles, God in heaven."

He went and stood by the window, looking out at the green lawns. "It's going to rain," he said. "Thank God it's going to rain at last."

"What happened?" I said, "what did the coroner say? Why have you been there all this time?"

"He went over and over the same ground again," said Maxim. "Little details about the boat that no one cared about a damn. Were the sea-cocks hard to turn on? Where exactly was the first hole in relation to the second? What was ballast? What effect upon the stability of the boat would the shifting of the ballast have? Could a woman do this unaided? Did the cabin door shut firmly? What pressure of water was necessary to burst open the door? I thought I should go mad. I kept my temper though. Seeing you there, by the door, made me remember what I had to do. If you had not fainted like that, I should never have done it. It brought me up with a jerk. I knew exactly what I was going to say. I faced Horridge all the time, I never took my eyes off his thin, pernickety, little face and those gold-rimmed pince-nez. I shall remember that face of his to my dying day. I'm tired, darling; so tired I can't see, or hear, or feel anything."

He sat down on the window seat. He leant forward, his head in his hands. I went and sat beside him. In a few minutes Frith came in, followed by Robert carrying the table for tea. The solemn ritual went forward as it always did, day after day, the leaves of the table pulled out, the legs adjusted, the laying of the snowy cloth, the putting down of the silver tea-pot and the kettle with the little flame beneath. Scones, sandwiches, three different sorts of cake. Jasper sat close to the table, his tail thumping now and again upon the floor, his eyes fixed expectantly on me. It's funny, I thought, how the routine of life goes on, whatever happens, we do the same things, go through the little performances of eating, sleeping, washing. No crisis can break through the crust of habit. I poured out Maxim's tea, I took it to him on the window seat, gave him his scone, and buttered one for myself.

"Where's Frank?" I asked.

"He had to go and see the vicar. I would have gone too but I wanted to come straight back to you. I kept thinking of you, waiting here, all by yourself, not knowing what was going to happen."

"Why the vicar?" I said.

"Something has to happen this evening," he said. "Something at the church."

I stared at him blankly. Then I understood. They were going to bury Rebecca. They were going to bring Rebecca back from the mortuary.

"It's fixed for six-thirty," he said. "No one knows but Frank, and Colonel

Julyan, and the vicar, and myself. There won't be anyone hanging about. This was arranged yesterday. The verdict doesn't make any difference."

"What time must you go?"

"I'm meeting them there at the church at twenty-five past six."

I did not say anything. I went on drinking my tea. Maxim put his sandwich down untasted. "It's still very hot, isn't it?" he said.

"It's the storm," I said. "It won't break. Only little spots at a time. It's there in the air. It won't break."

"It was thundering when I left Lanyon," he said, "the sky was like ink over my head. Why in the name of God doesn't it rain?"

The birds were hushed in the trees. It was still very dark.

"I wish you did not have to go out again," I said.

He did not answer. He looked tired, so deathly tired.

"We'll talk over things this evening when I get back," he said presently. "We've got so much to do together, haven't we? We've got to begin all over again. I've been the worst sort of husband for you."

"No!" I said. "No!"

"We'll start again, once this thing is behind us. We can do it, you and I. It's not like being alone. The past can't hurt us if we are together. You'll have children too." After a while he glanced at his watch. "It's ten past six," he said, "I shall have to be going. It won't take long, not more than half-an-hour. We've got to go down to the crypt."

I held his hand. "I'll come with you. I shan't mind. Let me come with you."

"No," he said. "No, I don't want you to come."

Then he went out of the room. I heard the sound of the car starting up in the drive. Presently the sound died away, and I knew he had gone.

Robert came to clear away the tea. It was like any other day. The routine was unchanged. I wondered if it would have been so had Maxim not come back from Lanyon. I wondered if Robert would have stood there, that wooden expression on his young sheep's face, brushing the crumbs from the snow-white cloth, picking up the table, carrying it from the room.

It seemed very quiet in the library when he had gone. I began to think of them down at the church, going through that door and down the flight of stairs to the crypt. I had never been there. I had only seen the door. I wondered what a crypt was like, if there were coffins standing there. Maxim's father and mother. I wondered what would happen to the coffin of that other woman who had been put there by mistake. I wondered who she was, poor unclaimed soul, washed up by the wind and tide. Now another coffin would stand there. Rebecca would lie there in the crypt as well. Was the vicar reading the burial service there, with Maxim, and Frank, and Colonel Julyan standing by his side? Ashes to ashes. Dust to dust. It seemed to me that Rebecca had no reality any more. She had crumbled away when they had found her on the cabin floor. It was not Rebecca who was lying in that coffin in the crypt, it was dust. Only dust.

Just after seven the rain began to fall. Gently at first, a light pattering in the trees, and so thin I could not see it. Then louder and faster, a driving torrent falling slantways from the slate sky, like water from a sluice. I left the windows open wide. I stood in front of them and breathed the cold clean air. The rain splashed into my face and on my hands. I could not see beyond the lawns, the falling rain came thick and fast. I heard it sputtering in the gutter-pipes above the window, and splashing on the stones of the terrace. There was no more thunder. The rain smelt of moss and earth and of the black bark of trees.

I did not hear Frith come in at the door. I was standing by the window, watching the rain. I did not see him until he was beside me.

"Excuse me, Madam," he said, "do you know if Mr. de Winter will be long?"

"No," I said, "not very long."

"There's a gentleman to see him, Madam," said Frith, after a moment's hesitation. "I'm not quite sure what I ought to say. He's so very insistent about seeing Mr. de Winter."

"Who is it?" I said. "Is it anyone you know?"

Frith looked uncomfortable. "Yes, Madam," he said, "it's a gentleman who used to come here frequently at one time, when Mrs. de Winter was alive. A gentleman called Mr. Favell."

I knelt on the window seat and shut the window. The rain was coming in on to the cushions. Then I turned round and looked at Frith.

"I think perhaps I had better see Mr. Favell," I said.

"Very good, Madam."

I went and stood over on the rug beside the empty fireplace. It was just possible that I should be able to get rid of Favell before Maxim came back. I did not know what I was going to say to him, but I was not frightened.

In a few moments Frith returned and showed Favell into the library. He looked much the same as before but a little rougher if possible, a little more untidy. He was the sort of man who invariably went hatless, his hair was bleached from the sun of the last days and his skin was deeply tanned. His eyes were rather blood-shot. I wondered if he had been drinking.

"I'm afraid Maxim is not here," I said. "I don't know when he will be back. Wouldn't it be better if you made an appointment to see him at the office in the morning?"

"Waiting doesn't worry me," said Favell, "and I don't think I shall have to wait very long, you know. I had a look in the dining-room as I came along, and I see Max's place is laid for dinner all right."

"Our plans have been changed," I said. "It's quite possible Maxim won't be home at all this evening."

"He's run off has he?" said Favell, with a half-smile I did not like. "I wonder if you really mean it. Of course under the circumstances it's the wisest thing he can do. Gossip is an unpleasant thing to some people. It's more pleasant to avoid it, isn't it?"

"I don't know what you mean," I said.

"Don't you?" he said. "Oh, come, you don't expect me to believe that, do you? Tell me, are you feeling better? Too bad fainting like that at the inquest this afternoon. I would have come and helped you out but I saw you had one knight-errant already. I bet Frank Crawley enjoyed himself. Did you let him drive you home? You wouldn't let me drive you five yards when I offered to."

"What did you want to see Maxim about?" I asked.

Favell leant forward to the table and helped himself to a cigarette. "You don't mind my smoking, I suppose?" he said, "it won't make you sick, will it? One never knows with brides."

He watched me over his lighter. "You've grown up a bit since I saw you last, haven't you?" he said. "I wonder what you have been doing. Leading Frank Crawley up the garden-path?" He blew a cloud of smoke in the air. "I say, do you mind asking old Frith to get me a whisky-and-soda?"

I did not say anything. I went and rang the bell. He sat down on the edge of the sofa, swinging his legs, that half-smile on his lips. Robert answered the bell. "A whisky-and-soda for Mr. Favell," I said.

"Well, Robert?" said Favell, "I haven't seen you for a very long time. Still breaking the hearts of the girls in Kerrith?"

Robert flushed. He glanced at me, horribly embarrassed.

"All right, old chap, I won't give you away. Run along and get me a double whisky, and jump on it."

Robert disappeared. Favell laughed, dropping ash all over the floor.

"I took Robert out once on his half-day," he said. "Rebecca bet me a fiver I wouldn't ask him. I won my fiver all right. Spent one of the funniest evenings of my life. Did I laugh? Oh, boy! Robert on the razzle takes a lot of beating, I tell you. I must say he's got a good eye for a girl. He picked the prettiest of the bunch we saw that night."

Robert came back again with the whisky-and-soda on a tray. He still looked very red, very uncomfortable. Favell watched him with a smile as he poured out his drink, and then he began to laugh, leaning back on the arm of the sofa. He whistled the bar of a song, watching Robert all the while.

"That was the one, wasn't it?" he said, "that was the tune. Do you still like ginger hair, Robert?"

Robert gave him a flat weak smile. He looked miserable. Favell laughed louder still. Robert turned and went out of the room.

"Poor kid," said Favell. "I don't suppose he's been on the loose since. That old ass Frith keeps him on a leading string."

He began drinking his whisky-and-soda, glancing round the room, looking at me every now and again, and smiling.

"I don't think I shall mind very much if Max doesn't get back to dinner," he said. "What say you?"

I did not answer. I stood by the fireplace, my hands behind my back. "You wouldn't waste that place at the dining-room table would you?" he said. He looked at me, smiling still, his head on one side.

"Mr. Favell," I said, "I don't want to be rude, but as a matter of fact I'm very tired. I've had a long and fairly exhausting day. If you can't tell me what you want to see Maxim about it's not much good your sitting here. You had far better do as I suggest, and go round to the estate office in the morning."

He slid off the arm of the sofa and came towards me, his glass in his hand. "No, no," he said. "No, no, don't be a brute. I've had an exhausting day too. Don't run away and leave me. I'm quite harmless, really I am. I suppose Max has been telling tales about me to you?"

I did not answer. "You think I'm the big, bad wolf, don't you?" he said, "but I'm not, you know. I'm a perfectly ordinary, harmless bloke. And I think you are behaving splendidly over all this, perfectly splendidly. I take off my hat to you, I really do." This last speech of his was very slurred and thick. I wished I had never told Frith I would see him.

"You come down here to Manderley," he said, waving his arm vaguely, "you take on all this place, meet hundreds of people you've never seen before, you put up with old Max and his moods, you don't give a fig for anyone, you just go your own way, I call it a damn good effort, and I don't care who hears me say so. A damn good effort." He swayed a little as he stood. He steadied himself, and put the empty glass down on the table. "This business has been a shock to me, you know," he said. "A bloody awful shock. Rebecca was my cousin. I was damn fond of her."

"Yes," I said. "I'm very sorry for you."

"We were brought up together," he went on. "Always tremendous pals. Liked the same things, the same people. Laughed at the same jokes. I suppose I was fonder of Rebecca than anyone else in the world. And she was fond of me. All this has been a bloody shock."

"Yes," I said. "Yes, of course."

"And what is Max going to do about it, that's what I want to know? Does he think he can sit back quietly now that sham inquest is over? Tell me that?" He was not smiling any more. He bent towards me.

"I'm going to see justice is done to Rebecca," he said, his voice growing louder. "Suicide. . . . God Almighty, that doddering old fool of a coroner got the jury to say suicide. You and I know it wasn't suicide, don't we?" He leant closer to me still. "Don't we?" he said slowly.

The door opened and Maxim came into the room, with Frank just behind him. Maxim stood quite still, with the door open, staring at Favell. "What the hell are you doing here?" he said.

Favell turned round, his hands in his pockets. He waited a moment, and then he began to smile. "As a matter of fact, Max, old chap, I came to congratulate you on the inquest this afternoon."

"Do you mind leaving the house?" said Max, "or do you want Crawley and me to chuck you out?"

"Steady a moment, steady a moment," said Favell. He lit another cigarette, and sat down once more on the arm of the sofa.

"You don't want Frith to hear what I'm going to say, do you?" he said. "Well, he will, if you don't shut that door."

Maxim did not move. I saw Frank close the door very quietly.

"Now, listen here, Max," said Favell, "you've come very well out of this affair, haven't you? Better than you ever expected. Oh, yes, I was in the court this afternoon, and I dare say you saw me. I was there from start to finish. I saw your wife faint, at a rather critical moment, and I don't blame her. It was touch and go, then, wasn't it, Max, what way the enquiry would go? And luckily for you it went the way it did. You hadn't squared those thick-headed fellows who were acting jury, had you? It looked damn like it to me."

Maxim made a move towards Favell, but Favell held up his hand.

"Wait a bit, can't you?" he said. "I haven't finished yet. You realise, don't you, Max, old man, that I can make things damned unpleasant for you if I choose? Not only unpleasant, but shall I say dangerous?"

I sat down on the chair beside the fireplace. I held the arms of the chair very tight. Frank came over and stood behind the chair. Still Maxim did not move. He never took his eyes off Favell.

"Oh, yes?" he said, "in what way can you make things dangerous?"

"Look here, Max," said Favell, "I suppose there are no secrets between you and your wife, and from the look of things Crawley there just makes the happy trio. I can speak plainly then, and I will. You all know about Rebecca and me. We were lovers, weren't we? I've never denied it, and I never will. Very well then. Up to the present I believed, like every other fool, that Rebecca was drowned sailing in the bay, and that her body was picked up at Edgecoombe weeks afterwards. It was a shock to me then, a bloody shock. But I said to myself, 'That's the sort of death Rebecca would choose, she'd go out like she lived, fighting.'" He paused, he sat there on the edge of the sofa, looking at all of us in turn. "Then I pick up the evening paper a few days ago and I read that Rebecca's boat had been stumbled on by the local diver and that there was a body in the cabin. I couldn't understand it. Who the hell would Rebecca have as a sailing companion? It didn't make sense. I came down here, and put up at a pub just outside Kerrith. I got in touch with Mrs. Danvers. She told me then that the body in the cabin was Rebecca's. Even so I thought like everyone else that the first body was a mistake and Rebecca had somehow got shut in the cabin when she went to fetch a coat. Well, I attended that inquest to-day, as you know. And everything went smoothly, didn't it, until Tabb gave his evidence? But after that? Well, Max, old man, what have you got to say about those holes in the floorboards, and those sea-cocks turned full on?"

"Do you think," said Maxim slowly, "that after those hours of talk this afternoon I am going into it again—with you? You heard the evidence, and you heard the verdict. It satisfied the coroner, and it must satisfy you."

"Suicide, eh?" said Favell. "Rebecca committing suicide. The sort of thing she would do, wasn't it? Listen, you never knew I had this note, did you? I kept it, because it was the last thing she ever wrote to me. I'll read it to you. I think it will interest you."

He took a piece of paper out of his pocket. I recognised that thin, pointed, slanting hand. "*I tried to ring you from the flat, but could get no answer,*" he read. "*I'm going down to Manderley right away. I shall be at the cottage this evening, and if you get this in time will you get the car and follow me. I'll spend the night at the cottage, and leave the door open for you. I've got something to tell you and I want to see you as soon as possible. Rebecca."*

He put the note back in his pocket. "That's not the sort of note you write when you're going to commit suicide, is it?" he said. "It was waiting for me at my flat when I got back about four in the morning. I had no idea Rebecca was to be in London that day or I should have got in touch with her. It happened, by a vile stroke of fortune, I was on a party that night. When I read the note at four in the morning I decided it was too late to go crashing down on a six-hour run to Manderley. I went to bed, determined to put a call through later in the day. I did. About twelve o'clock. And I heard Rebecca had been drowned!"

He sat there, staring at Maxim. None of us spoke.

"Supposing the coroner this afternoon had read that note, it would have made it a little bit more tricky for you, wouldn't it, Max, old man?" said Favell.

"Well," said Maxim. "Why didn't you get up and give it to him?"

"Steady, old boy, steady. No need to get rattled. I don't want to smash you, Max. God knows you've never been a friend to me, but I don't bear malice about it. All married men with lovely wives are jealous, aren't they? And some of 'em just can't help playing Othello. They're made that way. I don't blame them. I'm sorry for them. I'm a bit of a Socialist in my way, you know, and I can't think why fellows can't share their women instead of killing them. What difference does it make? You can get your fun just the same. A lovely woman isn't like a motor tyre, she doesn't wear out. The more you use her the better she goes. Now, Max. I've laid all my cards on the table. Why can't we come to some agreement? I'm not a rich man. I'm too fond of gambling for that. But what gets me down is never having any capital to fall back upon. Now if I had a settlement of two or three thousand a year for life I could jog along quite comfortably. And I'd never trouble you again. I swear before God I would not."

"I've asked you before to leave the house," said Maxim. "I'm not going to ask you again. There's the door behind me. You can open it yourself."

"Half a minute, Maxim," said Frank, "it's not quite so easy as all that." He turned to Favell. "I see what you're driving at. It happens, very unfortunately, that you could, as you say, twist things round and make it difficult for Maxim. I don't think he sees it as clearly as I do. What is the exact amount you propose Maxim should settle on you?"

I saw Maxim go very white, and a little pulse began to show on his forehead. "Don't interfere with this, Frank," he said, "this is my affair entirely. I'm not going to give way to blackmail."

"I don't suppose your wife wants to be pointed out as Mrs. de Winter, the widow of a murderer, of a fellow who was hanged," said Favell. He laughed, and glanced towards me.

"You think you can frighten me, don't you, Favell?" said Maxim. "Well, you are wrong. I'm not afraid of anything you can do. There is the telephone, in the next room. Shall I ring up Colonel Julyan and ask him to come over? He's the magistrate. He'll be interested in your story." Favell stared at him, and laughed.

"Good bluff," he said, "but it won't work. You wouldn't dare ring up old Julyan. I've got enough evidence to hang you, Max, old man." Maxim walked slowly across the room and passed through to the little room beyond. I heard the click of the telephone.

"Stop him!" I said to Frank. "Stop him, for God's sake."

Frank glanced at my face, he went swiftly towards the door.

I heard Maxim's voice, very cool, very calm. "I want Kerrith 17," he said. Favell was watching the door, his face curiously intense.

"Leave me alone," I heard Maxim say to Frank. And then, two minutes afterwards: "Is that Colonel Julyan speaking? It's de Winter here. Yes. Yes, I know. I wonder if you could possibly come over here at once. Yes, to Manderley. It's rather urgent. I can't explain why on the telephone, but you shall hear everything directly you come. I'm very sorry to have to drag you out. Yes. Thank you very much. Good-bye."

He came back again into the room. "Julyan is coming right away," he said. He crossed over and threw open the windows. It was still raining very hard. He stood there, with his back to us, breathing the cold air.

"Maxim," said Frank quietly. "Maxim."

He did not answer. Favell laughed, and helped himself to another cigarette. "If you want to hang yourself, old fellow, it's all the same to me," he said. He picked up a paper from the table and flung himself down on the sofa, crossed his legs, and began to turn over the pages. Frank hesitated, glancing from me to Maxim. Then he came beside me.

"Can't you do something?" I whispered. "Go out and meet Colonel Julyan, prevent him from coming, say it was all a mistake?" Maxim spoke from the window without turning round.

"Frank is not to leave this room," he said. "I'm going to manage this thing alone. Colonel Julyan will be here in exactly ten minutes."

We none of us said anything. Favell went on reading his paper. There was no sound but the steady falling rain. It fell without a break, steady, straight, and monotonous. I felt helpless, without strength. There was nothing I could do. Nothing that Frank could do. In a book or in a play I would have found a revolver, and we should have shot Favell, hidden his body in a cupboard. There was no revolver. There was no cupboard. We were ordinary people. These things did not happen. I could not go to Maxim now and beg him on my knees to give Favell the money. I had to sit there, with my hands in my lap, watching the rain, watching Maxim with his back turned to me, standing by the window.

It was raining too hard to hear the car. The sound of the rain covered all other sounds. We did not know Colonel Julyan had arrived until the door opened, and Frith showed him into the room.

Maxim swung round from the window. "Good evening," he said. "We meet again. You've made very good time."

"Yes," said Colonel Julyan, "you said it was urgent, so I came at once. Luckily, my man had left the car handy. What an evening."

He glanced at Favell uncertainly, and then came over and shook hands with me, nodding to Frank. "A good thing the rain has come," he said. "It's been hanging about too long. I hope you're feeling better."

I murmured something, I don't know what, and he stood there looking from one to the other of us, rubbing his hands.

"I think you realise," Maxim said, "that I haven't brought you out on an evening like this for a social half-hour before dinner. This is Jack Favell, my late wife's first cousin. I don't know if you have ever met."

Colonel Julyan nodded. "Your face seems familiar. I've probably met you here in the old days."

"Quite," said Maxim. "Go ahead, Favell."

Favell got up from the sofa and chucked the paper back on the table. The ten minutes seemed to have sobered him. He walked quite steadily. He was not smiling any longer. I had the impression that he was not entirely pleased with the turn in the events, and he was ill-prepared for the encounter with Colonel Julyan. He began speaking in a loud, rather domineering voice. "Look here, Colonel Julyan," he said, "there's no sense in beating about the bush. The reason why I'm here is that I'm not satisfied with the verdict given at the inquest this afternoon."

"Oh?" said Colonel Julyan, "isn't that for de Winter to say, not you?"

"No, I don't think it is," said Favell. "I have a right to speak, not only as Rebecca's cousin, but as her prospective husband, had she lived."

Colonel Julyan looked rather taken aback. "Oh," he said. "Oh, I see. That's rather different. Is this true, de Winter?"

Maxim shrugged his shoulders. "It's the first I've heard of it," he said.

Colonel Julyan looked from one to the other doubtfully. "Look here, Favell," he said, "what exactly is your trouble?"

Favell stared at him a moment. I could see he was planning something in his mind, and he was still not sober enough to carry it through. He put his hand slowly in his waistcoat pocket and brought out Rebecca's note. "This was written a few hours before Rebecca was supposed to have set out on that suicidal sail. Here it is. I want you to read it, and say whether you think a woman who wrote that note had made up her mind to kill herself."

Colonel Julyan took a pair of spectacles from a case in his pocket and read the note. Then he handed it back to Favell. "No," he said, "on the face of it, no. But I don't know what the note refers to. Perhaps you do. Or perhaps de Winter does?"

Maxim did not say anything. Favell twisted the piece of paper in his fingers, considering Colonel Julyan all the while. "My cousin made a definite appointment in that note, didn't she?" he said. "She deliberately asked me to drive down to Manderley that night because she had something to tell me. What it actually was I don't suppose we shall ever know, but that's beside the point. She made the appointment, and she was to spend the night in the cottage on purpose to see me alone. The mere fact of her going for a sail never surprised me. It was the sort of thing she did, for an hour or so, after a long day in London. But to plug holes in the cabin and deliberately drown herself, the hysterical, impulsive freak of a neurotic girl—oh, no, Colonel Julyan, by Christ, no!" The colour had flooded into his face, and the last words were shouted. His manner was not helpful to him, and I could see by the thin line of Colonel Julyan's mouth that he had not taken to Favell.

"My dear fellow," he said, "it's not the slightest use your losing your temper with me. I'm not the coroner who conducted the enquiry this afternoon, nor am I a member of the jury who gave the verdict. I'm merely the magistrate of the district. Naturally I want to help you all I can, and de Winter, too. You say you refuse to believe your cousin committed suicide. On the other hand you heard, as we all did, the evidence of the boat-builder. The sea-cocks were open, the holes were there. Very well. Suppose we get to the point. What do you suggest really happened?"

Favell turned his head and looked slowly towards Maxim. He was still twisting the note between his fingers. "Rebecca never opened those sea-cocks, nor split the holes in the planking. Rebecca never committed suicide. You've asked for my opinion, and by God you shall have it. Rebecca was murdered. And if you want to know who the murderer is, why there he stands, by the window there, with that God-damned superior smile on his face. He couldn't even wait, could he, until the year was out, before marrying the first girl he set eyes on? There he is, there's your murderer for you, Mr. Maximilian de Winter. Take a good long look at him. He'd look well hanging, wouldn't he?"

And Favell began to laugh, the laugh of a drunkard, high-pitched, forced and foolish, and all the while twisting Rebecca's note between his fingers.

CHAPTER TWENTY-FOUR

THANK GOD for Favell's laugh. Thank God for his pointing finger, his flushed face, his staring blood-shot eyes. Thank God for the way he stood there swaying on his two feet. Because it made Colonel Julyan antagonistic, it put him on our side. I saw the disgust on his face, the quick movement of his lips. Colonel Julyan did not believe him. Colonel Julyan was on our side.

"The man's drunk," he said quietly. "He doesn't know what he's saying."

"Drunk, am I?" shouted Favell. "Oh, no, my fine friend. You may be a magistrate and a colonel into the bargain, but it won't cut any ice with me. I've got the law on my side for a change, and I'm going to use it. There are other magistrates in this bloody county besides you. Fellows with brains in their heads, who understand the meaning of justice. Not soldiers who got the sack years ago for incompetence and walk about with a string of putty medals on their chest. Max de Winter murdered Rebecca and I'm going to prove it."

"Wait a minute, Mr. Favell," said Colonel Julyan quietly, "you were present at the enquiry this afternoon, weren't you? I remember you now. I saw you sitting there. If you felt so deeply about the injustice of the verdict why didn't you say so then, to the jury, to the coroner himself? Why didn't you produce that letter in court?"

Favell stared at him, and laughed. "Why?" he said, "because I did not choose to, that's why. I preferred to come and tackle de Winter personally."

"That's why I rang you up," said Maxim, coming forward from the window; "we've already heard Favell's accusations. I asked him the same question. Why didn't he tell his suspicions to the coroner? He said he was not a rich man, and that if I cared to settle two or three thousand on him for life he would never worry me again. Frank was here, and my wife. They both heard him. Ask them."

"It's perfectly true, sir," said Frank. "It's blackmail pure and simple."

"Yes, of course," said Colonel Julyan, "the trouble is that blackmail is not very pure, nor is it particularly simple. It can make a lot of unpleasantness for a great many people, even if the blackmailer finds himself in gaol at the end of it. Sometimes innocent people find themselves in gaol as well. We want to avoid that, in this case. I don't know whether you are sufficiently sober, Favell, to answer my questions, and if you keep off irrelevant personalities we may get through with the business quicker. You have just made a serious accusation against de Winter. Have you any proof to back that accusation?"

"Proof?" said Favell. "What the hell do you want with proof? Aren't those holes in the boat proof enough?"

"Certainly not," said Colonel Julyan, "unless you can bring a witness who saw him do it. Where's your witness?"

"Witness be damned," said Favell. "Of course de Winter did it. Who else would kill Rebecca?"

"Kerrith has a large population," said Colonel Julyan. "Why not go from door to door making enquiries? I might have done it myself. You appear to have no more proof against de Winter there than you would have against me."

"Oh, I see," said Favell, "you're going to hold his hand through this. You're going to back de Winter. You won't let him down because you've dined with him, and he's dined with you. He's a big name down here. He's the owner of Manderley. You poor bloody little snob."

"Take care, Favell, take care."

"You think you can get the better of me, don't you? You think I've got no case to bring to a court of law. I'll get my proof for you all right. I tell you de Winter killed Rebecca because of me. He knew I was her lover, he was jealous, madly jealous. He knew she was waiting for me at the cottage on the beach, and he went down that night and killed her. Then he put her body in the boat and sank her."

"Quite a clever story, Favell, in its way, but I repeat again you have no proof. Produce your witness who saw it happen and I might begin to take you seriously. I know that cottage on the beach. A sort of picnic place, isn't it? Mrs. de Winter used to keep the gear there for the boat. It would help your story if you could turn it into a bungalow with fifty replicas alongside of it. There would be a chance then that one of the inhabitants might have seen the whole affair."

"Hold on," said Favell slowly, "hold on. . . . There is a chance de Winter might have been seen that night. Quite a good chance too. It's worth finding out. What would you say if I did produce a witness?"

Colonel Julyan shrugged his shoulders. I saw Frank glance enquiringly at Maxim. Maxim did not say anything. He was watching Favell. I suddenly knew what Favell meant. I knew who he was talking about. And in a flash of fear and horror I knew that he was right. There had been a witness that night. Little sentences came back to me. Words I had not understood, phrases I believed to be the fragments of a poor idiot's mind. "She's down there, isn't she? She won't come back again." "I didn't tell no one." "They'll find her there, won't they? The fishes have eaten her, haven't they?" "She'll not come back no more." Ben knew. Ben had seen. Ben, with his queer crazed brain, had been a witness all the time. He had been hiding in the woods that night. He had seen Maxim take the boat from the moorings, and pull back in the dinghy, alone. I knew all the colour was draining away from my face. I leant back against the cushion of the chair.

"There's a local half-wit who spends his time on the beach," said Favell. "He was always hanging about, when I used to come down and meet Rebecca. I've often seen him. He used to sleep in the woods, or on the beach, when the nights were hot. The fellow's cracked, he would never have come forward on his own. But I could make him talk, if he did see anything that night. And there's a bloody big chance he did."

"Who is this? What's he talking about?" said Colonel Julyan.

"He must mean Ben," said Frank, with another glance at Maxim. "He's the son of one of our tenants. But the man's not responsible for what he says or does. He's been an idiot since birth."

"What the hell does that matter?" said Favell. "He's got eyes, hasn't he? He knows what he sees. He's only got to answer yes or no. You're getting windy now, aren't you? Not so mighty confident?"

"Can we get hold of this fellow and question him?" asked Colonel Julyan.

"Of course," said Maxim. "Tell Robert to cut down to his mother's cottage, Frank, and bring him back."

Frank hesitated. I saw him glance at me out of the tail of his eye.

"Go on, for God's sake," said Maxim. "We want to end this thing, don't we?" Frank went out of the room. I began to feel the old nagging pain beneath my heart.

In a few minutes Frank came back again into the room.

"Robert's taken my car," he said. "If Ben is at home he won't be more than ten minutes."

"The rain will keep him at home all right," said Favell, "he'll be there. And I think you will find I shall be able to make him talk." He laughed, and looked at Maxim. His face was still very flushed. Excitement had made him sweat; there were beads of perspiration on his forehead. I noticed how his neck bulged over the back of his collar, and how low his ears were set on his head. Those florid good looks would not last him very long. Already he was out of condition, puffy. He helped himself to another cigarette. "You're like a little trades union here at Manderley, aren't you?" he said; "no one going to give anyone else away. Even the local magistrate is on the same racket. We must exempt the bride of course. A wife doesn't give evidence against her husband. Crawley of course has been squared. He knows he would lose his job if he told the truth. And if I guess rightly there's a spice of malice in his soul towards me too. You didn't have much success with Rebecca, did you, Crawley? That garden-path wasn't quite long enough, eh? It's a bit easier this time, isn't it? The bride will be grateful for your fraternal arm every time she faints. When she hears the judge sentence her husband to death that arm of yours will come in very handy."

It happened very quickly. Too quick for me to see how Maxim did it. But I saw Favell stagger and fall against the arm of the sofa, and down on to the floor. And Maxim was standing just beside him. I felt rather sick. There was something degrading in the fact that Maxim had hit Favell. I wished I had not known. I wished I had not been there to see. Colonel Julyan did not say anything. He looked very grim. He turned his back on them and came and stood beside me.

"I think you had better go upstairs," he said quietly.

I shook my head. "No," I whispered. "No."

"That fellow is in a state capable of saying anything," he said. "What you have just seen was not very attractive, was it? Your husband was right of course, but it's a pity you saw it."

I did not answer. I was watching Favell who was getting slowly to his feet. He sat down heavily on the sofa and put his handkerchief to his face.

"Get me a drink," he said, "get me a drink."

Maxim looked at Frank. Frank went out of the room. None of us spoke. In a moment Frank came back with the whisky-and-soda on a tray. He mixed some in a glass and gave it to Favell. Favell drank it greedily, like an animal. There was something sensual and horrible the way he put his mouth to the glass. His lips folded upon the glass in a peculiar way. There was a dark red patch on his jaw where Maxim had hit him. Maxim had turned his back on him again and had returned to the window. I glanced at Colonel Julyan and saw that he was looking at Maxim. His gaze was curious, intent. My heart began beating very quickly. Why did Colonel Julyan look at Maxim in that way?

Did it mean that he was beginning to wonder, to suspect?

Maxim did not see. He was watching the rain. It fell straight and steady as before. The sound filled the room. Favell finished his whisky-and-soda and put the glass back on the table beside the sofa. He was breathing heavily. He did not look at any of us. He was staring straight in front of him at the floor.

The telephone began ringing in the little room. It struck a shrill, discordant note. Frank went to answer it.

He came back at once and looked at Colonel Julyan. "It's your daughter," he said; "they want to know if they are to keep dinner back."

Colonel Julyan waved his hand impatiently. "Tell them to start," he said, "tell them I don't know when I shall be back." He glanced at his watch. "Fancy ringing up," he muttered, "what a moment to choose."

Frank went back into the little room to give the message. I thought of the daughter at the other end of the telephone. It would be the one who played golf. I could imagine her calling to her sister, "Dad says we're to start. What on earth can he be doing? The steak will be like leather." Their little household disorganised because of us. Their evening routine upset. All these foolish inconsequent threads hanging upon one another, because Maxim had killed Rebecca. I looked at Frank. His face was pale and set.

"I heard Robert coming back with the car," he said to Colonel Julyan. "The window in there looks on to the drive."

He went out of the library to the hall. Favell had lifted his head when he spoke. Then he got to his feet once more and stood looking towards the door. There was a queer, ugly smile on his face.

The door opened, and Frank came in. He turned and spoke to someone in the hall outside.

"All right, Ben," he said quietly, "Mr. de Winter wants to give you some cigarettes. There's nothing to be frightened of."

Ben stepped awkwardly into the room. He had his sou'wester in his hands. He looked odd and naked without his hat. I realised for the first time that his head was shaved all over, and he had no hair. He looked different, dreadful.

The light seemed to daze him. He glanced foolishly round the room, blinking his small eyes. He caught sight of me, and I gave him a weak, rather tremulous smile. I don't know if he recognised me or not. He just blinked his eyes. Then Favell walked slowly towards him and stood in front of him.

"Hullo," he said, "how's life treated you since we last met?"

Ben stared at him. There was no recognition on his face. He did not answer.

"Well?" said Favell, "you know who I am, don't you?"

Ben went on twisting his sou'wester, "Eh?" he said.

"Have a cigarette," said Favell, handing him the box. Ben glanced at Maxim and Frank.

"All right," said Maxim, "take as many as you like."

Ben took four and stuck two behind each ear. Then he stood twisting his cap again.

"You know who I am, don't you?" repeated Favell.

Still Ben did not answer. Colonel Julyan walked across to him. "You shall go home in a few moments, Ben," he said. "No one is going to hurt you. We just want you to answer one or two questions. You know Mr. Favell, don't you?"

This time Ben shook his head. "I never seen 'un," he said.

"Don't be a bloody fool," said Favell roughly; "you know you've seen me.

You've seen me go to the cottage on the beach, Mrs. de Winter's cottage. You've seen me there, haven't you?"

"No," said Ben. "I never seen no one."

"You damned half-witted liar," said Favell, "are you going to stand there and say you never saw me, last year, walk through those woods with Mrs. de Winter, and go into the cottage? Didn't we catch you once, peering at us from the window?"

"Eh?" said Ben.

"A convincing witness," said Colonel Julyan sarcastically.

Favell swung round on him. "It's a put-up job," he said. "Someone has got at this idiot and bribed him too. I tell you he's seen me scores of times. Here. Will this make you remember?" He fumbled in his hip-pocket and brought out a note-case. He flourished a pound note in front of Ben. "Now do you remember me?" he said.

Ben shook his head. "I never seen 'un," he said, and then he took hold of Frank's arm. "Has he come here to take me to the asylum?" he said.

"No," said Frank. "No, of course not, Ben."

"I don't want to go to the asylum," said Ben. "They'm cruel to folk in there. I want to stay home. I done nothing."

"That's all right, Ben," said Colonel Julyan. "No one's going to put you in the asylum. Are you quite sure you've never seen this man before?"

"No," said Ben, "I've never seen 'un."

"You remember Mrs. de Winter, don't you?" said Colonel Julyan.

Ben glanced doubtfully towards me.

"No," said Colonel Julyan gently, "not this lady. The other lady, who used to go to the cottage."

"Eh?" said Ben.

"You remember the lady who had the boat?"

Ben blinked his eyes. "She's gone," he said.

"Yes, we know that," said Colonel Julyan. "She used to sail the boat, didn't she? Were you on the beach when she sailed the boat the last time? One evening, over twelve months ago. When she didn't come back again?"

Ben twisted his sou'wester. He glanced at Frank, and then at Maxim. "Eh?" he said.

"You were there, weren't you?" said Favell, leaning forward. "You saw Mrs. de Winter come down to the cottage, and presently you saw Mr. de Winter too. He went into the cottage after her. What happened then? Go on. What happened?"

Ben shrank back against the wall. "I seen nothing," he said. "I want to stay home. I'm not going to the asylum. I never seen you. Never before. I never seen you and she in the woods." He began to blubber like a child.

"You crazy little rat," said Favell slowly, "you bloody crazy little rat."

Ben was wiping his eyes with the sleeve of his coat.

"Your witness does not seem to have helped you," said Colonel Julyan. "The performance has been rather a waste of time, hasn't it? Do you want to ask him anything else?"

"It's a plot," shouted Favell. "A plot against me. You're all in it, every one of you. Someone's paid this half-wit, I tell you. Paid him to tell his string of dirty lies."

"I think Ben might be allowed to go home," said Colonel Julyan.

"All right, Ben," said Maxim. "Robert shall take you back. And no one will put you in the asylum, don't be afraid. Tell Robert to find him something in the kitchen," he added to Frank. "Some cold meat, whatever he fancies."

"Payment for services rendered, eh?" said Favell. "He's done a good day's work for you, Max, hasn't he?"

Frank took Ben out of the room. Colonel Julyan glanced at Maxim. "The fellow appeared to be scared stiff," he said, "he was shaking like a leaf. I was watching him. He's never been ill-treated, has he?"

"No," said Maxim, "he's perfectly harmless, and I've always let him have the run of the place."

"He's been frightened at some time," said Colonel Julyan. "He was showing the whites of his eyes, just like a dog does, when you're going to whip him."

"Well, why didn't you?" said Favell, "he'd have remembered me all right if you'd whipped him. Oh, no, he's going to be given a good supper for his work to-night. Ben's not going to be whipped."

"He has not helped your case, has he?" said Colonel Julyan quietly, "we're still where we are. You can't produce one shred of evidence against de Winter and you know it. The very motive you gave won't stand the test. In a court of law, Favell, you wouldn't have a leg to stand on. You say you were Mrs. de Winter's prospective husband, and that you held clandestine meetings with her in that cottage on the beach. Even the poor idiot we have just had in this room swears he never saw you. You can't even prove your own story, can you?"

"Can't I?" said Favell. I saw him smile. He came across to the fireplace and rang the bell.

"What are you doing?" said Colonel Julyan.

"Wait a moment and you'll see," said Favell.

I guessed already what was going to happen. Frith answered the bell.

"Ask Mrs. Danvers to come here," said Favell.

Frith glanced at Maxim. Maxim nodded shortly.

Frith went out of the room. "Isn't Mrs. Danvers the housekeeper?" said Colonel Julyan.

"She was also Rebecca's personal friend," said Favell. "She was with her for years before she married, and practically brought her up. You are going to find Danny a very different sort of witness to Ben."

Frank came back into the room. "Packed Ben off to bed?" said Favell. "Given him his supper and told him he was a good boy? This time it won't be quite so easy for the trades union."

"Mrs. Danvers is coming down," said Colonel Julyan. "Favell seems to think he will get something out of her."

Frank glanced quickly at Maxim. Colonel Julyan saw the glance. I saw his lips tighten. I did not like it. No, I did not like it. I began biting my nails.

We all waited, watching the door. And Mrs. Danvers came into the room. Perhaps it was because I had generally seen her alone, and beside me she had seemed tall and gaunt, but she looked shrunken now in size, more wizened, and I noticed she had to look up to Favell and to Frank and Maxim. She stood by the door, her hands folded in front of her, looking from one to the other of us.

"Good evening, Mrs. Danvers," said Colonel Julyan.

"Good evening, sir," she said.

Her voice was that old, dead, mechanical one I had heard so often.

"First of all, Mrs. Danvers, I want to ask you a question," said Colonel Julyan, "and the question is this. Were you aware of the relationship between the late Mrs. de Winter and Mr. Favell here?"

"They were first cousins," said Mrs. Danvers.

"I was not referring to blood-relationship, Mrs. Danvers," said Colonel Julyan. "I mean something closer than that."

"I'm afraid I don't understand, sir," said Mrs. Danvers.

"Oh, come off it, Danny," said Favell, "you know damn well what he's driving at. I've told Colonel Julyan already, but he doesn't seem to believe me. Rebecca and I had lived together off and on for years, hadn't we? She was in love with me, wasn't she?"

To my surprise Mrs. Danvers considered him a moment without speaking, and there was something of scorn in the glance she gave him.

"She was not," she said.

"Listen here, you old fool . . ." began Favell, but Mrs. Danvers cut him short.

"She was not in love with you, or with Mr. de Winter. She was not in love with anyone. She despised all men. She was above all that."

Favell flushed angrily. "Listen here. Didn't she come down the path through the woods to meet me, night after night? Didn't you wait up for her? Didn't she spend the week-ends with me in London?"

"Well," said Mrs. Danvers, with sudden passion, "and what if she did? She had a right to amuse herself, didn't she? Love-making was a game with her, only a game. She told me so. She did it because it made her laugh. It made her laugh, I tell you. She laughed at you like she did at the rest. I've known her come back and sit upstairs on her bed and rock with laughter at the lot of you."

There was something horrible in the sudden torrent of words, something horrible and unexpected. It revolted me, even though I knew. Maxim had gone very white. Favell stared at her blankly, as though he had not understood. Colonel Julyan tugged at his small moustache. No one said anything for a few minutes. And there was no sound but that inevitable falling rain. Then Mrs. Danvers began to cry. She cried like she had done that morning in the bedroom. I could not look at her. I had to turn away. No one said anything. There were just the two sounds in the room, the falling rain and

Mrs. Danvers crying. It made me want to scream. I wanted to run out of the room and scream and scream.

No one moved towards her, to say anything, or to help her. She went on crying. Then at last, it seemed eternity, she began to control herself. Little by little the crying ceased. She stood quite still, her face working, her hands clutching the black stuff of her frock. At last she was silent again. Then Colonel Julyan spoke, quietly, slowly.

"Mrs. Danvers," he said, "can you think of any reason, however remote, why Mrs. de Winter should have taken her own life?"

Mrs. Danvers swallowed. She went on clutching at her frock. She shook her head. "No," she said. "No."

"There you see?" Favell said swiftly. "It's impossible. She knows that as well as I do. I've told you already."

"Be quiet, will you?" said Colonel Julyan. "Give Mrs. Danvers time to think. We all of us agree that on the face of it the thing's absurd, out of the question. I'm not disputing the truth or veracity of that note of yours. It's plain for us to see. She wrote you that note sometime during those hours she spent in London. There was something she wanted to tell you. It's just possible that if we knew what that something was we might have an answer to the whole appalling problem. Let Mrs. Danvers read the note. She may be able to throw light on it." Favell shrugged his shoulders. He felt in his pocket for the note and threw it on the floor at Mrs. Danvers' feet. She stooped and picked it up. We watched her lips move as she read the words. She read it twice. Then she shook her head. "It's no use," she said. "I don't know what she meant. If there was something important she had to tell Mr. Jack she would have told me first."

"You never saw her that night?"

"No, I was out. I was spending the afternoon and evening in Kerrith. I shall never forgive myself for that. Never till my dying day."

"Then you know of nothing on her mind, you can't suggest a solution, Mrs. Danvers? Those words '*I have something to tell you,*' do not convey anything to you at all?"

"No," she answered. "No, sir, nothing at all."

"Does anybody know how she spent that day in London?"

Nobody answered. Maxim shook his head. Favell swore under his breath. "Look here, she left that note at my flat at three in the afternoon," he said. "The porter saw her. She must have driven down here straight after that, and gone like the wind too."

"Mrs. de Winter had a hair appointment from twelve until one-thirty," said Mrs. Danvers. "I remember that, because I had to telephone through to London from here earlier in the week and book it for her. I remember doing it. Twelve to one-thirty. She always lunched at her club after a hair appointment so that she could leave the pins in her hair. It's almost certain she lunched there that day."

"Say it took her half-an-hour to have lunch, what was she doing from two until three? We ought to verify that," said Colonel Julyan.

"Oh, Christ Jesus, who the hell cares what she was doing?" shouted Favell. "She didn't kill herself, that's the only bloody thing that matters, isn't it?"

"I've got her engagement diary locked in my room," said Mrs. Danvers slowly. "I kept all those things. Mr. de Winter never asked me for them. It's just possible she may have noted down her appointments for that day. She was methodical in that way. She used to put everything down and then tick the items off with a cross. If you think it would be helpful I'll go and fetch the diary."

"Well, de Winter?" said Colonel Julyan, "what do you say? Do you mind us seeing this diary?"

"Of course not," said Maxim. "Why on earth should I?"

Once again I saw Colonel Julyan give him that swift, curious glance. And this time Frank noticed it. I saw Frank look at Maxim too. And then back again to me. This time it was I who got up and went towards the window. It seemed to me that it was no longer raining quite so hard. The fury was spent. The rain that was falling now had a quieter, softer note. The grey light of evening had come into the sky. The lawns were dark and drenched with the heavy rain, and the trees had a shrouded humped appearance. I could hear the housemaid overhead drawing the curtains for the night, shutting down the windows that had not been closed already. The little routine of the day going on inevitably as it had always done. The curtains drawn, shoes taken down to be cleaned, the towel laid out on the chair in the bathroom and the water run for my bath. Beds turned down, slippers put beneath a chair. And here were we in the library, none of us speaking, knowing in our hearts that Maxim was standing trial here for his life.

I turned round when I heard the soft closing of the door. It was Mrs. Danvers. She had come back again with the diary in her hand.

"I was right," she said quietly. "She had marked down the engagements as I said she would. Here they are on the date she died."

She opened the diary, a small, red leather book. She gave it to Colonel Julyan. Once more he brought his spectacles from his case. There was a long pause while he glanced down the page. It seemed to me then that there was something about that particular moment, while he looked at the page of the diary, and we stood waiting, that frightened me more than anything that had happened that evening.

I dug my nails in my hands. I could not look at Maxim. Surely Colonel Julyan must hear my heart beating and thumping in my breast?

"Ah!" he said. His finger was in the middle of the page. Something is going to happen, I thought, something terrible is going to happen. "Yes," he said, "yes, here it is. Hair at twelve, as Mrs. Danvers said. And a cross beside it. She kept her appointment then. Lunch at the club, and a cross beside that. What have we here, though? Baker, two o'clock. Who was Baker?" He looked at Maxim. Maxim shook his head. Then at Mrs. Danvers.

"Baker?" repeated Mrs. Danvers. "She knew no one called Baker. I've never heard the name before."

"Well here it is," said Colonel Julyan, handing her the diary. "You can see for yourself. Baker. And she's put a great cross beside it as though she wanted to break the pencil. She evidently saw this Baker whoever he may have been."

Mrs. Danvers was staring at the name written in the diary, and the black cross beside it. "Baker," she said. "Baker."

"I believe if we knew who Baker was we'd be getting to the bottom of the whole business," said Colonel Julyan. "She wasn't in the hands of money-lenders, was she?"

Mrs. Danvers looked at him with scorn. "Mrs. de Winter?" she said.

"Well, blackmailers perhaps?" said Colonel Julyan, with a glance at Favell.

Mrs. Danvers shook her head. "Baker," she repeated. "Baker."

"She had no enemy, no one who had ever threatened her, no one she was afraid of?"

"Mrs. de Winter afraid?" said Mrs. Danvers. "She was afraid of nothing and no one. There was only one thing ever worried her, and that was the idea of getting old, of illness, of dying in her bed. She has said to me a score of times, 'When I go, Danny, I want to go quickly, like the snuffing out of a candle.' That used to be the only thing that consoled me, after she died. They say drowning is painless, don't they?"

She looked searchingly at Colonel Julyan. He did not answer. He hesitated, tugging at his moustache. I saw him throw another glance at Maxim.

"What the hell's the use of all this?" said Favell, coming forward. "We're streaking away from the point the whole bloody time. Who cares about this Baker fellow? What's he got to do with it? It was probably some damn merchant who sold stockings, or face-cream. If he had been anyone important Danny here would know him. Rebecca had no secrets from Danny."

But I was watching Mrs. Danvers. She had the book in her hands and was turning the leaves. Suddenly she gave an exclamation.

"There's something here," she said, "right at the back among the telephone numbers. Baker. And there's a number beside it: 0488. But there is no exchange."

"Brilliant Danny," said Favell, "becoming quite a sleuth in your old age, aren't you? But you're just twelve months too late. If you'd done this a year ago there might have been some use in it."

"That's his number all right," said Colonel Julyan, "0488, and the name Baker beside it. Why didn't she put the exchange?"

"Try every exchange in London," jeered Favell. "It will take you through the night but we don't mind. Max doesn't care if his telephone bill is a hundred pounds, do you, Max? You want to play for time and so should I, if I were in your shoes."

"There is a mark beside the number but it might mean anything," said Colonel Julyan, "take a look at it, Mrs. Danvers. Could it possibly be an M?"

Mrs. Danvers took the diary in her hands again. "It might be," she said doubtfully. "It's not like her usual M, but she may have scribbled it in a hurry. Yes, it might be M."

"Mayfair 0488," said Favell, "what a genius, what a brain!"

"Well?" said Maxim, lighting his first cigarette, "something had better be done about it. Frank? Go through and ask the exchange for Mayfair 0488."

The nagging pain was strong beneath my heart. I stood quite still, my hands by my side. Maxim did not look at me.

"Go on, Frank," he said. "What are you waiting for?"

Frank went through to the little room beyond. We waited while he called the exchange. In a moment he was back again. "They're going to ring me," he said quietly. Colonel Julyan clasped his hands behind his back and began walking up and down the room. No one said anything. After about four minutes the telephone rang shrill and insistent, that irritating, monotonous note of a long-distance call. Frank went through to answer it. "Is that Mayfair 0488?" he said. "Can you tell me if anyone of the name of Baker lives there? Oh, I see. I'm so sorry. Yes, I must have got the wrong number. Thank you very much."

The little click as he replaced the receiver. Then he came back into the room. "Someone called Lady Eastleigh lives at Mayfair 0488. It's an address in Grosvenor Street. They've never heard of Baker."

Favell gave a great cackle of laughter. "The butcher, the baker, the candlestick-maker, They all jumped out of a rotten potato," he said. "Carry on, detective Number One, what's the next exchange on the list?"

"Try Museum," said Mrs. Danvers.

Frank glanced at Maxim. "Go ahead," said Maxim.

The farce was repeated all over again. Colonel Julyan repeated his walk up and down the room. Another five minutes went by, and the telephone rang again. Frank went to answer it. He left the door wide open, I could see him lean down to the table where the telephone stood, and bend to the mouth-piece.

"Hullo? Is that Museum 0488? Can you tell me if anyone of the name of Baker lives there? Oh; who is that speaking? A night porter. Yes. Yes, I understand. Not offices. No, no of course. Can you give me the address? Yes, it's rather important." He paused. He called to us over his shoulder. "I think we've got him," he said.

Oh, God, don't let it be true. Don't let Baker be found. Please, God, make Baker be dead. I knew who Baker was. I had known all along. I watched Frank through the door, I watched him lean forward suddenly, reach for a pencil and a piece of paper. "Hullo? Yes, I'm still here. Could you spell it? Thank you. Thank you very much. Good night." He came back into the room, the piece of paper in his hands. Frank who loved Maxim, who did not know that the piece of paper he held was the one shred of evidence that was worth a damn in the whole nightmare of our evening, and that by producing it he could destroy Maxim as well and truly as though he had a dagger in his hand and stabbed him in the back.

"It was the night porter from an address in Bloomsbury," he said. "There are no residents there at all. The place is used during the day as a doctor's consulting rooms. Apparently Baker's given up practice, and left six months ago. But we can get hold of him all right. The night porter gave me his address. I wrote it down on this piece of paper."

CHAPTER TWENTY-FIVE

IT WAS THEN that Maxim looked at me. He looked at me for the first time that evening. And in his eyes I read a message of farewell. It was as though he leant against the side of a ship, and I stood below him on the quay. There would be other people touching his shoulder, and touching mine, but we would not see them. Nor would we speak or call to one another, for the wind and the distance would carry away the sound of our voices. But I should see his eyes and he would see mine before the ship drew away from the side of the quay. Favell, Mrs. Danvers, Colonel Julyan, Frank with the slip of paper in his hands, they were all forgotten at this moment. It was ours, inviolate, a fraction of time suspended between two seconds. And then he turned away and held out his hand to Frank.

"Well done," he said. "What's the address?"

"Somewhere near Barnet, north of London," said Frank, giving him the paper. "But it's not on the telephone. We can't ring him up."

"Satisfactory work, Crawley," said Colonel Julyan, "and from you too, Mrs. Danvers. Can you throw any light on the matter now?"

Mrs. Danvers shook her head. "Mrs. de Winter never needed a doctor. Like all strong people she despised them. We only had Doctor Phillips from Kerrith here once, that time she sprained her wrist. I've never heard her speak of this Doctor Baker, she never mentioned his name to me."

"I tell you the fellow was a face-cream mixer," said Favell. "What the hell does it matter who he was? If there was anything to it Danny would know. I tell you it's some fool fellow who had discovered a new way of bleaching hair or whitening the skin, and Rebecca had probably got the address from her hair-dresser that morning and went along after lunch out of curiosity."

"No," said Frank. "I think you're wrong there. Baker wasn't a quack. The night porter at Museum 0488 told me he was a very well-known woman's specialist."

"H'm," said Colonel Julyan, pulling at his moustache, "there must have been something wrong with her after all. It seems very curious that she did not say a word to anybody, not even to you, Mrs. Danvers."

"She was too thin," said Favell, "I told her about it, but she only laughed. Said it suited her. Banting I suppose, like all these women. Perhaps she went to this chap Baker for a diet sheet."

"Do you think that's possible, Mrs. Danvers?" asked Colonel Julyan.

Mrs. Danvers shook her head slowly. She seemed dazed, bewildered by this sudden news about Baker. "I can't understand it," she said. "I don't know what it means. Baker. A Doctor Baker. Why didn't she tell me? Why did she keep it from me? She told me everything."

"Perhaps she didn't want to worry you," said Colonel Julyan. "No doubt she made an appointment with him, and saw him, and then when she came down that night she was going to have told you all about it."

"And the note to Mr. Jack," said Mrs. Danvers suddenly. "That note to Mr. Jack, '*I have something to tell you. I must see you.*' She was going to tell him too?"

"That's true," said Favell slowly. "We were forgetting the note." Once more he pulled it out of his pocket and read it to us aloud. "'*I've got something to tell you and I want to see you as soon as possible. Rebecca.*'"

"Of course, there's no doubt about it," said Colonel Julyan, turning to Maxim. "I wouldn't mind betting a thousand pounds on it. She was going to tell Favell the result of that interview with this Doctor Baker."

"I believe you're right after all," said Favell. "The note and that appointment seem to hang together. But what the hell was it all about, that's what I want to know? What was the matter with her?"

The truth screamed in their faces and they did not see. They all stood there, staring at one another, and they did not understand. I dared not look at them. I dared not move lest I betray my knowledge. Maxim said nothing. He had gone back to the window and was looking out into the garden that was hushed and dark and still. The rain had ceased at last, but the spots fell from the dripping leaves and from the gutter above the window.

"It ought to be quite easy to verify," said Frank. "Here is the doctor's present address. I can write him a letter and ask him if he remembers an appointment last year with Mrs. de Winter."

"I don't know if he would take any notice of it," said Colonel Julyan, "there is so much of this etiquette in the medical profession. Every case is confidential you know. The only way to get anything out of him would be to get de Winter to see him privately and explain the circumstances. What do you say, de Winter?"

Maxim turned round from the window. "I'm ready to do whatever you care to suggest," he said quietly.

"Anything for time, eh?" said Favell, "a lot can be done in twenty-four hours, can't it? Trains can be caught, ships can sail, aeroplanes can fly?"

I saw Mrs. Danvers look sharply from Favell to Maxim, and I realised then, for the first time, that Mrs. Danvers had not known about Favell's accusation. At last she was beginning to understand. I could tell from the expression on her face. There was doubt written on it, then wonder and hatred mixed, and then conviction. Once again those lean, long hands of hers clutched convulsively at her dress, and she passed her tongue over her lips. She went on staring at Maxim. She never took her eyes away from Maxim. It's too late, I thought, she can't do anything to us now, the harm is done. It does not matter what she says to us now, or what she does. The harm is done. She can't hurt us any more. Maxim did not notice her, or if he did he gave no sign. He was talking to Colonel Julyan.

"What do you suggest?" he said. "Shall I go up in the morning, drive to this address at Barnet? I can wire Baker to expect me."

"He's not going alone," said Favell, with a short laugh. "I have a right to insist on that, haven't I? Send him up with Inspector Welch and I won't object."

If only Mrs. Danvers would take her eyes away from Maxim. Frank had seen her now. He was watching her, puzzled, anxious. I saw him glance once more at the slip of paper in his hands, on which he had written Doctor Baker's address. Then he too glanced at Maxim. I believe then that some faint idea of the truth began to force itself to his conscience, for he went very white and put the paper down on the table.

"I don't think there is any necessity to bring Inspector Welch into the affair—yet," said Colonel Julyan. His voice was different, harsher. I did not like the way he used the word "yet." Why must he use it at all? I did not like it. "If I go with de Winter, and stay with him the whole time, and bring him back, will that satisfy you?" he said.

Favell looked at Maxim, and then at Colonel Julyan. The expression on his face was ugly, calculating, and there was something of triumph too in his light blue eyes. "Yes," he said slowly, "yes, I suppose so. But for safety's sake do you mind if I come with you too?"

"No," said Colonel Julyan, "unfortunately I think you have the right to ask that. But if you do come, I have the right to insist on your being sober."

"You needn't worry about that," said Favell, beginning to smile, "I'll be sober all right. Sober as the judge will be when he sentences Max in three months' time. I rather think this Doctor Baker is going to prove my case, after all."

He looked around at each one of us and began to laugh. I think he too had understood at last the significance of that visit to the doctor.

"Well?" he said, "what time are we going to start in the morning?"

Colonel Julyan looked at Maxim. "How early can you be ready?"

"Any time you say," said Maxim.

"Nine o'clock?"

"Nine o'clock," said Maxim.

"How do we know he won't do a bolt in the night?" said Favell. "He's only got to cut round to the garage and get his car."

"Is my word enough for you?" said Maxim, turning to Colonel Julyan. And for the first time Colonel Julyan hesitated. I saw him glance at Frank. And a flush came over Maxim's face. I saw the little pulse beating on his forehead. "Mrs. Danvers," he said slowly, "when Mrs. de Winter and I go to bed to-night will you come up yourself and lock the door on the outside? And call us yourself, at seven in the morning."

"Yes, sir," said Mrs. Danvers. Still she kept her eyes on him, still her hands clutched at her dress.

"Very well then," said Colonel Julyan brusquely. "I don't think there is anything else we need discuss, to-night. I shall be here sharp at nine in the morning. You will have room for me in your car, de Winter?"

"Yes," said Maxim.

"And Favell will follow us in his?"

"Right on your tail, my dear fellow, right on your tail," said Favell.

Colonel Julyan came up to me and took my hand. "Good night," he said. "You know how I feel for you in all this, there's no need for me to tell you. Get your husband to bed early, if you can. It's going to be a long day." He held my hand a minute, and then he turned away. It was curious how he avoided my eye. He looked at my chin. Frank held the door for him as he went out. Favell leant forward and filled his case with cigarettes from the box on the table.

"I suppose I'm not going to be asked to stop to dinner?" he said.

Nobody answered. He lit one of the cigarettes, and blew a cloud of smoke into the air. "It means a quiet evening at the pub on the high-road then," he said, "and the barmaid has a squint. What a hell of a night I'm going to spend! Never mind, I'm looking forward to to-morrow. Good night, Danny, old lady, don't forget to turn the key on Mr. de Winter, will you?"

He came over to me and held out his hand.

Like a foolish child I put my hands behind my back. He laughed, and bowed.

"It's just too bad, isn't it?" he said. "A nasty man like me coming and spoiling all your fun. Don't worry, it will be a great thrill for you when the yellow Press gets going with your life story, and you see the headlines 'From Monte Carlo to Manderley. Experiences of murderer's girl-bride,' written across the top. Better luck next time."

He strolled across the room to the door, waving his hand to Maxim by the window. "So long, old man," he said, "pleasant dreams. Make the most of your night behind that locked door." He turned and laughed at me, and then he went out of the room. Mrs. Danvers followed him. Maxim and I were alone. He went on standing by the window. He did not come to me. Jasper came trotting in from the hall. He had been shut outside all the evening. He came fussing up to me, biting the edge of my skirt.

"I'm coming with you in the morning," I said to Maxim. "I'm coming up to London with you in the car."

He did not answer for a moment. He went on looking out of the window. Then "Yes," he said, his voice without expression. "Yes, we must go on being together."

Frank came back into the room. He stood in the entrance, his hand on the door. "They've gone," he said, "Favell and Colonel Julyan. I watched them go."

"All right, Frank," said Maxim.

"Is there anything I can do?" said Frank, "anything at all? Wire to anyone, arrange anything? I'll stay up all night if only there's anything I can do. I'll get that wire off to Baker of course."

"Don't worry," said Maxim, "there's nothing for you to do—yet. There may be plenty—after to-morrow. We can go into all that when the time comes. To-night we want to be together. You understand, don't you?"

"Yes," said Frank. "Yes, of course."

He waited a moment, his hand on the door. "Good night," he said.

"Good night," said Maxim.

When he had gone, and shut the door behind him, Maxim came over to me where I was standing by the fireplace. I held out my arms to him and he came to me like a child. I put my arms round him and held him. We did not say anything for a long time. I held him and comforted him as though he were Jasper. As though Jasper had hurt himself in some way and had come to me to take his pain away.

"We can sit together," he said, "driving up in the car."

"Yes," I said.

"Julyan won't mind," he said.

"No," I said.

"We shall have to-morrow night too." he said. "They won't do anything at once, not for twenty-four hours perhaps."

"No," I said.

"They aren't so strict now," he said. "They let one see people. And it all takes such a long time. If I can I shall try and get hold of Hastings. He's the best. Hastings or Birkett. Hastings used to know my father."

"Yes," I said.

"I shall have to tell him the truth," he said. "It makes it easier for them. They know where they are."

"Yes," I said.

The door opened and Frith came into the room. I pushed Maxim away, I stood up straight and conventional, patting my hair into place.

"Will you be changing, Madam, or shall I serve dinner at once?"

"No, Frith, we won't be changing, not to-night," I said.

"Very good, Madam," he said.

He left the door open. Robert came in and began drawing the curtains. He arranged the cushions, straightened the sofa, tidied the books and papers on the table. He took away the whisky-and-soda and the dirty ash-trays. I had seen him do these things as a ritual every evening I had spent at Manderley, but to-night they seemed to take on a special significance, as though the memory of them would last forever and I should say, long after, in some other time, "I remember this moment."

Then Frith came in and told us that dinner was served.

I remember every detail of that evening. I remember the ice-cold consommé in the cups, and the filets of sole, and the hot shoulder of lamb.

I remember the burnt-sugar sweet, the sharp savoury that followed.

We had new candles in the silver candlesticks; they looked white and slim and very tall. The curtains had been drawn here too against the dull grey evening. It seemed strange to be sitting in the dining-room and not look out on to the lawns. It was like the beginning of autumn.

It was while we were drinking our coffee in the library that the telephone rang. This time it was I who answered it. I heard Beatrice speaking at the other end. "Is that you?" she said, "I've been trying to get through all the evening. Twice it was engaged."

"I'm so sorry," I said, "so very sorry."

"We had the evening papers about two hours ago," she said, "and the verdict was a frightful shock to both Giles and myself. What does Maxim say about it?"

"I think it was a shock to everybody," I said.

"But, my dear, the thing is preposterous. Why on earth should Rebecca have committed suicide? The most unlikely person in the world. There must have been a blunder somewhere."

"I don't know," I said.

"What does Maxim say, where is he?" she said.

"People have been here," I said, "Colonel Julyan, and others. Maxim is very tired. We're going up to London to-morrow."

"What on earth for?"

"Something to do with the verdict. I can't very well explain."

"You ought to get it squashed," she said. "It's ridiculous, quite ridiculous. And so bad for Maxim, all this frightful publicity. It's going to reflect on him."

"Yes," I said.

"Surely Colonel Julyan can do something?" she said. "He's a magistrate. What are magistrates for? Old Horridge from Lanyon must have been off his head. What was her motive supposed to be? It's the most idiotic thing I've ever heard in my life. Someone ought to get hold of Tabb. How can he tell whether those holes in the boat were made deliberately or not? Giles said of course it must have been the rocks."

"They seemed to think not," I said.

"If only I could have been there," she said. "I should have insisted on speaking. No one seems to have made any effort. Is Maxim very upset?"

"He's tired," I said, "more tired than anything else."

"I wish I could come up to London and join you," she said, "but I don't see how I can. Roger has a temperature of 103, poor old boy, and the nurse we've got in is a perfect idiot, he loathes her. I can't possibly leave him."

"Of course not," I said. "You mustn't attempt it."

"Whereabouts in London will you be?"

"I don't know," I said. "It's all rather vague."

"Tell Maxim he must try and do something to get that verdict altered. It's so bad for the family. I'm telling everybody here it's absolutely wicked. Rebecca would never have killed herself, she wasn't the type. I've a good mind to write to the coroner myself."

"It's too late," I said. "Much better leave it. It won't do any good."

"The stupidity of it gets my goat," she said. "Giles and I think it much more likely that if those holes weren't done by the rocks they were done deliberately, by some tramp or other. A Communist perhaps. There are heaps of them about. Just the sort of thing a Communist would do."

Maxim called to me from the library. "Can't you get rid of her? What on earth is she talking about?"

"Beatrice," I said desperately, "I'll try and ring you up from London."

"Is it any good my tackling Dick Godolphin?" she said. "He's your M.P.

I know him very well, much better than Maxim does. He was at Oxford with Giles. Ask Maxim whether he would like me to telephone Dick and see if he can do anything to squash the verdict. Ask Maxim what he thinks of this Communist idea."

"It's no use," I said. "It can't do any good. Please, Beatrice, don't try and do anything. It will make it worse, much worse. Rebecca may have had some motive we don't know anything about. And I don't think Communists go ramming holes in boats, what would be the use? Please, Beatrice, leave it alone."

Oh, thank God she had not been with us to-day. Thank God for that at least. Something was buzzing in the telephone. I heard Beatrice shouting, "Hullo, hullo, don't cut us off, exchange," and then there was a click, and silence.

I went back into the library, limp and exhausted. In a few minutes the telephone began ringing again. I did not do anything. I let it ring. I went and sat down at Maxim's feet. It went on ringing. I did not move. Presently it stopped, as though cut suddenly in exasperation. The clock on the mantelpiece struck ten o'clock. Maxim put his arms round me and lifted me against him. We began to kiss one another, feverishly, desperately, like guilty lovers who have not kissed before.

CHAPTER TWENTY-SIX

WHEN I AWOKE the next morning, just after six o'clock, and got up and went to the window there was a foggy dew upon the grass like frost, and the trees were shrouded in a white mist. There was a chill in the air and a little, fresh wind, and the cold, quiet smell of autumn.

As I knelt by the window looking down on to the rose-garden where the flowers themselves drooped upon their stalks, the petals brown and dragging after last night's rain, the happenings of the day before seemed remote and unreal. Here at Manderley a new day was starting, the things of the garden were not concerned with our troubles. A blackbird ran across the rose-garden to the lawns in swift, short rushes, stopping now and again to stab at the earth with his yellow beak. A thrush, too, went about his business, and two stout, little wagtails, following one another, and a little cluster of twittering sparrows. A gull poised himself high in the air, silent and alone, and then spread his wings wide and swooped beyond the lawns to the woods and the Happy Valley. These things continued, our worries and anxieties had no power to alter them. Soon the gardeners would be astir, brushing the first leaves from the lawns and the paths, raking the gravel in the drive. Pails would clank in the courtyard behind the house, the hose would be turned on the car, the little scullery maid would begin to chatter through the open door to the men in the yard. There would be the crisp, hot smell of bacon.

The housemaids would open up the house, throw wide the windows, draw back the curtains.

The dogs would crawl from their baskets, yawn and stretch themselves, wander out on to the terrace and blink at the first struggles of the pale sun coming through the mist. Robert would lay the table for breakfast, bring in those piping scones, the clutch of eggs, the glass dishes of honey, jam, and marmalade, the bowl of peaches, the cluster of purple grapes with the bloom upon them still, hot from the greenhouses.

Maids sweeping in the morning-room, the drawing-room, the fresh clean air pouring into the long open windows. Smoke curling from the chimneys, and little by little the autumn mist fading away and the trees and the banks and the woods taking shape, the glimmer of the sea showing with the sun upon it below the valley, the beacon standing tall and straight upon the headland.

The peace of Manderley. The quietude and the grace. Whoever lived within its walls, whatever trouble there was and strife, however much uneasiness and pain, no matter what tears were shed, what sorrows borne, the peace of Manderley could not be broken or the loveliness destroyed. The flowers that died would bloom again another year, the same birds build their nests, the same trees blossom. That old quiet moss smell would linger in the air, and bees would come, and crickets, the herons build their nests in the deep dark woods. The butterflies would dance their merry jig across the lawns, and spiders spin foggy webs, and small startled rabbits who had no business to come trespassing poke their faces through the crowded shrubs. There would be lilac, and honeysuckle still, and the white magnolia buds unfolding slow and tight beneath the dining-room window. No one would ever hurt Manderley. It would lie always in its hollow like an enchanted thing, guarded by the woods, safe, secure, while the sea broke and ran and came again in the little shingle bays below.

Maxim slept on and I did not wake him. The day ahead of us would be a weary thing and long. High-roads, and telegraph poles, and the monotony of passing traffic, the slow crawl into London. We did not know what we should find at the end of our journey. The future was unknown. Somewhere to the north of London lived a man called Baker who had never heard of us, but he held our future in the hollow of his hand. Soon he too would be waking, stretching, yawning, going about the business of his day. I got up, and went into the bathroom, and began to run my bath. These actions held for me the same significance as Robert and his clearing of the library had the night before. I had done these things before mechanically, but now I was aware as I dropped my sponge into the water, as I spread my towel on the chair from the hot rail, as I lay back and let the water run over my body. Every moment was a precious thing, having in it the essence of finality. When I went back to the bedroom and began to dress I heard a soft footstep come and pause outside the door, and the key turn quietly in the lock. There was silence a moment, and then the footsteps went away. It was Mrs. Danvers.

She had not forgotten. I had heard the same sound the night before, after we had come up from the library. She had not knocked upon the door, she had not made herself known; there was just the sound of footsteps and the turning of the key in the lock. It brought me to reality, and the facing of the immediate future.

I finished dressing, and went and turned on Maxim's bath. Presently Clarice came with our tea. I woke Maxim. He stared at me at first like a puzzled child, and then he held out his arms. We drank our tea. He got up and went to his bath and I began putting things methodically in my suit-case. It might be that we should have to stay in London.

I packed the brushes Maxim had given me, a nightdress, my dressing-gown and slippers, and another dress too and a pair of shoes. My dressing-case looked unfamiliar as I dragged it from the back of a wardrobe. It seemed so long since I had used it, and yet it was only four months ago. It still had the Customs mark upon it they had chalked at Calais. In one of the pockets was a concert ticket from the casino in Monte Carlo. I crumpled it and threw it into the waste-paper basket. It might have belonged to another age, another world. My bedroom began to take on the appearance of all rooms when the owner goes away. The dressing-table was bare without my brushes. There was tissue-paper lying on the floor, and an old label. The beds where we had slept had a terrible emptiness about them. The towels lay crumpled on the bathroom floor. The wardrobe doors gaped open. I put on my hat so that I should not have to come up again, and I took my bag and my gloves and my suit-case. I glanced round the room to see if there was anything I had forgotten. The mist was breaking, the sun was forcing its way through and throwing patterns on the carpet. When I was half-way down the passage I had a curious, inexplicable feeling that I must go back and look in my room again. I went without reason, and stood a moment looking at the gaping wardrobe and the empty bed, and the tray of tea upon the table. I stared at them, impressing them forever on my mind, wondering why they had the power to touch me, to sadden me, as though they were children that did not want me to go away.

Then I turned and went downstairs to breakfast. It was cold in the dining-room, the sun not yet on the windows, and I was grateful for the scalding bitter coffee and heartening bacon. Maxim and I ate in silence. Now and again he glanced at the clock. I heard Robert put the suit-cases in the hall with the rug, and presently there was the sound of the car being brought to the door.

I went out and stood on the terrace. The rain had cleared the air, and the grass smelt fresh and sweet. When the sun was higher it would be a lovely day. I thought how we might have wandered in the valley before lunch, and then sat out afterwards under the chestnut tree with books and papers. I closed my eyes a minute and felt the warmth of the sun on my face and on my hands.

I heard Maxim calling to me from the house. I went back, and Frith helped me into my coat. I heard the sound of another car. It was Frank.

"Colonel Julyan is waiting at the lodge gates," he said. "He did not think it worth while to drive right up to the house."

"No," said Maxim.

"I'll stand by in the office all day and wait for you to telephone," said Frank. "After you've seen Baker you may find you want me, up in London."

"Yes," said Maxim. "Yes, perhaps."

"It's just nine now," said Frank. "You've up to time. It's going to be fine too. You should have a good run."

"Yes."

"I hope you won't get over-tired, Mrs. de Winter," he said to me. "It's going to be a long day for you."

"I shall be all right," I said. I looked at Jasper who was standing by my feet with ears drooping and sad reproachful eyes.

"Take Jasper back with you to the office," I said. "He looks so miserable."

"Yes," he said. "Yes, I will."

"We'd better be off," said Maxim. "Old Julyan will be getting impatient. All right, Frank."

I climbed in the car beside Maxim. Frank slammed the door.

"You will telephone, won't you?" he said.

"Yes, of course," said Maxim.

I looked back at the house. Frith was standing at the top of the steps, and Robert just behind. My eyes filled with tears for no reason. I turned away and groped with my bag on the floor of the car so that nobody should see. Then Maxim started up the car and we swept round and into the drive and the house was hidden.

We stopped at the lodge gates and picked up Colonel Julyan. He got in at the back. He looked doubtful when he saw me.

"It's going to be a long day," he said. "I don't think you should have attempted it. I would have taken care of your husband you know."

"I wanted to come," I said.

He did not say any more about it. He settled himself in the corner. "It's fine, that's one thing," he said.

"Yes," said Maxim.

"That fellow Favell said he would pick us up at the cross-roads. If he's not there don't attempt to wait, we'd do much better without him. I hope the damned fellow has over-slept himself."

When we came to the cross-roads though I saw the long green body of his car, and my heart sank. I had thought he might not be on time. Favell was sitting at the wheel, hatless, a cigarette in his mouth. He grinned when he saw us, and waved us on. I settled down in my seat for the journey ahead, one hand on Maxim's knee. The hours passed, and the miles were covered. I watched the road ahead in a kind of stupor. Colonel Julyan slept at the back from time to time, I turned occasionally and saw his head loll against the cushions, and his mouth open. The green car kept close beside us. Sometimes it shot ahead, sometimes it dropped behind. But we never lost it. At one we stopped for lunch at one of those inevitable old-fashioned hotels in the main street of a county town. Colonel Julyan waded through the whole set lunch, starting with soup and fish, and going on to roast beef and Yorkshire pudding. Maxim and I had cold ham and coffee.

I half expected Favell to wander into the dining-room and join us, but when we came out to the car again I saw his car had been drawn up outside a café on the opposite side of the road. He must have seen us from the window, for three minutes after we had started he was on our tail again.

We came to the suburbs of London about three o'clock. It was then that I began to feel tired, the noise and the traffic blocks started a humming in my head. It was warm in London too. The streets had that worn dusty look of August, and the leaves hung listless on dull trees. Our storm must have been local, there had been no rain here.

People were walking about in cotton frocks and the men were hatless. There was a smell of waste-paper, and orange-peel, and feet, and burnt dried grass. Buses lumbered slowly, and taxis crawled. I felt as though my coat and skirt were sticking to me, and my stockings pricked my skin.

Colonel Julyan sat up and looked out through his window. "They've had no rain here," he said.

"No," said Maxim.

"Looks as though the place needed it, too."

"Yes."

"We haven't succeeded in shaking Favell off. He's still on our tail."

"Yes."

Shopping centres on the outskirts seemed congested. Tired women with crying babies in prams stared into windows, hawkers shouted, small boys hung on to the back of lorries. There were too many people, too much noise. The very air was irritable and exhausted and spent.

The drive through London seemed endless, and by the time we had drawn clear again and were out beyond Hampstead there was a sound in my head like the beating of a drum, and my eyes were burning.

I wondered how tired Maxim was. He was pale, and there were shadows under his eyes, but he did not say anything. Colonel Julyan kept yawning at the back. He opened his mouth very wide and yawned aloud, sighing heavily afterwards. He would do this every few minutes. I felt a senseless stupid irritation come over me, and I did not know how to prevent myself from turning round and screaming to him to stop.

Once we had passed Hampstead he drew out a large-scale map from his coat-pocket and began directing Maxim to Barnet. The way was clear and there were sign-posts to tell us, but he kept pointing out every turn and twist in the road, and if there was any hesitation on Maxim's part Colonel Julyan would turn down the window and call for information from a passerby.

When we came to Barnet itself he made Maxim stop every few minutes. "Can you tell us where a house called Roselands is? It belongs to a Doctor Baker, who's retired, and come to live there lately," and the passerby would stand frowning a moment, obviously at sea, ignorance written plain upon his face.

"Doctor Baker? I don't know a Doctor Baker. There used to be a house called Rose Cottage near the church, but a Mrs. Wilson lives there."

"No, it's Roselands we want, Doctor Baker's house," said Colonel Julyan, and then we would go on and stop again in front of a nurse and a pram. "Can you tell us where Roselands is?"

"I'm sorry. I'm afraid I've only just come to live here."

"You don't know a Doctor Baker?"

"Doctor Davidson. I know Doctor Davidson."

"No, it's Doctor Baker we want."

I glanced up at Maxim. He was looking very tired. His mouth was set hard. Behind us crawled Favell, his green car covered in dust.

It was a postman who pointed out the house in the end. A square house, ivy-covered, with no name on the gate, which we had already passed twice. Mechanically I reached for my bag and dabbed my face with the end of the powder puff. Maxim drew up outside at the side of the road. He did not take the car into the short drive. We sat silently for a few minutes.

"Well, here we are," said Colonel Julyan, "and it's exactly twelve minutes past five. We shall catch them in the middle of their tea. Better wait for a bit."

Maxim lit a cigarette, and then stretched out his hand to me. He did not speak. I heard Colonel Julyan crinkling his map.

"We could have come right across without touching London," he said, "saved us forty minutes I dare say. We made good time the first two hundred miles. It was from Chiswick on we took the time."

An errand-boy passed us whistling on his bicycle. A motor-coach stopped at the corner and two women got out. Somewhere a church clock chimed the quarter. I could see Favell leaning back in his car behind us and smoking a cigarette. I seemed to have no feeling in me at all. I just sat and watched the little things that did not matter. The two women from the bus walk along the road. The errand-boy disappear round the corner. A sparrow hop about in the middle of the road pecking at dirt.

"This fellow Baker can't be much of a gardener," said Colonel Julyan. "Look at those shrubs tumbling over his wall. They ought to have been pruned right back." He folded up the map and put it back in his pocket. "Funny sort of place to choose to retire in," he said. "Close to the main road and overlooked by other houses. Shouldn't care about it myself. I dare say it was quite pretty once before they started building. No doubt there's a good golf-course somewhere handy."

He was silent for a while, then he opened the door and stood out on the road. "Well, de Winter," he said, "what do you think about it?"

"I'm ready," said Maxim.

We got out of the car. Favell strolled up to meet us.

"What were you all waiting for, cold feet?" he said.

Nobody answered him. We walked up the drive to the front door, a strange incongruous little party. I caught sight of a tennis lawn beyond the house, and I heard the thud of balls. A boy's voice shouted "Forty-fifteen, not thirty all. Don't you remember hitting it out, you silly ass?"

"They must have finished tea," said Colonel Julyan.

He hesitated a moment, glancing at Maxim. Then he rang the bell.

It tinkled somewhere in the back premises. There was a long pause. A very young maid opened the door to us. She looked startled at the sight of so many of us.

"Doctor Baker?" said Colonel Julyan.

"Yes, sir, will you come in?"

She opened a door on the left of the hall as we went in. It would be the drawing-room, not used much in the summer. There was a portrait of a very plain dark woman on the wall. I wondered if it was Mrs. Baker. The chintz covers on the chairs and on the sofa were new and shiny. On the mantelpiece were photographs of two schoolboys with round, smiling faces. There was a very large wireless in the corner of the room by the window. Cords trailed from it, and bits of aerial. Favell examined the portrait on the wall. Colonel Julyan went and stood by the empty fireplace. Maxim and I looked out of the window. I could see a deck-chair under a tree, and the back of a woman's head. The tennis court must be round the corner. I could hear the boys shouting to each other. A very old Scotch terrier was scratching himself in the middle of a path. We waited there for about five minutes. It was as though I was living the life of some other person and had come to this house to call for a subscription to a charity. It was unlike anything I had ever known. I had no feeling, no pain.

Then the door opened and a man came into the room. He was medium height, rather long in the face, with a keen chin. His hair was sandy, turning grey. He wore flannels, and a dark blue blazer.

"Forgive me for keeping you waiting," he said, looking a little surprised, as the maid had done, to see so many of us. "I had to run up and wash. I was playing tennis when the bell rang. Won't you sit down?" He turned to me. I sat down in the nearest chair and waited.

"You must think this a very unorthodox invasion, Doctor Baker," said Colonel Julyan, "and I apologise very humbly for disturbing you like this. My name is Julyan. This is Mr. de Winter, Mrs. de Winter, and Mr. Favell. You may have seen Mr. de Winter's name in the papers recently."

"Oh," said Doctor Baker, "yes, yes I suppose I have. Some inquest or other wasn't there? My wife was reading all about it."

"The jury brought in a verdict of suicide," said Favell coming forward, "which I say is absolutely out of the question. Mrs. de Winter was my cousin, I knew her intimately. She would never have done such a thing, and what's more she had no motive. What we want to know is what the devil she came to see you about on the very day she died."

"You had better leave this to Julyan and myself," said Maxim quietly. "Doctor Baker has not the faintest idea what you are driving at."

He turned to the doctor who was standing between them with a line between his brows, and his first polite smile frozen on his lips. "My late wife's cousin is not satisfied with the verdict," said Maxim, "and we've driven up to see you to-day because we found your name, and the telephone number of your old consulting rooms, in my wife's engagement diary. She seems to have made an appointment with you, and kept it, at two o'clock on the last day she ever spent in London. Could you possibly verify this for us?"

Doctor Baker was listening with great interest, but when Maxim had finished he shook his head. "I'm most awfully sorry," he said, "but I think you've made a mistake. I should have remembered the name de Winter. I've never attended a Mrs. de Winter in my life."

Colonel Julyan brought out his note-case and gave him the page he had torn from the engagement diary. "Here it is, written down," he said, "Baker, two o'clock. And a big cross beside it, to show that the appointment was kept. And here is the telephone address. Museum 0488."

Doctor Baker stared at the piece of paper. "That's very odd, very odd indeed. Yes, the number is quite correct as you say."

"Could she have come to see you and given a false name?" said Colonel Julyan.

"Why, yes, that's possible. She may have done that. It's rather unusual of course. I've never encouraged that sort of thing. It doesn't do us any good in the profession if people think they can treat us like that."

"Would you have any record of the visit in your files?" said Colonel Julyan. "I know it's not etiquette to ask, but the circumstances are very unusual. We do feel her appointment with you must have some bearing on the case and her subsequent—suicide."

"Murder," said Favell.

Doctor Baker raised his eyebrows, and looked enquiringly at Maxim. "I'd no idea there was any question of that," he said quietly. "Of course I understand, and I'll do anything in my power to help you. If you will excuse me a few minutes I will go and look up my files. There should be a record of every appointment booked throughout the year, and a description of the case. Please help yourself to cigarettes. It's too early to offer you sherry, I suppose?"

Colonel Julyan and Maxim shook their heads. I thought Favell was going to say something but Doctor Baker had left the room before he had a chance.

"Seems a decent sort of fellow," said Colonel Julyan.

"Why didn't he offer us whisky-and-soda?" said Favell. "Keeps it locked up I suppose. I didn't think much of him. I don't believe he's going to help us now."

Maxim did not say anything. I could hear the sound of the tennis balls from the court. The Scotch terrier was barking. A woman's voice shouted to him to be quiet. The summer holidays. Baker playing with his boys. We had interrupted their routine. A high-pitched, gold clock in a glass case ticked very fast on the mantelpiece. There was a post-card of the Lake of Geneva leaning against it. The Bakers had friends in Switzerland.

Doctor Baker came back into the room with a large book and a file-case in his hands. He carried them over to the table. "I've brought the collection for last year," he said. "I haven't been through them yet since we moved. I only gave up practice six months ago you know." He opened the book and began turning the pages. I watched him fascinated. He would find it of course. It was only a question of moments now, of seconds. "The seventh, eighth, tenth," he murmured, "nothing here. The twelfth did you say? At two o'clock? Ah!"

We none of us moved. We all watched his face.

"I saw a Mrs. Danvers on the twelfth at two o'clock," he said.

"Danny? What on earth . . ." began Favell, but Maxim cut him short.

"She gave a wrong name of course," he said. "That was obvious from the first. Do you remember the visit now, Doctor Baker?"

But Doctor Baker was already searching his files. I saw his fingers delve into the pocket marked with D. He found it almost at once. He glanced down rapidly at his own hand-writing. "Yes," he said slowly. "Yes, Mrs. Danvers. I remember now."

"Tall, slim, dark, very handsome?" said Colonel Julyan quietly.

"Yes," said Doctor Baker. "Yes."

He read through the files, and then replaced them in the case. "Of course," he said, glancing at Maxim, "this is unprofessional you know? We treat patients as though they were in the confessional. But your wife is dead, and I quite understand the circumstances are exceptional. You want to know if I can suggest any motive why your wife should have taken her life? I think I can. The woman who called herself Mrs. Danvers was very seriously ill."

He paused. He looked at every one of us in turn.

"I remember her perfectly well," he said, and he turned back to the files again. "She came to me for the first time a week previously to the date you mentioned. She complained of certain symptoms, and I took some X-rays of her. The second visit was to find out the result of those X-rays. The photographs are not here, but I have the details written down. I remember her standing in my consulting room and holding out her hand for the photographs. 'I want to know the truth,' she said, 'I don't want soft words and a bedside manner. If I'm for it you can tell me right away.'" He paused, he glanced down at the files once again.

I waited, waited. Why couldn't he get done with it and finish and let us go? Why must we sit there, waiting, our eyes upon his face?

"Well," he said, "she asked for the truth, and I let her have it. Some patients are better for it. Shirking the point does them no good. This Mrs. Danvers, or Mrs. de Winter rather, was not the type to accept a lie. You must have known that. She stood it very well. She did not flinch. She said she had suspected it for some time. Then she paid my fee and went out. I never saw her again."

He shut up the box with a snap, and closed the book. "The pain was slight as yet but the growth was deep-rooted," he said, "and in three or four months' time she would have been under morphia. An operation would have been no earthly use at all. I told her that. The thing had got too firm a hold.

There is nothing anyone can do in a case like that, except give morphia, and wait."

No one said a word. The little clock ticked on the mantelpiece, and the boys played tennis in the garden. An aeroplane hummed overhead.

"Outwardly of course she was a perfectly healthy woman," he said, "rather too thin I remember, rather pale, but then that's the fashion nowadays, pity though it is. It's nothing to go upon with a patient. No, the pain would increase week by week, and as I told you, in four or five months' time she would have had to be kept under morphia. The X-rays showed a certain malformation of the uterus, I remember, which meant she could never have had a child, but that was quite apart, it had nothing to do with the disease."

I remember hearing Colonel Julyan speak, saying something about Doctor Baker being very kind to have taken so much trouble. "You have told us all we want to know," he said, "and if we could possibly have a copy of the memoranda in your file it might be very useful."

"Of course," said Doctor Baker. "Of course."

Everyone was standing up. I got up from my chair too. I shook hands with Doctor Baker. We all shook hands with him. We followed him out into the hall. A woman looked out of the room on the other side of the hall and darted back when she saw us. Someone was running a bath upstairs, the water ran loudly. The Scotch terrier came in from the garden and began sniffing at my heels.

"Shall I send the report to you or to Mr. de Winter?" said Doctor Baker.

"We may not need it at all," said Colonel Julyan. "I rather think it won't be necessary. Either de Winter or I will write. Here is my card."

"I'm so glad to have been of use," said Doctor Baker; "it never entered my head for a moment that Mrs. de Winter and Mrs. Danvers could be the same person."

"No, naturally," said Colonel Julyan.

"You'll be returning to London I suppose?"

"Yes. Yes, I imagine so."

"Your best way then is to turn sharp left by that pillar-box, and then right by the church. After that it's a straight road."

"Thank you. Thank you very much."

We came out on to the drive and went towards the cars. Doctor Baker pulled the Scotch terrier inside the house. I heard the door shut. A man with one leg and a barrel-organ began playing Roses in Picardy, at the end of the road.

CHAPTER TWENTY-SEVEN

WE WENT and stood by the car. No one said anything for a few minutes. Colonel Julyan handed round his cigarette case. Favell looked grey, rather shaken. I noticed his hands were trembling as he held the match. The man with the barrel-organ ceased playing for a moment and hobbled towards us, his cap in his hand. Maxim gave him two shillings. Then he went back to the barrel-organ and started another tune. The church clock struck six o'clock. Favell began to speak. His voice was diffident, careless, but his face was still grey. He did not look at any of us, he kept glancing down at his cigarette and turning it over in his fingers. "This cancer business," he said, "does anybody know if it's contagious?"

No one answered him. Colonel Julyan shrugged his shoulders.

"I never had the remotest idea," said Favell jerkily. "She kept it a secret from everyone, even Danny. What a God-damned appalling thing, eh? Not the sort of thing one would ever connect with Rebecca. Do you fellows feel like a drink? I'm all out over this, and I don't mind admitting it. Cancer! Oh, my God!"

He leant up against the side of the car and shaded his eyes with his hands. "Tell that bloody fellow with the barrel-organ to clear out," he said. "I can't stand that God-damned row."

"Wouldn't it be simpler if we went ourselves?" said Maxim. "Can you manage your own car or do you want Julyan to drive it for you?"

"Give me a minute," muttered Favell. "I'll be all right. You don't understand. This thing has been a damned unholy shock to me."

"Pull yourself together, man, for heaven's sake," said Colonel Julyan. "If you want a drink go back to the house and ask Baker. He knows how to treat for shock I dare say. Don't make an exhibition of yourself in the street."

"Oh, you're all right, you're fine," said Favell, standing straight and looking at Colonel Julyan and Maxim. "You've got nothing to worry about any more. Max is on a good wicket now, isn't he? You've got your motive, and Baker will supply it in black and white free of cost, whenever you send the word. You can dine at Manderley once a week on the strength of it and feel proud of yourself. No doubt Max will ask you to be god-father to his first child."

"Shall we get into the car and go?" said Colonel Julyan to Maxim. "We can make our plans going along."

Maxim held open the door of the car, and Colonel Julyan climbed in. I sat down in my seat in the front. Favell still leant against the car and did not move. "I should advise you to get straight back to your flat and go to bed," said Colonel Julyan shortly, "and drive slowly, or you will find yourself in gaol for manslaughter. I may as well warn you now, as I shall not be seeing you again, that as a magistrate I have certain powers that will prove effective if you ever turn up in Kerrith or the district. Blackmail is not much of a profession, Mr. Favell. And we know how to deal with it in our part of the world, strange though it may seem to you."

Favell was watching Maxim. He had lost the grey colour now, and the old unpleasant smile was forming on his lips. "Yes, it's been a stroke of luck for you, Max, hasn't it?" he said slowly; "you think you've won, don't you? The law can get you yet, and so can I, in a different way. . . ."

Maxim switched on the engine. "Have you anything else you want to say?" he said. "Because if you have you had better say it now."

"No," said Favell. "No, I won't keep you. You can go." He stepped back on to the pavement, the smile still on his lips. The car slid forward. As we turned the corner I looked back and saw him standing there, watching us, and he waved his hand and he was laughing.

We drove on for a while in silence. Then Colonel Julyan spoke. "He can't do anything," he said. "That smile and that wave was part of his bluff. They're all alike, those fellows. He hasn't a thread of a case to bring now. Baker's evidence would squash it."

Maxim did not answer. I glanced sideways at his face but it told me nothing. "I always felt the solution would lie in Baker," said Colonel Julyan, "the furtive business of that appointment, and the way she never even told Mrs. Danvers. She had her suspicions you see. She knew something was wrong. A dreadful thing, of course. Very dreadful. Enough to send a young and lovely woman right off her head."

We drove on along the straight main road. Telegraph poles, motor-coaches, open sports cars, little semi-detached villas with new gardens, they flashed past making patterns in my mind I should always remember.

"I suppose you never had any idea of this, de Winter?" said Colonel Julyan.

"No," said Maxim. "No."

"Of course some people have a morbid dread of it," said Colonel Julyan. "Women especially. That must have been the case with your wife. She had courage for every other thing but that. She could not face pain. Well, she was spared that at any rate."

"Yes," said Maxim.

"I don't think it would do any harm if I quietly let it be known down in Kerrith and in the county that a London doctor has supplied us with a motive," said Colonel Julyan. "Just in case there should be any gossip. You never can tell, you know. People are odd, sometimes. If they knew about Mrs. de Winter it might make it a lot easier for you."

"Yes," said Maxim, "yes, I understand."

"It's curious and very irritating," said Colonel Julyan slowly, "how long stories spread in country districts. I never know why they should but unfortunately they do. Not that I anticipate any trouble over this but it's as well to be prepared. People are inclined to say the wildest things if they are given half a chance."

"Yes," said Maxim.

"You and Crawley of course can squash any nonsense in Manderley or the estate, and I can deal with it effectively in Kerrith. I shall say a word to my girl too. She sees a lot of the younger people, who very often are the worst offenders in story-telling. I don't suppose the newspapers will worry you any more, that's one good thing. You'll find they will drop the whole affair in a day or two."

"Yes," said Maxim.

We drove on through the northern suburbs and came once more to Finchley and Hampstead.

"Half-past six," said Colonel Julyan, "what do you propose doing? I've got a sister living in St. John's Wood, and feel inclined to take her unawares and ask for dinner, and then catch the last train from Paddington. I know she doesn't go away for another week. I'm sure she would be delighted to see you both as well."

Maxim hesitated, and glanced at me. "It's very kind of you," he said, "but I think we had better be independent. I must ring up Frank, and one thing and another. I dare say we shall have a quiet meal somewhere and start off again afterwards, spending the night at a pub, on the way. I rather think that's what we shall do."

"Of course," said Colonel Julyan, "I quite understand. Could you throw me out at my sister's? It's one of those turnings off the Avenue Road."

When we came to the house Maxim drew up a little way ahead of the gate. "It's impossible to thank you," he said, "for all you've done to-day. You know what I feel about it without my telling you."

"My dear fellow," said Colonel Julyan, "I've been only too glad. If only we'd known what Baker knew of course there would have been none of this at all. However, never mind about that now. You must put the whole thing behind you as a very unpleasant and unfortunate episode. I'm pretty sure you won't have any more trouble from Favell. If you do, I count on you to tell me at once. I shall know how to deal with him." He climbed out of the car, collecting his coat and his map. "I should feel inclined," he said, not looking directly at us, "to get away for a bit. Take a short holiday. Go abroad perhaps."

We did not say anything. Colonel Julyan was fumbling with his map. "Switzerland is very nice this time of the year," he said. "I remember we went once for the girl's holidays, and thoroughly enjoyed ourselves. The walks are delightful." He hesitated, cleared his throat. "It is just faintly possible certain little difficulties might arise," he said, "not from Favell, but from one or two people in the district. One never knows quite what Tabb has been saying, and repeating, and so on. Absurd of course. But you know the old saying? Out of sight, out of mind. If people aren't there to be talked about the talk dies. It's the way of the world."

He stood a moment, counting his belongings. "I've got everything I think. Map, glasses, stick, coat. Everything complete. Well, good-bye, both of you. Don't get over-tired. It's been a long day."

He turned in at the gate and went up the steps. I saw a woman come to the window and smile and wave her hand. We drove away down the road and turned the corner. I leant back in my seat and closed my eyes. Now that we were alone again and the strain was over, the sensation was one of almost unbearable relief. It was like the bursting of an abscess. Maxim did not speak. I felt his hand cover mine. We drove on through the traffic and I saw none of it. I heard the rumble of the buses, the hooting of taxis, that inevitable, tireless London roar, but I was not part of it. I rested in some other place that was cool and quiet and still. Nothing could touch us any more. We had come through our crisis.

When Maxim stopped the car I opened my eyes and sat up. We were opposite one of those numerous little restaurants in a narrow street in Soho. I looked about me, dazed and stupid.

"You're tired," said Maxim briefly. "Empty and tired and fit for nothing. You'll be better when you've had something to eat. So shall I. We'll go in here and order dinner right away. I can telephone to Frank, too."

We got out of the car. There was no one in the restaurant but the maître d'hôtel and a waiter and a girl behind a desk. It was dark and cool. We went to a table right in the corner. Maxim began ordering the food. "Favell was right about wanting a drink," he said. "I want one too and so do you. You're going to have some brandy."

The maître d'hôtel was fat and smiling. He produced long thin rolls in paper envelopes. They were very hard, very crisp. I began to eat one ravenously. My brandy-and-soda was soft, warming, curiously comforting.

"When we've had dinner we'll drive slowly, very quietly," said Maxim. "It will be cool, too, in the evening. We'll find somewhere on the road we can put up for the night. Then we can get along to Manderley in the morning."

"Yes," I said.

"You didn't want to dine with Julyan's sister and go down by the late train?"

"No."

Maxim finished his drink. His eyes looked large and they were ringed with shadows. They seemed very dark against the pallor of his face.

"How much of the truth," he said, "do you think Julyan guessed?"

I watched him over the rim of my glass. I did not say anything.

"He knew," said Maxim slowly, "of course he knew."

"If he did," I said, "he will never say anything. Never, never."

"No," said Maxim. "No."

He ordered another drink from the maître d'hôtel. We sat silent and peaceful in our dark corner.

"I believe," said Maxim, "that Rebecca lied to me on purpose. The last supreme bluff. She wanted me to kill her. She foresaw the whole thing. That's why she laughed. That's why she stood there laughing when she died."

I did not say anything. I went on drinking my brandy-and-soda. It was all over. It was all settled. It did not matter any more. There was no need for Maxim to look white and troubled.

"It was her last practical joke," said Maxim, "the best of them all. And I'm not sure if she hasn't won, even now."

"What do you mean? How can she have won?" I said.

"I don't know," he said. "I don't know." He swallowed his second drink. Then he got up from the table. "I'm going to ring up Frank," he said.

I sat there in my corner, and presently the waiter brought me my fish. It was lobster. Very hot and good. I had another brandy-and-soda, too. It was pleasant and comfortable sitting there and nothing mattered very much. I smiled at the waiter. I asked for some more bread in French for no reason. It was quiet and happy and friendly in the restaurant. Maxim and I were together. Everything was over. Everything was settled. Rebecca was dead. Rebecca could not hurt us. She had played her last joke as Maxim had said. She could do no more to us now. In ten minutes Maxim came back again.

"Well," I said, my own voice sounding far away, "how was Frank?"

"Frank was all right," said Maxim. "He was at the office, been waiting there for me to telephone him ever since four o'clock. I told him what had happened. He sounded glad, relieved."

"Yes," I said.

"Something rather odd though," said Maxim slowly, a line between his brows. "He thinks Mrs. Danvers has cleared out. She's gone, disappeared. She said nothing to anyone but apparently she'd been packing up all day, stripping her room of things, and the fellow from the station came for her boxes at about four o'clock. Frith telephoned down to Frank about it, and Frank told Frith to ask Mrs. Danvers to come down to him at the office. He waited, and she never came. About ten minutes before I rang up, Frith telephoned to Frank again and said there had been a long-distance call for Mrs. Danvers which he had switched through to her room, and she had answered. This must have been about ten past six. At a quarter-to-seven he knocked on the door and found her room empty. Her bedroom too. They looked for her and could not find her. They think she's gone. She must have gone straight out of the house and through the woods. She never passed the lodge gates."

"Isn't it a good thing?" I said. "It saves us a lot of trouble. We should have had to send her away, anyway. I believe she guessed, too. There was an expression on her face last night. I kept thinking of it, coming up in the car."

"I don't like it," said Maxim. "I don't like it."

"She can't do anything," I argued. "If she's gone, so much the better. It was Favell who telephoned of course. He must have told her about Baker. He would tell her what Colonel Julyan said. Colonel Julyan said if there was any attempt at blackmail we were to tell him. They won't dare do it. They can't. It's too dangerous."

"I'm not thinking of blackmail," said Maxim.

"What else can they do?" I said. "We've got to do what Colonel Julyan said. We've got to forget it. We must not think about it any more. It's all over, darling, it's finished. We ought to go down on our knees and thank God that it's finished."

Maxim did not answer. He was staring in front of him at nothing.

"Your lobster will be cold," I said; "eat it, darling. It will do you good, you want something inside you. You're tired." I was using the words he had used to me. I felt better and stronger. It was I now who was taking care of him. He was tired, pale. I had got over my weakness and fatigue and now he was the one to suffer from reaction. It was just because he was empty, because he was tired. There was nothing to worry about at all. Mrs. Danvers had gone. We should praise God for that, too. Everything had been made so easy for us, so very easy. "Eat up your fish," I said.

It was going to be very different in the future. I was not going to be nervous and shy of the servants any more. With Mrs. Danvers gone I should learn bit by bit to control the house. I would go and interview the cook in the kitchen. They would like me, respect me. Soon it would be as though Mrs. Danvers had never had command. I would learn more about the estate, too. I should ask Frank to explain things to me. I was sure Frank liked me. I liked him, too. I would go into things, and learn how they were managed. What they did at the farm. How the work in the grounds was planned. I might take to gardening myself, and in time have one or two things altered. That little square lawn outside the morning-room window with the statue of the satyr. I did not like it. We would give the satyr away. There were heaps of things that I could do, little by little. People would come and stay and I should not mind. There would be the interest of seeing to their rooms, having flowers and books put, arranging the food. We would have children. Surely we would have children.

"Have you finished?" said Maxim suddenly. "I don't think I want any more. Only coffee. Black, very strong, please, and the bill," he added to the maître d'hôtel.

I wondered why we must go so soon. It was comfortable in the restaurant, and there was nothing to take us away. I liked sitting there, with my head against the sofa back, planning the future idly in a hazy pleasant way. I could have gone on sitting there for a long while.

I followed Maxim out of the restaurant, stumbling a little, and yawning. "Listen," he said, when we were on the pavement, "do you think you could sleep in the car if I wrapped you up with the rug, and tucked you down in the back? There's the cushion there, and my coat as well."

"I thought we were going to put up somewhere for the night?" I said blankly. "One of those hotels one passes on the road."

"I know," he said, "but I have this feeling I must get down tonight. Can't you possibly sleep in the back of the car?"

"Yes," I said doubtfully. "Yes, I suppose so."

"If we start now, it's a quarter-to-eight, we ought to be there by half-past two," he said. "There won't be much traffic on the road."

"You'll be so tired," I said. "So terribly tired."

"No," he shook his head. "I shall be all right. I want to get home. Something's wrong. I know it is. I want to get home."

His face was anxious, strange. He pulled open the door and began arranging the rugs and the cushion at the back of the car.

"What can be wrong?" I said. "It seems so odd to worry now, when everything's over. I can't understand you."

He did not answer. I climbed into the back of the car and lay down with my legs tucked under me. He covered me with the rug. It was very comfortable. Much better than I imagined. I settled the pillow under my head.

"Are you all right?" he said. "Are you sure you don't mind?"

"No," I said smiling. "I'm all right. I shall sleep. I don't want to stay anywhere on the road. It's much better to do this and get home. We'll be at Manderley long before sunrise."

He got in front and switched on the engine. I shut my eyes. The car drew away and I felt the slight jolting of the springs under my body. I pressed my face against the cushion. The motion of the car was rhythmic, steady, and the pulse of my mind beat with it. A hundred images came to me when I closed my eyes, things seen, things known, and things forgotten. They were jumbled together in a senseless pattern. The quill of Mrs. Van Hopper's hat, the hard straight-backed chairs in Frank's dining-room, the wide window in the west wing at Manderley, the salmon-coloured frock of the smiling lady at the fancy dress ball, a peasant-girl in a road near Monte Carlo.

Sometimes I saw Jasper chasing butterflies across the lawns; sometimes I saw Doctor Baker's Scotch terrier scratching his ear beside a deck-chair. There was the postman who had pointed out the house to us to-day, and there was Clarice's mother wiping a chair for me in the back parlour. Ben smiled at me, holding winkles in his hands, and the bishop's wife asked me if I would stay to tea. I could feel the cold comfort of my sheets in my own bed, and the gritty shingle in the cove. I could smell the bracken in the woods, the wet moss, and the dead azalea petals. I fell into a strange broken sleep, waking now and again to the reality of my narrow cramped position and the sight of Maxim's back in front of me. The dusk had turned to darkness. There were the lights of passing cars upon the road. There were villages with drawn curtains and little lights behind them. And I would move, and turn upon my back, and sleep again.

I saw the staircase at Manderley, and Mrs. Danvers standing at the top in her black dress, waiting for me to go to her. As I climbed the stairs she backed under the archway and disappeared. I looked for her and I could not find her. Then her face looked at me through a hollow door and I cried out and she had gone again.

"What's the time?" I called. "What's the time?"

Maxim turned round to me, his face pale and ghostly in the darkness of the car. "It's half-past eleven," he said. "We're over half-way already. Try and sleep again."

"I'm thirsty," I said.

He stopped at the next town. The man at the garage said his wife had not gone to bed and she would make us some tea. We got out of the car and stood inside the garage. I stamped up and down to bring the blood back to my hands and feet. Maxim smoked a cigarette. It was cold. A bitter wind blew in through the open garage door, and rattled the corrugated roof. I shivered, and buttoned up my coat.

"Yes, it's nippy to-night," said the garage man, as he wound the petrol pump. "The weather seemed to break this afternoon. It's the last of the heat-waves for this summer. We shall be thinking of fires soon."

"It was hot in London," I said.

"Was it?" he said. "Well, they always have the extremes up there, don't they? We get the first of the bad weather down here. It will blow hard on the coast before morning."

His wife brought us the tea. It tasted of bitter wood, but it was hot. I drank it greedily, thankfully. Already Maxim was glancing at his watch.

"We ought to be going," he said. "It's ten minutes to twelve." I left the shelter of the garage reluctantly. The cold wind blew in my face. The stars raced across the sky. There were threads of cloud too. "Yes," said the garage man, "summer's over for this year."

We climbed back into the car. I settled myself once more under the rug. The car went on. I shut my eyes. There was the man with the wooden leg winding his barrel-organ, and the tune of Roses in Picardy hummed in my head against the jolting of the car. Frith and Robert carried the tea into the library. The woman at the lodge nodded to me abruptly, and called her child into the house. I saw the model boats in the cottage in the cove, and the feathery dust. I saw the cobwebs stretching from the little masts. I heard the rain upon the roof and the sound of the sea. I wanted to get to the Happy Valley and it was not there. There were woods about me, there was no Happy Valley. Only the dark trees and the young bracken. The owls hooted. The moon was shining in the windows of Manderley. There were nettles in the garden, ten foot, twenty foot high.

"Maxim!" I cried. "Maxim!"

"Yes," he said. "It's all right. I'm here."

"I had a dream," I said. "A dream."

"What was it?" he said.

"I don't know. I don't know."

Back again into the moving unquiet depths. I was writing letters in the morning-room. I was sending out invitations. I wrote them all myself with a thick black pen. But when I looked down to see what I had written it was not my small square hand-writing at all, it was long, and slanting, with curious pointed strokes. I pushed the cards away from the blotter and hid them. I got up and went to the looking-glass. A face stared back at me that was not my own. It was very pale, very lovely, framed in a cloud of dark hair. The eyes narrowed and smiled. The lips parted. The face in the glass stared back at me and laughed. And I saw then that she was sitting on a chair before the dressing-table in her bedroom, and Maxim was brushing her hair. He held her hair in his hands, and as he brushed it he wound it slowly into a thick long rope. It twisted like a snake, and he took hold of it with both hands and smiled at Rebecca and put it round his neck.

"No," I screamed. "No, no. We must go to Switzerland. Colonel Julyan said we must go to Switzerland."

I felt Maxim's hand upon my face. "What is it?" he said. "What's the matter?"

I sat up and pushed my hair away from my face.

"I can't sleep," I said. "It's no use."

"You've been sleeping," he said. "You've slept for two hours. It's quarter-past two. We're four miles the other side of Lanyon."

It was even colder than before. I shuddered in the darkness of the car.

"I'll come beside you," I said. "We shall be back by three."

I climbed over and sat beside him, staring in front of me through the wind-screen. I put my hand on his knee. My teeth were chattering.

"You're cold," he said.

"Yes," I said.

The hills rose in front of us, and dipped, and rose again. It was quite dark. The stars had gone.

"What time did you say it was?" I asked.

"Twenty past two," he said.

"It's funny," I said. "It looks almost as though the dawn was breaking over there, beyond those hills. It can't be though, it's too early."

"It's the wrong direction," he said, "you're looking west."

"I know," I said. "It's funny, isn't it?"

He did not answer and I went on watching the sky. It seemed to get lighter even as I stared. Like the first red streaks of sunrise. Little by little it spread across the sky.

"It's in winter you see the northern lights, isn't it?" I said. "Not in summer?"

"That's not the northern lights," he said, "that's Manderley."

I glanced at him and saw his face. I saw his eyes.

"Maxim," I said. "Maxim, what is it?"

He drove faster, much faster. We topped the hill before us and saw Lanyon lying in a hollow at our feet. There to the left of us was the silver streak of the river, widening to the estuary at Kerrith six miles away. The road to Manderley lay ahead. There was no moon. The sky above our heads was inky black. But the sky on the horizon was not dark at all. It was shot with crimson, like a splash of blood. And the ashes blew towards us with the salt wind from the sea.